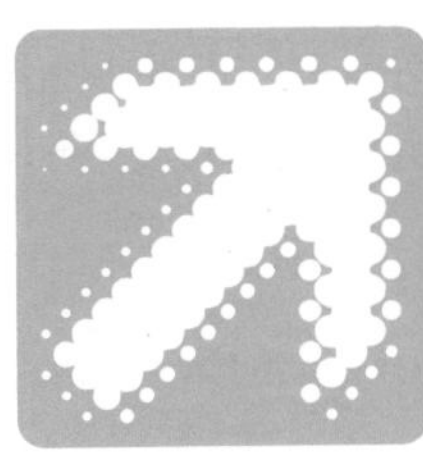

# ART WORLD DIRECTORY 2002



## ArtReview

Published by Art Review Ltd
Hereford House
23–24 Smithfield Street
London EC1A 9LF
Tel: 020 7236 4880
Fax: 020 7236 4881
EMail: info@art-review.co.uk
Web: www.art-review.co.uk
ISBN 0 904831

**Project Manager**
Joyce Cronin

**Art Direction**
Robin Hawes
**Financial Controller**
Dilip Chauhan
**Production Manager**
Piers Bebbington
**Marketing Manager**
Sophia Dempsey
**Advertisement Manager**
Emily Palmer
**Editorial**
Ossian Ward, Ruth Corb
**Executive Publisher**
Dennis Hotz

**Database Consultant**
Desktop Solutions
**Reprographics**
The Westside Group
**Printing & Binding**
Scotprint



Every effort has been made to ensure the accuracy of the information contained in the Directory. However, it is advisable to check with galleries prior to visiting.

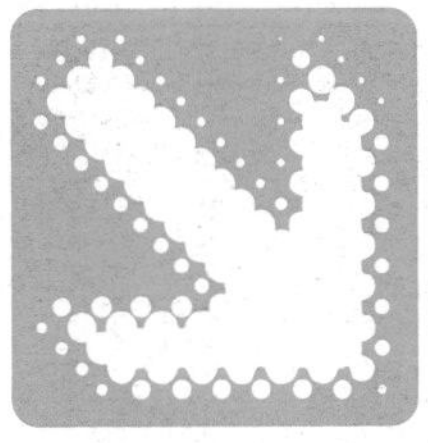

# CONTENTS

# HOW TO USE THE DIRECTORY

### Galleries and exhibition spaces

Where this has been supplied, entries are designated 'C' for a purely commercial enterprise, 'P' for a public gallery or museum or 'PS' for a public gallery or museum holding selling shows.

### Work stocked and sold

Where provided, the media in which commercial establishments specialise is listed as part of their entry.

### Price range

A guide to commercial establishments' price range may also be found as part of their entry.

### Indices

At the back of the Directory will you find a number of useful indices.

***Commercial Galleries by Media:***
*Use this index to find galleries stocking work in your chosen media*

***Commercial Gallery Artists:***
*This index lists by gallery, a sample of the artists whose work is sold by that establishment*

***Artists' Index:***
*This index lists by artist, the establishments which sell the artist's work*

***General Index:***
*The alphabetical index to all entries listed in the Directory.*

# WELCOME TO THE 2002 ART WORLD DIRECTORY

It's an exciting time to be in the art publishing business. And it's particularly exciting for *ArtReview* and for the *Art World Directory*, because both publications are evolving and expanding. This edition of the redesigned *Art World Directory* for the first time sees the introduction of short, informative and above all interesting editorial articles at the beginning of each section, which we hope you will enjoy reading.

The success of the listings has seen an increase in the number of a diverse range of art organisations included in the publication.

I would like to thank all the galleries and art service providers who have given their support to this new edition, particularly Caroline Mornement for her help with the new Crafts section. This section is long overdue and I hope it will expand and develop in future editions.

There has never been a better time to call *ArtReview* and find out how we can help you.

Watch this space. *ArtReview* and the *Art World Directory* are going places.

***The Publisher***

Showcase Wales

Michael Tomlinson 'Portrait of Arnold Wesker'
Heol Penrallt
Machynlleth
Powys SY20 8AJ
Tel 01654 703355
YR AMGUEDDFA GYMREIG OGELFYDDYD FODERN
Y TABERNACL
THE MUSEUM OF MODERN ART, WALES
email: momawales@tabernac.dircon.co.uk
www.tabernac.dircon.co.uk

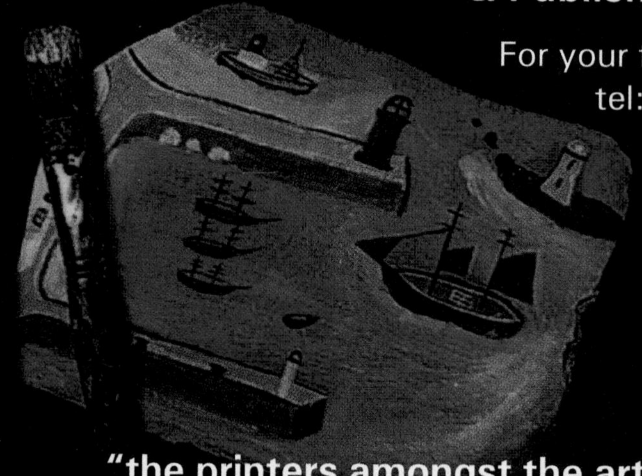

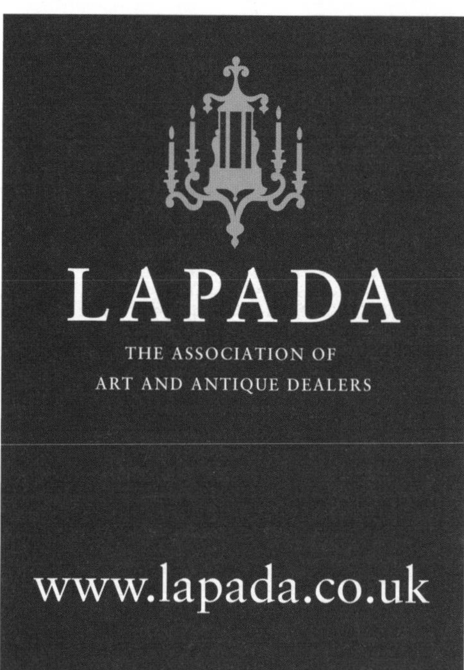
LAPADA
THE ASSOCIATION OF
ART AND ANTIQUE DEALERS
www.lapada.co.uk

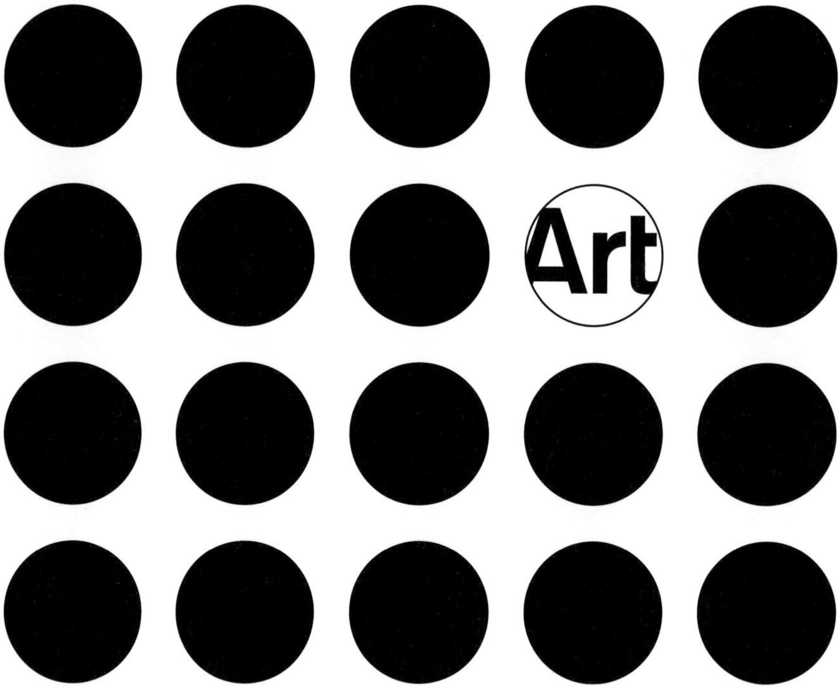

# Calendar of Exhibitions

UK & IRELAND

INTERNATIONAL

This is a selection of exhibitions due to take place from November 2001 to spring 2003 at public and commercial galleries throughout Britain and Ireland. Exhibitions are listed under the month in which they start so if you want to know what is on in a particular month, don't forget to check previous months for continuing exhibitions. It is advisable to contact the venues before visiting in order to ensure that the details have not changed since publication.

## UK & IRELAND

### Continuing from previous months

▶ **Beyond Function**
Millennium Galleries, Sheffield
1 Sep–4 Nov 0114 278 26 00

▶ **Shinto: The Sacred Art of Ancient Japan**
The British Museum, London
5 Sep–2 Dec 020 7323 8000

▶ **Shirin Neshat**
IMMA, Dublin
5 Sep–Dec 00353 1 612 9900

▶ **Memphis Remembered**
Design Museum, London
7 Sep–4 Nov 020 7940 8790

▶ **Katharina Fritsch**
Tate Modern, London
7 Sep–5 Dec 020 7887 8008

▶ **John Kobal Photographic Portrait Award 2001**
National Portrait Gallery, London
12 Sep–20 Jan 020 7306 0055

▶ **Julian Opie**
Ikon Gallery, Birmingham
12 Sep–4 Nov 0121 248 0708

▶ **Masaccio: The Pisa Altarpiece**
The National Gallery, London
12 Sep–11 Nov 020 7747 2865

▶ **Doris Salcedo**
Camden Arts Centre, London
14 Sep–11 Nov 020 7435 2643

▶ **Jose Davila**
Camden Arts Centre, London
14 Sep–11 Nov 020 7435 2643

▶ **Sophie Ristelhueber**
Camden Arts Centre, London
14 Sep–11 Nov 020 7435 2643

▶ **Frank Auerbach**
Royal Academy of Arts, London
14 Sep–12 Dec 020 7300 8000

▶ **Trauma**
Firstsite, Colchester (National Touring Exhib. organised by the Hayward)
15 Sep–17 Nov Hayward: 020 7921 0600

▶ **Here and Now: Scottish Art 1990–2001**
Dundee Contemporary Arts
15 Sep–4 Nov 01382 606 220

▶ **Bryan Wynter: Paintings and Kinetic Sculpture 1945–74**
Tate St Ives
15 Sep–2 Dec 01736 796 226

▶ **Thomas Joshua Cooper: Photographs**
Tate St Ives
15 Sep–2 Dec 01736 796 226

▶ **Fluid**
Wolverhampton Art Gallery
15 Sep–24 Nov 01902 552 055

▶ **Elefuntastic**
City Museum, Sheffield
15 Sep–Dec 0114 278 2600

▶ **My Generation**
Wolverhampton Art Gallery
15 Sep–10 Nov 01902 552 055

▶ **Medieval Sculpture**
Tate Britain, London
17 Sep–3 Mar 020 7887 8000

▶ **The Golden Age of Watercolours – The Hickman Bacon Collection**
Dulwich Picture Gallery, London
19 Sep–6 Jan 020 8693 5254

▶ **Teresa Pemberton – Fragile Boundaries**
Frasco, London
20 Sep–6 Nov 020 7834 7773

▶ **Surrealism: Desire Unbound**
Tate Modern, London
20 Sep–16 Dec 020 7887 8008

▶ **Out of Japan**
V&A, London
20 Sep–3 Feb 020 7938 8500

▶ **Robert Davies and Gary Coyle**
Model Arts and Niland Gallery, Sligo
21 Sep–3 Nov

▶ **Textural Space**
Whitworth Art Gallery, Manchester
21 Sep–18 Nov 0161 275 7450

▶ **Michael Snow Almost Cover to Cover**
Arnofini, Bristol
22 Sep–18 Nov 0117 929 9191

▶ **Rembrandt's Women**
Royal Academy of Arts, London
22 Sep–16 Dec 020 7300 8000

▶ **Jean Dubuffet: Maquettes for Monuments**
Leeds City Art Gallery, Leeds
26 Sep–6 Jan 0113 247 8248

▶ **The Print in Italy 1550–1620**
The British Museum, London
27 Sep–13 Jan 020 7323 8000

▶ **The Prints of Stanley William Hayter 1901–88**
The British Museum, London
27 Sep–13 Jan 020 7323 8000

▶ **Tim Harrison**
The New Art Centre Sculpture Park and Gallery, Wiltshire
28 Sep–18 Nov 01980 862 244

▶ **Magnetic North**
The New Art Gallery, Walsall
28 Sep–18 Nov 01922 654 400

▶ **Travelling Companions: Chardin & Freud**
Ulster Museum, Belfast
(Touring National Gallery Exhibition)
29 Sep–25 Nov 028 9038 1251

▶ **Richard Murphy**
Fruitmarket, The Gallery Lower, Edinburgh
29 Sep–24 Nov 0131 225 2383

▶ **Nick Hess**
Fruitmarket, The Gallery Upper, Edinburgh
29 Sep–24 Nov 0131 225 2383

▶ **Rachel Whiteread**
Scottish National Gallery of Modern Art, Edinburgh
29 Sep–9 Dec 0131 624 6200

▶ **Drawing Distinctions: 20th Century Drawings and Watercolours from the British Council Collections**
Milton Keynes Gallery
29 Sep–25 Nov 01908 676 900

▶ **Picasso: Histoire Naturelle**
Gosport Gallery (National Touring Exhib. organised by the Hayward)
29 Sep–2 Dec Hayward: 020 7921 0600

▶ **David Hockney: Grimm's Fairy Tales**
Lynn Museum, King's Lynn (National Touring Exhib. organised by the Hayward)
29 Sep–1 Dec Hayward: 020 7921 0600

▶ **Solid State: Reflections On the Real**
Kettle's Yard, Cambridge
29 Sep–4 Nov 01223 352124

▶ **Mike Nelson**
ICA, London
30 Sep–11 Nov 020 7930 3647

▶ **Peugeot Design Awards**
mac, Birmingham
1 Oct–11 Nov 0121 440 3838

▶ **In Ruins: Ruins from the Renaissance to the present day**
Holburne Museum of Art, Bath
2 Oct–2 Dec 01225 466 669

▶ **Carey Young**
John Hansard Gallery, Southampton
2 Oct–10 Nov 023 8059 2158

▶ **Peter Friedl and Daniel Dale Johnston**
Chisenhale, London
3 Oct–11 Nov 020 8981 4518

▶ **Andreas Serrano**
Barbican, London
4 Oct–Dec 020 7638 4141

**▶ Dan Holdsworth**
Barbican, London
4 Oct–Dec 020 7638 4141

**▶ Portuguese Contemporary Design**
Design Museum, London
4 Oct–4 Nov 020 7940 8790

**▶ Facts of Life: Contemporary Japanese Art**
Hayward Gallery, London
4 Oct–9 Dec 020 7921 0600

**▶ Janet Mullarney**
Crawford Municipal Art Gallery, Cork
5 Oct–3 Nov 00353 021 4273 377

**▶ Richard Wentworth and Eugene Atget**
The Photographers' Gallery, London
5 Oct–18 Nov 020 7831 1772

**▶ Phil Morsman**
Broughton House Gallery, Cambridge
6–27 Oct 01223 314 960

**▶ Winifred Nicholson**
Graves Art Gallery, Sheffield (National Touring Exhib. organised by the Hayward)
6 Oct–17 Nov Hayward: 020 7921 0600

**▶ 200 Cold Heaven: Don McCullin on Aids in Africa**
mac, Birmingham
6 Oct–15 Nov 0121 440 3838

**▶ Mnemosyne: Iona Montgomery**
Lille Art Gallery, Glasgow
6 Oct–17 Nov 0141 578 8847

**▶ Creating a Presence: Landscape**
Lille Art Gallery, Glasgow
6 Oct–17 Nov 0141 578 8847

**▶ Vistas: Landscapes and Interiors**
Portal Gallery, London
8–20 Oct 020 7493 0706

**▶ Profile of an Irish Practice: Shay Cleary Architects**
Architecture Centre, Dublin
8–25 Oct 00353 01 676 1703

**▶ John Hoyland**
Beaux Arts, London
9 Oct–24 Nov 020 7437 5799

**▶ Siobhan McLaren**
Viewpoint Gallery, Plymouth
10–26 Oct 01752 203441

**▶ Gillian Ayres: New Works**
Alan Cristea Gallery, London
10 Oct–10 Nov 020 7439 1899

**▶ Guy Portelli Sculpture**
The Gallery Manchester
10 Oct–3 Nov 0161 237 3551

**▶ Carlo Carra: Works on Paper**
Estorick Collection of Modern Italian Art
10 Oct–20 Jan 020 7704 9522

**▶ Art For Youth 2001: Charity**
Mall Galleries, London
11–Oct 020 79306844

**▶ The Stuart Portrait: Status and Legacy**
Southampton City Art Gallery
11 Oct–30 Dec 023 8083 2277

**▶ Painted Ladies: Women at the Court of Charles II**
National Portrait Gallery, London
11 Oct–6 Jan 020 7306 0055

**▶ Doug Aitken**
Serpentine Gallery, London
12 Oct–25 Nov 020 7402 6075

**▶ Sacred and Profane**
Mappin Art Gallery, Sheffield
13 Oct–14 Jan 0114 276 8588

**▶ Immediate 2**
Site Gallery, Sheffield
13 Oct–24 Nov 0114 281 2077

**▶ Mixed show**
The Open Eye Gallery, Edinburgh
13 Oct–1 Nov 0131 557 1020

**▶ At Home with Art**
Mold Library, Museum and Art Gallery (National Touring Exhib. organised by the Hayward)
13 Oct–10 Nov Hayward: 020 7921 0600

**▶ Patrick Caulfield: The Poems of Jules Laforgue**
mac, Birmingham (National Touring Exhib. organised by the Hayward)
13 Oct–17 Nov Hayward: 020 7921 0600

**▶ Wil Rowlands & William Selwyn**
Oriel Plas Glyn-y-Weddw Gallery, Llanbedrog
14 Oct–24 Dec 01758 740 763

**▶ Jean do Gale**
Mall Galleries, London
16–28 Oct 020 7930 6844

**▶ Recent Paintings by Marj Bond**
Solomon Gallery, Dublin
16–31 Oct 01 679 4237

**▶ Royal Society of Marine Artists: Annual Exhibition**
Mall Galleries, London
17–28 Oct 020 7930 6844

**▶ Christopher Cook: Changing the Need**
Hirschl Contemporary Art, London
17 Oct–17 Nov 020 7495 2565

**▶ Art on The Line: The Royal Academy Exhibitions at Somerset House 1780–1836**
Courtauld Institute Gallery, London
18 Oct–20 Jan 020 7848 2526

**▶ Venetian Drawings**
Christ Church Picture Gallery, Oxford
18 Oct–Feb 01865 276 172

**▶ Marking the Territory: Performance Event**
IMMA, Dublin
18–21 Oct 00353 1 612 9900

**▶ Radical Fashion**
V&A, London
18 Oct–6 Jan 020 7938 8500

**▶ The Fine Art of Photography**
Scottish National Portrait Gallery, Edinburgh
19 Oct–13 Jan 0131 624 6200

**▶ Paul McCarthy**
Tate Liverpool
19 Oct–13 Jan 0151 702 7400

**▶ Street Level: Samuel Coulthurst**
The Lowry, Manchester
20 Oct–Jan 0161 876 2020

**▶ Open City: Street Photography 1950–2000**
The Lowry, Manchester
20 Oct–2 Jan 0161 876 2020

**▶ Martin Murrey: Paintings**
The Lowry, Manchester
20 Oct–6 Jan 0161 876 2020

**▶ Street Level: L S Lowry's Street Life**
The Lowry, Manchester
20 Oct–6 Jan 0161 876 2020

**▶ Fleeting Arcadias**
Newcastle School of Art and Design (National Touring Exhib. organised by the Hayward)
20 Oct–18 Nov Hayward: 020 7921 0600

**▶ Margaret Hunter: Changing Perceptions II**
Collins Gallery, Glasgow
20 Oct–17 Nov 0141 548 4145

**▶ Watercolour Society of Wales**
Brecon
20 Oct–24 Nov 01291 690260

**▶ LS Lowry: Street Life**
The Lowry, Manchester
20 Oct–Jan 0161 870 2020

**▶ Shooting People**
The Lowry, Manchester
20 Oct–Jan 0161 876 2020

**▶ Open City: Street Photography**
The Lowry, Manchester
20 Oct–Jan 0161 870 2020

**▶ Martin Murrey: Paintings**
The Lowry, Manchester
20 Oct–Jan 0161 870 2020

**▶ Oxford Reflections by Malcolm Sparkes**
Christ Church Picture Gallery, Oxford
21 Oct–18 Nov 01865 276 172

**▶ Beryl Cook: New Paintings**
Portal Gallery, London
22 Oct–10 Nov 020 7493 0706

▶ **June Berry: Watercolours and Prints**
Bankside Gallery, London
24 Oct–17 Nov 020 7928 2820

▶ **Pisanello: Painter to the Renaissance Court**
The National Gallery, London
24 Oct–13 Jan 020 7747 2865

▶ **Mirror, Mirror: Self Portraits by Women Artists**
National Portrait Gallery, London
24 Oct–10 Feb 020 7306 0055

▶ **The Americans**
Barbican, London
25 Oct–6 Jan 020 7638 4141

▶ **Art in the Age of Queen Victoria**
Royal Academy of Arts,
London Permanent Collection
Leeds City Art Gallery, Leeds
25 Oct–20 Jan 0113 247 8248

▶ **AFF London**
The Gallery Manchester
25–28 Oct 0161 237 3551

▶ **Unknown Amazon Culture and Nature in Ancient Brazil**
The British Museum, London
26 Oct–1 Apr 020 7323 8000

▶ **A Tribute to Edwin Morgan**
Scottish National Portrait Gallery, Edinburgh
26 Oct–3 Feb 0131 624 6200

▶ **Newly Acquired Drawings in the National Gallery**
National Gallery of Scotland, Edinburgh
26 Oct–31 Jan 0131 624 6200

▶ **Adorn, Equip, Accessorise**
Oriel 31, Newtown Powys
27 Oct–1 Dec 01 686 625 041

▶ **Out of Line: Arts Council Collection of Drawing 1950–2001**
Graves Art Gallery, Sheffield
27 Oct–8 Dec 0114 273 5158

▶ **The Fuji/AOP Assistant Awards**
AOP Gallery, London
29 Oct–10 Nov 020 7739 6669

▶ **Nicky Philipps**
Fine Art Commissions Ltd London
29 Oct–10 Nov 020 7589 4111

▶ **Kathe Kollwitz: Artist of the People**
The Oakham Theatre, Oakham (National Touring Exhib. organised by the Hayward)
29 Oct–17 Nov Hayward: 020 7921 0600

▶ **Melanie Guy**
Viewpoint Gallery, Plymouth
30 Oct–8 Nov 01752 203 441

▶ **Miwa Kojima/ Takuro Mikame: Tsunami**
198 Gallery, London
30 Oct–14 Dec 020 7978 8309

## November 2001

▶ **Tate Centenary Development**
Tate Britain, London
1 Nov 020 7887 8000

▶ **Raymond McGrath**
Architecture Centre, Dublin
1–16 Nov 00353 01 676 1703

▶ **Bartolomeu dos Santos**
The London Institute Gallery, London
1 Nov–7 Dec 020 514 8033

▶ **Exposed: The Victorian Nude**
Tate Britain, London
1 Nov–13 Jan 020 7887 8000

▶ **New English Art Club: Annual Exhibition**
Mall Galleries, London
2–12 Nov 020 7930 6844

▶ **Identity**
Project A, Glasgow
2–30 Nov 0141 552 2822

▶ **Ed Rusha**
MOMA, Oxford
3 Nov–13 Jan 01865 728 608

▶ **Victorian Watercolours from Gallery Collection**
Leeds City Art Gallery, Leeds
3 Nov–Jan 0113 247 8248

▶ **Mixed Show**
The Open Eye Gallery, Edinburgh
3–22 Nov 0131 557 1020

▶ **Jean Lodge**
Broughton House Gallery, Cambridge
3–24 Nov 01223 314 960

▶ **Gillian Wearing**
Angel Row Gallery, Nottingham
3 Nov–5 Jan 0115 915 2869

▶ **Edward Western**
The Jersey Arts Centre, Jersey (National Touring Exhib. organised by the Hayward)
5 Nov–2 Dec Hayward: 020 7921 0600

▶ **Anthony Frost: Walking into Red**
Advanced Graphics, London
5 Nov–21 Dec 020 8691 1330

▶ **Ana Duncan & Anthony Scott: Sculpture exhibition**
Solomon Gallery, Dublin
6–21 Nov 01 679 4237

▶ **Richard Gorman**
Crawford Municipal Art Gallery, Cork
7 Nov–4 Dec 00353 021 4273 377

▶ **The Turner Prize Exhibition 2001**
Tate Britain, London
7 Nov–20 Jan 020 7887 8000

▶ **Beuys to Hirst: Art Works at Deutsche Bank**
Dean Gallery, Scottish National Gallery of Modern Art, Edinburgh
7 Nov–13 Jan 0131 624 6200

▶ **Kitaj: In the Aura of Cézanne and Other Masters**
The National Gallery, London
7 Nov–10 Feb 020 7747 2865

▶ **Ross Loveday**
Frasco, London
8 Nov–22 Dec 020 7834 7773

▶ **Simon English and Varvara Shavrova**
Model Arts and Niland Gallery, Sligo
8 Nov–8 Dec

▶ **Agatha Christie and Archaeology: Mystery in Mesopotamia**
The British Museum, London
9 Nov–24 Mar 020 7323 8000

▶ **Home World**
Northern Gallery for Contemporary Art, Sunderland
9 Nov–29 Dec 0191 514 8460

▶ **Britten's Landscape**
Kettle's Yard, Cambridge
10 Nov–6 Jan 01223 352 124

▶ **Shot Up North**
AOP Gallery, London
12–24 Nov 020 7739 6669

▶ **Haydn Cornner**
Portal Gallery, London
12 Nov–1 Dec 020 7493 2667

▶ **At Home with Art**
Colwyn Bay, Library (National Touring Exhib. organised by the Hayward)
13 Nov–8 Dec Hayward: 020 7921 0600

▶ **Mimmo Paladino: A Print Retrospective**
Alan Cristea Gallery, London
13 Nov–15 Dec 020 7439 1866

▶ **Braco Dimitrijevic**
Ikon Gallery, Birmingham
14 Nov–20 Jan 0121 248 0708

▶ **Light Motifs: An Aomori Float and Japanese Kites**
The British Museum, London
14 Nov–3 Mar 020 7323 8000

▶ **Richard Hamilton**
Ikon Gallery, Birmingham
14 Nov–Dec 0121 248 0708

▶ **Irish Art Now: From the Poetic to the Political**
IMMA, Dublin
14 Nov–Mar 00353 1 612 9900

▶ **Open Day Exhibition**
Viewpoint Gallery, Plymouth
14–22 Nov 01752 203441

▶ **Roger Hampson and the Northern School**
The Gallery Manchester
15–24 Nov 0161 237 3551

▶ **The Discerning Eye**
Mall Galleries, London
16–25 Nov 020 7930 6844

▶ **Matisse: Jazz, from the Arts Council Collection**
Plymouth City Museum and Art Council
(National Touring Exhib. organised by the Hayward)
17 Nov–16 Dec Hayward: 020 7921 0600

▶ **Goya The Disparates**
Red House Museum and Gardens, Christchurch
(National Touring Exhib. organised by the Hayward)
17 Nov–16 Dec Hayward: 020 7921 0600

▶ **Dubuffet's Walls: Lithographs for Les Murs**
York College For Further Education
(National Touring Exhib. organised by the Hayward)
17 Nov–16 Dec Hayward: 020 7921 0600

▶ **Crafts For Christmas**
Millennium Galleries, Sheffield
17 Nov–31 Dec 0114 278 26 00

▶ **Marianne Ryan**
Hirschl Contemporary Art, London
21 Nov–21 Dec 020 7495 2565

▶ **Art Textiles 2**
mac, Birmingham
24 Nov–6 Jan 0121 440 3838

▶ **Prints by Mila Judge-Furstova**
mac, Birmingham
24 Nov–6 Jan 0121 440 3838

▶ **Contemporary Folk Art from Hu Country, Shangxi Province, China**
mac, Birmingham
24 Nov–1 Jan 0121 440 3838

▶ **Christmas Art and Craft**
Lille Art Gallery, Glasgow
24 Nov–19 Dec 0141 578 8847

▶ **The Dawn of the Floating World**
Royal Academy of Arts, London
24 Nov–17 Feb 020 7300 8000

▶ **Artist's Choice: David Shrigley's Selection from the Permanent Collection**
Scottish National Gallery of Modern Art, Edinburgh
24 Nov–24 Feb 0131 624 6200

▶ **Collins' Christmas Show**
Collins Gallery, Glasgow
24 Nov–21 Dec 0141 548 4145

▶ **Saul Bass**
Design Museum, London
24 Nov–Mar 020 7940 8790

▶ **Conran Foundation Collection – Marc Newson**
Design Museum, London
24 Nov–Feb 020 7940 8790

▶ **Will Maclean**
Dundee Contemporary Arts, Dundee
24 Nov–20 Jan 01382 606 220

▶ **Christmas Show**
The Open Eye Gallery, Edinburgh
24 Nov–24 Dec 0131 557 1020

▶ **High Summer**
Wolverhampton Art Gallery
24 Nov–19 Jan 01902 552055

▶ **David Tress**
Oriel Plas Glyn-y-Weddw Gallery, Llanbedrog
25 Nov–Jan 01758 740 763

▶ **Exhibition of Drawings by Martin Reynolds**
Architecture Centre, Dublin
26 Nov–14 Dec 00353 01 676 1703

▶ **Paul Benny**
Fine Art Commissions Ltd London
26 Nov–2 Dec 020 7589 4111

▶ **IDEA Awards**
AOP Gallery, London
26 Nov–8 Dec 020 7739 6669

▶ **Norman Adams**
Beaux Arts, London
27 Nov–21 Dec 020 7437 5799

▶ **Christmas/Small Works:**
Gallery and invited artists. Solomon Gallery, Dublin
27 Nov–23 Dec 01 679 4237

▶ **Gina Pane**
John Hansard Gallery, Southampton
27 Nov–19 Jan 023 8059 2158

▶ **Design Crafts Exhibtion**
Viewpoint Gallery, Plymouth
27 Nov–6 Dec 01752 203 441

▶ **Hanna Volmer**
Mall Galleries, London
28 Nov–2 Dec 020 7930 6844

▶ **Paul Benney**
Mall Galleries, London
28 Nov–2 Dec 020 7930 6844

▶ **Carolyn Henderson**
Mall Galleries, London
28 Nov–2 Dec 020 7930 6844

▶ **Alasdair and Sally MacDonell**
The McHardy Sculpture Company, London
28 Nov–Dec 020 7378 7300

▶ **Roman Signer**
Camden Arts Centre, London
30 Nov–3 Feb 020 7435 2643

▶ **John Galliano at Christian Dior**
Design Museum, London
30 Nov–28 Apr 020 7940 8790

▶ **Remote**
The Photographers' Gallery, London
30 Nov–Jan 020 7831 1772

## December 2001

▶ **Winter Exhibition**
The Gallery, Manchester
Dec 0161 237 3551

▶ **Christmas Exhibition**
Linton Court Gallery
1–16 Dec 01729 822 695

▶ **Christmas Mixture**
Broughton House Gallery, Cambridge
1–22 Dec 01223 314 960

▶ **Dalziel & Scullion**
Fruitmarket The Gallery, Edinburgh
1 Dec–12 Jan 0131 22 2383

▶ **The Silbury Group**
Milton Keynes Gallery
1 Dec–13 Jan 01908 676 900

▶ **Travelling Companions: Chardin & Freud (The National Gallery Touring Exhibition)**
Christchurch Museum, Ipswich
1 Dec–3 Feb 01473 253 246

▶ **Goya: The Family of the Infante Don Luis**
The National Gallery, London
1 Dec–3 Mar 020 7747 2865

▶ **Kiss and Kill: Film Visions of Brighton**
Brighton Museum and Art Gallery
1 Dec–7 Apr 01273 290 900

▶ **The Little Picture Show: Small Paintings by Great Artists**
Portal Gallery, London
3–21 Dec 020 7493 0706

▶ **Fleeting Arcadias**
Clotsworthy Arts Centre, Antrim (National Touring Exhib. organised by the Hayward)
4–21 Dec Hayward: 020 7921 0600

▶ **Royal Institute of Oil Painters: Annual Exhibition**
Mall Galleries, London
5–18 Dec 020 7930 6844

▶ **Olwen, Julia & Naomi**
Mall Galleries, London
5–18 Dec 020 7930 6844

▶ **Annual Christmas Show**
Project A, Glasgow
7–21 Dec 0141 552 2822

▶ **Janet Cardiff: Spem in Alium – 40 Part Motet**
The New Art Gallery, Walsall
7 Dec–13 Jan 01922 654 400

▶ **Walsall Society of Artists**
The New Art Gallery, Walsall
7 Dec–13 Jan 01922 654 400

▶ **Recent Gifts to the Collection**
The New Art Gallery, Walsall
7 Dec–13 Jan
01922 654400

▶ **Views of Germany**
Whitworth Art Gallery, Manchester
7 Dec–10 Mar 0161 275 7450

▶ **Nigel Henderson: Parallel of Life and Art**
Graves Art Gallery, Sheffield
8 Dec–2 Feb 0114 273 5158

▶ **Harold Harvey**
Wolverhampton Art Gallery
8 Dec–26 Jan 01902 552 055

▶ **Richard Artschwager**
Serpentine Gallery, London
12 Dec–10 Feb 020 7402 6075

▶ **Dairmuid Delargy**
Model Arts and Niland Gallery, Sligo
13 Dec–19 Jan

▶ **Out of Line**
Oriel Mostyn Gallery, Llandudno (National Touring Exhib. organised by the Hayward)
15 Dec–27 Jan Hayward: 020 7921 0600

▶ **BP Wildlife Photographer of the Year competition 2001**
Exhibition Gallery, Bristol Museums and Art Gallery
15 Dec–19 Jan 0117 922 3571

▶ **Sandra Blow: Paintings**
Tate St Ives
15 Dec–3 Mar 01736 796 226

▶ **Vicken Parsons: Paintings**
Tate St Ives
15 Dec–3 Mar 01736 796 226

▶ **Gallery Print Publications from 2001: works by Opie, Dine, Yass**
Alan Cristea Galler, London
19 Dec–Jan 020 7439 1866

▶ **Jeremy Moon: A Retrospective**
Graves Art Gallery, Sheffield
22 Dec–2 Mar 0114 273 5158

## January 2002

▶ **Keith Tyson**
South London Gallery
Jan–Feb 020 7703 6120

▶ **Rufus Jon Wilson**
198 Gallery, London
Jan–Feb 020 7978 8309

▶ **Monet, Renoir and the Impressionist Landscape**
National Gallery of Ireland, Dublin
Jan–Apr 0033 01 661 5133

▶ **The Lowry Collection**
The Lowry, Manchester
Jan–Apr 0161 870 2020

▶ **Intimacy: Contemporary Portraits**
The Lowry, Manchester
Jan–Apr 0161 870 2020

▶ **David Walker: No Man's Land**
The Lowry, Manchester
Jan–Apr 0161 870 2020

▶ **The Vaughan Bequest of Turner Watercolours**
National Gallery of Scotland, Edinburgh
1–31 Jan 0131 624 6200

▶ **Mixed Show**
The Open Eye Gallery, Edinburgh
5–24 Jan 0131 557 1020

▶ **Manga: Short Comics from Modern Japan**
The London Institute Gallery, London
9 Jan–8 Feb 020 7514 8083

▶ **Coins of the Princely States of India**
The British Museum, London
10 Jan–May 020 7323 8000

▶ **Flights of Reality**
Kettle's Yard, Cambridge
12 Jan–3 Mar 01223 352124

▶ **Changing Face: Photographs of the Bullring Project by Luke Unsworth**
mac, Birmingham
12 Jan–3 Mar 0121 440 3838

▶ **New York Rhythm: Photographs by Silas Wood**
mac, Birmingham
12 Jan–3 Mar 0121 440 3838

▶ **Spotlight on Kenneth Martin**
Peter Scott Gallery, Lancaster (National Touring Exhib. organised by the Hayward)
12 Jan–24 Feb Hayward: 020 7921 0600

▶ **Picasso: Histoire Naturelle**
Mclean Museum and Art Gallery, Greenlock (National Touring Exhib. organised by the Hayward)
12 Jan–10 Feb Hayward: 020 7921 0600

▶ **David Hockney: Grimm's Fairy Tales**
Black Swan Guild, Frome (National Touring Exhib. organised by the Hayward)
12 Jan–10 Feb Hayward: 020 7921 0600

▶ **Fleeting Arcadias**
The Ucheldre Centre, Holyhead (National Touring Exhib. organised by the Hayward)
12 Jan–10 Feb Hayward: 020 7921 0600

▶ **A City's Pride: The Lowry L S Collection**
The Lowry, Manchester
12 Jan– 0161 876 2020

▶ **Intimacy**
The Lowry, Manchester
12 Jan–Apr 0161 876 2020

▶ **New Artists**
Oriel Plas Glyn-y-Weddw Gallery, Llanbedrog
13 Jan–25 Feb 01758 740 763

▶ **Fleeting Arcadias**
Brighton College, Burstow Gallery (National Touring Exhib. organised by the Hayward)
16 Jan–17 Mar Hayward: 020 7921 0600

▶ **Japanese Prints from the Occupation**
The British Museum, London
17 Jan–19 May 020 7323 8000

▶ **Paul Klee**
Hayward Gallery, London
17 Jan–1 Apr 020 7921 0600

▶ **Ann-Sofi Siden**
Hayward Gallery, London
17 Jan–16 Apr 020 723 8000

▶ **Patricia Mackinnon-Day**
Whitworth Art Gallery, Manchester
17 Jan–12 Apr 0161 275 7450

▶ **Sport**
Project A, Glasgow
18 Jan–22 Feb 0141 552 2822

▶ **Matthew Collings**
Milton Keynes Gallery
19 Jan–3 Mar 01908 676 900

▶ **Mt Fuji: Photographs by Chris Steeele-Perkins**
mac, Birmingham
19 Jan–10 Mar 0121 440 3838

▶ **Art Textiles 2**
Collins Gallery, Glasgow
20 Jan–2 Mar 0141 548 4145

▶ **Nan Goldin**
Whitechapel Art Gallery, London
25 Jan–31 Mar 020 7522 7898

▶ **Great Houses of Scotland**
Scottish National Portrait Gallery, Edinburgh
25 Jan–21 Apr 0131 624 6200

▶ **Trauma**
MoMA, Oxford (National Touring Exhib. organised by the Hayward)
25 Jan–12 Apr Hayward: 020 7921 0600

▶ **Naoya Hatakeyama**
Northern Gallery for Contemporary Art, Sunderland
25 Jan–23 Mar 0191 514 8460

▶ **Mixed Show**
The Open Eye Gallery, Edinburgh
26 Jan–14 Feb 0131 557 1020

▶ **Light**
Bristol City Museum and Art Gallery, Bristol
26 Jan–7 Mar 0117 922 3571

▶ **No Man's Land: Photographs by David Walker**
The Lowry, Manchester
26 Jan–Apr 0161 876 2020

▶ **Paris: Capital of the Arts 1900–68**
Royal Academy of the Arts, London
26 Jan–12 Apr 020 7300 8000

▶ **Fifties Art in Britain**
Barbican Gallery, London
31 Jan–Apr 020 7638 4141

**▶ Touring Exhibition**
The New Art Gallery, Walsall
31 Jan–13 Mar 01922 654 400

**▶ Imagining Ulysses: Richard Hamilton's Illustrations to James Joyce**
The British Museum, London
31 Jan–19 May 020 7323 8000

**▶ The Art of Calligraphy in Modern China**
The British Museum, London
31 Jan–19 May 020 7323 8000

## February 2002

**▶ Raymond Booth**
Leeds City Art Gallery, Leeds
Feb–early Apr 0113 247 8255

**▶ Terbrugghen's Crucifixion**
National Gallery of Ireland, Dublin
Feb–May 0033 01 661 5133

**▶ At Home with Art**
Bowes Museum, Barnard Castle (National Touring Exhib. organised by the Hayward)
2 Feb–17 Mar Hayward: 020 7921 0600

**▶ Mario Testino: Portraits**
Brighton and Hove Museum and Gallery
2 Feb–2 Jun 01273 202 900

**▶ Magic/Object/Action**
Site Gallery, Sheffield
2 Feb–16 Mar 0114 281 2077

**▶ Critical Interventions III, Unprincipled Passions**
John Hansard Gallery, Southampton
5 Feb–23 Mar 023 8059 2158

**▶ Katarina Ivanisin**
Beaux Arts, London
5 Feb–2 Mar 020 7437 5799

**▶ William Beckford**
Dulwich Picture Gallery, London
6 Feb–14 Apr 020 8693 5254

**▶ Paul Morrison**
Southampton City Art Gallery
7 Feb–14 Apr 023 8083 2277

**▶ Travelling Companions: Chardin & Freud (The National Gallery Touring Exhibition)**
Victoria Art Gallery, Bath
9 Feb–7 Apr 01225 477 772

**▶ Sea**
Wolverhampton Art Gallery
9 Feb–13 Apr 01902 552 055

**▶ Katharina Grosse & Santiago Sierra**
Ikon Gallery, Birmingham
12 Feb–7 Apr 0121 248 0708

**▶ Aelbert Cuyp**
The National Gallery, London
13 Feb–12 May 020 7747 2865

**▶ Kathe Kollwitz: Artist of the People**
Blackwell, Kendal (National Touring Exhib. organised by the Hayward)
14 Feb–21 Apr Hayward: 020 7921 0600

**▶ Adapt NOW: eclectic contemporary group show in aid of the ADAPT Trust**
Kelingrove Museum, Glasgow
Tel: 0131 346 1999; Fax: 0131 346 1991
Email: adapt.trust@virgin.net

**▶ Zero - Hans Schleger: A Life of Design**
The London Institute Gallery, London
15 Feb–14 Mar 020 7514 8083

**▶ Douglas Huebler**
Camden Arts Centre, London
15 Feb–14 Apr 020 7435 2643

**▶ Nigel Henderson: Parallel of Life and Art**
Dean Gallery, Scottish National Gallery of Modern Art, Edinburgh
16 Feb–7 Apr 0131 624 6200

**▶ David Hockney: Grimm's Fairy Tales**
Wednesbury Musuem and Art Gallery (National Touring Exhib. organised by the Hayward)
16 Feb–17 Mar Hayward: 020 7921 0600

**▶ Mixed Show**
The Open Eye Gallery, Edinburgh
16 Feb–7 Mar 0131 557 1020

**▶ The Barbican Show**
The Barbican, London
20 Feb–8 Apr 020 7638 4141

**▶ Seeing Things: Photographing Objects**
V&A, London
20 Feb–Aug 020 7938 8500

**▶ Wolfgang Suschitzky**
Scottish National Portrait Gallery, Edinburgh
21 Feb–Apr 0131 624 6200

**▶ Saving Faces: Portraits by Mark Gilbert**
Brighton and Hove Museum and Gallery
27 Feb–21 Apr 01273 202 900

## March 2002

**▶ Eduardo Padilha**
198 Gallery, London
Mar–Apr 020 7978 8309

**▶ Mike Kelly**
South London Gallery
Mar–Apr 020 7703 6120

**▶ A Pelican in the Wilderness: Hermits and Hermitages**
Holburne Museum of Art, Bath
Mar–May 01225 466 669

**▶ Beck's Futures 3**
ICA, London
Mar–May 020 7930 3647

**▶ Spotlight on Kenneth Martin**
Rhyl Library (National Touring Exhib. organised by the Hayward)
2 Mar–14 Apr Hayward: 020 7921 0600

**▶ Andie Clay**
Oriel Plas Glyn-y-Weddw Gallery, Llanbedrog
3 Mar–3 Apr 01758 740 763

**▶ Mark Gilbert**
Beaux Arts, London
5 Mar–6 Apr 020 7437 5799

**▶ Group Show**
Project A, Glasgow
8 Mar–12 Apr 0141 552 2822

**▶ Mixed Show**
The Open Eye Gallery, Edinburgh
9–28 Mar 0131 557 1020

**▶ Tim Noble and Sue Webster**
Milton Keynes Gallery
9 Mar–28 Apr 01908 676 900

**▶ Terry Setch: Retrospective**
Collins Gallery, Glasgow
9 Mar–13 Apr 0141 548 4145

**▶ Carey Young: Video Work**
Angel Row Gallery, Nottingham
9 Mar–28 Apr 0115 915 2869

**▶ Ian Hamilton Finlay: Martime Works**
Tate St Ives
11 Mar–2 Jun 01736 796 226

**▶ Simon Starling**
Tate St Ives
11 Mar–2 Jun 01736 796 226

**▶ Hussein Chalayan**
Tate St Ives
11 Mar–2 Jun 01736 796 226

**▶ Baroque Painting in Genoa**
The National Gallery, London
13 Mar–16 Jun 020 7747 2865

**▶ Loni Kreduder**
The McHardy Sculpture Company, London
13 Mar–Apr 020 7378 7300

**▶ Earth and Fire: Italian Terracotta Sculpture from Donatello to Canova**
V&A, London
14 Mar–Jul 020 7938 8500

**▶ The Tiara Today**
V&A, London
21 Mar–Jul 020 7938 8500

**▶ Young at Art**
The London Institute Gallery, London
21 Mar–19 Apr 020 7514 8083

**▶ Outside Art**
Whitworth Art Gallery, Manchester
22 Mar–2 Jun 0161 275 7450

▶ **The Art of Star Wars**
City Art Centre, Edinburgh
23 Mar–6 Sep 0131 529 3993

▶ **David Hockney: Grimm's Fairy Tales**
Luton, Museum and Art Gallery (National Touring Exhib. organised by the Hayward)
23 Mar–21 Apr Hayward: 020 7921 0600

▶ **Out of Line**
Middlesborough Art Gallery (National Touring Exhib. organised by the Hayward)
23 Mar–30 Jun Hayward: 020 7921 0600

▶ **Brazilian Artists**
The New Art Gallery, Walsall
28 Mar–9 Jun 01922 654400

▶ **Mixed Show**
The Open Eye Gallery, Edinburgh
30 Mar–18 Apr 0131 557 1020

## April 2002

▶ **Paintings & Prints from Henry Rothschild Collection**
Broughton House Gallery, Cambridge
Apr 01223 314 960

▶ **Mirror Mirror: Self Portraits by Women Artists (National Portrait Gallery Touring Exhibition)**
Leeds City Art Gallery, Leeds
mid-Apr–13 Jun 0113 247 8255

▶ **New Acquisitions of Contemporary Art**
Scottish National Gallery of Modern Art, Edinburgh
Easter–Jul 0131 624 6200

▶ **Matisse: Jazz**
Thelma Hulbert Gallery, Honiton (National Touring Exhib. organised by the Hayward)
6 Apr–5 May Hayward: 020 7921 0600

▶ **Goya: The Disparates**
Bedales Gallery, Peters Gallery (National Touring Exhib. organised by the Hayward)
6 Apr–5 May Hayward: 020 7921 0600

▶ **Friends Exhibition, Elis Gwyn Jones and Jan Barnes**
Oriel Plas Glyn-y-Weddw Gallery, Llanbedrog
6-Apr–10 May 01758 740 763

▶ **Graham Gussin**
Ikon Gallery, Birmingham
16 Apr–2 Jun 0121 248 0708

▶ **Rosslyn: Country of Painter and Poet**
National Gallery of Scotland, Edinburgh
19 Apr–7 Jul 0131 624 6200

▶ **Hai Huang: Tales of Two Cities**
Collins Gallery, Glasgow
20 Apr–18 May 0141 548 4145

▶ **Mixed Show**
The Open Eye Gallery, Edinburgh
20 Apr–9 May 0131 557 1020

▶ **Light**
National Gallery, Laing Art & Bristol City Museums Touring Exhibition. Newcastle Laing Art Gallery, Newcastle
20 Apr–7 Jul 0191 232 2000

▶ **Michael Snow**
John Hansard Gallery, Southampton
23 Apr–8 Jun 023 8059 2158

▶ **Artist: William Ratcliffe and Harold Gilman**
Southampton City Art Gallery
25 Apr–2 Jun 023 8083 2277

▶ **One Tree**
Bristol Museums and Art Gallery
27 Apr–9 Jun 0117 922 3571

▶ **Mythical Echoes Sculptures by Steve West**
Wolverhampton Art Gallery
27 Apr–15 Jun 01902 552 055

## May 2002

▶ **Tess Recordon**
Broughton House Gallery, Cambridge
May– 01223 314 960

▶ **New Contemporaries**
Barbican Gallery, London
May–Jun 020 7638 4141

▶ **Carlos Madriz**
198 Gallery, London
May–Jun 020 7978 8309

▶ **Scots in Film: Portraits by Donald Maclellan**
Scottish National Portrait Gallery, Edinburgh
May–Sep 0131 624 6200

▶ **Drummond of Hawthornden**
Scottish National Portrait Gallery, Edinburgh
May–Sep 0131 624 6200

▶ **David Octavius Hill and Robert Adamson**
Scottish National Portrait Gallery, Edinburgh
May–Sep 0131 624 6200

▶ **European Coinage**
The British Museum, London
May–15 Sep 020 7323 8000

▶ **Boyd Webb**
Estorick Collection, London
1 May–9 Jun 020 7704 9522

▶ **[X] hibit**
The London Institute Gallery, London
1 May–13 Jun 020 7514 8083

▶ **Sarah Lucas**
Milton Keynes Gallery
4 May–23 Jun 01908 676 900

▶ **Sacred and Profane**
Brighton Museum and Art Gallery
4 May–30 Jun 01273 290 900

▶ **Mali Morris: Abstract Painting**
Angel Row Gallery, Nottingham
7 May–29 Jun 0115 915 2869

▶ **Mixed Show**
The Open Eye Gallery, Edinburgh
11–30 May 0131 557 1020

▶ **Matisse: Jazz**
Yale College, Wrexham (National Touring Exhib. organised by the Hayward)
11 May–9 Jun Hayward: 020 7921 0600

▶ **Elin Huws: Textiles**
Oriel Plas Glyn-y-Weddw Gallery, Llanbedrog
12 May 01758 740 763

▶ **The Hunt for Paradise: Court Arts of Safavi Iran 1501–1576**
The British Museum, London
17 May–15 Sep 020 7323 8000

▶ **Out of Line**
Wingfield Arts (National Touring Exhib. organised by the Hayward)
18 May–30 Jun Hayward: 020 7921 0600

▶ **Wolverhampton Society of Artists**
Wolverhampton Art Gallery
18 May–28 Jun 01902 552 055

▶ **The Dutch Italianates 1600–1700**
Dulwich Picture Gallery, London
22 May–26 Aug 020 8693 5254

▶ **Giles Penny**
The McHardy Sculpture Company, London
22 May– 020 7378 7300

▶ **Boxes**
Collins Gallery, Glasgow
25 May–29 Jun 0141 548 4145

▶ **George Romney 1734–1802**
Brighton and Hove Museum and Gallery
30 May–18 Aug 01273 202 900

## June 2002

▶ **Mixed Show**
The Open Eye Gallery, Edinburgh
1–20 Jun 0131 557 1020

▶ **Printers including Recent British Prints**
Whitstable Museum and Art Gallery (National Touring Exhib. organised by the Hayward)
1–30 Jun Hayward: 020 7921 0600

▶ **Picasso: Histoire Naturelle**
The Oakham Theatre, Oakham (National Touring Exhib. organised by the Hayward)
1–30 Jun Hayward: 020 7921 0600

▶ **Pickpocketing the Rich: Portrait Painters in Bath from 1720–1793**
Holburne Museum of Art, Bath
Jun–Aug 01225 466 669

▶ **American Beauty: Painting and Sculpture from the Detroit Museum of Arts**
National Gallery of Ireland, Dublin
Jun–Aug 0033 01 661 5133

**▶ Once Upon a Time: Beatrix Potter to Harry Potter**
Brighton and Hove Museum and Gallery
Jun–Sep 01273 202 900

**▶ Archway to Angel**
Sadlers's Wells, London
Jun–Sep 020 7863 8112/4

**▶ Paul Signac: Travels in France**
The Courtauld Institute Gallery
7 Jun–19 Aug 020 7848 2526

**▶ The Queen of Sheba: Treasures from the Yemen**
The British Museum, London
7 Jun–13 Oct 020 7323 8000

**▶ Spotlight on Kenneth Martin**
Huddersfield Art Gallery (National Touring Exhib. organised by the Hayward)
8 Jun–21 Jul Hayward: 020 7921 0600

**▶ Richard Long**
Tate St Ives
10 Jun–1 Sep 01736 796 226

**▶ Naum Gabo**
Tate St Ives
10 Jun–2 Sep 01736 796 226

**▶ St Ives International: Ceramicforum**
Tate St Ives
10 Jun–2 Sep 01736 796 226

**▶ Jean Frederic Schnyder**
Ikon Gallery, Birmingham
12 Jun–21 Jul 0121 248 0708

**▶ George Abrams Collection of Dutch and Flemish Drawings and 16th Century Italian Medals**
The British Museum, London
13 Jun–22 Sep 020 7323 8000

**▶ Behind the Lines: Vietnamese Images of War**
The British Museum, London
13 Jun–22 Sep 020 7323 8000

**▶ Douglas Allsop**
Southampton City Art Gallery
13 Jun–8 Sep 023 8083 2277

**▶ Rubens and Italian Art**
National Gallery of Scotland, Edinburgh
14 Jun–1 Sep 0131 624 6200

**▶ Matisse: Jazz**
Riverhouse Barn, Walton on Thames (National Touring Exhib. organised by the Hayward)
15 Jun–14 Jul Hayward: 020 7921 0600

**▶ Anthony Van Dyck: Ecce Homo and the Mocking of Christ**
National Gallery of Ireland, Dublin
19 Jun–11 Aug 0033 01 661 5133

**▶ Fabric of Vision: Dress and Drapery in Painting**
The National Gallery, London
19 Jun–8 Sep 020 7747 2865

**▶ Japanese Swords from the Peter Moores Project**
The British Museum, London
20 Jun–autumn 020 7323 8000

**▶ Mixed Show**
The Open Eye Gallery, Edinburgh
22 Jun–11 Jul 0131 557 1020

**▶ Potential**
John Hansard Gallery, Southampton
25 Jun–24 Aug 023 8059 2158

**▶ Pasta: Italian Culture on a Plate**
Estorick Collection, London
26 Jun–15 Sep 020 7704 9522

**▶ 100 Posters: The Odermatt Collection**
The London Institute Gallery, London
26 Jun–Aug 020 7514 8083

**▶ Fauve Painting 1905–07: The Triumph of Pure Colour**
Courtauld Institute Gallery, London
27 Jun–27 Aug 020 7848 2589

**▶ Act It Out**
Wolverhampton Art Gallery
29 Jun–31 Aug 01902 552 055

## July 2002

**▶ Urban Vision Project Exhibition**
198 Gallery, London
Jul 020 7978 8309

**▶ Saving Faces: Portraits by Mark Gilbert**
Leeds City Art Gallery, Leeds
Jul–Aug 0113 247 8255

**▶ Game On**
Barbican Gallery, London
Jul–early Sep 020 7638 4141

**▶ Mary Maclean: Foiled**
Collins Gallery, Glasgow
6 Jul–10 Aug 0141 548 4145

**▶ Ravi Depres**
Angel Row Gallery, Nottingham
6 Jul–2 Nov 0115 915 2869

**▶ Collect and Connect**
Wolverhampton Art Gallery
13 Jul–14 Sep 01902 552 055

**▶ Light**
The National Gallery, London (Laing Art & Bristol City Museums Touring Exhibition)
17 Jul–13 Oct 020 7747 2865

**▶ Matisse: Jazz**
St Barbe Museum, Lymington (National Touring Exhib. organised by the Hayward)
20 Jul–18 Aug Hayward: 020 7921 0600

**▶ Nicola Hicks Sculpture and Drawings**
Brighton and Hove Museum and Gallery
20 Jul–15 Sep 01273 202 900

**▶ Ben Nicholson**
Kettle's Yard, Cambridge
27 Jul–2 Oct 01223 352124

**▶ Vladimir Arkhipov**
Ikon Gallery, Birmingham
30 Jul–8 Sep 0121 248 0708

## August 2002

**▶ Howard Hodgkin**
Dean Gallery, Scottish National Gallery of Modern Art, Edinburgh
Aug–Oct 0131 624 6200

**▶ Mixed show**
The Open Eye Gallery, Edinburgh
9 Aug–5 Sep 0131 557 1020

**▶ Picasso: Histoire Naturelle**
Washington Arts Centre (National Touring Exhib. organised by the Hayward)
10 Aug–8 Sep Hayward: 020 7921 0600

**▶ Making Journeys: Textiles by Inge Hueber Anne Keith and Veronica Togneri**
Collins Gallery, Glasgow
17 Aug–21 Sep 0141 548 4145

**▶ John Freeman – Memorial**
Leeds City Art Gallery, Leeds
25 Aug–25 Nov 0113 247 9689

## September 2002

**▶ Leeds Photographic Society: Anniversary Exhibition**
Leeds City Art Gallery, Leeds
Sep 0113 247 8255

**▶ Mike Lyons**
Whitworth Art Gallery, Manchester
Sep–Dec 0161 275 7450

**▶ Dressing Down Contemporary Art, Fashion and Photography**
Barbican, London
Sep–early Jan 020 7638 4141

**▶ Cocteau**
Barbican, London
Sep–Jan 020 7638 4141

**▶ Charles Masson: Collections in Afghanistan**
The British Museum, London
Sep–Jan 020 7323 8000

**▶ Watercolour Society of Wales**
MOMA, Machynlleth
2 Sep–5 Oct 01291 690 260

**▶ Asylum: Places of Refuge in Art and Life**
Angel Row Gallery, Nottingham
7 Sep–2 Nov 0115 915 2869

**▶ Dubuffet's Walls: Lithographs for Les Murs**
Piece Hall Art Gallery, Halifax (National Touring Exhib. organised by the Hayward)
8 Sep–7 Oct Hayward: 020 7921 0600

**▶ Again Again**
John Hansard Gallery, Southampton
10 Sep–26 Oct 023 8059 2158

▶ **David Wilkie**
Dulwich Picture Gallery, London
11 Sep–1 Dec 020 8693 5254

▶ **Jules Breton**
National Gallery of Ireland, Dublin
15 Sep–Nov 0033 01 661 5133

▶ **Tim Pomeroy**
The McHardy Sculpture Company, London
25 Sep– 020 7378 7300

▶ **Double Take: Jon Mills Metalwork and Michele Walker Textiles**
Brighton Museum and Gallery
28 Sep–16 Nov 01273 202 900

## October 2002

▶ **I Don't Want To Look Anymore, I Just Want To See**
Leeds City Art Gallery, Leeds
Oct–Dec 0113 247 8255

▶ **Under Mussolini: Decorative & Propaganda arts in the 1920s–30s**
Estorick Collection, London
2 Oct–22 Dec 020 7704 9522

▶ **Americans: Portraits from the National Portrait Gallery, Washington DC**
Brighton and Hove Museum and Gallery
3 Oct–12 Jan 01273 202 900

▶ **Tom McKendrick: Heavier Than Air**
Collins Gallery, Glasgow
5 Oct–23 Nov 0141 548 4145

▶ **ARTAID 2002**
10 Oct–10 Nov
Following the huge success of ARTAID 2000, this will be the 3rd ARTAID Biennial contemporary group show to raise money for Crusaid. Some of the artists who have been included in previous ARTAID shows are David Bowie, Antony Gormley, Damien Hirst, Gary Hume, Howard Hodgkin, Martin Maloney, Ron Mueck and Mark Wallinger.

For venue details and further information re ARTAID 2002:
Tel: 020 7833 3939
Fax: 020 7833 8644
Email: artaid@crusaid.org.uk

▶ **The Mare's Tale**
Bristol Museums and Art Gallery
12 Oct–23 Nov 0117 922 3571

▶ **Madame de Pompadour: Images of a Mistress**
The National Gallery, London
16 Oct–12 Jan 020 7747 2865

▶ **Byronism**
Brighton and Hove Museum and Gallery
16 Oct–9 Feb 01273 202 900

▶ **On Top of the World: Scottish Mountaineers at Home and Abroad**
Scottish National Portrait Gallery, Edinburgh
25 Oct–19 Jan 0131 624 6200

## November 2002

▶ **Thomas Newbolt**
Broughton House Gallery, Cambridge
Nov 01223 314 960

▶ **Gold Matters: Value of Gold in diverse cultures**
Angel Row Gallery, Nottingham
9 Nov–11 Jan 0115 915 2869

▶ **Antony Gormley's Field for the British Isles**
The British Museum, London
15 Nov–12 Jan 020 7323 8000

▶ **Christmas Exhibition**
The McHardy Sculpture Company, London
20 Nov– 020 7378 7300

▶ **Barbara Hepworth**
The New Art Centre Sculpture Park and Gallery, Wiltshire
23 Nov 01980 862 244

▶ **Josephine Pryde**
The New Art Centre Sculpture Park and Gallery, Wiltshire
23 Nov 01980 862 244

▶ **Francois Roche Pierre Huygue, Philippe Parreno and graphic designers M/M**
ICA, London
23 Nov–13 Jan 020 7930 3647

▶ **The Collins' Christmas Show**
Collins Gallery, Glasgow
30 Nov–21 Dec 0141 548 4145

## December 2002

▶ **Cecily Sash**
Broughton House Gallery, Cambridge
Dec – phone for details 01223 314 960

▶ **Albrecht Dürer and his Influence: The Graphic Work of a Renaissance Artist**
The British Museum, London
6 Dec–23 Mar 020 7323 8000

▶ **Photography and Memory: A Seaside Album**
Brighton and Hove Museum and Gallery
7 Dec–9 Feb 01273 202 900

▶ **David Hockney: Grimm's Fairy Tales**
Ards Art Centre, Newtownards (National Touring Exhib. organised by the Hayward)
8 Dec–6 Jan Hayward: 020 7921 0600

▶ **Fixation 2**
AOP Gallery, London
10 Dec–12 Jan 020 7739 6669

▶ **Crawford Open 2**
Crawford Municipal Art Gallery, Cork
14 Dec–26 Jan 00353 021 4273 377

▶ **Duane Hanson**
Scottish National Gallery of Modern Art, Edinburgh
15 Dec–25 Feb 0131 624 6200

▶ **Arthur Rackham**
Dulwich Picture Gallery, London
18 Dec–spring 020 8693 5254

## INTERNATIONAL

### Continuing from previous months

**▶ Massimo Campigli**
Mona Bismarck Foundation, 34 avenue de New York, 75116 Paris, France
Sep–Nov 0033 01 47 23 38 33

**▶ Francesc Vidal**
Centre d'Art Santa Monica, Adreça, Rambla de Santa Monica 7, 08002, Barcelona, Spain
Sep–Dec 0034 93 316 28 10

**▶ Balthus**
Palazzo Grassi, San Samuele 3231, Italy
6 Sep–6 Jan 0039 041 523 1680

**▶ Linda McCartney: Retrospective**
Schloß Schoënbrunn, Kaiserliches Hoffmobiliendepot, 7 Mariahilfer Straße 88, Vienna, Austria
6 Sep–9 Dec 0043 1 524 33 57

**▶ Landscapes from Brueghel to Kandinsky**
Art and Exhibition Hall of the Republic of Germany, D-53113 Bonn, Museumsmeile Bonn, Friedrich-Ebert-Allee 4, Germany
7 Sep–25 Nov 0049 0228 9171200

**▶ Miracle de la Couleur**
Wallraf-Richartz-Museum, Fondation Corboud, Offentlichkeitsarbeit, Martinstraße 39, 50666 Cologne, Germany
7 Sep–9 Dec 0049 0221 2212371

**▶ Ernst Ludwig Kirchner**
Brücke Museum, Bussardsteig 9, 14195 Berlin, Germany
7 Sep–25 Nov 0049 030 8312029

**▶ The Wild West**
Arken, Museum for Modern Art, Skovvej 100, DK 2635 ISHØJ, Denmark
8 Sep–20 Jan 0045 43 54 02 22

**▶ Frederick Carl Frieseke: The Evolution of an American Impressionist**
San Diego Museum of Art. 1450 El Prado, Balboa Park, San Diego, California, USA
8 Sep–11 Nov 001 619 232 7931

**▶ The Short Century: Independence and Liberation Movements in Africa 1945–1994**
Museum of Contemporary Art in Chicago, 220 East Chicago Avenue, Chicago, Illinois 60611-2604, USA
8 Sep–30 Dec 001 312 280 660

**▶ Bruce Nauman**
Denver Art Museum, 13 Avenue and Acoma, Downtown Denver, Colorado, USA
8 Sep–30 Dec 001 720 865 5000

**▶ Art, Community and Identity**
Denver Art Museum, 13 Avenue and Acoma, Downtown Denver, Colorado, USA
8 Sep–25 Nov 001 720 865 5000

**▶ Samuel Mockbee**
The Contemporary Arts Center, Cincinnati, Ohio 45202-3998, USA
8 Sep–11 Nov 001 513 721 0390

**▶ Selections Fall 2001**
The Drawing Center, 35 Wooster Street, New York, New York 10013, USA
8 Sep–20 Oct 001 212 219 2166

**▶ Rob Pruitt: 101 Art Ideas You Can Do Yourself**
The Contemporary Arts Center, Cincinnati, Ohio 45202-3998, USA
8 Sep–11 Nov 001 513 721 0390

**▶ Iran do Espirito Santo**
The Contemporary Arts Center, Cincinnati, Ohio 45202-3998, USA
8 Sep–11 Nov 001 513 721 0390

**▶ Christo and Jeanne Claude**
Neuer Berliner Kunstverein, Chaussseestr, 128/129, 10115 Berlin, Germany
8 Sep–30 Dec 0049 030 2807020

**▶ Change of Scene XX**
Museum für Moderne Kunst, Domstrasse 10, D 60311, Frankfurt, Germany
9 Sep–Mar 0049 069 21235844

**▶ Along the Nile: Early Photographs of Egypt**
The Metropolitan Museum of Art, 1000 Fifth Ave, New York 10028, USA
11 Sep–30 Dec 001 212 535 7710

**▶ The Pharaoh's Photographers: Harry Burton, Tutankhamun, and the Metropolitan's Egyptian Expedition**
The Metropolitan Museum of Art, 1000 Fifth Ave, New York 10028, USA
11 Sep–30 Dec 001 212 535 7710

**▶ Caspar David Friedrich: Moonwatchers**
The Metropolitan Museum, 1000 Fifth Ave, New York 10028, USA
11 Sep–11 Nov 001 212 535 7710

**▶ Helen Levitt**
Centre Nationale de la Photographie. Hotel Salomon de Rothschild, 11 rue Berryer, 75008 Paris, France
12 Sep–19 Nov 0033 01 53 76 12 32

**▶ Martin Puryear: Sculpture of the 1990s**
University of California, Berkeley Art Museum, 2625 Durant Avenue, Berkeley, California 94720-2250, USA
12 Sep–16 Dec 001 510 642 0808

**▶ The Dream of the Audience: Theresa Hak Kyung Cha 1951–1982**
University of California, Berkeley Art Museum, 2625 Durant Avenue, Berkeley, California 94720-2250, USA
12 Sep–16 Dec 001 510 642 0808

**▶ The Surrounding Walls of Paris**
The French Army Museum, 129 rue de Grenelle, 75007 Paris, France
12 Sep–11 Nov 0033 01 44 42 37 72

**▶ The Venetian Cinquecento: Paintings from the State Hermitage in Saint Petersburg**
Museu National d'Art de Catalunya, Palau Nacional, Parc de Montjuïc, 08038 Barcelona, Spain
12 Sep–9 Dec 0034 93 622 03 76

**▶ Children in Murillo's Paintings**
Prado, P del Prado s/n, 28014 Madrid, Spain
13 Sep–18 Nov 0034 91 330 28 00

**▶ Christopher Wool**
Secession, Friedrichstraße 12, 1010 Vienna, Austria
13 Sep–11 Nov 0043 1 587 53 07 34

**▶ Linda Bilda**
Secession, Friedrichstraße 12, 1010 Vienna, Austria
13 Sep–11 Nov 0043 1 587 53 07 34

**▶ Jean Dubuffett: Centennial Exhibition**
Centre national d'art et de culture Georges Pompidou, 75191 Paris, France
13 Sep–31 Dec 0033 01 44 78 12 33

**▶ Pieter Boel 1622–1674**
Musée du Louvre, 75058, Paris, France
14 Sep–17 Dec 0033 01 40 20 53 17

**▶ Jeffry Mitchell**
Henry Art Gallery, University of Washington, Seattle, Washington 98195-1410, USA
14 Sep–1 Jan 001 206 543 2280

**▶ Loop: Back to the Beginning**
Kunsthalle der Hypo-Kulturstiftung, Theatinerstraße 8, Perusahof, D-80333, Munich, Germany
14 Sep–4 Nov 0049 089 224412

**▶ Stanley Spencer**
Art Gallery of Ontario, 317 Dundas St West, Toronto, Ontario, Canada M5T 1G4
14 Sep–16 Dec 001 416 977 0414

**▶ Ido Bar El**
Museum van Hedendaagse Kunst Antwerpen, Leuvestraat 32, B-2000, Antwerp, Belgium
15 Sep–18 Nov 0032 3 238 59 60

**▶ Robert Jacobsen: The Poetry of Space**
Statens Museum for Kunst, 48-50 Solvgade, D-K 1307 Copenhagen K, Denmark
15 Sep–13 Jan 0045 33 74 84 40

**▶ Antioch: The Lost Ancient City**
The Baltimore Museum of Art, 10 Art Museum Drive, Baltimore, MD 21218-3898, USA
16 Sep–30 Dec 001 410 396 7100

**▶ Ceal Floyer: Matrix 192**
University of California, Berkeley Art Museum, 2625 Durant Avenue, Berkeley, California 94720-2250, USA
16 Sep–11 Nov 001 510 642 0808

**▶ Jessica Bronson: Matrix 194**
University of California, Berkeley Art Museum, 2625 Durant Avenue, Berkeley, California 94720-2250, USA
16 Sep–11 Nov 001 510 642 0808

▶ **Architectures of Discourse**
Fundació Antoni Tapies, c/d Aragó no 255, ES 08007, Barcelona, Spain
18 Sep–11 Nov 0034 93 487 03 15

▶ **Hélio Oiticica: Quasi Cinemas**
Wexner Center for the Arts, 1871 North High Street, Columbus, Ohio 43210-1393, USA
18 Sep–30 Dec 001 614 292 3535

▶ **Johan van der Keuken: From the Body and City**
Wexner Center for the Arts, 1871 North High Street, Columbus, Ohio 43210-1393, USA
18 Sep–30 Dec 001 614 292 3535

▶ **Eduardo Arroyo**
Galeria Trama, Petritxol 8, 08002 Barcelona, Spain
20 Sep–16 Oct 0034 93 317 48 77

▶ **Annie Leibovitz: Women**
Seattle Art Museum, 100 University Street, Seattle, Washington 98101-2902, USA
20 Sep–6 Jan 001 206 654 3100

▶ **Anne Deacock-Van Raef**
Palais des Beaux Arts de Bruxelles, 10 rue Royale, 1000 Brussels, Belgium
21 Sep–4 Nov 0032 2 507 84 66

▶ **Brazil: Body and Soul**
Guggenheim Museum, New York 10128, USA
21 Sep–20 Jan 001 212 423 3500

▶ **Sol LeWitt: Incomplete Open Cubes**
Cleveland Museum of Art, 11150 East Boulevard, Cleveland, Ohio 44106, USA
22 Sep–30 Dec 001 216 421 7350

▶ **Pieter Bruegel the Elder: Drawings and Prints**
The Metropolitan Museum, 1000 Fifth Ave, New York 10028, USA
25 Sep–2 Dec 001 212 535 7710

▶ **Courtly Radiance: Metalwork from Islamic India**
The Metropolitan Museum, 1000 Fifth Ave, New York 10028, USA
25 Sep–25 Mar 001 212 535 7710

▶ **Lam Metis: Peinture de l'artiste cubain**
Musée Dapper, 35 rue Paul Valéry, 75116 Paris, France
26 Sep–20 Jan 0033 01 45 00 01 50

▶ **Contemporary Japanese Photography**
Finnish Museum of Photography, Cable Factory, Tallberginkaten 1G, FIN 00180, Helsinki, Finland
27 Sep–10 Nov 00358 96866 360

▶ **New Connections**
National Gallery in Prague, Palac Kinsky, Starom_stské nàm.12, 120 00, Praha 2, Prague, Czech Republic
27 Sep–13 Jan 00420 2 24 81 07 58 9

▶ **Wilde Americk: Discovery and Exploration**
Yale Center for British Art, 161 York Street, New Haven, Connecticut 06520, USA
27 Sep–30 Dec 001 203 432 2800

▶ **Great British Paintings from American Collections**
Yale Center for British Art, 161 York Street, New Haven, Connecticut 06520, USA
27 Sep–30 Dec 001 203 432 2800

▶ **La Vertigine della non forma: da Kandinsky a Polloock**
Museo Cantonale d'Arte Lugano, Via Canova 10, 6900 Lugano, Italy
29 Sep–6 Jan 0039 091 910 4780

▶ **Vito Acconci: Acts of Architecture**
Contemporary Arts Museum, 5216 Montrose Blvd, Houston, Texas 77006-6598, USA
29 Sep–25 Nov 001 713 284 8250

▶ **Design Positions in Art**
Museum für Angewandte Kunst, An der Rechtschule Kunst, D 5000, Cologne 1, Germany
29 Sep–9 Dec 0049 221 22126714

▶ **Venezia 1501: Petrucci e la stampa musicale**
Biblioteca Nazionale Marciana, Venice 30124, Italy
30 Sep–30 Oct 0039 041 240 7241

▶ **Virtue and Beauty: Leonardo's Ginevra de Benci and Renaissance Portraits of Women**
National Gallery of Art, Fourth Str at Constitution Ave, NW, Washington, DC 20565
30 Sep–6 Jan 001 202 842 6353

▶ **Wishing Welles**
Museum of Photographic Art, 1649 El Prado, San Diego, California 921101, USA
Oct–Nov 001 619 238 7559

▶ **Pedro G Romero**
Centre d'Art Santa Monica, Adreça, Rambla de Santa Monica 7, 08002, Barcelona, Spain
Oct–Dec 0034 93 316 28 10

▶ **The Lady at the Window: Figure Painting in the Qing Dynasty 1644–1911**
University of California, Berkeley Art Museum, 2625 Durant Avenue, Berkeley, California, USA 94720-2250
Oct–Jan 001 510 642 0808

▶ **Facing Museums**
The Walters Art Museum, 600 North Charles Street, Baltimore, Maryland 21201-5185, USA
Oct–Jun 001 410 547 9000

▶ **Fabrizio Plessi: Roma**
Guggenheim Bilbao, Abandoibarra Et 2, 48001 Bilbao, Spain
1 Oct–20 Jan 0034 94 435 90 80

▶ **Louise Bourgeois**
Guggenheim Bilbao, Abandoibarra Et 2, 48001 Bilbao, Spain
1 Oct–20 Jan 0034 94 435 90 80

▶ **Jeff Koons**
Guggenheim Bilbao, Abandoibarra Et 2, 48001 Bilbao, Spain
1 Oct–20 Jan 0034 94 435 90 80

▶ **The Thannhauser Collection**
Guggenheim Bilbao, Abandoibarra Et 2, 48001 Bilbao, Spain
1 Oct–20 Jan 0034 94 435 90 80

▶ **The Modern City**
Guggenheim Bilbao, Abandoibarra Et 2, 48001 Bilbao, Spain
1 Oct–20 Jan 0034 94 435 90 80

▶ **Form: The Classical Ideal in Modern Art from Renoir to Picasso**
Museo Thyssen Bornemisza, Carrer Sant Lu, 08010 Barcelona, Spain
2 Oct–13 Jan 0034 932 80 14 34

▶ **Neo-Impressionism: The Circle of Paul Signac**
The Metropolitan Museum, 1000 Fifth Ave, New York 10028, USA
2 Oct–30 Dec 001 212 535 7710

▶ **Glass of the Sultans**
The Metropolitan Museum, 1000 Fifth Ave, New York 10028, USA
2 Oct–13 Jan 001 212 535 7710

▶ **Arnold Böcklin 1827–1901**
Musée d'Orsay, 62 rue de Lille, 75343 Paris, France
2 Oct–14 Jan 0033 01 45 48 21 25

▶ **Klinger/Brahms**
Musée d'Orsay, 62 rue de Lille, 75343 Paris, France
2 Oct–14 Jan 0033 01 45 48 21 25

▶ **Europalia Pologne**
Palais des Beaux Arts de Bruxelles, 10 rue Royale, 1000 Brussels, Belgium
3 Oct–6 Jan 0032 2 507 84 66

▶ **Form Follows Fiction**
Museo d'Arte Contemporanea, Piazza Mafalda di Savoia, 10098 Rivoli, Torino, Italy
3 Oct–13 Jan 0039 011 956 5222

▶ **Ten Shades of Green**
University of California, Berkeley Art Museum, 2625 Durant Avenue, Berkeley, California, USA 94720-2250
3 Oct–2 Dec 001 510 642 0808

▶ **Anna Gaskell**
Museo d'Arte Contemporanea, Piazza Mafalda di Savoia, 10098 Rivoli, Torino, Italy
3 Oct–13 Jan 0039 011 956 5222

▶ **Ferdinand Hodler**
Fundación La Caixa, C/ Serrano 60, Madrid 28001, Spain
4 Oct–25 Nov 0034 91 435 48 33

▶ **Giorgio Morandi**
Musée d'Art Moderne de la Ville de Paris, 11 Avenue du Président Wilson, 75116 Paris, France
4 Oct–6 Jan 0033 1 53 67 40 00

▶ **The Spanish Civil War**
Museu National d'Art de Catalunya, Palau Nacional, Parc de Montjuïc, 08038

Barcelona, Spain
4 Oct–15 Jan 0034 93 622 03 76

▶ **Ludwig Meidner 1884–1966: A German Expressionist**
Jewish Museum Vienna,
Dorotheergassse 11, 1010 Vienna, Austria
4 Oct–20 Jan 0043 01 535 04 31

▶ **Ecrivains confronts leur image de Sandrine Jousseaume**
Le Botanique, Rue Royale 236,
1210 Brussels, Belgium
5 Oct–4 Nov 0032 2 218 37 32

▶ **12x12 New Artists/New Works**
Museum of Contemporary Art in Chicago,
220 East Chicago Avenue, Chicago,
Illinois 60611-2604, USA
5 Oct–ongoing 001 312 280 660

▶ **Henri Matisse: Spirit and Sense**
Fundación Juan March, Castelló, 77,
28006 Madrid, Spain
5 Oct–20 Jan 0034 91 435 42 40

▶ **Masterpieces from Fra Angelico to Bonnard: The Rau Collection**
Haus der Kunst, Prinzregentenstraße 1,
D 80538 Munich, Germany
5 Oct–13 Jan 0049 089 211270

▶ **Jacqueline Fraser: Portrait of the Lost Boys**
New Museum of Contemporary Art, 583
Broadway, New York, New York 10012, USA
5 Oct–13 Jan 001 212 431 5328

▶ **Klee Figures**
The Metropolitan Museum, 1000 Fifth Ave,
New York 10028, USA
5 Oct–13 Jan 001 212 535 7710

▶ **Jason Middelbrook: Dig**
New Museum of Contemporary Art, 583
Broadway, New York, New York 10012, USA
5 Oct–13 Jan 001 212 431 5328

▶ **Aat Veldhoen: Retrospective**
Rembrandt House Museum, Jodenbreestraat 4,
1011 NK Amsterdam, Netherlands
6 Oct–6 Jan 0031 020 5200 4000

▶ **Francis Al s/Phone Labyrinth/Matrix 145**
Wadsworth Atheneum Museum of Art,
600 Main St, Hartford, Connecticut, USA
6 Oct–6 Jan 001 860 278 2670

▶ **Architects of American Fashion: Norman Norell and Pauline Trigre**
Wadsworth Atheneum Museum of Art,
600 Main Str, Hartford, Connecticut, USA
6 Oct–17 Feb 001 860 278 2670

▶ **Alice Neel**
Denver Art Museum, 13 Avenue and Acoma,
Downtown Denver, Colorado, USA
6 Oct–30 Dec 001 720 865 5000

▶ **Vik Muniz: Seeing is Believing**
Contemporary Arts Center, 900 Camp Street,
New Orleans, Louisiana 70130, USA
6 Oct–30 Dec 001 504 528 3805

▶ **Cultural Fusion: Recent Works by Kimberly Dummons, Clifton Faust, Theresa Herrera and Edie Tsong**
Contemporary Arts Center, 900 Camp Street,
New Orleans, Louisiana 70130, USA
6 Oct–30 Dec 001 504 528 3805

▶ **Taking Positions**
Georg-Kolbe-Museum, Sensburger Allee 25,
14055 Berlin, Germany
7 Oct–6 Jan 0049 030 3047041

▶ **Goltzius and the Third Dimension**
Clark Art Insstitute, Williamstown,
Massachusetts, USA
7 Oct–6 Jan 001 413 458 2303

▶ **Great Masters of Mexican Folk Art**
Dallas Museum of Art,
1717 North Harwood Street at
St Pauls Avenue, Dallas, Texas 75201, USA
7 Oct–6 Jan 001 214 922 1200

▶ **Exodus: Photographs by Sebastiao Salgado**
Deutscheshistoriches Museum,
Kronprinzenpalais, Unter den Linden 3,
D-10117 Berlin, Germany
8 Oct–27 Nov 0049 030 203040

▶ **Transient Homes Novembre d'Anne Penders**
Le Botanique, Rue Royale 236,
1210 Brussels, Belgium
9 Oct–16 Dec 0032 2 218 37 32

▶ **Tunga: Mira Schendel**
Galerie nationale du Jeu de Paume, 1,
Place de la Concorde, 75008, France
9 Oct–18 Nov 0033 01 47 60 69 69

▶ **Signac 1863–1935: Master Neo-Impressionist**
The Metropolitan Museum,
1000 Fifth Ave, New York 10028, USA
9 Oct–30 Dec 001 212 535 7710

▶ **Nan Goldin**
Centre national d'art et de culture Georges
Pompidou, 75191 Paris, France
10 Oct–10 Dec 0033 01 44 78 12 33

▶ **Marlene Dumas**
Centre national d'art et de culture Georges
Pompidou, 75191 Paris, France
10 Oct–31 Dec 0033 01 44 78 12 33

▶ **Antoine Pevsner dans les collections du Centre Pompidou**
Centre national d'art et de culture Georges
Pompidou, 75191 Paris, France
10 Oct–31 Dec 0033 01 44 78 12 33

▶ **Candace Wheeler: The Art and Enterprise of American Design, 1875–1900**
The Metropolitan Museum, 1000 Fifth Ave,
New York 10028, USA
10 Oct–6 Jan 001 212 535 7710

▶ **Alberto Giacometti**
MoMA, 11 West 53 Street,
New York, New York, USA
11 Oct–8 Jan 001 212 708 9400

▶ **The Spirit of the Forest: The UPM Kymmene Collection**
Kunsthalle Helsinki, Nervanderinkatu 3,
00100 Helsinki, Finland
11 Oct–11 Nov 00358 9 454 2060

▶ **Canvas of War: Masterpieces from the Candian War Museum**
Art Gallery of Ontario, 317 Dundas Str West,
Toronto, Ontario, Canada M5T 1G4
12 Oct–6 Jan 416 977 0414

▶ **Dora Maar and Pablo Picasso: A Dangerous Liason**
Haus der Kunst, Prinzregentenstraße 1,
D 80538 Munich, Germany
12 Oct–13 Jan 0049 089 211270

▶ **Maria Austria: Photographs**
Jewish Historical Museum, Jonas Daniël
Meijerplein 2–4, Amsterdam, Netherlands
12 Oct–3 Mar 0031 020 6269 945

▶ **Tom Freidman**
New Museum of Contemporary Art, 583
Broadway, New York, New York 10012, USA
12 Oct–3 Feb 001 212 431 5328

▶ **Heli Hiltunen: Ars Fennica 2001 Prize**
Amos Anderson Art Museum,
PL 14, 00101 Helsinki, Finland
13 Oct–18 Nov 00358 09 68444632

▶ **X-rummet**
Statens Museum for Kunst, 48–50 Solvgade,
D-K 1307 Copenhagen K, Denmark
13 Oct–6 Jan 0045 33 74 84 40

▶ **Zero to Infinity: Arte Povera 1962–1972**
Walker Art Center, Vineland Place,
Minneapolis, Minnesota 55403, USA
13 Oct–13 Jan 001 612 375 7622

▶ **The Age of Rembrandt: Etchings from Holland's Golden Century**
San Diego Museum of Art. 1450 El Prado,
Balboa Park, San Diego, California, USA
13 Oct–13 Jan 001 619 232 7931

▶ **Picasso's Studio: David Douglas Duncan Photographs**
Cleveland Museum of Art, 11150 East Boulevard,
Cleveland, Ohio 44106, USA
13 Oct–19 Dec 001 216 421 7350

▶ **Artists Photographing Artists**
Cleveland Museum of Art, 11150 East Boulevard,
Cleveland, Ohio 44106, USA
13 Oct–27 Feb 001 216 421 7350

▶ **Animations**
PS1 Contemporary Art Center, 22–25
Jackson Ave at 46th Ave,
Long Island City, New York, 11101, USA
14 Oct–winter 001 718 784 2084

▶ **Joe Brainard**
PS1 Contemporary Art Center,
22–25 Jackson Ave at 46th Ave,
Long Island City, New York, 11101, USA
14 Oct–winter 001 718 784 2084

▶ **Janet Cardiff**
PS1 Contemporary Art Center,
22–25 Jackson Ave at 46th Ave, Long Island City, New York, 11101, USA
14 Oct–winter 001 718 784 2084

▶ **Richard Deacon**
PS1 Contemporary Art Center,
22–25 Jackson Ave at 46th Ave,
Long Island City, New York, 11101, USA
14 Oct–winter 001 718 784 2084

▶ **Yayoi Kusama**
Bass Museum of Art, 2121 Park Avenue,
Miami Beach, Florida 33139, USA
15 Oct–31 Dec 001 305 673 7530

▶ **August Strinberg 1849–1912**
Musée d'Orsay, 62 rue de Lille,
75343 Paris, France
16 Oct–27 Jan 0033 01 45 48 21 25

▶ **Ellen Gallagher**
ICA, 955 Boylston Street, Boston,
Massachussetts 02115, USA
17 Oct–31 Dec 001 617 927 6617

▶ **Erotic Picasso**
Museu Picasso de Barcelona,
Montcada 15–19, E 08003, Barcelona, Spain
17 Oct–20 Jan 0034 93 319 63 10

▶ **Assumpci Mateu**
Galeria Trama, Petritxol 8,
08002 Barcelona, Spain
18 Oct–17 Nov 0034 93 317 48 77

▶ **Treasury of the World: Jewelled Arts of India in the Age of the Mughals**
The Metropolitan Museum, 1000 Fifth Ave,
New York 10028, USA
18 Oct–13 Jan 001 212 535 7710

▶ **The Most Modest Art: J Apek**
National Gallery in Prague, Palac Kinsky,
Starom_stské nàm.12, 120 00, Praha 2, Prague,
Czech Republic
18 Oct–3 Feb 00420 2 24 81 07 58 9

▶ **Collection of J Kola**
National Gallery in Prague, Palac Kinsky,
Starom_stské nàm.12, 120 00, Praha 2,
Prague, Czech Republic
18 Oct–3 Feb 00420 2 24 81 07 58 9

▶ **La Peinture comme crime ou la part maudite de la modernité**
Musée du Louvre, 75058, Paris, France
19 Oct–14 Jan 0033 01 40 20 53 17

▶ **The Promise of Photography**
Le Botanique, Rue Royale 236,
1210 Brussels, Belgium
19 Oct–16 Dec 0032 2 218 37 32

▶ **Images from the World Between: The Circus in 20th Century American Art**
Wadsworth Atheneum Museum of Art,
600 Main Str, Hartford, Connecticut, USA
19 Oct–6 Jan 001 860 278 2670

▶ **Invitation à l'Atelier de Gilbert Boyer**
Musée Zadkine, 100 bis, rue d'Assas,
75006 Paris, France
19 Oct–20 Jan 0033 01 43 26 91 90

▶ **Travers es**
Musée d'Art Moderne de la Ville de Paris,
11 avenue du Président Wilson,
75116 Paris, France
19 Oct–13 Jan 0033 01 53 67 40 00

▶ **Images of the Family**
Neue Gesellschaft fuer Bildende Kunst,
Oranienstrasse 25, D 10999, Berlin, Germany
20 Oct–25 Nov 0049 030 6153031

▶ **William Kentridge**
Museum of Contemporary Art in Chicago,
220 East Chicago Avenue, Chicago,
Illinois 60611-2604, USA
20 Oct–20 Jan 001 312 280 660

▶ **The Motion Pictures of Eadward Muybridge and Dr Harold Egerton**
Denver Art Museum, 13 Avenue and Acoma,
Downtown Denver, Colorado, USA
20 Oct–14 Apr 001 720 865 5000

▶ **Quadriënnale Casino 2001**
Museum of Contemporary Art,
Citadelpark 9000, Ghent, Belgium
20 Oct–13 Jan 0032 9 221 17 03

▶ **Desire and Devotion: Art from India, Nepal and Tibet in the John and Berthe Ford Collection**
The Walters Art Museum,
600 North Charles Street,
Baltimore, Maryland 21201-5185, USA
20 Oct–13 Jan 001 410 547 9000

▶ **The American Artist as Painter and Draftsmen**
The Walters Art Museum, 600 North Charles Street, Baltimore, Maryland 21201-5185, USA
20 Oct–1 Jan 001 410 547 9000

▶ **Aelbert Cuyp**
National Gallery of Art, Fourth Str at Constitution Ave, NW, Washington, DC 20565
21 Oct–27 Jan 001 202 842 6353

▶ **Art Deco and Streamlined Modern Design: 1920–1940**
Dallas Museum of Art,
1717 North Harwood Street at
St Pauls Avenue, Dallas, Texas 75201, USA
21 Oct–17 Feb 001 214 922 1200

▶ **Trenton Hancock: The Life and Death of Number 1**
Modern Art Museum of Fort Worth, 1309
Montgomery Street, Camp Bowie Boulevard,
Fort Worth, Texas 76107, USA
21 Oct–20 Jan 001 817 738 9215

▶ **Artists Take on Detroit**
Detroit Institute of Art, 5200 Woodward Avenue,
Detroit, Michigan 48202, USA
21 Oct–6 Jan 001 313 833 7900

▶ **Henry Moore**
National Gallery of Art, Fourth Str at
Constitution Ave, NW, Washington, DC 20565
21 Oct–27 Jan 001 202 842 6353

▶ **Stairs**
Centre de Cultura Contemporania de Barcelona,
C/ Montalegre 5, 08001 Barcelona, Spain
23 Oct–27 Jan 0034 93 306 41 48

▶ **Kannibals et Vahines: Imagerie des mers du sud**
Musée National des Arts d'Afrique et d'Oceanie,
293 avenue Daumesnil, 75012 Paris, France
24 Oct–18 Feb 0033 01 473 46 51 61

▶ **Martin Kippenberger**
Österreichische Galerie Belvedere,
Prinz Eugen-Straße 27, A-1037 Vienna, Austria
24 Oct–24 Feb 0043 1 79 55 70

▶ **Judith Rothschild: An Artists Search**
SFMOMA, 151 Third Street, San Francisco,
California 94103, USA
25 Oct–17 Feb 001 415 357 4000

▶ **Norman Foster: Retrospective**
Museum für Angewandte Kunst,
An der Rechtschule Kunst, D 5000,
Cologne 1, Germany
26 Oct–31 Dec 0049 221 22126714

▶ **Rachel Whiteread: Transient Spaces**
Deutsche Guggenheim Berlin,
Unter den Linden 13–15, 10117 Berlin, Germany
27 Oct–13 Jan 0049 030 2020930

▶ **Tim Beeby**
Museum voor Schone Kunsten, Wapenplein,
B8400, Oostende, Belgium
27 Oct–25 Nov 0032 059 80 53 35

▶ **Werner Watty**
Museum voor Schone Kunsten,
Wapenplein, B8400, Oostende, Belgium
27 Oct–25 Nov 0032 059 80 53 35

▶ **Audible Images: Sound and Photography**
Museum of Contemporary Photography,
600 South Michigan Avenue, Chicago,
Illinois 60605, USA
27 Oct–22 Dec 001 312 663 5554

▶ **The Cos Cob Art Colony: Impressionists on the Connecticut Shore**
Denver Art Museum, 13 Avenue and Acoma,
Downtown Denver, Colorado, USA
27 Oct–20 Jan 001 720 865 5000

▶ **Elisabeth Marx**
Kölnisches Stadtmuseum, Bischofsgartenstraße
1, 1-50667, Cologne, Germany
27 Oct–30 Dec 0049 0221 212388

▶ **The Discovery of the World: The World of Discoveries**
K Haus, Karlsplatz 5, A 1010, Vienna, Austria
27 Oct–13 Jan 0043 1 587 96 63 21

▶ **Central Art Award: Ernesto Neto**
Koelnischer Kunstverein, Caecilienstrasse 33, D
50667, Cologne, Germany
27 Oct–23 Dec 0049 221 217021

▶ **Frank O Gehry: Retrospective**
Guggenheim Bilbao, Abandoibarra Et 2,

48001 Bilbao, Spain
28 Oct–Mar 0034 94 435 90 80

▶ **Picasso: The Artist's Studio**
Cleveland Museum of Art, 11150 East Boulevard, Cleveland, Ohio 44106, USA
28 Oct–6 Jan 001 216 421 7350

▶ **Bill Brandt: A Retrospective**
Museum of Photographic Art, 1649 El Prado, San Diego, California 921101, USA
28 Oct–6 Jan 001 619 238 7559

▶ **Goya and the Feminine World**
Prado, P del Prado s/n, 28014 Madrid, Spain
30 Oct–27 Jan 0034 91 330 28 00

▶ **Posing for Posterity: Portrait Drawings from the Collection**
J Paul Getty Museum, 1200 Getty Center Drive, Los Angeles, California 90049-1681, USA
30 Oct–20 Jan 001 310 440 7360

▶ **Heavenly Vision: Shaker Gift Drawings and Gift Songs**
The Drawing Center, 35 Wooster Street, New York, New York 10013, USA
31 Oct–15 Dec 001 212 219 2166

▶ **Bracha Lichtenberg Ettinger**
The Drawing Center, 40 Wooster Street, New York, New York 10013, USA
31 Oct–15 Dec 001 212 219 2166

▶ **Heather Ackroyd and Dan Harvey**
Isabella Stewart Gardner Museum, 2 Palace Road, Boston, Massachussetts 02115, USA
31 Oct–30 Dec 001 617 566 1401

## November 2001

▶ **Gure Artea**
Centre d'Art Santa Monica, Adreça, Rambla de Santa Monica 7, 08002, Barcelona, Spain
Nov–Dec 0034 93 316 28 10

▶ **Krijin de Koning**
Site Odéon No 5, 5 Place de l'Odéon, 75006 Paris, France
Nov–Dec 0033 01 44 41 05 05

▶ **Trésor de Conques**
Musée du Louvre, 75058, Paris, France
1 Nov–11 Mar 0033 01 40 20 53 17

▶ **Isa Genzken, Berlin/ Wolfgang Tilmans, London**
Museum Ludwig, Biscofsgarten 1, D-50667, Cologne, Germany
1 Nov–Feb 0049 221 2210

▶ **Thomas Bayrle, Frankfurt/ Bodys Isek Kingelez, Kinshasa**
Museum Ludwig, Biscofsgarten 1, D-50667, Cologne, Germany
1 Nov–Feb 0049 221 2210

▶ **Our Ideal Museum**
Museum Ludwig, Biscofsgarten 1, D-50667, Cologne, Germany
1 Nov–Apr 0049 221 2210

▶ **New Aquisitions: The Royal Collection of Prints and Drawings**
Statens Museum for Kunst, 48–50 Solvgade, D-K 1307 Copenhagen K, Denmark
3 Nov–20 Jan 0045 33 74 84 40

▶ **Rococo**
Rijksmuseum, 1070 DN, Amsterdam, Netherlands
3 Nov–1 Feb 0031 020 6747 171

▶ **Speak Softly and Carry a Beagle: The Art of Charles Schultz**
The Norman Rockwell Museum, Route 183, Stockbridge, Massachussetts 01262, USA
3 Nov–27 Jan 001 413 298 4100

▶ **Best Impressions: 35 Years of Prints and Sculpture ffrom Gemini GEL**
National Gallery of Art, Fourth Str at Constitution Ave, NW, Washington, DC 20565
4 Nov–20 Jan 001 202 842 6353

▶ **Kokoschka: Max Schmidt, Adolf Loos and His Friends**
Museo Thyssen Bornemisza, Carrer Sant Lu, 08010 Barcelona, Spain
6 Nov–17 Feb 00 34 932 80 14 34

▶ **Gottlieb**
Museo de Arte Abstracto Español, Casas Colgadas, 16001 Cuenca, Spain
8 Nov–13 Jan 0034 96 921 29 83

▶ **Frank Herzog**
artothek, Am Hof 50, 50667 Cologne, Germany
8 Nov–21 Dec 0049 0221 1212332

▶ **New Works: Jim Mendiola, Ordo Amoris Cabinet, Ruben Ortiz-Torres**
Art Pace, 445 North Main Avenue, San Antonio, Texas 78205, USA
8 Nov–13 Jan 001 210 212 4900

▶ **War and Peace: A German Empress at the Castle of Pavlovsk**
Haus der Kunst, Prinzregentenstraße 1, D 80538 Munich, Germany
9 Nov–10 Feb 0049 089 211270

▶ **SFMOMA Experimental Design Award**
SFMOMA, 151 Third Street, San Francisco, California 94103, USA
9 Nov–5 Feb 001 415 357 4000

▶ **Superflat**
Henry Art Gallery, University of Washington, Seattle, Washington 98195-1410, USA
10 Nov–3 Feb 001 206 543 2280

▶ **Philip Huyghe**
Museum van Hedendaagse Kunst Antwerpen, Leuvestraat 32, B-2000, Antwerp, Belgium
10 Nov–20 Jan 0032 3 238 59 60

▶ **Jan van Munster and Belu Simeon Fainarru**
Museum van Hedendaagse Kunst Antwerpen, Leuvestraat 32, B-2000, Antwerp, Belgium
10 Nov–10 Feb 0032 3 238 59 60

▶ **A Fleur de Peau: Le Moulage sur Nature au 19ème siècle**
Musée d'Orsay, 62 rue de Lille, 75343 Paris, France
13 Nov–10 Feb 0033 01 45 48 21 25

▶ **Manuel Alvarez Bravo: Optical Parables**
J Paul Getty Museum, 1200 Getty Center Drive, Los Angeles, California 90049-1681, USA
13 Nov–17 Feb 001 310 440 7360

▶ **Jean Nouvel**
Centre national d'art et de culture Georges Pompidou, 75191 Paris, France
14 Nov–4 Feb 0033 01 44 78 12 33

▶ **Picasso's Classicism**
The Baltimore Museum of Art, 10 Art Museum Drive, Baltimore, MD 21218-3898, USA
14 Nov–3 Feb 001 410 396 7100

▶ **Pavilion of Finland in Paris 1900**
Museum of Finnish Architecture, Kasarmikatu 24, 00130 Helsinki, Finland
14 Nov–13 Jan 00358 98 56 75 100

▶ **Finnish Art Nouveau Villas**
Museum of Finnish Architecture, Kasarmikatu 24, 00130 Helsinki, Finland
14 Nov–13 Jan 00358 9 8567 5100

▶ **Drawings of Suur-Merijoki Manor**
Museum of Finnish Architecture, Kasarmikatu 24, 00130 Helsinki, Finland
14 Nov–13 Jan 00358 9 8567 5100

▶ **Displaced: Paul Celan in Vienna 1947–8**
Jewish Museum Vienna, Dorotheergassse 11, 1010 Vienna, Austria
14 Nov–24 Feb 0043 01 535 04 31

▶ **Carte di riso: antique maps from China and Japan**
Biblioteca Nazionale Marciana, Venice 30124, Italy
15 Nov–14 Feb 0039 041 240 7241

▶ **Troy: Dream and Reality**
Art and Exhibition Hall of the Republic of Germany, D-53113 Bonn, Museumsmeile Bonn, Friedrich-Ebert-Allee 4, Germany
16 Nov–17 Feb 0049 0228 9171200

▶ **Norman Rockwell: Pictures for the American People**
Guggenheim Museum, 1071 Fifth Ave, New York 10128, USA
16 Nov–3 Mar 001 212 423 3500

▶ **NY Abstraction 1976–88**
Arken, Museum for Modern Art, Skovvej 100, DK 2635 ISHØJ, Denmark
17 Nov–17 Feb 0045 43 54 02 22

▶ **Kimmo Kaivanto: A Retrospective**
Kunsthalle Helsinki, Nervanderinkatu 3, 00100 Helsinki, Finland
17 Nov–30 Dec 00358 9 454 2060

▶ **Points of Departure II: Connecting with Contemporary Art**
SFMOMA, 151 Third Street, San Francisco, California 94103, USA
17 Nov–9 Jun 001 415 357 4000

▶ **En Cada Barrio Revolucion**
The Contemporary Arts Center, Cincinnati, Ohio 45202-3998, USA
17 Nov–13 Jan 001 513 721 0390

▶ **Paul Tzanotopoulos**
The Contemporary Arts Center, Cincinnati, Ohio 45202-3998, USA
17 Nov–7 Apr 001 513 721 0390

▶ **William Eggleston and Mario Merz**
Fondation Cartier pour l'art Contemporain, 261 boulevard Raspail, F 75014 Paris, France
18 Nov–Feb 0033 1 42 18 56 50

▶ **The Stamp of Impulse: Abstract Expressionist Prints**
Cleveland Museum of Art, 11150 East Boulevard, Cleveland, Ohio 44106, USA
18 Nov–27 Jan 001 216 421 7350

▶ **Thomas Scheibitz: Matrix 195**
University of California, Berkeley Art Museum, 2625 Durant Avenue, Berkeley, California 94720-2250, USA
18 Nov–13 Jan 001 510 642 0808

▶ **A Century of Drawing**
National Gallery of Art, Fourth Str at Constitution Ave, NW, Washington, DC 20565
18 Nov–7 Apr 001 202 842 6353

▶ **Jeune Peinture Belge**
Palais des Beaux Arts de Bruxelles, 10 rue Royale, 1000 Brussels, Belgium
20 Nov–6 Jan 0032 2 507 84 66

▶ **Gonzalo Scire**
Galeria Trama, Petritxol 8, 08002 Barcelona, Spain
22 Oct–29 Dec 0034 93 317 48 77

▶ **Hans-Peter Feldmann**
Fundació Antoni Tapies, c/d Aragó no 255, ES 08007, Barcelona, Spain
22 Nov–27 Jan 0034 93 487 03 15

▶ **Silent Reading: In the Inner Chambers of Fantasy 17th–19th Century Painting**
Residenzgalerie Salzburg, Postfach 527, A 5010 Salzburg, Austria
23 Nov–3 Feb 0043 662 840 451

▶ **The Hamsen Collection**
Denver Art Museum, 13 Avenue and Acoma, Downtown Denver, Colorado, USA
23 Nov–21 Apr 001 720 865 5000

▶ **Claude Monet and the Modern Art**
Kunsthalle der Hypo-Kulturstiftung, Theatinerstraße 8, Perusahof, D-80333, Munich, Germany
23 Nov–10 Mar 0049 089 224412

▶ **Weinnachten rund um den Globus**
Schloß Schönbrunn, 1130 Vienna, Austria
24 Nov–26 Dec 0043 01 81113

▶ **Muka Youth Prints**
Museum van Hedendaagse Kunst Antwerpen, Leuvestraat 32, B-2000, Antwerp, Belgium
0032 3 238 5960

▶ **Annual Christmas Tree and Neopolitain Baroque Creche**
The Metropolitan Museum, 1000 Fifth Ave, New York 10028, USA
24 Nov–6 Jan 001 212 535 7710

▶ **Dreaming Without Dreams**
Secession, Friedrichstraße 12, 1010 Vienna, Austria
28 Nov–3 Feb 0043 1 587 53 07 34

▶ **Karel Svolinsk**
National Gallery in Prague, Palac Kinsky, Starom_stské nàm.12, 120 00, Praha 2, Prague, Czech Republic
29 Nov–24 Feb 00420 2 24 81 07 58 9

## December 2001

▶ **Livio Mehus: The Genius of Painting**
Prado, P del Prado s/n, 28014 Madrid, Spain
Dec–Jan 0034 91 330 28 00

▶ **Tauromachy I**
Prado, P del Prado s/n, 28014 Madrid, Spain
Dec–Jan 0034 91 330 28 00

▶ **Films from the R John McGee Collection**
Museum of Photographic Art, 1649 El Prado, San Diego, California 921101, USA
Dec–Mar 001 619 238 7559

▶ **Reinventing Art**
Wadsworth Atheneum Museum of Art, 600 Main Str, Hartford, Connecticut, USA
Dec–Sep 001 860 278 2670

▶ **Liza Lou II**
Bass Museum of Art, 2121 Park Avenue, Miami Beach, Florida 33139, USA
1–31 Dec 001 305 673 7530

▶ **Jan Van Imschoot, Yishai Jusidman, Steven Aalders**
Museum of Contemporary Art, Citadelpark 9000, Ghent, Belgium
1 Dec–3 Feb 0032 9 221 17 03

▶ **Portretten**
Museum voor Schone Kunsten, Wapenplein, B8400, Oostende, Belgium
1 Dec–15 Feb 0032 059 80 53 35

▶ **The Treasury of Basle Cathedral**
Bavarian National Museum, Prinzregentenstraße 3, 80538 Munich, Germany
1 Dec–24 Feb 0049 089 2112401

▶ **A Table au 19ème siècle**
Musée d'Orsay, 62 rue de Lille, 75343 Paris, France
4 Dec–17 Feb 0033 01 45 48 21 25

▶ **Rembrandt on Paper**
Bayerische Staatsgemaldesammlungen, Barer Str 29, 80799 Munich, Germany
5 Dec–6 Feb 0049 089 23805118

▶ **Extreme Beauty: The Body Transformed**
The Metropolitan Museum, 1000 Fifth Ave, New York 10028, USA
6 Dec–3 Mar 001 212 535 7710

▶ **Christmas A–Z**
Deutscheshistoriches Museum, Kronprinzenpalais, Unter den Linden 3, D-10117 Berlin, Germany
6 Dec–1 Jan 0049 030 203040

▶ **12th National Salon of Army Painters**
The French Army Museum, 129 rue de Grenelle, 75007 Paris, France
7–20 Dec 0033 01 44 42 37 72

▶ **Interrupted Careers: Ull Horn and Tom Burr**
Neue Gesellschaft fuer Bildende Kunst, Oranienstrasse 25, D 10999, Berlin, Germany
8 Dec–13 Jan 0049 030 6153031

▶ **New Acquisitions**
Museum van Hedendaagse Kunst Antwerpen, Leuvestraat 32, B-2000, Antwerp, Belgium
8 Dec–20 Jan 0032 3 238 59 60

▶ **Christian Marclay**
SFMOMA, 151 Third Street, San Francisco, California 94103, USA
8 Dec–24 Mar 001 415 357 4000

▶ **The Frame in America 1860–1960**
San Diego Museum of Art, 1450 El Prado, Balboa Park, San Diego, California, USA
8 Dec–3 Feb 001 619 232 7931

▶ **The Inward Eye: Transcendence in Contemporary Art**
Contemporary Arts Museum, 5216 Montrose Blvd, Houston, Texas 77006-6598, USA
8 Dec–17 Feb 001 713 284 8250

▶ **Die Brücke**
Brücke Museum, Bussardsteig 9, 14195 Berlin, Germany
8 Dec–23 Jun 0049 030 8312029

▶ **Oscar Niemeyer**
Galerie nationale du Jeu de Paume, 1, Place de la Concorde, 75008, France
10 Dec–3 Feb 0033 01 47 60 69 69

▶ **Ansel Adams in the University of California Collections**
University of California, Berkeley Art Museum, 2625 Durant Avenue, Berkeley, California 94720-2250, USA
12 Dec–10 Mar 001 510 642 0808

▶ **Splendid Isolation: Art of Easter Island**
The Metropolitan Museum, 1000 Fifth Ave, New York 10028, USA
12 Dec–4 Aug 001 212 535 7710

▶ **Max Vabinsk**
National Gallery in Prague, Palac Kinsky, Starom_stské nàm.12, 120 00, Praha 2, Prague, Czech Republic
13 Dec–31 Mar 00420 2 24 81 07 58 9

▶ **Willem de Kooning**
Fundación La Caixa, C/ Serrano 60, Madrid 28001, Spain
20 Dec–25 Mar 0034 91 435 48 33

▶ **Gordon Parks: Photojournalism**
Cleveland Museum of Art, 11150 East Boulevard,

Cleveland, Ohio 44106, USA
22 Dec–27 Feb 001 216 421 7350

▶ **Cultural Coatings**
Denver Art Museum, 13 Avenue and Acoma, Downtown Denver, Colorado, USA
22 Dec–16 Jun 001 720 865 5000

## January 2002

▶ **Art de la Plume en Amazonie**
Mona Bismarck Foundation, 34 avenue de New York, 75116 Paris, France
Jan–Feb 0033 01 47 23 38 33

▶ **Langlands and Bell**
Site Odéon No 5, 5 Place de l'Odéon, 75006 Paris, France
Jan–Mar 0033 01 44 41 05 05

▶ **Spanish Conceptual Art in the Rafael Tous Collection**
Centre Cultural Tecla Sala, Avinguda Josep Tarradellas, 44 08901 L'Hospitalet de Llobregat, Barcelona, Spain
Jan–Apr 0034 93 338 57 71

▶ **Zeichnungsehen**
Wallraf-Richartz Museum, Fondation Corboud, Offentlichkeitsarbeit, Martinstraße 39, 50667 Cologne, Germany
Jan–Apr 0049 0221 221 22372

▶ **Next Wave**
Contemporary Arts Center, 900 Camp Street, New Orleans, Louisiana 70130, USA
1 Jan–30 Jun 001 504 528 3805

▶ **Mariscal**
Galeria Trama, Petritxol 8, 08002 Barcelona, Spain
3 Jan–2 Feb 0034 93 317 48 77

▶ **Teemu M Ki**
Kunsthalle Helsinki, Nervanderinkatu 3, 00100 Helsinki, Finland
5 Jan–3 Feb 00358 9 454 2060

▶ **Masterworks of the Albertina**
Frick Art and Historical Center, 7227 Reynolds Street, Pittsburgh, Pennsylvania, USA
5 Jan–3 Mar 001 412 371 0600

▶ **Rome on the Grand Tour**
J Paul Getty Museum, 1200 Getty Center Drive, Los Angeles, California 90049-1681, USA
8 Jan–11 Aug 001 310 440 7360

▶ **Andy Warhol: Retrospective**
National Gallery in Prague, Palac Kinsky, Starom_stské nàm.12, 120 00, Praha 2, Prague, Czech Republic
10 Jan–17 Mar 00420 2 24 81 07 58 9

▶ **Suzan Frecon**
The Drawing Center, 40 Wooster Street, New York, New York 10013, USA
10 Jan–21 Feb 001 212 219 2166

▶ **Anna Maria Maiolino: A Life Line**
The Drawing Center, 35 Wooster Street, New York, New York 10013, USA
10 Jan–21 Feb 001 212 219 2166

▶ **Raffael Becker**
Kölnisches Stadtmuseum, Bischofsgartenstraße 1, 1-50667, Cologne, Germany
11 Jan–24 Feb 0049 0221 212388

▶ **William Lundberg**
Contemporary Arts Museum, 5216 Montrose Blvd, Houston, Texas 77006-6598, USA
11 Jan–3 Mar 001 713 284 8250

▶ **Zeitgenössische Fotokunst aus der Schweiz**
Neuer Berliner Kunstverein, Chaussseestr, 128/129, 10115 Berlin, Germany
12 Jan–24 Feb 0049 030 2807020

▶ **Out of Place: Contemporary Art and the Architectural Uncanny**
Museum of Contemporary Art in Chicago, 220 East Chicago Avenue, Chicago, Illinois 60611-2604, USA
12 Jan–12 May 001 312 280 660

▶ **Body Works**
Contemporary Arts Center, 900 Camp Street, New Orleans, Louisiana 70130, USA
12 Jan–24 Mar 001 504 528 3805

▶ **Expanding Universe: The Recent Painitngs of Al Held**
Contemporary Arts Center, 900 Camp Street, New Orleans, Louisiana 70130, USA
12 Jan–24 Mar 001 504 528 3805

▶ **Shifting Tides: Cuban Photography after the Revolution**
Museum of Contemporary Photography, 600 South Michigan Avenue, Chicago, Illinois 60605, USA
12 Jan–9 Mar 001 312 663 5554

▶ **Double Vision: The Strauss Collection**
Museum of Photographic Art, 1649 El Prado, San Diego, California 921101, USA
13 Jan–16 Mar 001 619 238 7559

▶ **Robots**
Museum für Angewandte Kunst, An der Rechtschule Kunst, D 5000, Cologne 1, Germany
14 Jan–14 Apr 0049 221 22126714

▶ **Earthly Bodies: Irving Penn's Nudes**
The Metropolitan Museum, 1000 Fifth Ave, New York 10028, USA
Mid-Jan–Apr 001 212 535 7710

▶ **Italia und Germania**
Bayerische Staatsgemaldesammlungen, Barer str. 29, 80799 Munich, Germany
16 Jan–17 Mar 0049 089 28927653

▶ **Migrations: Photographs by Sebastiao Salgado**
University of California, Berkeley Art Museum, 2625 Durant Avenue, Berkeley, California 94720-2250, USA
16 Jan–24 Mar 001 510 642 0808

▶ **The People of 1,000 Gods: The Hittites**
Art and Exhibition Hall of the Republic of Germany, D-53113 Bonn, Museumsmeile Bonn, Friedrich-Ebert-Allee 4, Germany
18 Jan–28 Apr 0049 0228 9171200

▶ **Alvar Aalto**
Schloß Schoënbrunn, Kaiserliches Hoffmobiliendepot, 7 Mariahilfer Straße 88, Vienna, Austria
18 Jan–21 Apr 0043 1 524 33 57

▶ **Antoni Tapies ou la penseé orientale**
Le Botanique, Rue Royale 236, 1210 Brussels, Belgium
18 Jan–24 Feb 0032 2 218 37 32

▶ **Everhard Jalxich 1618–1695**
Musée du Louvre, 75058, Paris, France
18 Jan–15 Apr 0033 01 40 20 53 17

▶ **Lucien Herv**
I H tel de Sully, 62 Rue Saint-Antoine, 75004 Paris, France
18 Jan–17 Mar 0033 01 42 74 30 60

▶ **Interrupted Careers: Jochen Klein and Wolfgang Tillmans**
Neue Gesellschaft fuer Bildende Kunst, Oranienstrasse 25, D 10999, Berlin, Germany
19 Jan–17 Feb 0049 030 6153031

▶ **My Reality: The Culture of Anime**
The Contemporary Arts Center, Cincinnati, Ohio 45202-3998, USA
19 Jan–7 Apr 001 513 721 0390

▶ **Liam Gillick**
The Contemporary Arts Center, Cincinnati, Ohio 45202-3998, USA
19 Jan–7 Apr 001 513 721 0390

▶ **Rainer Wolzl**
Georg-Kolbe-Museum, Sensburger Allee 25, 14055 Berlin, Germany
20 Jan–1 Mar 0049 030 304 7041

▶ **Carven**
Musée de la Mode de la Ville de Paris, 10 avenue Pierre Ier de Serbie, 75116 Paris, France
21 Jan–15 Jun 0033 01 56 52 86 03

▶ **Chic Clicks: Creativity and Commerce in Contemporary Fashion Photography**
ICA, 955 Boylston Street, Boston, Massachussetts 02115, USA
23 Jan–7 Apr 001 617 927 6617

▶ **Tirana/Tyranny**
Centre de Cultura Contemporania de Barcelona, C/ Montalegre 5, 08001 Barcelona
23 Jan–14 Apr 0034 93 306 41 48

▶ **Benjamin Brechnell Turner: Rural England through a Victorian Lens**
The Metropolitan Museum, 1000 Fifth Ave, New York 10028, USA
23 Jan–21 Apr 001 212 535 7710

▶ **Robert Kot**
Le Botanique, Rue Royale 236, 1210 Brussels, Belgium
25 Jan–24 Feb 0032 2 218 37 32

▶ **Painted Ladies: Women at the Court of Charles II**
Yale Center for British Art, 161 York Street, New Haven, Connecticut 06520, USA
25 Jan–17 Mar 001 203 432 2800

▶ **Sowon Kwon: Matrix 196**
University of California, Berkeley Art Museum, 2625 Durant Avenue, Berkeley, California 94720-2250, USA
27 Jan–24 Mar 001 510 642 0808

▶ **Cosm Tura and Ferrara: A Forgotten Renaissance**
Isabella Stewart Gardner Museum, 2 Palace Road, Boston, Massachussetts 02115, USA
30 Jan–12 May 001 617 566 1401

▶ **Ultrabaroque: Aspects of Post-Latin American Art**
Art Gallery of Ontario, 317 Dundas Str West, Toronto, Ontario, Canada M5T 1G4
30 Jan–28 Apr 001 416 977 0414

## February 2002

▶ **Inuit Project from the AGO Collection**
Art Gallery of Ontario, 317 Dundas Str West, Toronto, Ontario, Canada M5T 1G4
Feb– 001 416 977 0414

▶ **Hèlio Oiticica: Quasi Cinemas**
Koelnischer Kunstverein, Caecilienstrasse 33, D 50667, Cologne, Germany
Feb–Apr 0049 221 217021

▶ **Sonic Youth**
Palais des Beaux Arts de Bruxelles, 10 rue Royale, 1000 Brussels, Belgium
Feb–Apr 0032 2 507 84 66

▶ **James Welling**
Palais des Beaux Arts de Bruxelles, 10 rue Royale, 1000 Brussels, Belgium
Feb–May 0032 2 507 84 66

▶ **Rik Wouters**
Palais des Beaux Arts de Bruxelles, 10 rue Royale, 1000 Brussels, Belgium
Feb–May 0032 2 507 84 66

▶ **Jacques Charlier, Leo Copers**
Museum of Contemporary Art, Citadelpark 9000, Ghent, Belgium
mid-Feb–Apr 0032 9 221 17 03

▶ **Art on Art**
Haus der Kunst, Prinzregentenstraße 1, D 80538 Munich, Germany
1 Feb–5 May 0049 089 211270

▶ **NACKT**
Museum für Kunst und Gewerbe, Steintorplatz, 20099 Hamburg, Germany
1 Feb–28 Apr 0049 428 545353

▶ **Surrealism: Desire Unbound**
The Metropolitan Museum, 1000 Fifth Ave, New York 10028, USA
1 Feb–5 May 001 212 535 7710

▶ **Asger Jorn: Retrospective**
Arken, Museum for Modern Art, Skovvej 100, DK 2635 ISHØJ, Denmark
2 Feb–2 Jun 0045 43 54 02 22

▶ **Eva Hesse: A Retrospective**
SFMOMA, 151 Third Street, San Francisco, California 94103, USA
2 Feb–19 May 001 415 357 4000

▶ **Bill Viola: Commissioned Work for Deutsche Guggenheim Berlin**
Deutsche Guggenheim Berlin, Unter den Linden 13–15, 10117 Berlin, Germany
2 Feb–28 Apr 0049 030 2020930

▶ **UN Studio/MATRIX 146**
Wadsworth Atheneum Museum of Art, 600 Main Str, Hartford, Connecticut, USA
2 Feb–28 Apr 001 860 278 2670

▶ **Hairitage**
Wadsworth Atheneum Museum of Art, 600 Main Str, Hartford, Connecticut, USA
2 Feb–26 May 001 860 278 2670

▶ **Mood River**
Wexner Center for the Arts, 1871 North High Street, Columbus, Ohio 43210-1393, USA
3 Feb–ongoing 001 614 292 3535

▶ **Christo and Jeanne-Claude in the Vogel Collection**
National Gallery of Art, Fourth Str at Constitution Ave, NW, Washington, DC 20565, USA
3 Feb–23 Jun 001 202 842 6353

▶ **Braque**
Museo Thyssen Bornemisza, Carrer Sant Lu, 08010 Barcelona, Spain
5 Feb–19 May 0034 932 80 14 34

▶ **Viewing Italy in the 18th Century**
J Paul Getty Museum, 1200 Getty Center Drive, Los Angeles, California 90049-1681, USA
5 Feb–12 May 001 310 440 7360

▶ **Andres Rebago**
Galeria Trama, Petritxol 8, 08002 Barcelona, Spain
6 Feb–9 Mar 0034 93 317 48 77

▶ **Looking Forward/Looking Back**
The Baltimore Museum of Art, 10 Art Museum Drive, Baltimore, MD 21218-3898, USA
6 Feb–5 May 001 410 396 7100

▶ **Kneub Hler**
National Gallery in Prague, Palac Kinsky, Starom_stské nàm.12, 120 00, Praha 2, Prague, Czech Republic
7 Feb–28 Apr 00420 2 24 81 07 58 9

▶ **Long Steps Never Broke A Back: Art from Africa in America**
Seattle Art Museum, 100 University Street, Seattle, Washington 98101-2902, USA
7 Feb–19 May 001 206 654 3100

▶ **Josef Koudelka**
National Gallery in Prague, Palac Kinsky, Starom_stské nàm.12, 120 00, Praha 2, Prague, Czech Republic
7 Feb–28 Apr 00420 2 24 81 07 58 9

▶ **New New Painters**
National Gallery in Prague, Palac Kinsky, Starom_stské nàm.12, 120 00, Praha 2, Prague, Czech Republic
7 Feb–1 Sep 00420 2 24 81 07 58 9

▶ **Belles et inconnus, sculptures en terre cuite des ateliers du Maine 16-18$^{e}$ siècle**
Musée du Louvre, 75058, Paris, France
8 Feb–21 May 0033 01 40 20 53 17

▶ **24 Frames a Second: The Story of Animation**
The Norman Rockwell Museum, Route 183, Stockbridge, Massachussetts 01262, USA
9 Feb–26 May 001 413 298 4100

▶ **Master Drawings from the Collection of Alfred Moir**
San Diego Museum of Art. 1450 El Prado, Balboa Park, San Diego, California, USA
9 Feb–7 Apr 001 619 232 7931

▶ **Impressionism to Surrealism: Selections from the Cone and Adler Collections of The Baltimore Museum of Art**
Wadsworth Atheneum Museum of Art, 600 Main Str, Hartford, Connecticut, USA
9 Feb–21 Apr 001 860 278 2670

▶ **Bert de Beul**
Museum van Hedendaagse Kunst Antwerpen, Leuvestraat 32, B-2000, Antwerp, Belgium
9 Feb–5 May 0032 3 238 59 60

▶ **The Practice**
Museum van Hedendaagse Kunst Antwerpen, Leuvestraat 32, B-2000, Antwerp, Belgium
9 Feb–5 May 0032 3 238 59 60

▶ **Museums for a New Millennium: Concepts, Projects, Buildings**
Modern Art Museum of Fort Worth, 1309 Montgomery Street, Camp Bowie Boulevard, Fort Worth, Texas 76107, USA
10 Feb–14 Apr 001 817 738 9215

▶ **Austria: 2nd Republic**
Jewish Museum Vienna, Dorotheergassse 11, 1010 Vienna, Austria
12 Feb–28 Apr 0043 01 535 04 31

▶ **Orazio and Artemisia Gentileschi: Father and Daughter Painters in Baroque Italy**
The Metropolitan Museum, 1000 Fifth Ave, New York 10028, USA
14 Feb–12 May 001 212 535 7710

▶ **Arnold Brocklin**
Bayerische Staatsgemaldesammlungen, Barer Str 29, 80799 Munich, Germany
14 Feb–26 May 0049 089 23805118

▶ **Le Geste Kongo**
Musée Dapper, 35 rue Paul Valéry, 75116 Paris, France
14 Feb–14 Jul 0033 01 45 00 01 50

▶ **Matthew Barney: The CREMASTER Cycle**
Guggenheim Museum, 1071 Fifth Ave,

New York 10128 0173, USA
15 Feb–5 May 001 212 423 3500

▶ **Gary Simmons**
Museum of Contemporary Art in Chicago, 220 East Chicago Avenue, Chicago, Illinois 60611-2604, USA
16 Feb–26 May 001 312 280 660

▶ **Mies in America**
Museum of Contemporary Art in Chicago, East Chicago Avenue, Chicago, Illinois 60611-2604, USA
16 Feb–26 May 001 312 280 660

▶ **Turner and the Sea**
The Baltimore Museum of Art, 10 Art Museum Drive, Baltimore, MD 21218-3898, USA
17 Feb–26 May 001 410 396 7100

▶ **Vital Forms: American Art in the Atomic Age**
Walker Art Center, Vineland Place, Minnesota 55403, USA
17 Feb–12 May 001 612 375 7622

▶ **Arctic Diary: Paintings and Photographs by William Bradford**
Clark Art Institute, Williamstown, Massachusetts, USA
17 Feb–5 May 001 413 458 2303

▶ **The Age of Impressionism: European Masterpieces from Ordrupgaard, Copenhagen**
The Walters Art Museum, 600 North Charles Street, Baltimore, Maryland 21201-5185, USA
17 Feb–26 May 001 410 547 9000

▶ **Photographs from the Metropolitan Bank and Trust Collection**
Cleveland Museum of Art, 11150 East Boulevard, Cleveland, Ohio 44106, USA
17 Feb–28 Apr 001 216 421 7350

▶ **The Mystery of the Young Rembrandt**
Rembrandt House Museum, Jodenbreestraat 4, 1011 NK Amsterdam, Netherlands
20 Feb–26 May 0031 020 5200 4000

▶ **Yes Yoko Ono**
Art Gallery of Ontario, 317 Dundas Str West, Toronto, Ontario, Canada M5T 1G4
22 Feb–20 May 001 416 977 0414

▶ **Gerhard Richter: 40 Years of Painting**
MoMA, 11 West 53 Street, New York, New York, USA
21 Feb–21 May 001 212 708 9400

▶ **Interrupted Careers: Jimmy Desana and Laurie Simmons**
Neue Gesellschaft fuer Bildende Kunst, Oranienstrasse 25, D 10999, Berlin, Germany
23 Feb–24 Mar 0049 030 6153031

▶ **US Design**
Denver Art Museum, 13 Avenue and Acoma, Downtown Denver, Colorado, USA
23 Feb–26 May 001 720 865 5000

▶ **Elaine Sturtevant**
Neuer Berliner Kunstverein, Chausssestr, 128/129, 10115 Berlin, Germany
Mar–21 Apr 0049 030 2807020

▶ **Art and Home: Dutch Interiors in the Age of Rembrandt**
Denver Art Museum, 13 Avenue and Acoma, Downtown Denver, Colorado, USA
23 Feb–26 May 001 720 865 5000

▶ **Goya and the Feminine World**
from the Prado to Washington National Gallery, 6th Street and Constitution Ave, Washington, DC 20565, USA
24 Feb–19 May 001 202 737 4215

▶ **Treasury of the World: Jeweled Arts of India in the Age of the Mughals**
Cleveland Museum of Art, 11150 East Boulevard, Cleveland, Ohio 44106, USA
24 Feb–19 May 001 216 421 7350

▶ **Over the Line: The Art and Life of Jacob Lawrence**
Detroit Institute of Art, 5200 Woodward Avenue, Detroit, Michigan 48202, USA
24 Feb–19 May 001 313 833 7900

▶ **Ribera: La Piedad**
Museo Thyssen Bornemisza, Carrer Sant Lu, 08010 Barcelona, Spain
26 Feb–26 May 0034 932 80 14 34

▶ **Paris-Barcelona**
Museu Picasso de Barcelona, Montcada 15–19, E 08003, Barcelona, Spain
28 Feb–26 May 0034 93 319 63 10

▶ **The Victorian Nude**
Haus der Kunst, Prinzregentenstraße 1, D 80538 Munich, Germany
28 Feb–26 May 0049 089 211270

▶ **Lukas Cranach the Elder**
Statens Museum for Kunst, 48–50 Solvgade, D-K 1307 Copenhagen K, Denmark
spring 2002 0045 33 74 84 40

▶ **Master Drawings from the Smith College Museum of Art**
Fundación La Caixa, C/ Serrano 60, Madrid 28001, Spain
spring 2002 0034 91 435 48 33

▶ **From Goya to Picasso**
from Prado to Altes Museum, Lustgarten, Museuminsel, Berlin, Germany
spring 2002 0049 030 203550

## March 2002

▶ **Chinese Paintings by Cheng Shifa: Works from the Artists Collection**
Denver Art Museum, 13 Avenue and Acoma, Downtown Denver, Colorado, USA
Mar 001 720 865 5000

▶ **Yannis Kounellis**
Museum of Contemporary Art, Citadelpark 9000, Ghent, Belgium
Mar–May 0032 9 221 17 03

▶ **The Economy of Time**
Museum Ludwig, Biscofsgarten 1, D-50667, Cologne, Germany
Mar–May 0049 221 2210

▶ **The Classical Period of Ancient Greece: Notion or Reality**
Staatliche Museum zu Berlin, Bodestraße 1–3. D10178 Berlin, Germany
1 Mar–1 Jun 0049 030 20905200

▶ **Maria Teresa Kuczynska**
Musée Bourdelle, 16/18 rue Antoine Bourdelle, 75015 Paris, France
Mar–Jun 0033 01 49 54 73 73

▶ **Edward Weston: The Last Years in Carmel**
SFMOMA, 151 Third Street, San Francisco, California 94103, USA
1 Mar–9 Jul 001 415 357 4000

▶ **William Kentridge**
Contemporary Arts Museum, 5216 Montrose Blvd, Houston, Texas 77006-6598, USA
1 Mar–5 May 001 713 284 8250

▶ **Ellen Gallagher**
The Drawing Center, 35 Wooster Street, New York, New York 10013, USA
2 Mar–6 Apr 001 212 219 2166

▶ **Jack Stauffacher: Selections from a Permanent Collection of Architecture and Design**
SFMOMA, 151 Third Street, San Francisco, California 94103, USA
2 Mar–26 May 001 415 357 4000

▶ **Perfect Acts of Architecture**
SFMOMA, 151 Third Street, San Francisco, California 94103, USA
2 Mar–26 May 001 415 357 4000

▶ **Selections Winter 2002**
The Drawing Center, 40 Wooster Street, New York, New York 10013, USA
2 Mar–6 Apr 001 212 219 2166

▶ **Dimitri Van Grunderbeek**
Museum van Hedendaagse Kunst Antwerpen, Leuvestraat 32, B-2000, Antwerp, Belgium
2 Mar–26 May 0032 3 238 59 60

▶ **Guy Mees**
Museum van Hedendaagse Kunst Antwerpen, Leuvestraat 32, B-2000, Antwerp, Belgium
2 Mar–26 May 0032 3 238 59 60

▶ **The Flowering of Florence: Botanical Art for the Medici, 1550–1750**
National Gallery of Art, Fourth Str at Constitution Ave, NW, Washington, DC 20565, USA
3 Mar–27 May 001 202 842 6353

▶ **Eisenmeier**
Jewish Museum Vienna, Dorotheergassse 11, 1010 Vienna, Austria
5 Mar–21 Apr 0043 01 535 04 31

▶ **Treasures from a Lost Civilisation: Ancient Chinese Art from Sichuan**
The Metropolitan Museum, 1000 Fifth Ave, New York 10028, USA
5 Mar–16 Jun 001 212 535 7710

▶ **Railroads in Photography**
J Paul Getty Museum, 1200 Getty Center Drive, Los Angeles, California 90049-1681, USA
5 Mar–23 Jun 001 310 440 7360

▶ **Genesis: Contemporary Art Explores Human Genomics**
Henry Art Gallery, University of Washington, Seattle, Washington 98195-1410, USA
7 Mar–26 May 001 206 543 2280

▶ **Stories: Narrative Elements in Contemporary Art**
Haus der Kunst, Prinzregentenstraße 1, D 80538 Munich, Germany
8 Mar–2 Jun 0049 089 211270

▶ **Michael Sweerts**
Rijksmuseum, 1070 DN, Amsterdam, Netherlands
8 Mar–12 May 0031 020 6747 171

▶ **Bartolomé Esteban Murillo: Paintings from American Collections**
Kimbell Art Museum, 3333 Camp Bowie Boulevard, Fort Worth, Texas 76107-2792, USA
10 Mar–2 Jun 001 817 332 8451

▶ **Regina Gimenez**
Galeria Trama, Petritxol 8, 08002 Barcelona, Spain
13 Mar–13 Apr 0034 93 317 48 77

▶ **The Work of a Lifetime: Highlights from the Cahill Family Collection**
University of California, Berkeley Art Museum, 2625 Durant Avenue, Berkeley, California 94720-2250, USA
13 Mar–26 May 001 510 642 0808

▶ **New Works: Candice Breitz, Surasi Kusolwong, Chuck Ramirez**
Art Pace, 445 North Main Avenue, San Antonio, Texas 78205, USA
14 Mar–12 May 001 210 212 4900

▶ **Tapestry in the Renaissance: Art and Magnificence**
The Metropolitan Museum, 1000 Fifth Ave, New York 10028, USA
14 Mar–19 Jun 001 212 535 7710

▶ **Artistic Relations: Madrid–London**
Prado, P del Prado s/n, 28014 Madrid, Spain
15 Mar–2 Jun 0034 91 330 28 00

▶ **Artistes Brasiliens**
Le Botanique, Rue Royale 236, 1210 Brussels, Belgium
15 Mar–14 Apr 0032 2 218 37 32

▶ **Johan Scott**
Kunsthalle Helsinki, Nervanderinkatu 3, 00100 Helsinki, Finland
16 Mar–14 Apr 00358 9 454 2060

▶ **The Art of French Fashion**
Wadsworth Atheneum Museum of Art, 600 Main Str, Hartford, Connecticut, USA
16 Mar–18 Aug 001 860 278 2670

▶ **The World Seen from Fez**
Centre de Cultura Contemporania de Barcelona, C/ Montalegre 5, 08001 Barcelona, Spain
20 Mar–26 May 0034 93 306 41 48

▶ **Maurice Frydman**
Le Botanique, Rue Royale 236, 1210 Brussels, Belgium
21 Mar–28 Apr 0032 2 218 37 32

▶ **Charlotte Salomon**
Jewish Historical Museum, Jonas Daniël Meijerplein 2–4, Amsterdam, Netherlands
21 Mar–8 Sep 0031 20 62 69 945

▶ **The Russian Avant-Garde Book 1910–1934**
MoMA, 11 West 53 Street, New York, New York, USA
21 Mar–11 Jun 001 212 708 9400

▶ **Tulips: Beauty and Mania**
Residenzgalerie Salzburg, Postfach 527, A 5010 Salzburg, Austria
21 Mar–30 Jun 0043 662 840451

▶ **Barbara Crane: The Loop**
Museum of Contemporary Photography, 600 South Michigan Avenue, Chicago, Illinois 60605, USA
22 Mar–15 Jun 001 312 663 5554

▶ **Nolde und die Sudsee**
Kunsthalle der Hypo-Kulturstiftung, Theatinerstraße 8, Perusahof, D-80333, Munich, Germany
22 Mar–26 May 0049 089 224412

▶ **Visions of Passgae**
Museum of Photographic Art, 1649 El Prado, San Diego, California 921101, USA
24 Mar–2 Jun 001 619 238 7559

▶ **Violence in the Medieval World**
J Paul Getty Museum, 1200 Getty Center Drive, Los Angeles, California 90049-1681, USA
26 Mar–7 Jul 001 310 440 7360

▶ **Jan Kupek: The Master of Baroque Portrait**
National Gallery in Prague, Palac Kinsky, Starom_stské nàm.12, 120 00, Praha 2, Prague, Czech Republic
28 Mar–30 Jun 00420 2 24 81 07 58 9

▶ **L Novak**
National Gallery in Prague, Palac Kinsky, Starom_stské nàm.12, 120 00, Praha 2, Prague, Czech Republic
28 Mar–30 Jun 00420 2 24 81 07 58 9

▶ **J Autengruber**
National Gallery in Prague, Palac Kinsky, Starom_stské nàm.12, 120 00, Praha 2, Prague, Czech Republic
28 Mar–30 Jun 00420 2 24 81 07 58 9

▶ **La photographie et le rêve américain, 1840–1940**
Patrimoine Photographique, 62 rue Saint-Antoine, 75004 Paris, France
29 Mar–16 Jun 0033 01 42 74 30 80

▶ **West Points/Points West**
Denver Art Museum, 13 Avenue and Acoma, Downtown Denver, Colorado, USA
30 Mar–12 May 001 720 865 5000

▶ **Victorian Visions**
Frick Art and Historical Center, 7227 Reynolds Street, Pittsburgh, Pennsylvania, USA
30 Mar–2 Jun 001 412 371 0600

## April 2002

▶ **L'Or des Iles: Barbier-Mueller Museum Collection**
Mona Bismarck Foundation, 34 avenue de New York, 75116 Paris, France
Apr–May 0033 01 47 23 38 33

▶ **The Harem**
Centre de Cultura Contemporania de Barcelona, C/ Montalegre 5, 08001 Barcelona
Apr–Jul 0034 93 306 41 48

▶ **Sanford Biggers: Matrix 197**
University of California, Berkeley Art Museum, 2625 Durant Avenue, Berkeley, California 94720-2250, USA
7 Apr–2 Jun 001 510 642 0808

▶ **Komar and Melamid's Asian Elephant Art and Conservation Project**
University of California, Berkeley Art Museum, 2625 Durant Avenue, Berkeley, California 94720-2250, USA
10 Apr–14 Jul 001 510 642 0808

▶ **Le Theâtre de Victor Hugo mis en scène**
Maison de Victor Hugo, 6 Place des Vosges, 75004 Paris, France
11 Apr–28 Jul 0033 01 42 72 10 16

▶ **Markus Prachensky**
Österreichische Galerie Belvedere, Prinz Eugen-Straße 27, A-1037 Vienna, Austria
11 Apr–30 Jun 0043 01 79 55 70

▶ **Swetlana Heger/Plamen Dejanov**
Österreichische Galerie Belvedere, Prinz Eugen-Straße 27, A-1037 Vienna, Austria
11 Apr–25 Aug 0043 01 79 55 70

▶ **Competition: Shaping Society**
Neue Gesellschaft fuer Bildende Kunst, Oranienstrasse 25, D 10999, Berlin, Germany
13 Apr–5 May 0049 030 6153031

▶ **No Ghost, Just a Shell: The Lee Ann Project**
SFMOMA, 151 Third Street, San Francisco, California 94103, USA
13 Apr–28 Jul 001 415 357 4000

▶ **Sprawl**
The Contemporary Arts Center, Cincinnati, Ohio 45202-3998, USA
13 Apr–16 Jun 001 513 721 0390

▶ **The Sacred Spaces of Peter Saenredam**
J Paul Getty Museum, 1200 Getty Center Drive, Los Angeles, California 90049-1681, USA
16 Apr–7 Jul 001 310 440 7360

▶ **Anna Miquel**
Galeria Trama, Petritxol 8,
08002 Barcelona, Spain
17 Apr–25 May 0034 93 317 48 77

▶ **Emma Kunz, Hilma of Klint and Agnes Martin**
The Drawing Center, 35 Wooster Street,
New York, New York 10013, USA
18 Apr–15 Jun 001 212 219 2166

▶ **Cesar Paternosto and Cecilia Vicuna**
The Drawing Center, 40 Wooster Street,
New York, New York 10013, USA
18 Apr–29 May 001 212 219 2166

▶ **Paula Rego**
Yale Center for British Art, 161 York Street,
New Haven, Connecticut 06520, USA
18 Apr–30 Jun 001 203 432 2800

▶ **Deir el Medineh, le village des artistes de la vallée des rois**
Musée du Louvre, 75058, Paris, France
19 Apr–15 Jul 0033 01 40 20 53 17

▶ **Marc Ots**
Le Botanique, Rue Royale 236,
1210 Brussels, Belgium
19 Apr–26 May 0032 2 218 37 32

▶ **Carnegie Art Award**
Kunsthalle Helsinki, Nervanderinkatu 3,
00100 Helsinki, Finland
20 Apr–12 May 00358 9 454 2060

▶ **Building: Artists Address Architecture**
ICA, 955 Boylston Street, Boston,
Massachussetts 02115, USA
24 Apr–30 Jun 001 617 927 6617

▶ **Walter Malli**
Schloß Schoënbrunn, Kaiserliches
Hoffmobiliendepot,
7 Mariahilfer Straße 88, Vienna, Austria
24 Apr–14 Jul 0043 1 524 33 57

▶ **Masters of Firenze**
National Gallery in Prague, Palac Kinsky,
Starom_stské nàm.12, 120 00, Praha 2,
Prague, Czech Republic
25 Apr–15 Aug 00420 2 24 81 07 58 9

▶ **Alex Katz**
Art and Exhibition Hall of the Republic of
Germany, D-53113 Bonn, Museumsmeile Bonn,
Friedrich-Ebert-Allee 4, Germany
26 Apr–11 Aug 0049 0228 9171200

▶ **Ernst Epstein 1881-1938**
Jewish Museum Vienna, Dorotheergassse 11,
1010 Vienna, Austria
30 Apr–25 Aug 0043 01 535 04 31

## May 2002

▶ **Community Creations**
Isabella Stewart Gardner Museum, 2 Palace
Road, Boston, Massachussetts 02115, USA
May 001 617 566 1401

▶ **KunstenFestival des Arts**
Palais des Beaux Arts de Bruxelles, 10 rue
Royale, 1000 Brussels, Belgium
May–Jun 0032 2 507 84 66

▶ **Bernard Frieze, Mendella**
Museum of Contemporary Art,
Citadelpark 9000, Ghent, Belgium
May–Jun 0032 9 221 17 03

▶ **Dora Maar: A Retrospective**
Centre Cultural Tecla Sala, Avinguda Josep
Tarradellas, 44 08901 L'Hospitalet de Llobregat,
Barcelona, Spain
May–Jul 0034 93 338 57 71

▶ **Issey Miyake**
Museum für Angewandte Kunst, An der
Rechtschule Kunst, D 5000, Cologne 1,
Germany
May–Jul 0049 221 22126714

▶ **Invitation au musée de Raoul Marek**
Musée Zadkine, 100 bis, rue d'Assas,
75006 Paris, France
May–Sep 0033 01 43 26 91 90

▶ **Manfred Bischoff**
Isabella Stewart Gardner Museum, 2 Palace
Road, Boston, Massachussetts 02115, USA
May–Sep 001 617 566 1401

▶ **Bicentenary of Saint Cyr**
The French Army Museum,
129 rue de Grenelle,
75007 Paris, France
May–Oct 0033 01 44 42 37 72

▶ **Witches: History and Hysteria**
Deutscheshistoriches Museum,
Kronprinzenpalais, Unter den Linden 3,
D-10117 Berlin, Germany
2 May–6 Aug 0049 030 203040

▶ **Christine Borland**
Contemporary Arts Museum, 5216 Montrose
Blvd, Houston, Texas 77006-6598, USA
3 May–23 Jun 001 713 284 8250

▶ **Dressing Up: Costume in the Collection**
Museum of Contemporary Photography,
600 South Michigan Avenue, Chicago,
Illinois 60605, USA
3 May–10 Aug 001 312 663 5554

▶ **Nedko Solakov**
Neuer Berliner Kunstverein, Chaussseestr,
128/129, 10115 Berlin, Germany
4 May–16 Jun 0049 030 2807020

▶ **Young Art 2002**
San Diego Museum of Art. 1450 El Prado,
Balboa Park, San Diego, California, USA
4 May–9 Jun 001 619 232 7931

▶ **Deutsche Bank Collection**
Deutsche Guggenheim Berlin,
Unter den Linden 13–15, 10117 Berlin, Germany
11 May–30 Jun 0049 030 2020930

▶ **Thomas Struth**
Dallas Museum of Art, 1717 North Harwood
Street at St Pauls Avenue, Dallas,
Texas 75201, USA
12 May–18 Aug 001 214 922 1200

▶ **Johann Knapp: Masterworks**
Österreichische Galerie Belvedere,
Prinz Eugen-Straße 27, A-1037 Vienna, Austria
14 May–15 Sep 0043 01 79 55 70

▶ **Emigrants**
Jewish Museum Vienna,
Dorotheergassse 11, 1010 Vienna, Austria
14 May–18 Aug 0043 01 535 04 31

▶ **Toulouse Lautrec**
Museum für Kunst und Gewerbe,
Steintorplatz, 20099 Hamburg, Germany
17 May–28 Jul 0049 428 545353

▶ **Realism Studio: Cyber War**
Neue Gesellschaft fuer Bildende Kunst,
Oranienstrasse 25, D 10999, Berlin, Germany
18 May–16 Jun 0049 030 6153031

▶ **Sam Durant/MATRIX 147**
Wadsworth Atheneum Museum of Art,
600 Main Str, Hartford, Connecticut, USA
18 May–1 Sep 001 860 278 2670

▶ **From Paris to Provincetown: Blanche Lazzell and the Color Woodcut**
Cleveland Museum of Art, 11150 East Boulevard,
Cleveland, Ohio 44106, USA
19 May–28 Jul 001 216 421 7350

▶ **Les Cartoons de vitraux d'Ingres**
Musée du Louvre, 75058, Paris, France
24 May–19 Aug 0033 01 40 20 53 17

▶ **Kunst uber Kunst**
Wallraf-Richartz Museum, Fondation Corboud,
Offentlichkeitsarbeit, Martinstraße 39, 50667
Cologne, Germany
24 May–25 Aug 0049 221 22372

NOTES

# Fairs and Festivals

# Art fairs and festivals

In the art world, money talks – and from January 2002, it's even more of an international language. The advent of the single currency in 12 countries will have interesting ramifications for Europe's fairs and festivals, and it can't be a coincidence that one of the year's most promising events, Manifesta 4, has come in from the cold (Ljubljana 2000) and returned to the financial heart of Europe: Frankfurt. Founded in the late-1990s, Manifesta – which runs from 25 May to 25 August – stands out in an almost uncomfortably crowded calendar for its flexibility and includivism: artists are chosen for the quality of their work rather than their nationality, and special emphasis is placed on minority cultures and beliefs. National borders shouldn't work their way into a truly European, post-Cold War festival, insists the Manifesta committee – so a different cultural capital hosts the show each time. With Harald Szeemann's reign in Venice coming in for increasingly vociferous criticism, the big Biennials will have to look to their laurels to eclipse their younger and more energetic rivals.

Elsewhere in Europe, it's business as usual, and healthy attendances and sales last year bode well for the next, despite the seesawing stock market. Bologna's Artefiera – Italy's leading contemporary art fair – kicks off the year in January, ARCO Madrid and Strasbourg's St'art brighten up February, and Innsbruck and Maastricht TEFAF follow in March. The 33rd Art Basel – still unrivalled as the world's best modern and contemporary sale – runs from 12 to 17 June; Art Forum Berlin and Art Cologne jostle for supremacy in the autumn.

In the UK, the usual suspects are Art 2002 (Jan), Grosvenor House (Jun), Art London (Jun), Fresh Art (Jul), The 20/21 British Art Fair (Sep) and The Affordable Art Fair (Oct), while September marks the welcome return of the Liverpool Biennial. Bringing a little bit of Venice to Merseyside – admittedly without the razzle-dazzle – Liverpool's 1999 debut was a notable success, attracting a recorded 200,000 visitors. The 2001 Biennial was delayed by a year to allow for the completion of works on the Walker Art Gallery and the stylish new FACT Centre – a Foundation for Art and Creative Technology, dedicated to film, video and new media.

The international flavour of the first festival is tempered this time by a local curatorial team (from FACT, Tate Liverpool and Bluecoat Art Centre), who will be angling to strengthen Liverpool's bid to become the 2008 European Capital of Culture.

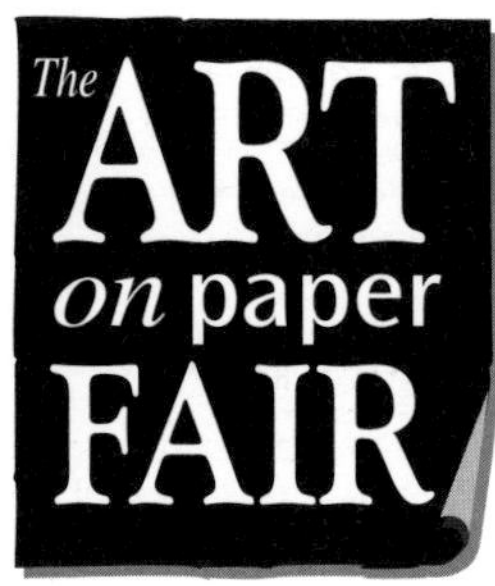


*London's only annual fair for original works of art on paper*

**7-10 February 2002**

**ROYAL COLLEGE OF ART**

Kensington Gore, London SW7 2EU

*For further information:*
Telephone: 020 8742 1611
e-mail: organisers@artfairs.demon.co.uk
Website: www.artonpaper.co.uk

2002

The *only* fair for BRITISH ART from 1900 to the present day

**18-22 September 2002**

NEW VENUE

**COMMONWEALTH INSTITUTE**

Kensington High Street, London W8 6NQ

*For further information:*
Telephone: 020 8742 1611
e-mail: organisers@artfairs.demon.co.uk
Website: www.britishartfair.co.uk

The following is a selection of the fine art and craft fairs and arts festivals taking place in the coming year. While many are open to visitors on the day, it is necessary to reserve places for some specialist festivals – please contact the organisers for further information.

## ▶ Art Miami International Art Exposition

Miami Beach Convention Center, 1901 Convention Centre Drive, Miami Beach, USA.
**Tel 001** 407 220 2690 **Fax 001** 407 220 3180
**Jan**

## ▶ Arte Fiere

January in the 'quartiere fieristico', Bolognafiere. Viale della Fiere, 20, 40128 Bologna, Italy.
**Tel 00**39 051 282111
**Email** Artefiere@bolognafiere.it
**Fax 00**39 051 282333
**Jan**

## ▶ Arte Sevilla

Palacio de Congreso y Exposiciones, Seville.
**Tel 00**34 954 254040
**Jan**

## ▶ Outsider Art Fair

Puck Building, Lafayettte and Houston Streets, New York, USA.
**Tel 00**1 212 777 5718 **Fax 00**1 212 477 6490
**Ws** www.sandfordsmith.com
**Jan**

## ▶ West London Antiques and Fine Art Fair

Kensington Town Hall, Hornton Street, London W8.
**Tel** 01444 482 514 **Fax** 01444 483 412
**Email** info@penman-fairs.co.uk
**Ws** www.penman-fairs.co.uk
**Jan**

## ▶ BDC Events

Business Design Centre, 52 Upper Street, Islington, London N1 0QH.
**Tel** 020 7359 3535 **Fax** 020 7288 6446
**Ws** www.art-fair.co.uk www.freshartfair.co.uk
**Contact:** Lucy Field
*ART 2002, THE 14TH LONDON CONTEMPORARY ART FAIR*
*16–20 January 2002.*
*See and buy works of art from over 100 of the UK's leading galleries.*
*www.art-fair.co.uk*
*FRESH ART July 2002*
*Discover new artists at London's freshest art fair*
*www.freshartfair.co.uk*
**16–20 Jan**

## ▶ WaterColours & Drawings Fair

The Park Lane Hotel, Piccadilly, London W1.
**Tel** 07000 785 613 **Fax** 07000 785 614
**Email** watercolours@talk21.com
**Ws** www.watercoloursfair.com
**31 Jan–3 Feb**

## ▶ ARCO

Parque Ferial Juan Carlos, 28042 Madrid, Spain.
**Tel 00**34 91 722 5017 **Fax 00**34 91 722 5798
**Feb**

## ▶ St'Art 2002

Place de la Foire, Exposition-BP 256 R/7. FR 67007 Strasbourg Cedex
**Tel** 0033 3 88 37 2121
**1–4 Feb**

## ▶ The Art on Paper Fair

Royal College of Art, Kensington Gore, London SW7.
**Tel** 020 7742 1611 **Fax** 020 7995 5094
**Email** organisers@artfairs.demon.co.uk
**Ws** www.artonpaper.co.uk
**Opening times** Thu–Fri 11–8, Sat–Sun 11–7.
*London's only annual fair for works on paper, now in its fourth year. Over 50 leading dealers from Europe and the USA show work on paper – watercolours, prints, drawings and photography. Admission £5*
**7–10 Feb**

## ▶ Chester Antiques and Fine Art Fair

The County Grandstand, Chester Racecourse, Chester.
**Tel** 01444 482514
**Email** info@penman-fairs.co.uk
**Ws** www.penman-fairs.co.uk
*Two floors of the racecourse are filled with antiques from dealers from all over the UK, presenting a wide selection of pieces mostly from before 1900. The 3rd floor contains fine paintings from all ages and room sets by furniture dealers. This event is widely regarded as the most prestigious of its kind in the Northwest. Admission £4 with catalogue. Also 14–17 February and 24–17 October 2002. Open from 11–8 on Thursday and Friday, 11–6 on Saturday, and 11–5 on Sunday.*
**14–17 Feb**

## ▶ Art Innsbruck

GutenbergstraBe 3, Innsbruck A-6020 00.
**Tel 00**43 (0)512 567101
**Ws** www.art-innsbruck.at
*20th-century art and design.*
**Mar**

## ▶ The Contemporary Print Show & The Contemporary Print Fair

6a Goodge Place, London W1P 1FL.
**Tel** 020 7436 4007 **Fax** 020 7436 2755
**Email** clivej@artnet.co.uk
**Ws** www.artnet.co.uk
**Opening times** Mon–Sat 10–7.30, Sun 12–7.30
**Contact:** Clive Jennings
**15–26 Mar, 29 Mar–10 Apr**

## ▶ International Asian Art Fair

Seventh Regiment Armory Park Avenue at 67th Street, New York, USA
**Tel** 020 7734 5491 **Fax** 020 7494 4604
**Email** info@haughton.com
**Ws** www.haughton.com
**22–27 Mar**

## ▶ Art Frankfurt

Ludwig-Erhard-An-Lage, 1 Frankfurt 6037.
**Tel 00**49 69 75456694 **Fax 00**49 69 75751674
**Ws** www.artfrankfurt.de
*Contemporary art.*
**Apr or May**

## ▶ Glasgow Art Fair

George Square, Glasgow.
**Tel** 0141 552 6027 **Fax** 0141 552 6048
*Scotland's only art fair and the largest fair dedicated to art outside London with over 40 of Britain's finest art dealers selling original works of art by both celebrated and lesser-known artists.*
**Apr**

## ▶ The Chelsea Art Fair

Chelsea Old Town Hall, Kings Road, London SW3.
**Tel** 01444 482 514
**Fax** 01444 483 412
**Email** info@penman-fairs.co.uk
**Ws** www.penman-fairs.co.uk
**Opening times** Thu/Fri 11–9, Sat 11–7, Sun 11–5
**Contact:** Caroline Penman
*Organising the Chelsea Art Fair run annually in April since 1996. Admission £6. Contemporary and 20th-century paintings, drawings, prints, sculptures and ceramics offered by 40 galleries from across Britain and a few international exhibitors.*
*Chelsea Fair offers works by renowned artists and newcomers, ranging from £100 to £25,000 for new collectors and connoisseurs alike. Preview: Wednesday 24 April 6–9pm – £10 admission & wine.*
**25–28 Apr**

## ▶ Art Chicago 2002

Festival Hall, Navy Pier 600 E. Grand Avenue, Chicago, USA.
**Tel 001** 312 5873300
*Established 1993. The leading US art fair for modern and contemporary art.*
**May**

## ▶ Museums and Galleries Month, National Association for Gallery Education

1 Herbal Hill, Clerkenwell, London EC1R 5EJ.
**Tel** 020 7278 8382
*Over 400 galleries and museums, from local establishments to national institutions; and will be hosting a variety of events to attract a wider audience to art.*
**1 May–2 Jun**

## ▶ Brighton Festival

12A Pavilion Buildings, Castle Square, Brighton BN1 1EE.
**Tel** 01273 700 747 **Fax** 01273 707 505
**Email** info@brighton-festival.org.uk
**Ws** www.brighton-festival.org.uk

*England's biggest arts festival, involving several exhibitions in the visual arts.*
**4–26 May**

### ► The Craft Show for Calke
Calke Abbey.
**Tel** 01263 734711
**Email** info@easternevents.com
**Ws** www.easternevents.com
**Opening times** 10–5 daily
*The shows aim to offer quality rather than quantity and maintain a high standard of exhibitors with a rigorous selection procedure. A variety of crafts, demonstrations and children's entertainment will be on offer.*
**4–6 May**

### ► Living Crafts
Hatfield House, Hatfield AL9 5NQ
**Tel** 023 9242 6523
**Email** admin@livingcrafts.co.uk
**Ws** www.livingcrafts.co.uk
**Opening times** 10–6
*Around 400 of Britain's top craftsmen and artists demonstrating and selling a wide range of work in a variety of styles and media including jewellery, textiles, prints, oils, acrylics and watercolours.*
**9–12 May**

### ► The International Fine Art Fair
The Seventh Regiment Armory, Park Avenue at 67th Street, New York, USA.
**Tel** 020 7734 5491
**Fax** 020 7494 4604
**Email** info@haughton.com
**Ws** www.haughton.com
*Western art: paintings, drawings and sculpture, c.1300 to the 1960s, from European countries including France, Italy, Germany, Belgium, Spain, Britain, The Netherlands plus work from the United States.*
**10–15 May**

### ► Chelmsford Cathedral Festival
New Street, Chelmsford CM1 1AT.
**Tel** 01245 359 890
**Fax** 01245 280 456
**Email** chelcathfest@lineone.net
*With one of the finest acoustics in Britain, this splendid building is the venue for seven days of music-making each May. Classical music, jazz, opera, art and sculpture exhibitions plus a massive Fringe, in total over 80 events in and around the County Town of Essex during Festival week.*
**11–18 May**

### ► Newbury International Spring Festival
1 Bridge Street,
Newbury RG14 5BH.
**Tel** 01635 32421/528766
*Two busy weeks in May provide the finest artistic entertainment from music to visual arts, hosted at a variety of beautiful venues in Newbury and the surrounding area, including parish churches, country houses and hotels.*
**11–25 May**

### ► The Highland Festival: Scotland
40 Huntly Street, Inverness IV3 5HR.
**Tel** 01463 719 000/711 112
**Email** info@highlandfestival.org.uk
**Ws** www.highland-festival.co.uk
*A celebration of a wide range of arts and culture throughout the Highlands and Islands.*
**24 May–8 Jun**

### ► The Affordable Art Fair, Bath
Green Park Station, Bath.
**Jun**

### ► Art Basel
Messe Basel, Messeplatz, Basel, Switzerland
**Tel** 0041 61 686 2706 **Fax** 0041 61 686 3130
**Jun**

### ► Aldeburgh Festival of Music and the Arts
Snape Maltings Concert Hall, Snape, Saxmundham IP17 1SP.
**Tel** 01728 687110 **Fax** 01728 687120
**Email** enquiries@aldeburghfestivals.co.uk
**Ws** www.aldeburgh.co.uk
*Mixed arts festival.*
**Jun**

### ► City of London Festival
Bishopsgate Hall, 230 Bishopsgate, London EC2M 4HW.
**Tel** 020 7377 0540
**Fax** 020 7377 1972
**Email** admin@colf.org
**Ws** www.colf.org
*A large variety of events in stunning heritage venues, many of which are not normally open to the public. Programme includes concerts, opera, dance, theatre, comedy exhibitions, cinema, architectural and garden walks, readings and workshops.*
**Jun–Jul**

### ► Felbrigg Coast and Country Show
Felbrigg Hall near Cromer.
**Tel** 01263 734 711
**Email** info@easternevents.com
**Ws** www.easternevents.com
*Eastern Events organise craft shows at some of the most beautiful and interesting properties across the country. The show offers a variety of high quality crafts, demonstrations and children's entertainment.*
**Jun**

### ► Grassington Festival
Grassington near Skipton.
**Tel** 01756 753 093
**Ws** www.grassington-festival.org.uk
*Grassington in the heart of the Yorkshire Dales National Park offers exciting performances and spectacular scenery at its annual festival of music and the arts. Held at venues throughout Grassington.*
**Jun**

### ► Summer Olympia Fine Art and Antiques Fair
Olympia Hall, Hammersmith Road, London W14.
**Tel** 020 7370 8188
**Email** www.olympia-antiques.com
*400 international dealers will be exhibiting and selling high-quality antiques in this fair, which has merged with the 20th Century at Olympia fair. Careful vetting of exhibits by a panel of experts ensures accuracy of identification, so the public can buy with confidence.*
**Jun**

### ► Spitalfields Festival (London)
75 Brushfield Street, London.
**Tel** 020 7377 0287 **Fax** 020 7347 0494
**Email** info@spitalfieldsfestival.org.uk
**Ws** www.spitalfieldsfestival.org.uk
*Music events in Spitalfields*
**Jun**

### ► The Grosvenor House of Art and Antiques Fair
Le Meridien, Grosvenor House, Park Lane, London W1.
**Tel** 020 7399 8100 **Fax** 020 7495 8747
**Email** info@grosvenor-antiquesfair.co.uk
**Ws** www.grosvenor-antiquesfair.co.uk
*Britain's pre-eminent fair in the international world of art and antiques, now in its 68th year and attracting an audience of some 21,000 visitors. The world's leading dealers will be exhibiting works of art from antiquity to the 21st century which range in price from £200 to over £5 million. Visitors to the fair will have the rare opportunity to see £400 million worth of art and antiques under one roof, including paintings, furniture, silver jewellery, oriental and a veritable cornucopia of other objets d'art, all of which are available to buy.*
**Jun**

### ► The International Ceramics Fair and Seminar
The Park Lane Hotel, Picadilly, London W1.
**Tel** 020 7734 5491 **Fax** 020 7494 4604
**Email** info@haughton.com
**Ws** www.haughton.com
**Opening times** 11–7.
*A synthesis of academia and commerce, now in its 21st year. Organised in three sections, the event comprises an exhibition drawn from the ceramics collections of the Winterthur Museum, USA; a series of 15 lectures covering a vast range of aspects of the history of world ceramics by academics and curators from all over the the world; and a fair involving 40 exhibitors who bring rare ceramics and glass from 5,000 BC to the present.*
**Jun**

### ► Working Craft Show
Kedleston Hall.
**Tel** 01263 734 711
**Email** info@easternevents.com
**Ws** www.easternevents.com
*Eastern Events organise craft shows at some of the most beautiful and interesting properties across the country. The show aims to*

*offer quality rather than quantity and maintain a high standard of exhibitors with a rigorous selection procedure. There will be a variety of crafts, demonstrations and children's entertainment on offer.*
**Jun**

### ▶ Patchings 2001 Art & Craft Festival
Patchings Farm Art Centre, Oxton Road, Calverton NG14 6NU.
**Tel** 0115 965 3479 **Fax** 0115 965 5308
**Ws** www.patchingsartcentre.co.uk
**Opening times** 10–5.30 each day except Sun 10–4.30
*Over 150 international artists and craft designers demonstrating, exhibiting and selling their work. Patchings Art & Craft Festival is now in its 8th year and again we are pleased to welcome the very best in fine art and designer craftsmanship to this unique event. One of the UK's most celebrated festivals set within the award-winning 60-acre countryside of Patchings Art Centre. The four-day event makes a special occasion whatever your interest. Enjoy the great variety of creative and inspiring work in action. Tickets £6, concessions £5, children under 11 free when part of a family group.*
**14–17 Jun**

### ▶ Bracknell Festival 2002
South Hill Park, Ringmead, Bracknell RG12 7PA.
**Tel** 01344 484 858
**Fax** 01344 411 427
**Email** marketing@southhillpark.org.uk
**Ws** www.southhillpark.org.uk
*Over three days, a festival primarily of music – a mixture of folk, jazz, rock, world music. However for the visual arts, there are also exhibitions, crafts stalls, and street theatre performances.*
**Jul**

### ▶ Greenwich and Docklands International Festivals
6 College Approach, London SE10 9HY.
**Tel** 020 8305 1818
**Fax** 020 8305 1188
**Email** info@festival.org
**Ws** www.festival.org
*Free outdoors spectaculars as well as ticketed events including theatre, music, dance and visual arts.*
**Jul**

### ▶ Harrogate International Festival
1 Victoria Avenue, Harrogate, North Yorks HG1 1EQ.
**Tel** 01423 562 303 **Fax** 01423 521 264
**Email** info@harrogate-festival.org.uk
**Ws** www.harrogate-festival.org.uk
*Mixed arts festival based in the beautiful spa town of Harrogate, including the best of the Edinburgh fringe... before Edinburgh! Art exhibitions are ongoing at the same time as the festival.*
**Jul–Aug**

### ▶ Ryedale Festival
The Memorial Hall, Potter Hill, Pickering YO18 8AA.
**Tel** 01751 475 777 box office
01751 475888 admin
**Ws** www.ryedalefestival.co.uk
*Mixed arts festival*
**Jul**

### ▶ Art in Action
Waterperry House, near Wheatley, OX33 9JZ.
**Tel** 020 738 3192 **Fax** 020 7381 0605
**Ws** www.artinaction.org.uk
**Opening times** 10.30–5.30
*Postponed to this date from 2001. An open-air event attracting some 25,000 visitors over a four-day period. More than 250 artists and craftsmen of the highest quality will be selling and demonstrating their work, with examples from both Western and non-Western cultures. Practical classes are available to book on the day. Also excellent food, live music, and dance performances.*
**18–21 Jul**

### ▶ National Eisteddfod of Wales
St David's.
**Tel** 02920 763 777 **Fax** 02920 763 737
**Email** info@eisteddfod.org.uk
**Ws** www.eisteddfod.org.uk
*Exhibition of contemporary art, crafts, sculpture, installation, video, photography, fashion, etc. by contributors who are of Welsh descent, are based in Wales or write or speak in Welsh.*
**3–10 Aug**

### ▶ Edinburgh International Festival
The Hub, Castlehill, Royal Mile, Edinburgh EH1 2NE.
**Tel** 0131 473 2000/2001 **Fax** 0131 473 2003
**Email** eif@eif.co.uk
**Ws** www.eif.co.uk
*Cultural feast featuring some of the world's greatest artists and companies.*
**11–30 Aug**

### ▶ The International Art and Design Fair
Seventh Regiment Armory, Park Avenue at 67th Street, New York, USA.
**Tel** 020 7734 5491 **Fax** 020 7494 4604
**Email** info@haughton.com
**Ws** www.haughton.com
*Asian and Islamic works of art, sculpture, ceramics and textiles from the Far East including China, Japan and Korea as well as South East Asia, India and the Middle East.*
**Sep–Oct**

### ▶ Rye Festival
PO Box 33, Rye TN31 7YB.
**Tel** 01797 224 442
**Email** info@ryefestival.co.uk
**Ws** www.ryefestival.co.uk
*Rye Festival promotes all forms of literature, music and the visual arts, and science in a celebration of the town's cultural life.*
**7–22 Sep**

### ▶ Liverpool Biennial of Contemporary Art
The View, Gostin House, 32–36 Hanover Street, Liverpool L1 4LN.
**Tel** 0151 709 7440 **Fax** 0151 709 7377
**14 Sep–24 Nov**

### ▶ The 20/21 Century British Art Fair
Commonwealth Institute, Kensington High Street, London W8 6NQ.
**Tel** 020 8742 1611 **Fax** 020 8995 5094
**Email** organisers@artfairs.demon.co.uk
**Ws** www.britishartfair.co.uk
**Opening times** 11–8.30 (18–20 Sep), 11–6 (21–22 Sep)
**Contact:** Gay Hutson.
*In 2002, this immensely popular fair moves to the Commonwealth Institute on Kensington High Street W8. Founded in 1988, this is the only fair for British art covering the period 1900 to the present day, which between 1991 and 2001 was held at the Royal College of Art and is undergoing refurbishment. On show from around 70 art dealers is a vast range of painting, sculpture, photography and ceramics featuring all the great names of 20th-century British art: Auerbach, Bacon, Freud, Frink, Hepworth, Hockney, Lowry, Moore, Nash, Sickert and Spencer as well as the young contemporaries of today. Prices range from a few hundred pounds up to many thousands. Admission £8, OAPs/students £4.*
**18–22 Sep**

### ▶ The Affordable Art Fair
Battersea Park, London.
www.affordableartfair.co.uk
**Tel** 020 7371 8787
**18-21 Oct**

### ▶ Cultura: the World Art and Antiques Fair
Messe Basel, Basel, Switzerland.
**Tel** 0041 61 2278787 **Fax** 0041 61 2278780
**Email** info@cultura-fair.ch
**Ws** www.cultura-fair.ch
**Oct**

### ▶ The International Fine Art and Antique Dealers Show
Seventh Regiment Armory, Park Avenue at 67th Street, New York, USA.
**Tel** 020 7734 5491
**Fax** 020 7494 4604
**Email** info@haughton.com
**Ws** www.haughton.com
*Art and antiques from all periods and countries, including pictures, sculpture, manuscripts, furniture, pottery and porcelain, glass, jewellery, silver, textiles and antiquities.*
**Oct**

### ▶ Art Cologne
Köln Messe, Cologne, Germany.
**Tel** +49 221 8210
**Ws** www.artcologne.de
*Germany's leading international modern and contemporary art fair.*
**Nov–Feb**

### ▶ The Craft Show
Chilford Vineyard, Linton, Cambridge.

**Tel** 01263 734 711
**Email** info@easternevents.com
**Ws** www.easternevents.com
*Eastern Events organise craft shows at some of the most beautiful and interesting properties across the country. There will be a variety of crafts, demonstrations and children's entertainment on offer.*
**Nov**

### ▶ Asian Art in London

32 Dover Street, Mayfair, London W1F 4NE.
**Tel** 020 7499 2215 **Fax** 020 7499 2216
**Email** info@asianartinlondon.com
**Ws** www.asianartinlondon.com
*A programme of exhibitions, auctions, and events to attract enthusiasts from all over the world. Over 50 dealers link up with auction houses, museums, and other institutions resulting in a multifaceted event supported by both the academic and commercial worlds. There will be a series of exhibitions, auctions, lectures, seminars and social events. An astonishing range of Chinese, Japanese, Indian, South East Asian, Himalayan, Korean and Islamic art will be on view.*
**7–15 Nov**

### ▶ The Bath Art Fair

The Pavillion, North Parade Road, Bath.
**Tel** 01444 482 514 **Fax** 01444 483 412
**Email** info@penman-fairs.co.uk
**Ws** www.penman-fairs.co.uk
**Opening times** Thu 12–8, Fri/Sat 10.30–6, Sun 10.30–5
*60 stands, including antiques before 1914, art, jewelry and the like until 1940, and some modern paintings. Admission is £3.*
**7–10 Nov**

### ▶ Westminster Gallery

Central Hall, Storey's Gate, London SW1 9NH.
**Tel** 020 7222 8010
**Fax** 020 7222 6883
**Email** eets@wch.co.uk
**Ws** www.wch.co.uk
**Opening times** Various
**Personnel** Senior Events Manager: Ms Cathy Williamson. General Manager: Michael Sharp.
**Services and Facilities** Café. Disabled Access. Gallery space for hire. Guided Tours

*Central Hall, Westminster*
*The Westminster Gallery offers an elegant, spacious and versatile exhibition area. The three rooms the gallery occupies can be hired individually or as a whole and are available throughout the year. Lighting, hanging and display facilities are easily managed. The adjacent café is open daily and is very happy to assist with refreshments for your private viewings.*

### ▶ Winter Olympia Fine Art and Antiques Fair

Olympia National Hall, Hammersmith Road, London W14.
**Tel** 020 7370 8234
**Email** olympia-antiques@eco.co.uk
**Ws** www.olympia-antiques.co.uk
*This prestigious fair, done in conjunction with the British Antique Dealers Association, involves around 230 leading dealers exhibiting and selling high quality antiques and outstanding works of art. Careful vetting of exhibits by a panel of experts ensures accuracy of identification, so the public can buy with confidence.*
**11–17 Nov**

# Competitions

This is only a selection of the competitions, awards and bursaries available, ranging from cash prizes and travel scholarships to opportunities for exhibitions and publishing. Further information can be obtained through art colleges, regional arts boards, local artists' groups and libraries. It is advisable to telephone the organisers and check details before submitting work or sending money.

**▶ Alastair Salvesen Art Scholarship**
DEADLINE FOR SUBMISSIONS IS 18 JAN 2002
*This is an enablement scholarship, offered by the Royal Scottish Academy, which comprises up to £10,000 in travel funds and a three-week exhibition, for any artist aged 24–35 who trained at a Scottish college of art.*
Details: Alastair Salvesen Art Scholarship, Royal Scottish Academy, 17 Waterloo Place, 3rd floor, Edinburgh EH1 3BG, tel: 0131 558 7097, fax: 0131 225 2349, email: info@royalscottishacademy.org, web: www.royalscottishacademy.org

**▶ Art Awards for the Over 60s**
*Competition open to amateur artists with top prizes of £1000 in each of the four categories: portrait, landscape/seascape, flora/fauna and still life.*
Details: Art Awards for the Over 60s, Elderly Accomodation Counsel, 11 Westrow, Westleigh Ave, London, tel: 020 8789 6185, fax: 020 8789 6185

**▶ Artist & Young Artist of the Year**
ENTRIES BY 1 MAR
*Categories for all artists, from beginners to professionals in all mediums, with awards totalling over £5,000 in prizes. The final paintings are exhibited in London.*
Details: Artist & Young Artist of the Year, PO Box 50, Newark, Nottinghamshire NG23 5GY, tel: 01949 844 050, fax: 01949 844 051, web: www.saa.co.uk

**▶ Creative Britons Awards**
*Prize money of £200,000 is being offered to 'heroes' of the arts world through the Creative Britons Awards – the biggest arts prize in the UK. The Awards, sponsored by Prudential, aim to highlight six individuals whose vision, leadership, and imagination have contributed most to the UK's cultural wealth. The overall winner receives £100,000 and five individuals receive £20,000 to donate to the arts project of their choice. Arts & Business, the Award's organiser, encourages nominations for individuals who have made a worthy contribution to the arts, such as encouraging artistic excellence, bringing the arts to new and wider audiences, helping to regenerate an area through the arts, build bridges between communities, schools, business and the arts or who have enabled a particular project to happen, by raising funds or support.*
Details: Creative Britons Awards, tel: 020 7378 8143

**▶ Delfina Studio Trust**
*The trust provides 18 free studio spaces: British artists are awarded two years' space and others one year with accommodation.*
Details: Delfina Studio Trust, 50 Bermondsey Street, Southwark, London SE1 3UD, tel: 020 7357 6600

**▶ Discerning Eye**
DEADLINE FOR ENTRIES IS 22 SEP
Details: Discerning Eye, Exhibition/Competition Organisers and PR, Parker Harris Partnership, PO Box 279, Esher, Surrey, tel: 01372 462190, fax: 01372 460032, email: info@parkerharris.com.uk

**▶ East Midlands Art Awards**
For details of various schemes/awards, contact the address.
Details: East Midlands Art Awards, Mountfields House, Epinal Way, Loughborough LE11 0QE

**▶ Eastern Arts Board (Visual and Media Arts Department)**
For details of various schemes/awards, contact the address.
Details: Eastern Arts Board (Visual and Media Arts Department), Cherry Hinton Hall, Cherry Hinton Road, Cambridge CB1 8DW, web: www.arts.org.uk

**▶ European Publishers Award for Photography**
*An open competition for the best set of photographs suitable for publication as a book, now in its 7th year. Judging normally takes place in April, and it is open to photographers worldwide. The winning book is published in five European countries.*
Details: European Publishers Award for Photography, Dewi Lewis Publishing, 8 Broomfield Road, Heaton Moor, Stockport SK4 4ND

**▶ Fine Art Trade Guild Business Awards Scheme**
*Winners in several nominated art and trade categories are presented with an artist-designed trophy in the spring.*
Details: Fine Art Trade Guild Business Awards Scheme, Fine Art Trade Guild, 16 Empress Place, London SW6 1TT, tel: 020 7381 6616, fax: 020 7381 2596

**▶ Fulbright Postgraduate Awards**
DEADLINE FOR SUBMISSIONS IS 8 NOV 2001
*Graduate students may apply for a year's postgraduate funding in the USA. A maintenance grant, full tuition fees, and transatlantic travel will be awarded to outstanding candidates. Send A4 SAE (39p) to address above for information. Applicants must be EU citizens, ordinarily resident in the UK.*
Details: Fulbright Postgraduate Awards, Fulbright Commission, 62 Doughty Street, London WC1N 2LS, tel: 020 7404 6880, web: www.fulbright.co.uk

**▶ Harlech Printmaking Open 2002**
*Entries are sought from artists around the world for the Harlech Printmaking Open to be held in the exhibition areas of Theatr Ardudwy Harlech, North Wales. There will be invited artists, selection by jury, purchase awards, and collection points in Harlech and London. Selection is by slide for artists from Wales, Scotland, England and Ireland. Artists from other parts of the world must submit actual work.*
Details: Harlech Printmaking Open 2002, Theatr Ardudwy, Harlech, Gwynedd LL4 62PU, web: ww.ucl.ac.uk/-uczc-crb/harlech.htm

**▶ The Hunting Art Prize**
SUBMISSION DEADLINE IS 30 NOV/1 DEC AT RCA, JUDGING BEGINS THE WEEK BEGINNING 3 DEC 2001
*Over 1,000 artists annually enter this prestigious competition which offers generous cash prizes and an exhibition at the RCA at the start of Feb, followed by a tour. Send A4 SAE to address below for details.*
Details: The Hunting Art Prize, Exhibition/ Competition Organisers and PR, Parker Harris Partnership, PO Box 279, Esher, Surrey KT10 8YZ, tel: 01372 462 190, fax: 01372 460 032, email: info@parkerharris.co.uk

**▶ John Kinross Memorial Fund**
*Students at Scottish colleges studying painting, sculpture, and architecture are eligible to apply for a 3-month scholarship to Florence in memory of the late John Kinross. Send a SAE to the address for details.*
Details: John Kinross Memorial Fund, Royal Scottish Academy, 10 Waterloo Place, Edinburgh EH1 3BG, tel: 0131 558 7097, fax: 0131 225 2349, email: info@royalscottishacademy.org, web: www.royalscottishacademy.org

**▶ Juliet Gomperts and Janet Konstam Trust**
*Young figurative and landscape artists, aged over 23 and under 45 are invited to apply for scholarships to attend courses for up to six weeks at the Verrochio Arts Centre in Tuscany. The value is approximately £2,000. Additionally, shortlisted candidates may apply for the £500 Janet Konstam Travelling Fellowship for travel and research in Italy. There is no application form: applicants should send up to 12 photographs or slides of current work (together with exploratory drawings), a CV, and the names, addresses and telephone numbers of two appropriate referees. For return of work, an A4 stamped addressed envelope must be enclosed. For details, send SAE to address above.*
Details: Juliet Gomperts and Janet Konstam Trust, Artists' Residencies in Tuscany, 31 Addison Avenue, London W11 4QS, email: b.gomperts@ucl.ac.uk

**▶ Kettle's Yard Fellowship**
*Annual Artist Fellowship, with a deadline for applications normally in early November.*
Details: Kettle's Yard Fellowship, Kettle's Yard, Castle Street, Cambridge CB3 0AQ, tel: 01223 352124, web: www.kettlesyard.co.uk

**▶ Kraszna-Krausz Book Awards**
*These international awards are made annually to encourage and recognise outstanding achievements in the publishing and writing of books on photography and the moving image (film, television and video). Books in any language are eligible, with entries submitted by publishers only.*
Details: Kraszna-Krausz Book Awards, 122 Fawnbrake Avenue, London SE24 0BZ, tel:

020 7738 6701, email: k-k@dial.pipex.com, web: www.editor.net/k-k

**▶ The Linbury Prize for Stage Design**

*Commissions and cash awards, sponsored by one of the Sainsbury family charitable trusts, are made biennially to final year graduate and postgraduate theatre design students from selected colleges. Finalists will exhibit in the autumn.*

Details: The Linbury Prize for Stage Design, Kallaway, tel: 020 7221 7883

**▶ The Macmillan Prize for a Children's Picture Book**

DEADLINE FOR SUBMISSIONS IS END OF APR 2002

*Art students in higher education are eligible to enter works that are original and will provide children with much enjoyment in this annual competition.*

Details: The Macmillan Prize for a Children's Picture Book, Marketing Department, Macmillan Children's Books, 25 Eccleston Place, London SW1W 9NF, tel: 020 7881 8356, fax: 020 7881 8357

**▶ Manhattan**

*A new collaboration opens the door to British artists. Christie-Wild and the major New York gallery, DFN Gallery, host a prestigious event in the heart of Manhattan to give emerging and established artists the oppurtunity to access this lucrative and challenging art market. Artists are accepted by invitation only. New artists are encouraged to apply by sending a SAE plus samples to the address above. The final list of exhibitors is announced in the spring. Artists are asked to contribute towards shipping, transportation, and export costs. All styles and forms of art are considered (excluding large conceptual or installation pieces).*

Details: Manhattan, NYAD 2000, Christie-Wild International, Hammerain House, Hookstone Avenue, Harrogate, North Yorkshire HG2 8ER, tel: 01423 546 365 fax: 01423 873 999 email: jmcwild7@aol.com

**▶ The National Art Library Illustration Awards**

*Organised by the National Art Library and sponsored by the Enid Linder Foundation, these annual awards are for book and magazine illustrations published in the calendar year preceding the date of the award.*

Details: The National Art Library Illustration Awards, The Victoria & Albert Museum, Cromwell Road, South Kensington, London SW7 2RL, tel: 020 7942 2000, web: www.nal.vam.ac.uk

**▶ National Eisteddfod of Wales**

DEADLINE FOR SUBMISSIONS IS 14 FEB

*The Eisteddfod hosts a large contemporary art and crafts exhibition. Awards include: Gold Medal and £5,000 in Fine Art; Gold Medal and £5,000 in Craft and Design; Young Artist Scholarship of £1, 500. Any person born in Wales, of Welsh parentage, able to speak or write the Welsh language or who has lived or worked in Wales for the three years prior to the date of the Eisteddfod is eligible.*

Details: National Eisteddfod of Wales, Eisteddfod Office, 40 Parc Ty Glas, Llanishen, Cardiff, CF4 5WU, tel: 029 2076 3777, email: info@eisteddfod.org.uk, web: www.eisteddfod.org.uk

**▶ National Print Exhibition 2002**

*February open exhibition at the Mall Galleries, London, offering 11 prizes for outstanding printmakers. For details, send SAE to address below.*

Details: National Print Exhibition 2002, Mall Galleries, 17 Carlton House Terrace, London SW1Y 5BD

**▶ New Designers Awards**

*This is part of the New Designers Exhibition held annually in July at the Business Design Centre, Islington, in 2002, and takes place in two parts: 3D work and 2D work. Business and sponsors from throughout the UK select winners from the exhibition representing the best graduates from British design courses.*

Details: New Designers Awards, tel: 020 7359 3535

**▶ The Open Drawing Competition, Cheltenham**

*Competition for professional artists which awards cash prizes every year during an exhibition held at Cheltenham & Gloucester College of Higher Education.*

Details: The Open Drawing Competition, Cheltenham, School of Fine Art, Cheltenham & Gloucester College of HIgher Education, Albert Road, Cheltenham, Glos GL52 3JG

**▶ Queen Elizabeth Scholarship Trust**

DEADLINE FOR SUBMISSIONS IS 19 JAN AND 19 JUL 2002

*Aimed at furthering education in crafts and trades, scholarships are granted (ranging from £2, 500 to £12,000) every June. For details, send A4 SAE stamped 31p to the address below.*

Details: Queen Elizabeth Scholarship Trust, 1 Buckingham Place, London SW1E 6HR, tel: 020 7828 2268, fax: 020 7828 1668, email: quest@rwha.co.uk, web: www.quest.org.uk

**▶ ROSL ART, Royal Over-Seas League**

*Annual exhibition of 5 artists, one from each of the 5 continents. Artists receive travel scholarship. For details, send SAE to the following address:*

Details: ROSL ART, Royal Over-Seas League, Over-Seas House, Park Place, St James's Street, London SW1A 1LR tel: 020 7408 0214, fax: 020 7499 6738, email: culture@rosl.org.uk, web: www.rosl.org.uk

**▶ Royal Institute of Painters in Watercolours**

*Open exhibition at the Mall Galleries in London in the spring. Many prizes are on offer.*

Details: Royal Institute of Painters in Watercolours, Mall Galleries, 17 Carlton House Terrace, London SW1Y 5BD

**▶ Royal Scottish Academy Annual Exhibition**

*The annual exhibition, sponsored by Maclay Murray & Spens, Solicitors, includes painting, printmaking, architecture and sculpture, with numerous awards in all categories including the M.S. Macfarlane Charitable Trust prizes for painting and sculpture and the Dumferline Building Society Award for painting.*

Details: Royal Scottish Academy Annual Exhibition, 17 Waterloo Place, Edinburgh EH1 3BG, tel: 0131 558 7097, web: www.royalscottishacademy.org.uk

**▶ Royal Scottish Academy (RSA) Art for Architecture**

*Grants are available to those involved in building or landscape projects to appoint, at the outset of a project, artists as part of the design team.*

Details: Royal Scottish Academy (RSA) Art for Architecture, 17 Waterloo Place, Edinburgh EH1 3BG, tel: 020 7451 6865 (JF) or 020 7451 6861 (GM), email: ferniej@rsa-uk.demon.co.uk or markovig@rsa-uk.demon.co.uk, web: www.rsa.org.uk/afa

**▶ Royal Scottish Academy (RSA) Student Design Awards**

*Awards in the form of Attachment or Travel awards are made to students submitting winning designs in response to the briefs offered in the Projects Book, which is published in September.*

Details: Royal Scottish Academy (RSA) Student Design Awards, RSA Design, 8 John Adam Street, London WC2N 6EZ, tel: 020 7451 6853, web: www.rsa.org.uk/projects/details

**▶ Royal Society of British Artists**

*Autumn open exhibition at the Mall Galleries in London, with nine awards on offer. For details, send SAE to address below.*

Details: Royal Society of British Artists, Mall Galleries, 17 Carlton House Terrace, London SW1Y 5BD

**▶ Royal Society of Marine Artists**

*Open exhibition in October at the Mall Galleries in London of works featuring the sea, with three prizes on offer. For details send SAE to the address below.*

Details: Royal Society of Marine Artists, Mall Galleries, 17 Carlton House Terrace, London SW1Y 5BD

**▶ Royal Society of Portrait Painters**

*Annual open exhibition in May at the Mall Galleries in London, offering three prestigious awards for portraiture: the Ondaatje Prize (£5,000) for the most distinguished painting in the exhibition; the Carroll Foundation Young Portrait Painters Award (£3,000) for a painter under 35; and the Prince of Wales's Award for Portrait Drawing (£2,000), sponsored by Prince Charles. For details send SAE to the address below.*

Details: Royal Society of Portrait Painters, Mall Galleries, 17 Carlton House Terrace, London SW1Y 5BD

**▶ The RPS International Print Competition**

SUBMISSION DEADLINE IS EARLY MAR

*Professional, student, and amateur photographers are invited to submit work.*

Details: The RPS International Print Competition, The Royal Photographic Society, Octagon Galleries, Milsom Street, Bath, BA1 1DN, tel: 01225 462 841, fax: 01225 448 688, web: www.rps.org

**▶ Scottish Arts Council**

*The Scottish Arts Council funds various projects covering the visual arts, combined arts, placements and travel, crafts and photography and commissions. There are also exhibition schemes. The help desk is open Monday to Friday, 10 to 4.*

Details: Scottish Arts Council, 12 Manor Place, Edinburgh EH3 7DD, tel: 0131 240 2433/2444

**▶ Singer & Friedlander/Sunday Times Watercolour Exhibition**

SUBMISSION DEADLINE IN MID-JUN

*A competition and selected exhibition, held from September to November at the Mall Galleries, Leeds, and Birmingham, for works 'upholding the finest traditions of contemporary British watercolour painting'. Finalists' exhibitions are held at the Mall Galleries and in several regional centres, and prizes are worth a total of around £25,000. For details, send an SAE to the address below.*

Details: Singer & Friedlander/Sunday Times Watercolour Exhibition, Exhibition/ Competition Organisers and PR, Parker Harris Partnership, PO Box 279, Esher, Surrey KT10 8YZ, tel: 01372 462190, fax: 01372 460032,

**▶ Society of Wildlife Artists**

*Summer open exhibition at the Mall Galleries in London of work depicting wildlife, with six prizes on offer.*

Details: Society of Wildlife Artists, Mall Galleries, 17 Carlton House Terrace, London SW1Y 5BD

**▶ Stockport Open Exhibition**

*Works made by artists in the North West are exhibited annually and merit awards are made. For details, send a SAE to the address below.*

Details: Stockport Open Exhibition, Stockport Art Gallery, Wellington Road South, Stockport SK3 8AB

**▶ Tabernacle Art Competition 2002**

SUBMISSION DEADLINE JUL, EXHIBITION RUNS FROM JUL TO SEP

*The Museum of Modern Art, Wales, invites artists to submit one new work in any format or media inspired by the title (theme to be decided).*

Details: Tabernacle Art Competition 2002, MOMA Wales, Heol Penrallt, Machynlleth, SY20 8AJ, tel: 01654 703355

**▶ The Turner Prize**

*This annual prize, supported by the Patrons of New Art, is usually sponsored by Channel 4. Nominations from the public are invited and four British contemporary artists under 50 are chosen by a selection panel for a popular finalists' exhibition at the end of each year on the strength of the previous year's exhibitions. A large cash prize (£20,000) is awarded at the Tate Gallery.*

Details: The Turner Prize, Tate Gallery, Millbank, London SW1P 4RG

**▶ University of Glamorgan Purchase Prize**

*Sponsored by the University of Glamorgan, the Purchase Art Prize is a competition open to all artists and students who are of Welsh parentage, born in Wales, or have lived in Wales for the last two years. Prizes are for the purchase of works in the category of painting in any medium consistent with contemporary practice. Initial submission is by slides with selected finalists exhibiting in the University Gallery y Bont/The Bridge in May.*

Details: University of Glamorgan Purchase Prize, School of Humanities and Social Sciences, University of Glamorgan, Pontypridd CF37 1DL

**▶ Watercolour C21**

*New open painting competition organised by the Royal Watercolour Society, encouraging innovative approaches to the use of watercolour. Artists are invited to submit three framed, glazed water-based paintings on paper and successful entries will be exhibited at Bankside Gallery, London, alongside works by internationally acclaimed artists. Prizes are awarded with a total value of over £10,000.*

Details: Watercolour C21, Bankside Gallery, 48 Hopton Street, London SE1 9JH, tel: 020 7928 7521

**▶ West Midlands Arts**

*For details of various schemes/awards, write to the address below.*

Details: West Midlands Arts, Finance Department, 82 Granville Street, Birmingham B1 2LH

**▶ Yorkshire Arts**

SUBMISSIONS THROUGHOUT THE YEAR

*Artists from the region are invited to submit applications for various schemes covering the visual arts, crafts, photography, film-making, multimedia and broadcasting. For details, write to the address below.*

Details: Yorkshire Arts, Visual & Media Arts unit, Yorkshire Arts Board, 21 Bond Street, Dewsbury, West Yorkshire WF13 1AX

# London Commercial Galleries

*All entries in this section are sorted alphabetically by gallery*

# The London Art Buyer's Map

No other city in the world can offer the same extraordinary richness and diversity of commercial art galleries as London, located from the far East End to Mayfair and beyond, according to the art to be sold. For the London art buyer's map is, in fact, a series of areas in which like-minded galleries cluster.

The Old Master galleries are dotted around St James's and gentlemen's clubland, for here is where their traditional aristocratic customers have trod since the establishment of White's coffee house and James Christie's auction house in Pall Mall in the 18th century. The tiny streets that run behind the great façades of St James are the natural haunt of dealers specialising in English, Flemish and Dutch pictures, housed in exquisite galleries. 19th-century picture dealers and the grand dealers who deal in mega-price Impressionists and early 20th-century masters such as Picasso, find that the former town houses of Bond Street and Mayfair are their natural home. Their extremely rich international clients can walk from their hotels to be delighted with perhaps a single Monet, sky lit in a grand 18th-century interior.

The moderns, those galleries dealing in 20th-century art, have traditionally claimed Cork Street as their home, which makes a great deal of sense; the slightly younger clientele feels at home in this attractive little street and its large late-19th-century houses offer vast, clean environments in which to hang very large modern pictures and place sculpture to its best advantage – in empty volumes of space.

But it is the huge surge of interest in contemporary art in London that has changed the map and offers the most excitement in terms of discovering galleries who not only pursue cutting edge exhibition policies but whose location and appearance add much to the adventure of buying art.

The move to the East End was partly spearheaded by Gilbert and George who moved to Spitalfields many years ago; since then the areas further to the east have provided impecunious artists with cheap studio space, carved out of iron-framed warehouses. In their wake came the galleries which show their work, taking over in Hoxton Square, strung along Old Street, dotted around Bethnal Green and Hackney. It makes sense; many young city types buy contemporary art – and the East End is on their doorstep. And what's next? South of the river is proving interesting, stimulated by the Tate Modern. Southwark and Bermondsey are, after all, just over the river from the City and will be even more accessible after the Canon Street Jubilee footbridge has been built in 2002. And even further afield in Deptford there are already two extremely interesting galleries.

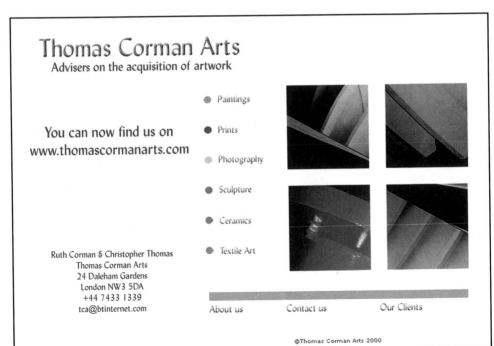

### ▶ 11 Duke Street Ltd
11 Duke Street, London SW1Y.
**Fax** 020 7976 2733
**Email** 020 7976 2744/2733

### ▶ 12 Dolland Street
2nd Floor, London SE11.
**Tel** 020 7494 1434

### ▶ 198 Gallery
194–198 Railton Road, Herne Hill, London SE24 0LU.
**Tel** 020 7978 8390
*See London Public section for details*

### ▶ 180 Gallery
182 Westbourne Grove, London W11 2RH.
**Tel** 020 7229 9309
**Fax** 020 7243 7215

### ▶ 291 Gallery
291 Hackney Road, London E2.
**Tel** 020 76135676

### ▶ 507 Gallery
507 Kings Road, Chelsea, London SW10 0TX.
**Nearest Underground** Sloane Sq./Earls Court

### ▶ Aaron Gallery
125 Mount Street, London W1K 3NS.
**Tel** 020 7499 9434
**Fax** 020 7499 0072
**Email** info@aarongallery.com
**Ws** www.aarongallery.com
**Opening times** Mon–Fri 10–6, Sat by appointment
**Personnel** Proprietor: Manouchehr Aaron. Proprietor: Simon Aaaron.
**Work Stocked and Sold**
*Dealers in Ancient art*

### ▶ Abbott & Holder
30 Museum Street, London WC1A 1LH.
**Tel** 020 7637 3981
**Fax** 020 7631 0575
**Email** abbott.holder@virgin.net
**Ws** www.abbottandholder.co.uk
**Opening times** Mon–Sat 9.30–6, Thu 9.30–7.
**Nearest Underground** Tottenham Court Road/Holborn.
**Personnel** Partners: Phillip Athill, John Abbott.
**Services and Facilities** Art Consultancy. Framing. Gallery space for hire. Restoration. Valuation.
**Work Stocked and Sold** Dr. Pa. Pr.
**Price range** £50–£5,000
For artists see Commercial Gallery Artists.

### ▶ Ackermann & Johnson
Lowndes Lodge Gallery, 27 Lowndes Street, London SW1X 9H7.
**Tel** 020 7235 6464
**Fax** 020 7823 1057
**Opening times** Mon–Fri 9–5, Sat by appointment only.
**Nearest Underground** Knightsbridge, Sloane Square.
**Personnel** Peter Johnson. Hugh Nixon. Claire Lauf.
**Services and Facilities** Commissioning Service. Framing. Restoration. Valuation.
**Work Stocked and Sold** Dr. Pa. Sc.
For artists see Commercial Gallery Artists.

### ▶ Actaeon Gallery
15 Motcomb Street, London SW1X 8LB.
**Tel** 020 7259 5095 **Fax** 020 7259 5069

### ▶ Adam Gallery
35 Ponsonby Terrace, London SW1P 4PZ.
**Tel** 020 7630 0599
**Email** enquiries@adamgallery.com
**Ws** www.adamgallery.com
**Opening times** Tue–Fri 10–6, Sat 10–4.
**Nearest Underground** Pimlico.
**Personnel** Directors: Paul Dye, Philip Dye. China Blake, Vanessa Wells, James McDonagh.
**Services and Facilities** Art Consultancy. Art for Offices. Framing. Restoration. Valuation.
**Work Stocked and Sold** Dr. Pa. Pr. Sc.
**Price range** £500–£60,000

### ▶ Addison Ross Gallery
40 Eaton Terrace, London SW1 W8TS.
**Tel** 020 7730 1536, 020 7730 6353
**Fax** 020 7823 5081
**Personnel** David Ross.

### ▶ Adonis Art
1B Coleherne Road, London SW10.
**Tel** 020 7460 3888

### ▶ Advanced Graphics London
B206 The Gallery and C103 The Studio Faircharm, 8–12 Creekside, London SE8 3DX.
**Tel** 020 8691 1330
**Fax** 020 8694 9930
**Email** gallery@advancedgraphics.co.uk
**Ws** www.advancedgraphics.co.uk
**Opening times** Mon–Fri 10–6, evenings & weekends by appointment.
**Nearest Station** Deptford, DLR: Deptford Bridge.
**Personnel** Louise Peck. Fay Davey. Charlotte Dixon.
**Services and Facilities** Art Consultancy. Art for Offices. Disabled Access. Framing. Parking.
**Work Stocked and Sold** Ab. Pr.
**Price range** £300–£2,000
For artists see Commercial Gallery Artists.

*Printers and publishers of limited edition original prints, specialising in silkscreen and woodblock. Own publications include prints made directly with the following artists: Craigie Aitchison, Basil Beattie, Paul Benjamins, Neil Canning, Anthony Frost, Terry Frost, Donald Hamilton Fraser, Tom Hammick, Clyde Hopkins, John Hoyland, James Hugonin, Albert Irvin, Trevor Jones, Anita Klein, John McLean, Matthew Radford, Ray Richardson and Kate Whiteford.*

### ▶ The Agency
35–40 Charlotte Road, London EC2.
**Tel** 020 7613 2080

### ▶ Agnew's
43 Old Bond Street, London W1S 4BA.
**Tel** 020 7290 9250 **Fax** 020 7629 4359
**Email** agnews@agnewsgallery.co.uk
**Ws** www.agnewsgallery.com
**Opening times** Mon–Fri 9.30–5.30
**Nearest Underground** Green Park.
**Personnel** Contemporary: Mark Adams.
**Services and Facilities** Art Consultancy. Framing. Restoration. Valuation.
**Work Stocked and Sold** Dr. Pa. Pr.
For artists see Commercial Gallery Artists.
*Paintings, drawings, prints and sculpture from 14th century to 20th century. Specialists – Old Masters: Julian Agnew, Christopher Kingzett; Watercolours: Andrew Wyld; Old Master Drawings: Gabriel Naughton.*

### ▶ Ainscough Contemporary Art
Drayton Gardens, London SW10 9QS.
**Tel** 020 7341 9442
**Opening times** Tue–Fri 12–7, Sat 12–5.
**Work Stocked and Sold** Pa.

### ▶ The Air Gallery
32 Dover Street, London W1X 3RA.
**Tel** 020 7409 1255/1516/1395
**Fax** 020 7409 1856
**Email** admin@airgallery.co.uk
**Ws** www.airgallery.co.uk
**Opening times** 10–6.
**Services and Facilities** Gallery space for hire.
**Work Stocked and Sold** Pr.

### ▶ Alan Cristea Gallery
31 Cork Street, London W1S 3NU.
**Tel** 020 7439 1866 **Fax** 020 7734 1549
**Email** info@alancristea.com
**Ws** www.alancristea.com
**Opening times** Mon–Fri 10–5.30, Sat 10–1.
**Nearest Underground** Green Park.
**Personnel** Director: Alan Cristea. Director: Kathleen Dempsey. Sales: David Cleaton-Roberts.
**Services and Facilities** Art Consultancy. Art for Offices. Disabled Access.
**Work Stocked and Sold** Pa. Ph. Pr.
**Price range** £400–£200,000
For artists see Commercial Gallery Artists.

***Langlands and Bell,* Air Routes of Britain (Night), *screenprint, 69.4 x 54.4 cm, 2000.***
*Europe's largest print dealer in top-rate 20th-century Master graphics including Braque, Miro, Matisse and Picasso. Dealers in important contemporary artists including Baselitz, Chillida, Close, Flanagan, Hockney, Johns, Lichtenstein, Scully and Warhol. The gallery is also the publisher of graphics by Ayres, Caulfield, Craig-Martin, Dibbets, Dine, Hamilton, Hodgkin, Langlands & Bell, McKeever, Milroy, Moon, Opie, Paladino,*

*Tilson and Yass. Exhibitions planned for 2001/02 include a Mimmo Paladino retrospective and new works by Gillian Ayres, Ian McKeever, and Michael Craig-Martin.*

### ▶ Albany Gallery
1 Bury Street, London SW1Y.
**Tel** 020 7839 6119

### ▶ Albemarle Gallery
49 Albemarle Street, London W1S 4JR.
**Tel** 020 7499 1616 **Fax** 020 7499 1717
**Email** albgall@aol.com
**Ws** www.albemarlegallery.co.uk
**Opening times** Mon–Fri 10–6. Sat 10–4.
**Nearest Underground** Green Park.
**Personnel** Managing Director: Tony Pontone.
**Services and Facilities** Art Consultancy. Art for Offices. Commissioning Service.
**Work Stocked and Sold** Pa. Sc.
**Price range** £1,000–£70,000
For artists see Commercial Gallery Artists.

**Iain Faulkner,** Trumpet and Straw Hat, **oil on board, 36" x 36".**
*Specialising in contemporary figurative, still life and trompe l'oeil paintings, together with urban and rural landscapes, the Albemarle Gallery has become renowned for its lively and stimulating group and one man shows, supported by full colour catalogues. With a unique reputation for introducing important from mainland Europe and North America as well as the UK, the Gallery boasts an impressive stable of established and emerging artists. Operating on two floors from its impressive Mayfair premises, the Gallery holds approximately 15 major shows each year.*

### ▶ Alchemy Gallery
157 Farringdon Road, London EC1R 3AD.
**Tel** 020 7278 5666 **Fax** 020 7278 9666
**Personnel** Daniela de Vendictis.
**Work Stocked and Sold**

### ▶ Alex Wengraf
The Old Knoll, Eliot Hill, London SE13 7EB.
**Tel** 020 8852 4552 **Fax** 020 8852 4554
**Email** info@wengraf.demon.uk
**Ws** www.wengraf.com

### ▶ Alexander Gotz
35 Connaught Square, London W2.
**Tel** 020 7724 4435 **Fax** 020 7262 9891

### ▶ Alexandra Gallery
Alexandra Palace Garden Centre, London N22 4BB.
**Tel** 020 8444 2674
**Email** judy@alexandragallery.demon.co.uk
**Ws** www.alexandragallery.demon.co.uk
**Opening times** Mon–Sat 10–5, Sun 10.30–4.30.
**Nearest Underground** Wood Green.
**Personnel** Gallery Owner: Judy Morell.
**Services and Facilities** Art Consultancy. Art for Offices. Commissioning Service. Craftshop. Framing. Parking. Restoration. Workshop Facilities.
**Work Stocked and Sold** Ab. App. Cer. Cra. Dec. Dr. Gla. Jew. Pa. Ph. Pr. Sc.
**Price range** £3–£5,000
For artists see Commercial Gallery Artists.

### ▶ Andrew Edmunds Prints & Drawings
44 Lexington Street, London W1R 3LH.
**Tel** 020 7437 8594
**Personnel** Andrew Edmunds.
**Work Stocked and Sold** Pr.

### ▶ Andrew Mummery Gallery
38 Great Sutton Street, London EC1V 0DX.
**Tel** 020 7251 6265 **Fax** 020 7251 6265
**Opening times** Tue–Sat 11–6.
**Nearest Underground** Barbican, Farringdon.
**Personnel** Andrew Mummery.
**Services and Facilities** Art Consultancy. Art for Offices.
**Work Stocked and Sold** Pa. Ph.
**Price range** £500–£5,000
For artists see Commercial Gallery Artists.
*Exhibiting international contemporary art.*

### ▶ Animation Art Gallery
13–14 Great Castle Street, London W1X.
**Tel** 020 7255 1456

### ▶ The Animation Gallery
Gray's Antique Market, London W1Y 1AR.
**Tel** 020 7493 3779

### ▶ Anna Bornholt Gallery
3–5 Weighhouse Street, London W1Y 1YL.
**Tel** 020 7499 6114

### ▶ Anna-Mei Chadwick
64 New Kings Road Parson's Green, London SW6 4LT.
**Tel** 020 7736 1928
**Personnel** Anna-Mei.
**Work Stocked and Sold** Pa.

### ▶ Anne Faggionato
Fourth Floor, 20 Dering Street, London W1R.
**Tel** 020 7493 6732 **Fax** 020 7493 9693
**Email** anne.faggionato@btinternet.com
**Ws** www.anne-faggionato.com
**Opening times** Mon–Fri 9.30–6.
**Nearest Underground** Bond Street, Oxford Circus.
**Personnel** Director: Anne Faggionato. Felicity Coupland. Alvaro Rodriguez-Fominaya.
**Services and Facilities** Art Consultancy.
**Work Stocked and Sold** Dr. Pa. Ph. Sc.
For artists see Commercial Gallery Artists.
*Dealers in impressionist, modern and contemporary paintings, sculpture and works on paper.*

### ▶ Annely Juda Fine Art
23 Dering Street, (off New Bond Street), London W1S 1AW.
**Tel** 020 7629 7578 **Fax** 020 7491 2139
**Email** ajfa@annelyjudafineart.co.uk
**Ws** www.annelyjudafineart.co.uk
**Opening times** Mon–Fri 10–6, Sat 10–1.
**Nearest Underground** Bond Street or Oxford Circus.
**Services and Facilities** Art Consultancy. Art for Offices. Commissioning Service. Valuation.
**Work Stocked and Sold** Dr. Pa. Sc.
For artists see Commercial Gallery Artists.
*Contemporary British and international artists including: Roger Ackling, Anthony Caro, Chillida, Christo, Alan Charlton, Prunella Clough, Nathan Cohen, Gloria Friedmann, Hamish Fulton, Funakoshi, Alan Green, Nigel Hall, David Hockney, Christine Hatt, Werner Haypeter, Al Held, Honegger, Malcolm Hughes, Iida, Kadishman, Kawamata, Leon Kossoff, Darren Lago, Edwina Leapman, Catherine Lee, Estate of Kenneth and Mary Martin, John McLaughlin, Michaeledes, Morellet, David Nash, Saito, Toko Shinoda, Yuko Shiraishi. Also specialising in Russian Constructivism, Bauhaus, de Stijl, etc., Arp, Gabo, Kliun, Lissitzky, Malevich, Moholy Nagy, Mondrian, Rodchenko, Schwitters, Vantongerloo, Vordemberge-Gildewart.*

### ▶ Anthony d'Offay Gallery
9, 21 & 23 & 24 Dering Street, off New Bond Street, London W1R 9AA.
**Tel** 020 7499 4100
**Fax** 020 7493 4443
**Opening times** Mon–Fri 10–5.30, Sat 10–1.
**Nearest Underground** Bond St/Green Park.
**Personnel** Directors: Anthony d'Offay, Marie-Louise Laband, Anne d'Offay, Robin Vousden, James Cohan, Lorcan O'Neill, Anders Kold, Margot Heller, Simon Lee.
For artists see Commercial Gallery Artists.

### ▶ Anthony Reynolds
5 Dering Street, London W1R 9AB.
**Tel** 020 7491 0621

### ▶ Anthony Wilkinson Fine Art
242 Cambridge Heath Road, London E2 9DA.
**Tel** 020 8980 2662
**Fax** 020 8980 0028
**Personnel** Anthony Wilkinson. Glen Baxter. Chris Bucklow. Simon Callery.

### ▶ The Approach
47 Approach Road, London E2.
**Tel** 020 8938 3878

### ▶ Art First
First Floor Gallery, 9 Cork Street, London W1S 3LL.
**Tel** 020 7734 0386 **Fax** 020 7734 3964
**Email** artfirst@dircon.co.uk
**Ws** www.artfirst.co.uk
**Opening times** Mon–Fri 10–6, Sat 11–2.
**Nearest Underground** Green Park
**Personnel** Executive Director: Clare Stracey. Executive Director: Geoffrey Bertram. Associate Director: Gillian Adam.
**Work Stocked and Sold** Dr. Pa. Pr. Sc.
**Price range** £250–£25,000
For artists see Commercial Gallery Artists.
*Art First is a first-floor contemporary art gallery exhibiting British and international artists. Alongside established figures we introduce less*

*well-known and younger artists. Among these there is a special focus on Scottish art and art from South Africa. Exhibitions change monthly.*

### ▶ Art For Offices
International Art Consultants, The Galleries, 15 Dock Street, London E1 8JL.
**Tel** 020 7481 1337 **Fax** 020 7481 3425
**Email** enquiries@afo.co.uk
**Ws** www.afo.co.uk
**Opening times** Open Mon–Fri 9.30–5.30.
**Nearest Underground** Tower Hill, Aldgate, Aldgate East.
**Personnel** Directors: Andrew Hutchinson, Peter Harris. Amanda Basker.
**Services and Facilities** Art Consultancy. Art for Offices. Commissioning Service. Framing. Parking.
**Work Stocked and Sold** Cer. Cra. Dr. Gla. Pa. Ph. Pr. Sc. Tx. Wd.
**Price range** £100–£50,000
*We have 20 years' experience advising architects, designers and corporate clients on the planning and implementation of art programmes. Our 10,000-square-foot galleries provide a central source of art, enabling clients and specifiers to view a comprehensive range of art on a single visit to one location. We deal directly with over 800 artists and have a large visual reference library covering art in all media which is cross-referenced by style and price. This makes it possible to research works of art or artists for commission quickly and effectively. Art can be purchased, commissioned or acquired on a flexible rental basis.*

### ▶ Art London. Com
Suite 958, 28 Old Brompton Road, London SW7 3SS.
**Tel** 020 7492 2897 **Fax** 020 7402 1028

### ▶ Art & Photographs
13 Masons Yard, St James's, London SW1Y.
**Tel** 020 7321 0495

### ▶ The Art Supermarket
28 Islington Park Street, Knightsbridge, London N1 1PX.
**Tel** 020 7359 2750 **Fax** 020 7359 2750
**Email** artsuper@aol.com
**Opening times** By appointment.
**Nearest Underground** Highbury & Islington. Buses 4, 19, 30, 43.
**Personnel** Directors: James West, Steve Hamblen.
**Services and Facilities** Art for Offices. Commissioning Service.
**Work Stocked and Sold** Pa.
**Price range** £100–£2,000
For artists see Commercial Gallery Artists.

### ▶ Arthaus
Old School House, 12 Pop Street, London SE1 3PR.
**Tel** 020 7232 1097
**Personnel** General Manager: Chris Stay.

### ▶ Arthouse
140 Lewisham Way, London SE14.
**Tel** 020 8694 9011

### ▶ Arthur Tooth & Sons
13 Dover Street, London W1X.
**Tel** 020 7499 6753

### ▶ Artmonsky Arts
108A Boundary Road, St Johns Wood, London NW8 0RH.
**Tel** 020 7604 3990 **Fax** 020 7604 3991
**Nearest Underground** Kilburn Park, Swiss Cottage. Buses: 139, 189.
**Work Stocked and Sold** Cer. Pr.
**Price range** From £150

### ▶ Asprey Jacques
4 Clifford Street, London W1.
**Tel** 020 7287 7675

### ▶ AOP Gallery (Association of Photographers)
81 Leonard Street, London EC2A 4QS.
**Tel** 020 7739 6669 **Fax** 020 7739 8707
**Ws** www.aophoto.co.uk
**Opening times** Mon–Fri 9.30–6, Sat 12–4.
**Nearest Underground** Old Street
**Personnel** Gallery Manager: Susan Bright. Gallery Assistant: Nick Jones. Marketing: Sascha Howard.
**Services and Facilities** Art for Offices. Disabled Access. Gallery space for hire.
**Work Stocked and Sold** Ph.
**Price range** From £100
*Exhibitions at the gallery offer the chance to buy photographs at affordable prices. The AOP Gallery also has a permanent collection of work for sale by contemporary photographers ideal for the private collector or corporate clients. Covering a wide range of subject matter, the collection is available for viewing by appointment. Ring Susan Bright on 020 7739 3631.*

### ▶ Atrium Gallery
1 Embankment Place, London.
**Tel** 020 7213 8511

### ▶ Audley Art
20 The Mall, Upper Street, Islington, London N1.
**Tel** 020 7704 9507

### ▶ Austin Desmond Fine Art
Pied Bull Yard, 68–69 Great Russell Street, London WC1B 3BN.
**Tel** 020 7242 4443

### ▶ Ballantyne & Date
38 Museum Street, London WC1A.
**Tel** 020 7242 4249

### ▶ Bar Room Bar
48 Rosslyn Hill, London NW3.
**Tel** 020 7435 0808
**Work Stocked and Sold** Pa.

### ▶ The Barnes Gallery
51 Church Road, Barnes, London SW13 9HH.
**Tel** 020 8741 1277

### ▶ Barry Davies Oriental Art
1 Davies Street, London W1Y 1LL.
**Tel** 020 7408 0207
**Fax** 020 7493 3422
**Email** bdoa@btinternet.com
**Ws** www.antiques-on-line.com/barrydavies
**Opening times** Mon–Fri 10–6.
**Nearest Underground** Bond Street or Green Park.
**Services and Facilities** Art Consultancy. Disabled Access. Valuation.

### ▶ Battersea Art Centre
176 Lavender Hill, London SW11 5QF.
**Tel** 020 7223 6557
**Opening times** Sat–Sun 10.30–6.
**Nearest Station** Clapham Junction.

### ▶ BCA Gallery
9 Cork Street, London W1X 1PD.
**Tel** 020 7734 6444
**Fax** 020 7287 1740
**Email** art@bca-gallery.com
**Ws** www.BCA-gallery.com
**Opening times** Mon–Fri 10–6, Sat 10–2.
**Nearest Underground** Green Park.
**Personnel** Director: B. Boukamel. Manager: Joanna Tonkinson. Assistant manager: Amy Samuel.
**Work Stocked and Sold** Dr. Pa. Ph. Pr. Sc.
**Price range** £500–£50,000
For artists see Commercial Gallery Artists.
*Contemporary British and European Art: Philip Braham, Ernesto Tatafiore, Ken Currie, Rainer Fetting, Markus Lüpertz, Luciano Castelli, Joumana Mourad, Cyril Olanier, E. R. Nele, François Delebecque, Hélène Delprat, Gérard Traquandi, Sandro Chia, Beverley Daniels.*

### ▶ Beaconsfield
22 Newport Street, London SE11.
**Tel** 020 7582 6465

### ▶ Beardsmore Gallery
22–24 Prince Of Wales Road, Kentish Town, London NW5 3LG.
**Tel** 020 7485 0923
**Fax** 020 7267 0824
**Personnel** Amanda Beardsmore. Brian Beardsmore.

### ▶ Beaux Arts London
22 Cork Street, London W1S 3NA.
**Tel** 020 7437 5799
**Fax** 020 7437 5798
**Email** info@beauxartslondon.co.uk
**Ws** www.beauxartslondon.co.uk
**Opening times** Mon–Fri 10–5.30, Sat 10–1.30.
**Nearest Underground** Green Park, Piccadilly Circus, Oxford Circus.
**Personnel** Director: Reg Singh. Director: Patricia Singh. Assistant Director: Lucy Gibson.
**Services and Facilities** Art for Offices. Commissioning Service.
**Work Stocked and Sold** Dr. Pa. Pr. Sc.
**Price range** £1,000–£100,000
For artists see Commercial Gallery Artists.
*Frank Auerbach, John Bellany, Lynn Chadwick, Elisabeth Frink, Terry Frost, Barbara Hepworth, Patrick Heron, Roger Hilton, Peter Lanyon, Jonathan Leaman, David Leapman, Mark Gilbert, John Hayland, William Scott, David Spiller.*

### ▶ Bengstrom
Studio 2N, Cooper House, 2 Michael Road, London SW6 2AD.
**Tel** 020 7731 2815, mobile 0370 966 741
**Fax** 020 7610 9212
**Ws** www.bengstromart.co.uk

### ▶ Benjamin Hargreaves
90 Kenyon Street, London SW6 6LB.
**Tel** 020 7385 7757

**Opening times** By appointment only.
**Work Stocked and Sold** Pa.

### ▶ Berkeley Square Gallery
23a Bruton Street, London W1X 8JJ.
**Tel** 020 7493 7939 **Fax** 020 7493 7798
**Opening times** Mon–Fri 10–6, Sat 10–2.
**Nearest Underground** Green Park
**Personnel** Tania Sutton. Peter Osborne. Janet Sturley. Brian Porter.
**Work Stocked and Sold** Pr.

### ▶ Bernard Jacobson Gallery
14a Clifford Street, London W1X 1RF.
**Tel** 020 7495 8575 **Fax** 020 7495 6210
**Opening times** Mon–Fri 10–6, Sat 10–1.
**Nearest Underground** Green Park
**Personnel** Bernard Jacobson. Robert Delaney. Jane McAllester. Amelia Johnson.
For artists see Commercial Gallery Artists.

### ▶ Blackheath Gallery
34a Tranquil Vale, Blackheath, London SE3 0AX.
**Tel** 020 8852 1802

### ▶ Blackman's Place
14 All Saints Road, London W11.
**Tel** 020 7243 4372

### ▶ Blains Fine Art
25 Bruton Place, Piccadilly, London W1X 7AB.
**Tel** 020 7495 5050
**Fax** 020 7495 4050
**Personnel** Charles Phillips.

### ▶ Bob Lawrence Gallery
93 Sloane Street, London SW1W.
**Tel** 020 7730 5900

### ▶ Bolton Street Gallery
28 Bolton Street, London W1Y 7PD.
**Tel** 020 7629 9933 **Fax** 020 7493 5561
**Email** info@boltonstreetgallery.co.uk
**Personnel** Vivien Lowenstein Moss. Tracey Holt.

### ▶ Boundary Gallery, Agi Katz Fine Art
98 Boundary Road, London NW8 0RH.
**Tel** 020 7624 1126
**Fax** 020 7681 7663 or 020 7624 1126
**Email** boundary@agikatz.demon.co.uk
**Opening times** Wed–Sat 11–6 and by appointment.
**Nearest Underground** St John's Wood or Swiss Cottage.
**Personnel** Director & Owner: Agi Katz. Gallery Assistant: Louise Homes.
**Services and Facilities** Art Consultancy. Art for Offices. Commissioning Service. Framing. Restoration. Valuation.
**Work Stocked and Sold** Dr. Pa. Pr.
**Price range** £300–£6,000
For artists see Commercial Gallery Artists.
*The gallery specialises in figurative art with emphasis on good draughtsmanship and strong use of colour. There are two periods of specialisation. 1. Modern British (1910–1950) including Bomberg, Brodzky, Dubsky, Epstein, Gotlib, Kramer Meninsky, Wolmark. Specialised knowledge of Anglo-Jewish artists – works in stock (available for sale) and will show by request. 2. Contemporary artists include Josef Herman, Morris Kestelman, Sonia Lawson, Albert Louden, Ana Maria Pacheco, Neil MacPherson, Peter Prendergast, David Tress, Anita Klein. Eight thematic or solo exhibitions a year. Catalogues published 3–4 times a year.*

### ▶ The Bow House Gallery
35 Wood Street, Barnet, EN5 4BE.
**Tel** 020 8441 5841
**Fax** 020 8441 5841
**Email** bowhousegallery@linone.net
**Ws** www.johnbrown-sculptor.co.uk
**Opening times** Thu–Sat 10–5, Sun 2–5 (during exhibitions).
**Nearest Underground** High Barnet
**Personnel** John Brown. Pauline Brown.
**Services and Facilities** Art Consultancy. Commissioning Service.
**Work Stocked and Sold** Cer. Pa. Pr. Sc.
**Price range** £150–£5,000
For artists see Commercial Gallery Artists.

*John Brown* Fidelity.
*We aim to present a wide range of paintings and sculpture by professional artists and to provide affordable art for home or workplace through a series of exhibitions, which includes Sculpture in the Garden shows in spring and summer.*

### ▶ Brixton Art Gallery
35 Brixton Station Road, London SW9 8PB.
**Tel** 020 7733 6957

### ▶ Browns Design Associates Ltd, The Flag Store
29 Queen Elizabeth Street, London SE1 2LP.

### ▶ Browse and Darby Gallery
19 Cork Street, London W1X 1HB.
**Tel** 020 7734 7984 **Fax** 020 7437 0750

### ▶ Burlington Paintings
10/12 Burlington Gardens, London W1X 1LG.
**Tel** 020 7734 9984/9228/4221
**Fax** 020 7494 3770
**Ws** www.burlington.co.uk
**Personnel** Lucinda Muschialli. Kate Black.
**Work Stocked and Sold** Pr.

### ▶ The Cable Street Gallery
Thames House, 566 Cable Street, Limehouse, London E1 9HB.
**Tel** 020 7790 1309 **Fax** 020 7790 1309
**Opening times** Thur–Sun 12–6.
**Personnel** Michael Cubey.

### ▶ Cadogan Contemporary Art
108 Draycott Avenue, South Avenue, London SW3 3AE.
**Tel** 020 7581 5451 **Fax** 020 7589 3222
**Email** alight@artcad.co.uk
**Ws** www.artcad.co.uk
**Opening times** Mon–Wed 10–7, Thu–Sat 10–6.
**Nearest Underground** South Kensington.
**Services and Facilities** Commissioning Service.
**Work Stocked and Sold** Dr. Pa. Sc.
**Price range** £500–£30,000
For artists see Commercial Gallery Artists.
*Modern contemporary art.*

### ▶ Camberwell Gallery
169 Camberwell Road, London SE5.
**Tel** 020 7740 6161

### ▶ Camden Art Gallery
22 Church Street, London NW8.
**Tel** 020 7262 3613 **Fax** 020 7723 2333
**Personnel** Alan Silver.

### ▶ Cato Miles Wynn
60 Lower Sloane Street, London SW1W.
**Tel** 020 7259 0306

### ▶ Catto Gallery
100 Heath Street, Hampstead, London NW3 1DP.
**Tel** 020 7435 6660 **Fax** 020 7431 5620
**Ws** www.catto.co.uk
**Opening times** Mon–Sat 10–6, Sun 2.30–6.
**Personnel** Gillian Catto.

### ▶ CCA Galleries Ltd
517–523 Fulham Road, London SW6 1HD.
**Tel** 020 7386 4900 **Fax** 020 7386 4919
**Email** gallery@ccagalleries.com
**Ws** www.ccagalleries.com
**Opening times** Mon–Sat 9.30–5.30.
**Nearest Underground** Fulham Broadway.
**Personnel** Retail Director: Marian Orchard-Webb. Gallery Manager: Lisa McLaren-Clark. Publishing Dept.: Teffany Tooke.
**Services and Facilities** Art Consultancy. Art for Offices. Framing.
**Work Stocked and Sold** Cer. Gla. Pa. Pr.
**Price range** £45–£3, 500
For artists see Commercial Gallery Artists.
*Leading publishers of limited edition silkscreens, etchings and lithographs. Catalogue of new publications produced three times a year. Exciting programme of exhibitions. Artists include Donald Hamilton-Fraser, Annora Spence, Sir Terry Frost, Richard Spare. An excellent bespoke framing service is also available.*

### ▶ Cell Project Space
Ideal House, 38–50 Arcola Street, London E8.
**Tel** 020 7241 3600
**Email** info@cell.org.uk

### ▶ Chaucer Fine Arts
45 Pimlico Road, London SW1W.
**Tel** 020 7730 2972

### ▶ Chinese Contemporary
11 New Burlington Place, London W1X 1FA.
**Tel** 020 7734 9808 **Fax** 020 7734 9818
**Personnel** Ludavic Bois.

### ▶ Chris Beetles
8 &10 Ryder Street, St James's, London SW1Y 6QB.
**Tel** 020 7839 7551 **Fax** 020 7839 1603
**Opening times** Mon–Sat 10–5.30.
**Nearest Underground** Green Park.
**Services and Facilities** Art Consultancy. Bookshop. Commissioning Service. Framing. Restoration. Valuation.
**Work Stocked and Sold** Dr. Pa. Sc.
**Price range** £150–£100,000
For artists see Commercial Gallery Artists.

### ▶ Christopher Drake
Flat 1, 19 Mason's Yard, Duke Street, St James's, London SW1Y 6BU.
**Tel** 020 7839 1198
**Work Stocked and Sold** Pr.

### ▶ Cinegrafix Gallery
4 Copper Row, Tower Bridge Piazza, London SE1. **Tel** 020 7234 0566

### ▶ The City Gallery
26 Copthall Avenue, London EC2R 7DN.
**Tel** 020 7256 5815 **Fax** 020 7256 6002
**Personnel** Anthony Hinton. Tiffany Panter.

### ▶ Clarges Gallery
1st Floor, 158 Walton Street, London SW3 2JL.
**Tel** 020 7584 3022
**Opening times** Mon–Fri 2.30–5.30. Periodic full-time shows as advertised.
**Nearest Underground** South Kensington.
**Services and Facilities** Framing. Restoration.
**Work Stocked and Sold** Dr. Pa. Pr.
**Price range** £250–£6,000
For artists see Commercial Gallery Artists.
*English watercolours from 1800 to present day, 20th century British School oils (including living painters in oils and watercolours). Limited edition 20th-century prints. Samuel Owen, David Cox, Samuel Prout, Harry Watson, Menzies Marshall, Cecil Hunt, Robert Bevan, Terrick Williams, John Piper, G. Denholm Armour, Egerton Cooper, Lucy Kemp-Welch, Bernard Dunstan, Diana Armfield.*

### ▶ Collins & Hastie Ltd
5 Park Walk, London SW10 0AJ.
**Tel** 020 7351 4292 **Fax** 020 7351 7929
**Email** caroline@chelseaart.co.uk
**Ws** www.chelseaart.co.uk
**Opening times** Mon–Fri 10–6, Sat 11–4.
**Nearest Underground** South Kensington
**Personnel** Director: Caroline Hastie. Director: Diana Collins.
**Services and Facilities** Art for Offices. Commissioning Service. Disabled Access. Gallery space for hire. Restoration.
**Work Stocked and Sold** Dec. Pa.
**Price range** £300–£20 000
*Collins & Hastie Ltd was established by Diana Collins and Caroline Hastie in 1993 and is situated in the heart of Chelsea. The gallery specialises in 20th-century and Contemporary British and European paintings. Our paintings are selected from artists whose work commands attention for the skill with which they, in their own distinctive way, portray the infinitely changing and interrelating qualities of light, colour, texture and form. We represent both figurative and abstract works, from the established artist to the recent graduate. Artists include: Guy Rodden, Alan Halliday, Alexander Chamberlain, Frederick Minard, Richard Hoare and Zoe Hope. Also a large collection of works by Paul Maze, the renowned British Impressionist. There is a series of exhibitions scheduled throughout the year. This provides an ideal forum for you to see the artists' latest works. Between these exhibitions we have a mixed show of the artists we represent.*

### ▶ Colnaghi
15 Old Bond Street, London W1X 4LJ.
**Tel** 020 7491 7408 **Fax** 020 7491 8851
**Opening times** Mon–Fri 9.30–6.
**Personnel** Directors: Richard Knight, Stephen Rudge.

### ▶ Colville Place Gallery
1 Colville Place, London W1P 1HN.
**Tel** 020 7436 1330 **Fax** 020 7436 1339
**Email** kwatson@romanesque.source.co.uk
**Ws** www.romanesque.co.uk/gallery.html
**Opening times** Mon–Fri 10–6, Sat 12–5.
**Nearest Underground** Goodge Street.
**Personnel** Ian Middleton. Keith Watson.
**Price range** £200–£2,000

### ▶ The Commercial Gallery
109 Commercial Street, London E1 6BG.
**Tel** 020 7392 9031 **Fax** 020 7377 8915
**Nearest Underground** Aldgate East and Liverpool Street.
**Personnel** Press Information: Yoav Hessayon. Press Information: Debbie Smith.

### ▶ The Coningsby Gallery
30 Tottenham Street, London W1T 4RJ.
**Tel** 020 7636 7478 **Fax** 020 7580 7017
**Email** debutart@coningsbygallery.demon.co.uk
**Ws** www.debutart.com
**Opening times** Mon–Fri 10–5.30. Weekends by appointment.
**Nearest Underground** Goodge Street
**Personnel** Proprietor: Andrew Coningsby. Marketing Director: Benjamin Cox.
**Services and Facilities** Art Consultancy. Art for Offices. Commissioning Service. Gallery space for hire.
**Work Stocked and Sold** App. Cra. Dr. Pa. Ph. Pr. Sc.
**Price range** £200–£8,000
For artists see Commercial Gallery Artists.
*Specialists in the exhibition and marketing of contemporary art photographers, illustrators and fine artists who work, or are interested in working, in the applied arts markets of advertising, design and publishing. Wide variety of hire and promotional options.*

### ▶ Connaught Brown
2 Albemarle Street, London W1X 3HF.
**Tel** 020 7408 0362 **Fax** 020 7495 3137
**Opening times** Mon–Fri 10–6, Sat 10–12.30.
**Nearest Underground** Green Park
**Personnel** Director: Anthony Brown.
**Work Stocked and Sold** Dr. Pa. Pr. Sc.
**Price range** £500–£500,000
For artists see Commercial Gallery Artists.
*Specialists in Impressionist, Post-Impressionist, Scandinavian, Modern Master and Modern British painting, drawing, sculpture and graphics – Bonnard, Chadwick, Chagall, Degas, Dubuffet, Dufy, Hitchens, Hockney, Holsoe, Matisse, Miró, Moore, Picasso, Pissarro, Renoir, Van Dongen, Vuillard and Warhol. The gallery has also represented Contemporary artist Paul Richards since its establishment in 1984.*

### ▶ The Contemporary Art Gallery/Group
59 Ebury Street, London SW1W 0NZ.
**Tel** 020 7730 6407 **Fax** 020 7823 6521
**Work Stocked and Sold** Cer.

### ▶ Coombs Contemporary
Tower Bridge Piazza, 1a Copper Row, Butlers Wharf, London SE1 2LH.
**Tel** 020 7403 6866
**Work Stocked and Sold** Pa.

### ▶ Corvi-Mora
22 Warren Street, London W1.
**Tel** 020 7383 2419

### ▶ Coskun & Co. Ltd
56a Walton Street, London SW3 1RB.
**Tel** 020 7581 9056 **Fax** 020 7581 1336
**Opening times** Tue–Sat 2–7 or by appointment.
**Nearest Underground** Knightsbridge.
**Personnel** Director: Gul Coskun.
**Services and Facilities** Art Consultancy. Art for Offices.
**Work Stocked and Sold** Dr. Pr.
For artists see Commercial Gallery Artists.

### ▶ Crane Kalman Gallery
178 Brompton Road, London SW3 1HQ.
**Tel** 020 7584 7566/7225 1931
**Fax** 020 7584 3843
**Opening times** Mon–Fri 10–6, Sat 10–4.
**Nearest Underground** Knightsbridge.
**Personnel** Directors: Andras Kalman. Andrew Kalman. Sally Kalman. Robin Light.
**Services and Facilities** Art Consultancy. Art for Offices.
**Work Stocked and Sold** Pa.
For artists see Commercial Gallery Artists.

### ▶ Cubitt Gallery
2–4 Caledonia Street, London N1.
**Tel** 020 7278 8226

### ▶ Curwen Gallery
4 Windmill Street, (off Charlotte Street), London W1T 2HZ.
**Tel** 020 7636 1459 **Fax** 020 7436 3059
**Email** gallery@curwengallery.com
**Ws** www.curwengallery.com
**Opening times** Mon–Fri 10–6, Sat 11–5 (closed bank holiday weekends).
**Nearest Underground** Goodge Street/ Tottenham Court Road.
**Personnel** Directors: Jill Hutchings, John Hutchings. Contact: Pryle Behrman.
**Services and Facilities** Art Consultancy. Art for Offices. Commissioning Service. Framing.
**Work Stocked and Sold** Dr. Pa. Pr. Sc.

**Price range** £40–£20,000
For artists see Commercial Gallery Artists.

*Johannes Von Stumm,* Bow, *stone, glass and steel, 69 x 33 x 29 cm.*

*Exhibition programme features Contemporary British Art, Modern Masters & International Graphics. Artists include: Edward Bawden, Kenneth Blackburn, Chloe Cheese, Glynn Boyd Harte, Phoebe Dingwall, Kieron Farrow, Jonathan Gibbs, Brendan Hansbro, Lallitha Jawahirilal, Stanley Jones, Thirza Kotzen, Ruth Martin, Toni Martina, Jennifer McRae, Alison Neville, Yuji Oki, Robin Richmond, Sophia Rizvi, Paul Ryan, Johannes von Stumm, Lucy Willis, Marjan Wouda. Master prints include: Basil Beattie, Prunella Clough, Elisabeth Frink RA, Barbara Hepworth, Josef Herman RA, John Hoyland RA, Albert Irvin, Henry Moore, John Piper and Ceri Richards.*

## ▶ The Cynthia Corbett Gallery

15 Claremont Lodge, 15 The Downs, Wimbledon, London SW20 8UA.
**Tel** 020 8947 6782, mobile 07939 085 076
**Fax** 020 8947 6782
**Email** corbettcc@hotmail.com
**Opening times** By appointment.
**Nearest Underground** Wimbledon.
**Personnel** Director: Cynthia Valianti-Corbett.
**Services and Facilities** Art Consultancy. Art for Offices. Commissioning Service. Lectures.
**Work Stocked and Sold** Dec. Dr. Pa. Ph. Pr. Sc.
**Price range** £250–£5,000
For artists see Commercial Gallery Artists.

*Andrew Burgess,* Downtown Manhattan, *oil on canvas, 36" x 48", 2000.*

*Gallery established in 1999 by former Christie's Education Art History graduate. Specialises in modern and contemporary art, particularly paintings, drawings and original prints of the highest quality. Promotes international artists from Britain, Continental Europe, Russia, Africa and America such as Ghislaine Howard, Andrew Burgess, Nicholas Moore, Colin Wiggins, John Monks, Day Bowman, Deborah Lanyon, Robert Shaft and Geoffrey Knoll. Group exhibitions and regular exhibitor at major contemporary London art fairs; solo and themed exhibitions at various venues. Emphasis is on personalised service for private, corporate and institutional clients and close relationships with the artists.*
*Available for consultancy to corporate or institutional art collections, private individuals, exhibition organisers and art filmmakers.*

## ▶ Daggett Gallery

153 Portobello Road, London W11 2DV.
**Tel** 020 7229 2248

## ▶ Daniel Hunt

60 Lower Sloane Street, London SW1W.
**Tel** 020 7259 0304

## ▶ Daniel Katz Ltd

59 Jermyn Street, St James's, London SW1Y 6LX.
**Tel** 020 7493 0688 **Fax** 020 7499 7493
**Email** info@katz.co.uk
**Ws** www.katz.co.uk
**Opening times** Mon–Fri 9–6.
**Nearest Underground** Green Park.
**Personnel** Directors: Daniel Katz, Stuart Lochhead. Researcher: Katherine Zock. Gallery Administrator: Sarah Goodbody.
**Services and Facilities** Art Consultancy.
**Work Stocked and Sold** Sc.
**Price range** From £5,000
For artists see Commercial Gallery Artists.
*European sculpture and works of art from the Renaissance, 17th and 18th centuries including bronze statuettes, marble and terracotta figures. Sales to all major museums worldwide plus collectors and private clients.*

## ▶ Danielle Arnaud Contemporary Arts

123 Kennington Road, London SE11 6SF.
**Tel** 020 7735 8292 **Fax** 020 7735 8292
**Opening times** Tue & Thu 10–2. Any other time by appointment.
**Personnel** Danielle Around.
**Work Stocked and Sold** Dr. Pa. Sc.

## ▶ David Gill Gallery

60 Fulham Road, London SW3.
**Tel** 020 7589 5946

## ▶ Davies & Tooth

The Air Gallery, 32 Dover Street, London W1X 3RA.
**Tel** 020 7409 1516
**Fax** 020 7409 1856
**Ws** www.art-net.co.uk/banca/toodav

## ▶ Delfina Project Space

51 Southwark Street, London SE1.
**Tel** 020 7357 6600

## ▶ Dilston Grove

Former Clare College Mission Church, Southwark Park, London SE16.
**Tel** 020 7237 1230

## ▶ Dissenters Chapel and Gallery

Kensal Green Cemetery, Harrow Road, London W10 4RA.
**Tel** 020 7402 2749
**Email** andred@vam.ac.uk
**Opening times** Mon–Sat 12.30–4. Admission free.
**Nearest Underground** Kensal Green.
**Personnel** André Davis.
**Work Stocked and Sold** Pa.
**Price range** £35–£1,000

## ▶ Dockroom

20 Dock Street, London E1.
**Tel** 020 7360 6000

## ▶ DomoBaal Contemporary Art

3 John Street, London WC1.
**Tel** 020 7242 9604

## ▶ Dot

41–45 Beak Street, London W1.
**Tel** 020 7494 0434

## ▶ Douwes Fine Art

38 Duke Street, St James's, London SW1Y 6DF.
**Tel** 020 7839 5795 **Fax** 020 7839 5904

## ▶ Dover Street Gallery

13 Dover Street, Green Park, London W1X 3PH.
**Tel** 020 7409 1540 **Fax** 020 7409 1565
**Personnel** Ben Hanly.

## ▶ Duncan Campbell Fine Art

15 Thackeray Street, Kensington, London W8 5ET.
**Tel** 020 7937 8665
**Opening times** Mon–Fri 11–6, Sat 10–5.
**Nearest Underground** High St Kensington.
**Work Stocked and Sold** Pa. Pr.

## ▶ Duncan R. Miller Fine Arts

17 Flask Walk, Hampstead, London NW3 1HJ.
**Tel** 020 7435 5462 **Fax** 020 7431 5352
**Opening times** Mon–Fri 10–6, Sat 11–6, Sun 2–5.
**Nearest Underground** Hampstead
**Personnel** Duncan R. Miller. Alexander R. Miller. Christabel Stewart.

## ▶ E M Arts

36 Tregunter Road, London SW10.
**Tel** 020 7373 3856

## ▶ E1 Gallery

10 Whites Row, London E1.
**Tel** 020 7721 8687

## ▶ Eagle Gallery - E M H Arts

159 Farringdon Road, London EC1R 3AL.
**Tel** 020 7833 2674
**Fax** 020 7833 2674/7624 6597
**Opening times** Thu–Fri 11–6, Sat–Sun 11–4, and by appointment.
**Nearest Underground** Farringdon.
**Personnel** Director: Emma Hill. Imogen Clarke.

## ▶ East 73rd Gallery

73 Curtain Road, London EC2.
**Tel** 020 7729 1590

## ▶ East West

8 Blenheim Crescent, London W11 1NN.
**Tel** 020 7229 7981 **Fax** 020 7221 0741
**Opening times** Wed–Sat 11–6 or by appointment.

**Services and Facilities** Art Consultancy. Commissioning Service.

### ▶ Eastern Art Gallery
40 Bloomsbury Way, London WC1A 2SE.
**Tel** 020 7430 1072

### ▶ Editions Graphiques
3 Clifford Street, London W1X 1RA.
**Tel** 020 7734 3944 **Fax** 020 7437 1859

### ▶ Edward Cohen
40 Duke Street, London SW1Y.
**Tel** 020 7839 5180

### ▶ Electrum Gallery
21 South Molton Street, London W1Y 1DD.
**Tel** 020 7629 6325 **Fax** 020 7435 9806
**Opening times** Mon–Fri 10–6, Sat 10–1.
**Work Stocked and Sold** Jew.

### ▶ Enid Lawson Gallery
36a Kensington Church Street, London W8 4BX.
**Tel** 020 7937 8444 **Fax** 020 7376 0552
**Email** 020 7938 4786
**Opening times** Mon–Sat 10–6.
**Nearest Underground** High Street Kensington or Notting Hill Gate.
**Services and Facilities** Art for Offices. Commissioning Service.
**Work Stocked and Sold** Cer. Pa.
**Price range** £20–£2,000
For artists see Commercial Gallery Artists.

### ▶ Entwistle
6 Cork Street, London W1X 2EE.
**Tel** 020 7734 6440 **Fax** 020 7734 7966
**Personnel** Lance Entwistle. Roberta Entwistle. Victoria Young. Katherine Wills-Sandford.

### ▶ Faggionato Fine Arts
49 Albemarle Street, London W1X.
**Tel** 020 7409 7979

### ▶ Fine Art Society
148 New Bond Street, London W1Y OJT.
**Tel** 020 7629 5116
**Work Stocked and Sold** Pr.

### ▶ Fischer Fine Art
49 Carlton Hill, London NW8 0EL.
**Tel** 020 7328 6502 **Fax** 020 7625 8341
**Opening times** By appointment.
**Personnel** Directors: Dr Wolfgang G. Fischer, Dr Jutta Fischer.

### ▶ Five
5 Princelet Street, London E1.
**Tel** 020 7247 0601

### ▶ Five Years
40 Underwood Street, London N1.
**Tel** 020 7608 0331 **Fax** 020 7608 0331

### ▶ Florence Trust Studios
St Saviour's, Aberdeen Park, Highbury, London N5 2AR.
**Tel** 020 7354 4771
**Fax** 020 7354 4771
**Email** info@florencetrust.org
**Ws** www.florencetrust.org
**Opening times** Please phone in advance to arrange an appointment.
**Nearest Underground** Highbury & Islington.
**Personnel** Director: Rod McIntosh.
**Services and Facilities** Art Consultancy. Art for Offices. Commissioning Service. Friends Society. Gallery space for hire. Lectures. Workshop Facilities.
**Work Stocked and Sold** Dr. Pa. Sc.
**Price range** £100–£6,000
*The Florence Trust is based at St Saviour's, Aberdeen Park, a Grade 1 listed 1866 Victorian Gothic church. The Studios offer visual artists studio awards, from 2 to 9 months, in an open-plan environment where they can work intensively and engage in critical exchange. Regular exhibitions are held at the Trust and we have 'Open Studio' events with invited guest artists exhibiting. Studio talks and slide presentations are also planned throughout the year. We have a comprehensive slide index of the artists we support, available for view by appointment. The studios and exhibition area are available for outside hire.*

### ▶ Flowers Central
21 Cork Street, London W1.
**Tel** 020 7439 7766

### ▶ Flowers East

Flowers East

199–205 Richmond Road, London E8 3NJ.
**Tel** 020 8985 3333
**Fax** 020 8985 0067
**Email** gallery@flowerseast.co.uk
**Ws** www.flowerseast.com
**Opening times** Tue–Sun 10–6.
**Nearest Underground** Bethnal Green, and 253/106 buses.
**Personnel** Chairman: Angela Flowers. Managing Director: Matthew Flowers. Director: Huei Flowers. Director of Graphics: Marian Stone.
**Services and Facilities** Art Consultancy. Art for Offices. Bookshop. Commissioning Service. Guided Tours. Parking.
**Work Stocked and Sold** Ab. Dr. Pa. Ph. Pr. Sc.
**Price range** £100–£100,000
For artists see Commercial Gallery Artists.
*Angela Flowers Gallery opened in Soho in 1970, with the aim of introducing young contemporary British artists and promoting established artists who deserved greater recognition.*
*In 1988 the gallery moved to London's East End and became Flowers East. Since then it has acquired Plc status and expanded into one of the biggest and most important commercial galleries in the country. Flowers East has two large gallery spaces and represents more than 35 artists, from young newcomers to major international figures. There is also a separate graphics department which publishes and sells limited edition prints by a wide range of contemporary artists. In October 2000, Flowers Central was opened at 21 Cork St, providing Flowers artists with a venue to exhibit their work, in the traditional heart of London's gallery scene.*

### ▶ Flying Colours Gallery
PO Box 9361, Chelsea, London SW3 3ZJ.
**Tel** 020 7351 5558 **Fax** 020 7351 5548
**Personnel** Jane Houldsworth. Laura Gowlett. John Honey. Rupert Russell.

### ▶ Focus Gallery
43 Museum Street, London WC1.
**Tel** 020 7242 7191

### ▶ Footstool Restaurant Gallery
St John's Smith Square, Westminster, London SW10 0AJ.
**Tel** 020 7222 2168
**Opening times** Mon–Fri 10–5, 6–10, and Sat–Sun concert eves.
**Nearest Underground** Westminster.
**Work Stocked and Sold** Pa.

### ▶ Fordham
20 Fordham Street, London E1.
**Tel** 020 7247 0410

### ▶ Foyles Art Gallery
2nd Floor, 113–119 Charing Cross Road, London WC2H 0EB.
**Tel** 020 8518 7685
**Email** rbalaz@sghms.ac.uk
**Opening times** Mon–Sat 10–6; closed Sun.

### ▶ Francis Graham-Dixon
48A Chalcot Road, London NW1 8LS.
**Tel** 020 7722 9922 **Fax** 020 7722 9922
**Email** fg-d@francisgrahamdixon.com
**Ws** www.francisgrahamdixon.com
**Opening times** By appointment.
**Nearest Underground** Chalk Farm.
**Personnel** Director: Francis Graham-Dixon.
**Services and Facilities** Art Consultancy. Commissioning Service. Valuation.
**Work Stocked and Sold** Dr. Pa. Ph. Pr. Sc.
**Price range** £250–£25,000
For artists see Commercial Gallery Artists.
*Artists represented/associated/sold – Emily Andersen, Sybille Berger, John Carter, Rowena Dring, Sheila Girling, Clyde Hopkins, Bryan Ingham, Oleg Kudryashov, Jane Langley, Françoise LaCampagne, Mali Morris, Derek Roberts, Sophie Smallhorn, Amanda Thesiger, Virginia Verran, Johanes Zechner.*

### ▶ Francis Kyle Gallery
9 Maddox Street, London W1R 9LE.
**Tel** 020 7499 6870

### ▶ Frederick Mulder
83 Belsize Park Gardens, London NW3 4NJ.
**Tel** 020 7722 2105
**Work Stocked and Sold** Pr.

### ▶ Frivoli
7a Devonshire Road, London W4 2EU.
**Tel** 020 8742 3255 **Fax** 020 8994 7372
**Opening times** Mon–Sat 10–6, Thu 10–7.
**Work Stocked and Sold** Cer. Cra. Fur. Gla. Jew. Tx. Wd.

### ▶ Frost & Reed
2–4 King Street, St James's, London SW1Y 6QP.
**Tel** 020 7839 4645
**Fax** 020 7839 1166
**Opening times** 9–5.30
**Nearest Underground** Green Park.

### ▶ Futuraneon, Interior Designers & Artists
11 Chase Side, London N14 5BP.
**Tel** 020 8882 6181
**Fax** 020 8886 1810
**Email** rocco@futuraneon.co.uk
**Price range** £190–£2, 500

### ▶ Gagliardi Gallery
509 Kings Road, Chelsea, London SW10 0TX.
**Tel** 020 7352 3663 **Fax** 020 7351 6283
**Opening times** Tue–Sat 12–5.30.
**Nearest Underground** Sloane Square/ Earl's Court.
**Personnel** Directors: Roberto Gagliardi, Marie Gagliardi.
**Services and Facilities** Art Consultancy. Art for Offices. Commissioning Service. Gallery space for hire. Restaurant.

### ▶ Gagosian Gallery
8 Heddon Street, London W1B 4BU.
**Tel** 020 7292 8222 **Fax** 020 7292 8220
**Email** info@gagosian.com
**Ws** www.gagosian.com
**Opening times** Tue–Sat 10–6

### ▶ Galerie Besson
15 Royal Arcade, 28 Old Bond Street, Green Park, London W1X 3HB.
**Tel** 020 7491 1706 **Fax** 020 7495 3203
**Opening times** Mon 1–5, Tue–Fri 10–5.30, Sat 10–12.30 during exhibitions.
**Work Stocked and Sold** Cer. Cra.

### ▶ Galerie Moderne/le Style Lalique
9–10 Halkin Arcade, Motcomb Street, Belgravia, London SW1X 8JT.
**Tel** 020 7245 6907 **Fax** 020 7245 6341
**Opening times** Mon–Fri 10–6 or by appointment.
**Nearest Underground** Knightsbridge/Hyde Park Corner.
**Personnel** Gallery Director: Mark Waller. Alison Allen.
**Work Stocked and Sold** Dr. Gla.
**Price range** £500–£50,000
For artists see Commercial Gallery Artists.

### ▶ Galleria Enterprise
606 Kings Road, London SW6 2DX.
**Tel** 020 7371 9940 **Fax** 020 7371 9950
**Email** info@galleria-art.co.uk
**Ws** www.galleria-art.co.uk
**Opening times** Mon–Sat 10.30–5.30.
**Nearest Underground** Fulham Broadway. Bus routes: 22, 11 and 14.
**Personnel** Owner: P. Vazifdar. Sales: R. Churchward-Viggers.
**Services and Facilities** Art Consultancy. Art for Offices. Commissioning Service. Framing.
**Work Stocked and Sold** Dec. Fur. Pa. Ph. Pr.

### ▶ The Gallery
Southwark Pk, London SE16.
**Tel** 020 7231 1230

### ▶ Gallery 75
75 Heath Street, Hampstead, London NW3 6UG.
**Tel** 020 7431 8711 **Fax** 020 7625 6100
**Personnel** Ms Maria Ximerez.

### ▶ Gallery Different
45 Shad Thames, Tower Bridge Piazza, London SE1 2NJ.
**Tel** 020 7357 8909 **Fax** 020 7403 9050
**Email** different@davidbegbie.com
**Ws** www.davidbegbie.com
**Opening times** Tue–Fri 10–6, Sat–Sun 12–6.
**Nearest Underground** Tower Hill/ London Bridge.
**Personnel** Karina Phillips. Tilly Rogers. Julie Keating.
**Services and Facilities** Art Consultancy. Art for Offices. Commissioning Service. Gallery space for hire. Lectures.
**Work Stocked and Sold** Dr. Pa. Ph. Pr. Sc.
**Price range** £500–£20,000
For artists see Commercial Gallery Artists.

*David Begbie,* Flourish 1, *steelmesh, 45 x 35 x 12 cm, 2001, £2,900.*
*Regular exhibitions of sculpture, drawings and prints.*

### ▶ Gallery Duncan Terrace
24 Duncan Terrace, London N1 8BS.
**Tel** 020 7837 5856 **Fax** 020 7278 2140
**Opening times** Phone for opening times
**Nearest Underground** Angel.
**Personnel** Maureen O'Donoughue.
**Work Stocked and Sold** Cer. Dr. Pa. Sc. Wd.
**Price range** £100–£10,000
For artists see Commercial Gallery Artists.

### ▶ Gallery K
101–103 Heath Street, London NW3 6SS.
**Tel** 020 7794 4949 **Fax** 020 7431 4833
**Email** art@gallery-k.co.uk
**Ws** www.gallery-k.co.uk
**Opening times** Tue–Fri 10–6, Sat 11–6, Sun 2.30–6.30.
**Nearest Underground** Hampstead.
**Personnel** Director: Mrs Ritsa Kyriacou. Exhibitions Manager–Curator: Elpida Karaba.
**Services and Facilities** Art Consultancy. Art for Offices. Restoration. Valuation.
**Work Stocked and Sold** Ab. App. Cer. Dr. Pa. Pr. Sc.
**Price range** £30–£50,000
For artists see Commercial Gallery Artists.

### ▶ Gallery Lingard
Walpole House, 35 Walpole Street, London SW3 4QS.
**Tel** 020 7730 9233 **Fax** 020 7730 9152
**Personnel** Timothy Lingard.

### ▶ Gallery M
London Fields, 282 Richmond Road, London E8 3QS.
**Tel** 020 8986 9922 **Fax** 020 8985 0067
**Opening times** Fri, Sat & Sun 10–6 and by appointment.
**Nearest Underground** Bethnal Green; train: Hackney Central.
**Personnel** Director: Huei Hong.
**Services and Facilities** Art for Offices. Framing. Parking.

### ▶ The Gallery of Architecture
6 Turnpin Lane, Greenwich, London SE10 9JA.
**Tel** 020 8293 3617
**Fax** 020 8305 2064
**Personnel** Elizabeth Gordon. Mr J. Brown. Betty Gordon.

### ▶ Gallery of Modern Art
9 Barmouth Road, London SW18 2DT.
**Tel** 020 8875 1481 **Fax** 020 8875 1481
**Opening times** Mon–Thu 10–4, and by appointment.
**Nearest Station** Wandsworth Town.
**Personnel** Art Director: Bea Newbery.
**Work Stocked and Sold** Cer. Dr. Gla. Pa. Pr. Sc.
**Price range** £50–£5,000
For artists see Commercial Gallery Artists.

### ▶ The Gallery
168 Pentonville Road, London N1.
**Tel** 020 7837 8490

### ▶ The Gallery Westland Place
13 Westland Place, London N1 7LP.
**Tel** 020 7251 6456 **Fax** 020 7251 9339
**Email** gallery@westlandplace.co.uk
**Opening times** Mon–Sat 10–6.
**Nearest Underground** Old Street.
**Personnel** Gallery Director: Michael Chanarin.
**Services and Facilities** Art Consultancy. Bar. Café. Gallery space for hire. Lectures. Parking. Restaurant.
**Work Stocked and Sold** Cer. Dr. Pa. Ph. Pr. Sc.
**Price range** £500–£10,000

### ▶ Gasogian
8 Heddon Street, London W1.
**Tel** 020 7292 8222

### ▶ Gasworks
155 Vauxhall Street, London SE11.
**Tel** 020 7582 6848

### ▶ Gavin Graham Gallery
47 Ledbury Road, London W11 2AA.
**Tel** 020 7229 4848 **Fax** 020 7792 9697

### ▶ Georgina Turner Fine Art
Haus, 23–25 Mortimer Street, London W1.
**Tel** 00331 4567 0334

### ▶ Gimpel Fils
30 Davies Street, London W1Y 1LG.
**Tel** 020 7493 2488
**Fax** 020 7629 5732
**Email** 101626.2002@compuserve.com
**Opening times** Mon–Fri 10–5.30, Sat 10–1.
**Nearest Underground** Bond St/Green Park.
**Personnel** Director: Peter Gimpel,.

### ▶ Gladwell & Co.
69 Queen Victoria Street, London EC4N.
**Tel** 020 7248 3824

### ▶ Goedhuis Contemporary
116 Mount Street, London W1K 3NH.
**Tel** 020 7629 2228
**Fax** 020 7409 3538
**Email** michael.goedhuis@btinternet.com
**Ws** www.goedhuiscontemporary.com
**Opening times** 9.30–5.30.
**Nearest Underground** Green Park/ Bond Street
**Personnel** Manager: Tiffany Lacey. Director: Michael Goedhuis.
**Work Stocked and Sold** Pa. Sc.
*Michael Goedhuis opened Goedhuis Contemporary Gallery at 116 Mount Street in Mayfair, London in 1995, after spending two decades specialising in early Asian art. His principal activity today is the promotion of the leading Chinese contemporary artists throughout the world. Goedhuis Contemporary's artists, painters, calligraphers and sculptors come from China, Taiwan, Hong Kong, Paris, Hawaii, New York and London. The only criterion for inclusion in the Goedhuis Contemporary Gallery and Exhibition Network is the quality of work and its capacity to be relevant to and significant for the modern world.*

### ▶ Gordon Reece Gallery
16 Clifford Street, London W1X 1RG.
**Tel** 020 7439 0007 **Fax** 020 7437 5715
**Opening times** Mon–Sat 11–5.30.
**Nearest Underground** Bond Street.
**Personnel** Director: Gordon Reece.
**Services and Facilities** Art Consultancy. Art for Offices.
**Work Stocked and Sold** Cer. Fur. Jew. Sc. Tx.
**Price range** £50–£5,000

***Carved wooden figure of Garuda.***
*Specialists in tribal, ethnic, folk arts, primitive and oriental antiques, the Gordon Reece gallery presents selling exhibitions alongside substantial permanent collections of Indian and African art, furniture, nomadic rugs, sculpture, jewellery and architectual antiques.*
*For details of our gallery in Knaresborough, North Yorkshire, please see Regional Galleries listing.*

### ▶ Greengrassi
39C Fitzroy Street, London W1.
**Tel** 020 7387 8747

### ▶ The Greenhouse at the Drill Hall
16 Chenies Street, London WC1E 7EX.
**Tel** 020 7631 1353
**Personnel** Gail Veasey.

### ▶ Grosvenor Gallery
18 Albemarle Street, London W1X 3HA.
**Tel** 020 7629 0891 **Fax** 020 7491 4391
**Opening times** Mon–Fri 10–5.
**Nearest Underground** Green Park.
**Personnel** Director: Mr Ray Perman.
**Services and Facilities** Art for Offices.
**Work Stocked and Sold** Dr. Pa. Sc.

### ▶ Grosvenor Prints
28–32 Shelton Street, London WC2H 9HP.
**Tel** 020 7836 1979
**Work Stocked and Sold** Pr.

### ▶ Guy Morrison
91a Jermyn Street, London SW1Y.
**Tel** 020 7839 1454
**Services and Facilities** Framing.

### ▶ Hackelbury Fine Art Limited
4 Launceston Place, London W8 5RL.
**Tel** 020 7937 8688 **Fax** 020 7937 8868
**Email** reception@hackelbury.co.uk
**Opening times** Tue–Sat 10–5.
**Nearest Underground** Gloucester Road, High Street Kensington.
**Personnel** Directors: S. Hackel, M. Bury. Gallery Manager: C. Harris.
**Services and Facilities** Art Consultancy. Art for Offices.
**Work Stocked and Sold** Ph.

### ▶ Hales Gallery
70 Deptford High Street, London SE8 4RT.
**Tel** 020 8694 1194 **Fax** 020 8692 0471
**Email** halesgallery@btclick.com
**Ws** www.halesgallery.com
**Opening times** Mon–Sat 10–5.
**Nearest Underground** Deptford, New Cross, Deptford Bridge DLR.
**Personnel** Partner: Paul Hedge. Partner: Paul Maslin. Gallery Manager: Clifton Steinberg. Coordinator: Ella Whitmarsh.
**Services and Facilities** Café. Parking.
**Work Stocked and Sold** Dr. Pa. Ph. Pr. Sc.
**Price range** £500–£20,000
For artists see Commercial Gallery Artists.

### ▶ The Hallway Gallery
35 April Court, Teale Street, London E2.
**Tel** 020 7684 9834

### ▶ Hall & Knight
15 Duke Street, St James's, London SW1Y 6DB.
**Tel** 020 7839 4090
**Fax** 020 7839 4091

### ▶ Hamilton's Gallery
13 Carlos Place, London W1Y 5AG.
**Tel** 020 7499 9493
**Fax** 020 7629 9919
**Opening times** Tue–Sat 10–6.
**Nearest Underground** Bond Street or Green Park.
**Personnel** Directors: Andrew Cowan, Tim Jefferies.
**Work Stocked and Sold** Ph.
For artists see Commercial Gallery Artists.

### ▶ Hanga Ten
Hurlingham Studios, Ranelagh Gardens, London SW6 3PA.
**Tel** 020 7371 9677, mobile 0780 115 1981
**Fax** 020 7371 9677
**Email** japanart@hangaten.co.uk
**Opening times** By appointment.
**Nearest Underground** Putney Bridge.
**Personnel** Hely Norton.
**Work Stocked and Sold** Pr.
**Price range** £35–£3,000
For artists see Commercial Gallery Artists.

*Shinoda Toko,* From the Past, *lithograph, 38 x 28 cm, 1999.*
*Hanga Ten is a new gallery specialising in modern and contemporary Japanese prints, hand-picked in Japan. Artists represented include many internationally known printmakers such as SHINODA Toko, ENDO Susumu and TAKAHASHI Rikio, but also those at the beginning of their careers. Techniques cover all printing methods: woodblock, silkscreen, lithograph, intaglio and combination processes. Artistic expression is also diverse, ranging from minimalist and abstract compositions to traditional Japanese themes. All the artists have one thing in common: their immense creative talent and the quality of their work, a reflection of their technical excellence and the genius of Japan's papermakers.*

### ▶ Hanina Gallery
180 Westbourne Grove, London W11 2RH.
**Tel** 020 7243 8877 **Fax** 020 7243 0132
**Opening times** Mon–Sat 10–6.
**Nearest Underground** Notting Hill Gate
**Personnel** Director: Mr Yuval Hanina.

### ▶ Hardware Gallery
162 Archway Road, Highgate, London N6 5BB.
**Tel** 020 8341 6415 **Fax** 020 8348 0561
**Opening times** Wed–Sat 2–6 and by appointment.
**Nearest Underground** Highgate/Archway.
**Services and Facilities** Framing.
**Work Stocked and Sold** Ab. Pr.
For artists see Commercial Gallery Artists.

### ▶ Hart Gallery
113 Upper Street, Islington, London N1 1QN.
**Tel** 020 7704 1131
**Fax** 020 7704 1707
**Opening times** Tue–Fri 11–7, Sat 11–6, Sun 2–6.

**Nearest Underground** Angel.
**Personnel** Directors: John Hart, Katherine Hart.
**Services and Facilities** Art Consultancy. Art for Offices. Disabled Access. Lectures.
**Work Stocked and Sold** Cer. Dr. Pa. Ph. Pr. Sc.
**Price range** £100–£20,000
For artists see Commercial Gallery Artists.

### ▶ Hazlitt, Gooden & Fox Ltd
38 Bury Street, St James's, London SW1Y 6BB.
**Tel** 020 7930 6422 **Fax** 020 7839 5984
**Personnel** John Morton Morris. Michael .
**Work Stocked and Sold** Dr. Pa.

### ▶ The Heifer Gallery
3 Calabria Road, Highbury, London N5 1JB.
**Tel** 020 7226 7380
**Personnel** Christian Duplessis.

### ▶ Henry Dyson Fine Art
129 Pepys Road, Telegraph Hill, London SE14 5SE.
**Tel** 020 7732 3636 or 0498 884 638

### ▶ Henry Peacock
38A Foley Street, London W1.
**Tel** 020 7323 4033

### ▶ Hicks Gallery
2 Leopold Road, Wimbledon, London SW19 7BD.
**Tel** 020 8944 7171

### ▶ Highgate Fine Art
26 Highgate High Street, London N6 5JG.
**Tel** 020 8340 7564 **Fax** 020 8347 7010
**Email** hfal26@aol.com
**Opening times** Tue–Sat 10–6, Sun, Mon by appointment.
**Nearest Underground** Archway.
**Personnel** Noël Oddy. Fiona Hutson.
**Services and Facilities** Art Consultancy. Commissioning Service. Framing. Valuation.
**Work Stocked and Sold** Dr. Pa. Pr. Sc.
**Price range** £50–£20,000
For artists see Commercial Gallery Artists.

### ▶ Hilary Chapman, 20th Century Gallery
821 Fulham Road, London SW6 5HG.
**Tel** 020 7731 5888
**Fax** 020 7731 5888
**Email** chapmanprints@cs.com
**Ws** www.hilarychapmanfineprints.co.uk
**Opening times** Mon–Fri 10–6, Sat 10–1.
**Nearest Underground** Parsons Green.
**Personnel** Hilary Chapman.
**Services and Facilities** Art for Offices. Framing. Lectures. Shop. Valuation.
**Work Stocked and Sold** Pr.
**Price range** £50–£1,000
For artists see Commercial Gallery Artists.
*Specialist print dealer in late-19th and early-20th-century British prints. Stock includes etchings, engravings, lithographs, wood-engravings and colour prints by major and minor artists of the period up to the 1950s. At least two exhibitions are held each year and illustrated lists issued periodically. Please send details to the gallery to be included on the mailing list. Exhibitions for 2001 include 'John Hassall RE 1906–1988' (October).*

### ▶ Hildegard Fritz-Denneville Fine Arts
31 New Bond Street, London W1Y 9HD.
**Tel** 020 7629 2466
**Fax** 020 7408 0604
**Nearest Underground** Bond Street.
**Personnel** Mrs Fritz-Denneville.
**Work Stocked and Sold** Dr. Pa. Pr.
For artists see Commercial Gallery Artists.

### ▶ Hirschl Contemporary Art
5 Cork Street, London W1S 3LQ.
**Tel** 020 7495 2565
**Fax** 020 7495 7535
**Email** jhirschl@dircon.co.uk
**Ws** www.hirschlcontemporary.com
**Opening times** Mon–Fri 10–7, Sat 10.30–1.
**Nearest Underground** Green Park, Bond Street, Oxford Circus.
**Personnel** Director: Jennifer Hirschl. Director: Robin Page.
**Services and Facilities** Art Consultancy. Art for Offices. Commissioning Service.
**Work Stocked and Sold** Pa. Ph. Sc.
**Price range** £500–£80,000
For artists see Commercial Gallery Artists.
*The gallery opened in September 2000. We exhibit and stock British and international contemporary art. For further information on our artists and exhibition programme, visit our website.*

### ▶ Home
1A Flodden Road, London SE5.
**Tel** 020 7274 3452

### ▶ Honor Oak Gallery
52 Honor Oak Park, London SE23 1DY.
**Tel** 020 8291 6094
**Opening times** Tue–Fri 9.30–6, Sat 9.30–5.
**Nearest Underground** Honor Oak Park.
**Personnel** Director: John Broad.
**Services and Facilities** Commissioning Service. Framing. Restoration.
**Work Stocked and Sold** Dr. Pa. Pr.
**Price range** £12–£2,000
For artists see Commercial Gallery Artists.
*Prints, drawings, watercolours and paintings by 20th-century and contemporary artists: Norman Ackroyd, Emiko Aida, Rosemary Benson, June Berry, Paul Bisson, Elizabeth Blackadder, Harry Brockway, Ashley Cook, Gill Day, Jenny Devereux, Paul Drury, David Evans, David Glück, Ellen Graubar, Margareta Berger-Hamerschlag, A. S. Hartrick, Thomas Hennell, John Houston, Sue Jameson, Rudolph Kortokraks, Karolina Larusdottir, Clare Leighton, Sanchia Lewis, Vincent Lines, George Mayer-Marton, Tiffany McNab, Donald Myall, John O'Connor, Trevor Price, Linda Richardson, Edward Stamp, Robin Tanner, Ann Tout, Erich Wagner, Richard Wardle, Gerd Winner, Adrian Wiszniewski, etc. Agent for Glasgow Print Studio.*

### ▶ Houldsworth
33–34 Cork Street, London W1S 3NQ.
**Tel** 020 7434 2333
**Fax** 020 7434 3636
**Email** contact@houldsworth.co.uk
**Ws** www.houldsworth.co.uk
**Opening times** Mon–Fri 10–5.30, Sat 10.30–1.
**Nearest Underground** Green Park, Bond Street.
**Personnel** Director: Pippy Houldsworth. Mariska Nietzman.
**Services and Facilities** Art Consultancy. Art for Offices.
**Work Stocked and Sold** Dr. Pa. Ph. Pr. Sc.
**Price range** £300–£200,000
For artists see Commercial Gallery Artists.
*Contemporary art.*

### ▶ Hybrid
98 Columbia Road, London E2.
**Tel** 020 7613 2628

### ▶ Hyde Park Gallery
16 Craven Terrace, London W2 3QD.
**Tel** 020 7402 2904

### ▶ IAP Fine Art
Viewing by Appointment at Island Studio, Hampton. Correspondence address: PO Box 2253, Iver Bucks SLO ODF.
**Tel** 01753 650 081 **Email** info@iapfineart.com
**Ws** www.iapfineart.com
**Opening times** By appointment at Island Studio, Hampton.
**Personnel** Proprietor: David Tregunna.
**Services and Facilities** Art Consultancy. Art for Offices. Commissioning Service. Restoration.
**Work Stocked and Sold** Pa. Pr. Sc.
**Price range** £150–£20,000
For artists see Commercial Gallery Artists.
*Contemporary British paintings and prints. We represent British painter Chris Gollon, and also hold work by Maggi Hambling, Peter Howson, and Fred Crayk.*

### ▶ Ice House
Central Library, Phillimore Walk, London W8 7RX.
**Tel** 020 7361 2295
**Personnel** Marketing Organiser: Mike Volpe. Organiser of Exhibitions: Michael Goggin.

### ▶ Independent Art Space
23a Smith Street, London SW3.
**Tel** 020 7259 9232

### ▶ Institute of Fine Art
5 Kirby Street, Hatton Garden, London EC1N.
**Tel** 020 7831 4048

### ▶ Interim Art
21 Herald Street, London E2 6JT.
**Tel** 020 7729 4112 **Fax** 020 7729 4113
**Opening times** Thu–Sun 11–6, and by appointment.
**Personnel** Director: Maureen Paley.

### ▶ International Art Project
57 Moreton Street, London SW1V.
**Tel** 020 7976 6200

### ▶ Jam Factory
Rothay Street, London SE1.
**Tel** 020 7403 2888

### ▶ James Colman Fine Arts
The Tower, 28 Mossbury Road, London SW11 2PB.
**Tel** 020 7924 3860 **Fax** 020 7924 3860
**Personnel** James Colman.

### ▶ James Roundell
58 Jermyn Street, London SW1Y.
**Tel** 020 7499 0722

### ▶ James West Fine Art
28 Islington Park Street, London N1 1PX.
**Personnel** James West.

### ▶ Japan Print Gallery
43 Pembridge Road, London W11.
**Tel** 020 7221 0927

### ▶ Jill George Gallery
38 Lexington Street, Soho, London W1F 0LL.
**Tel** 020 7439 7319 **Fax** 020 7287 0478
**Email** jill@jillgeorgegallery.co.uk
**Ws** www.jillgeorgegallery.co.uk
**Opening times** Mon–Fri 10–6, Sat 11–5.
**Nearest Underground** Piccadilly/Oxford Circus.
**Personnel** Director: Jill George.
**Services and Facilities** Art Consultancy. Art for Offices. Commissioning Service.
**Work Stocked and Sold** Dr. Pa. Pr.
**Price range** £200–£30,000
For artists see Commercial Gallery Artists.

Cell, *oil on canvas, 2000.*
*British contemporary art. Paintings, drawings, watercolours, limited edition prints and monoprints from the established artist to the recent graduate. The gallery handles both figurative and abstract originals and prints. Participates in national and international art fairs. Art consultancy and commissions organised on behalf of the artists. Exhibition every five weeks throughout the year.*

### ▶ Joanna Barnes Fine Arts
14 Mason's Yard, Duke Street, St James's, London SW1Y 6BU.
**Tel** 020 7930 4215
**Fax** 020 7839 8307
**Personnel** Joanna Barnes.

### ▶ John Bennett Gallery
206 Walton Street, London SW3 2JL.
**Tel** 020 7225 2223

### ▶ John Bloxham Fine Art
4 & 5 The Parade, St Johns Hill, London SW11 1TG.
**Tel** 020 7924 7500 **Fax** 020 7733 4451

### ▶ John Denham Gallery
50 Mill Lane, West Hampstead, London NW6 1NJ.
**Tel** 020 7794 2635
**Fax** 020 7794 2635
**Opening times** Sun & weekdays 11–5, closed Sat & Mon am.
**Nearest Underground** West Hampstead.
**Personnel** Director: John Denham.
**Services and Facilities** Framing. Restoration. Valuation.
**Work Stocked and Sold** Dr. Pa. Sc.
For artists see Commercial Gallery Artists.

### ▶ John Hunt
15 King Street, St James's, London SW1Y 6QU.
**Tel** 020 7839 2643 **Fax** 020 7839 2643
**Opening times** Mon–Fri 11–5.
**Personnel** John Hunt. Anne Bates.
**Work Stocked and Sold** Dr. Pa. Sc.

### ▶ John Martin of London
38 Albemarle Street, London W1X 3FB.
**Tel** 020 7499 1314 **Fax** 020 7493 2842
**Email** jmlondon@dircon.co.uk
**Opening times** Mon–Fri 10–6, Sat 10–3.
**Nearest Underground** Green Park.
**Personnel** John Martin.
**Services and Facilities** Art for Offices.
**Work Stocked and Sold** Dr. Pa. Sc.
**Price range** £300–£15,000
For artists see Commercial Gallery Artists.

### ▶ Jonathan Cooper
Park Walk Gallery, 20 Park Walk, London SW10 0AQ.
**Tel** 020 7351 0410 **Fax** 020 7351 0410
**Opening times** Mon–Fri 10–6.30, Sat 11–4.
**Nearest Underground** South Kensington.
**Personnel** Jonathan Cooper. Henrietta Dudley.
**Services and Facilities** Art Consultancy. Framing. Restoration. Valuation.
**Work Stocked and Sold** Pa. Ph.
**Price range** £120–£25,000
For artists see Commercial Gallery Artists.

### ▶ The Jonathan Wylder Gallery and Studio
2 Motcomb Street, Belgravia, London SW1X.
**Tel** 020 7245 9949 **Fax** 020 7245 9949
**Opening times** Mon–Fri 10–5, Sat 11–4.
**Nearest Underground** Knightsbridge.
**Personnel** Director: Jonathan Wylder.
**Work Stocked and Sold** Pa. Sc.

### ▶ Julian Hartnoll
14 Mason's Yard, off Duke Street, St James's, London SW1Y 6BU.
**Tel** 020 7839 3842 **Fax** 020 7930 8234
**Ws** www.art-on-line.com/hartnoll
**Opening times** Weekdays 10–12.30, 2.30–5, Sat 10–12.30.
**Nearest Underground** Green Park, Piccadilly Circus.
**Personnel** Director: Julian Hartnoll. Assistant: Rowena Williams.
**Services and Facilities** Art Consultancy. Art for Offices.
**Work Stocked and Sold** Cer. Dr. Pa. Pr.
**Price range** £100–£500,000
For artists see Commercial Gallery Artists.

### ▶ Julian Lax
37–39 Arkwright Road, London NW3 6BJ.
**Tel** 020 7794 9933 **Fax** 020 7431 5845
**Opening times** By appointment.
**Nearest Underground** Hampstead, Finchley Rd.
**Personnel** Director: Julian Lax.
**Services and Facilities** Art Consultancy. Art for Offices. Framing. Restoration. Valuation.
**Work Stocked and Sold** Dr. Pa. Pr. Sc.
**Price range** £100–£30,000
For artists see Commercial Gallery Artists.

### ▶ Julian Simon Fine Art
70 Pimlico Road, London SW1W 8LS.
**Tel** 020 7730 8673 **Fax** 020 7823 6116

### ▶ Kaleidoscope
64–66 Willesden Lane, London NW6 7SX.
**Tel** 020 7328 5833 **Fax** 020 7624 2913
**Opening times** Tue–Sat 10–6.
**Nearest Underground** Kilburn.
**Personnel** Director: Karl Barrie.
**Services and Facilities** Framing. Gallery space for hire. Restoration. Valuation.
**Work Stocked and Sold** Cer. Dec. Dr. Fur. Pa. Pr. Sc. Wd.
**Price range** £50–£5,000
For artists see Commercial Gallery Artists.

### ▶ Karen Griffiths
Chenil Galleries, 181–183 Kings Road, London SW3 5EB.
**Tel** 020 7352 8002

### ▶ Kathryn Bell/Fine Art Consultancy
Studio 123D, Canalot Production Studios, 222 Kensal Road, London W10 5BN.
**Tel** 020 8960 0070 **Fax** 020 8960 0209
**Opening times** By appointment.
**Nearest Underground** Westbourne Park.
**Personnel** Director: Kathryn Bell.
**Services and Facilities** Art Consultancy. Art for Offices. Commissioning Service. Lectures. Valuation.
**Work Stocked and Sold** App. Dr. Gla. Pa. Ph. Pr. Sc. Tx. Wd.
**Price range** £500–£40,000

### ▶ Keith Nickol
58 Sandringham Flats, Charing Cross Road, London WC2H 0BL.
**Tel** 020 7836 0216, mobile 041-141 4602
**Work Stocked and Sold** Pa.

### ▶ Kings Road Gallery
436 Kings Road, Chelsea, London SW10 0LJ.
**Tel** 020 7351 1367 **Fax** 020 7351 7007
**Email** tanya@kingsroadgallery.com
**Ws** www.kingsroadgallery.com
**Opening times** Mon–Fri 9.30–6, Sat 10–6, Sun appointment only.
**Nearest Underground** Sloane Square.
**Personnel** Director: Tanya Baxter. Gallery Manager: Sarah Boyle. Gallery Assistant: Ijil Yalat.
**Services and Facilities** Art Consultancy. Art for Offices. Commissioning Service. Framing. Valuation.
**Work Stocked and Sold** Pa. Ph. Sc.
**Price range** £500–£20,000
For artists see Commercial Gallery Artists.

*Yin Xin,* High Society, *acrylic on canvas, 162 x 130 cm, 2001, £12,000.*
*Kings Road Gallery is situated in the heart of Chelsea, which bears host to a number of*

*international antique and designer shops. The gallery represents established artists from East and West with a strong leaning towards figurative works. The Asian theme is prevalent amongst the works by both Western and Eastern artists, such as the Mongolian and Tibetan landscapes of Pip Todd Warmoth and the colourful Rajastan oils by Susan Jayne Hocking. The Buddhist monks by Min Wae Aung are striking compositions in acrylic on canvas. The gallery also has a corporate art department consulting to hotels, banks, private collectors and art loan facilites. The cultural diversity of Kings Road Gallery has artworks to suit all tastes.*

### ▶ Knapp Gallery
Regents College, Inner Circle, Regents Park, London NW1.

### ▶ L'Acquaforte
49a Ledbury Road, London W11.
**Tel** 020 7221 3388
**Services and Facilities** Framing.

### ▶ La Galerie
225 Ebury Street, London SW1W.
**Tel** 020 7730 9210
**Services and Facilities** Framing.

### ▶ Lamont Gallery
The Organ Factory, Swanscoombe Rd, London W11 4SU.
**Tel** 020 7602 3232 **Ws** www.lamontart.com
**Opening times** Tue–Sat 11–6.
**Nearest Underground** Bethnal Green.
**Personnel** Director: Andrew Lamont. Gallery Manager: Sigrid Williams.
**Services and Facilities** Art Consultancy. Art for Offices.
**Work Stocked and Sold** Cer. Pa. Pr. Sc.
**Price range** £200–£10,000
For artists see Commercial Gallery Artists.
*The first commercial art gallery to open in London's East End, Lamont Gallery has been a leading representative of contemporary British art for over ten years. The gallery shows at the UK's major art fairs and past exhibitions have toured to museums and abroad. Specialists in collection management, Lamont Gallery has a viewing room for private and corporate collectors. Also work by Cutting Edge Ceramicists.*

### ▶ Lefevre Gallery
30 Bruton Street, London W1X 8JD.
**Tel** 020 7493 2107 **Fax** 020 7499 9088
**Email** impressionist@lefevre-gallery.co.uk or contemporary@lefevre-gallery.co.uk
**Ws** www.lefevre-gallery.com
**Opening times** Mon–Fri 10–5
**Nearest Underground** Green Park
**Personnel** Director: Alexander Corcoran. Director: Desmond Corcoran. Director: Martin Summers .
**Services and Facilities** Art Consultancy. Commissioning Service. Valuation. Dr. Pa. Sc.
*19th–20th-century art. Contemporary art*

### ▶ The Leger Galleries Ltd
13 Old Bond Street, London W1X 3DB.
**Tel** 020 7629 3538

### ▶ Lena Boyle Fine Art
40 Drayton Gardens, London SW10 9SA.
**Tel** 020 7373 8247, 020 7259 2700
**Fax** 020 7370 7460
**Email** lenaa.boyle@btinternet.com
**Opening times** By appointment only.
**Nearest Underground** Gloucester Road, South Kensington.
**Personnel** Director: Lena Boyle. John Boyle.
**Services and Facilities** Art Consultancy. Art for Offices. Commissioning Service.
**Work Stocked and Sold** Cer. Dec. Dr. Pa. Pr. Sc. Wd.
**Price range** £75–£6,000
For artists see Commercial Gallery Artists.

### ▶ Lennox Gallery (London)
77 Moore Park Road, London SW6 2HH.
**Tel** 020 7736 3326,
Exhibitions: 01349 884 083

### ▶ Lenz
401 Langham House, 302 Regent Street, London W1R 6HH.
**Tel** 020 7580 4242 or 01954 231 006
**Fax** 020 7580 4792

### ▶ Lesley Craze Gallery
34 Clerkenwell Green, London EC1R 0DU.
**Tel** 020 7608 0393 **Fax** 020 7251 9200
**Opening times** Mon–Sat 10–5.30.
**Work Stocked and Sold** Jew.

### ▶ Linda Anne Landers & Spoon Print Press
337 Westbourne Park Road, London W11 1EG.
**Tel** 020 7229 2763
**Opening times** By appointment only.
**Work Stocked and Sold** Ab.
**Price range** £22–£400

### ▶ Linda Blackstone Gallery
The Old Slaughterhouse, R/O 13 High Street, Pinner, HA5 5QQ.
**Tel** 020 8868 5765
**Fax** 020 8868 4465
**Email** blackstoneart@talk21.com
**Ws** www.blackstoneart.com
**Opening times** Wed–Sat 10–6.
**Nearest Underground** Pinner (Metropolitan Line – Watford branch).
**Personnel** Proprietor: Linda Blackstone. Gallery Manageress: Bobbie Jones.
**Services and Facilities** Art for Offices. Commissioning Service. Framing. Parking. Restoration.
**Work Stocked and Sold** Ab. Cer. Pa. Pr. Sc. Tx. Wd.
**Price range** £100–£5,000
For artists see Commercial Gallery Artists.
*Established 1985. High-quality representational paintings, ceramics and sculpture by contemporary British artists. Continually changing exhibition punctuated by six major exhibitions a year. Subjects include: landscape, marine, wildlife and the figure. Gallery artists include: Mat Barber Kennedy RI, G. John Blockley RI PPPS NEAC, Richard Bolton, Catherine Brennand RI, Pamela Davis RMS, Stephanie Harrison RMS, Moira Huntly RI VPPS RSMA, Colin Kent RI, Robert King RI RSMA, Janet Ledger, John Lidzey, Debra Manifold PS, Leo McDowell RI, Ken Paine PS, J. Richard Plincke RI, Sue Read RI, Jackie Simmonds, Alan Simpson RSMA, Jacquie Turner. Fine art framing and restoration. In 1998 staged a special exhibition of paintings, prints and cards by British Artists (including Ken Howard RA and Norman Ackroyd RA) to commemorate the 50th Anniversary of the State of Israel; their first visit and first impressions of the Holy Land.*

### ▶ Lisson Gallery
67 Lisson Street and 52–54 Bell Street, London NW1 5DA.
**Tel** 020 7724 2739 **Fax** 020 7724 7124
**Email** contact@lisson.co.uk
**Ws** www.lisson.co.uk
**Opening times** Mon–Fri 10–6, Sat 10–5.
**Nearest Underground** Edgware Road, Marylebone.
**Personnel** Chairman: Nicholas Logsdail. Chief Executive: Jill Silverman van Coenegrachts. Directors: Michelle Souza, Pilar Corias.
For artists see Commercial Gallery Artists.

### ▶ Llewellyn Alexander (Fine Paintings) Ltd
124–126 The Cut, Waterloo, London SE1 8LN.
**Tel** 020 7620 1322/1324
**Fax** 020 7928 9469
**Nearest Underground** Waterloo
**Personnel** Contact: Diana Holdsworth.
**Work Stocked and Sold** Pa. Sc.
For artists see Commercial Gallery Artists.

### ▶ Loggia
15 Buckingham Gate, London SW1E 6LB.
**Tel** 020 7828 5963
**Opening times** Mon–Fri 6–8, Sat/Sun 2–6.
**Nearest Underground** St James's Park.
**Personnel** Chairman: Robert de Quin.

### ▶ London Contemporary Art Ltd
88 Peterborough Rd, London SW6 3HH.
**Tel** 020 7731 7770
**Personnel** Piers Johnstone.
**Work Stocked and Sold** Pr.

### ▶ Long & Ryle Art International
4 John Islip Street, London SW1P 4PX.
**Tel** 020 7834 1434 **Fax** 020 7821 9409
**Email** gallery@long-and-ryle.demon.co.uk
**Ws** www.long-and-ryle.demon.co.uk
**Opening times** Tue–Fri 10–5.30, Sat 2–5.
**Nearest Underground** Pimlico.
**Personnel** Directors: Sarah Long, Carolyn Ryle-Hodges. Manager: Linda Elliott.
**Services and Facilities** Art Consultancy. Art for Offices. Commissioning Service.
**Work Stocked and Sold** Pa. Pr. Sc.
**Price range** £400–£8,0000
For artists see Commercial Gallery Artists.
*Commercial art gallery and consultancy specialising in contemporary painting, sculpture and prints. Holds around eight exhibitions annually and participates in leading international art fairs.*

### ▶ Lucy B. Campbell Gallery
123 Kensington Church Street, London W8 7LP.
**Tel** 020 7727 2205
**Work Stocked and Sold** Pr.

### ▶ Lumley Cazalet
33 Davies Street, London W1Y 1FN.
**Tel** 020 7491 4767 **Fax** 020 7493 8644
**Email** lumleycaz@cwcom.net
**Ws** www.slad.org/lumley-cazalet-ltd

**Opening times** Mon–Fri 10–6.
**Nearest Underground** Bond Street.
**Personnel** Directors: Camilla Cazalet, Caroline Lumley, Catherine Hodgkinson.
**Work Stocked and Sold** Dr. Pr. Sc.
**Price range** £50–£300,000
For artists see Commercial Gallery Artists.

### ▶ Lutz Riester
PO Box 2769, London W2 6ZJ.
**Tel** 020 7258 3467
**Work Stocked and Sold** Pr.

### ▶ Lux Gallery
2–4 Hoxton Square, London N1.
**Tel** 020 7684 2785 **Fax** 020 7684 1111

### ▶ The Maas Gallery
15a Clifford Street, London W1X 1RF.
**Tel** 020 7734 2302
**Fax** 020 7287 4836
**Opening times** Daily 10–5.30.
**Nearest Underground** Green Park.
**Personnel** Directors: Rupert Maas, Fiona Halpin.
**Work Stocked and Sold** Dr. Pa. Pr. Sc.
**Price range** £200–£2,000,000
For artists see Commercial Gallery Artists.

### ▶ Mafuji Gallery
2nd floor, 28 Shacklewell Lane, London E8 2EZ.
**Tel** 020 8567 8222
**Fax** 020 8567 8222
**Email** mafuji@cwcom.net
**Opening times** Thu–Sat 1–5.
**Nearest Underground** Dalston Kingsland.
**Personnel** Director: Haruo Mafuji. Administrator: Peter Head.
**Services and Facilities** Disabled Access. Lectures.
**Work Stocked and Sold** Pa. Ph. Sc.
**Price range** £100–£5,000
*Opened in September 1999 as an artist-run space. The aim of the gallery is to find answers to the questions: what is art? what is the meaning of art? what is the relationship of art to human society? Art works exhibited in the gallery are adventurous and experimental, in all media, trying to explore profound issues such as who we are, where we live and where we are going in this global culture.*

### ▶ Malcolm Innes Gallery
7 Bury Street, St James's, London SW7Y 6AL.
**Tel** 020 7839 8083/4 **Fax** 020 7839 8085
**Personnel** Malcolm Innes: Malcolm Innes. A. R. B. Wood. Director: Sarah Stewart. Director: P. C. S. Allfrey.

### ▶ Mall Arcade
Camden Passage, Islington, London N1.
**Tel** 020 7930 1904
**Fax** 020 7839 7509
**Opening times** Wed and Sat 9–5. Other times by appointment.
**Work Stocked and Sold** Ph.

### ▶ Manya Igel Fine Arts
21–22 Peter's Court, Porchester Road, London W2 5DR.
**Tel** 020 7229 1669/8429
**Fax** 020 7229 6770
**Personnel** Manya Igel. Bernard Prydal. David Duncan. Rosalin Naqi.

### ▶ Marble Arch Art Gallery
14 Old Quebec Street, London W1H.
**Tel** 020 7629 5159
**Services and Facilities** Framing.

### ▶ Marina Henderson Gallery
11 Langton Street, London SW10.
**Tel** 020 7352 1667

### ▶ The Mark Gallery
9 Porchester Place, Marble Arch, London W2 2BS.
**Tel** 020 7262 4906 **Fax** 020 7224 9416
**Opening times** Mon–Fri 10–1 & 2–6, Sat 11–1.
**Nearest Underground** Marble Arch.
**Personnel** Director: Helen Mark.
**Work Stocked and Sold** Pr.

### ▶ Markovitch Gallery
108A Boundary Road, St John's Wood, London NW8 0RH.
**Tel** 020 7372 1333
**Work Stocked and Sold** Ph.

### ▶ Marlborough Graphics
6 Albemarle Street, London W1X 4BY.
**Tel** 020 7629 5161
**Fax** 020 7495 0641
**Email** graphics@marlboroughfineart.com
**Ws** www.marlboroughfineart.com
**Opening times** Mon–Fri 10–5.30, Sat 10–12.30.
**Nearest Underground** Green Park.
**Personnel** Director: David Case. Assistant: Nicola Togneri. Assistant: Ole Koch.
**Services and Facilities** Art Consultancy. Art for Offices. Framing. Valuation.
**Work Stocked and Sold** Ab. Cer. Dr. Ph. Pr. Sc.
**Price range** £300–£60,000
For artists see Commercial Gallery Artists.
*The leading dealers in Freud etchings. Contemporary publications and prints available by the following gallery artists: Arikha, Auerbach, Conroy, Davies, Hambling, Jacklin, KIiff, Kitaj, Le Brun, Oulton, Pasmore, Paul, Piper and Rego. Modern Master prints available by: Bacon, Hepworth, Kokoschka, Matisse, Miró, Moore, Nicholson, Picasso, Riley and Sutherland.*

### ▶ Marsden Contemporary Art
21 Dulwich Village, London SE21 7BT.
**Tel** 020 8488 4169
**Fax** 020 8693 2700
**Personnel** Gary Marsden. Helen Marsden.

### ▶ Martyn Gregory
34 Bury Street, St James's, London SW1Y 6AU.
**Tel** 020 7839 3731
**Fax** 020 7930 0812
**Email** mgregory@dircon.co.uk
**Opening times** 10–6.
**Nearest Underground** Green Park.
*British watercolours and paintings; China Trade pictures.*

### ▶ Matt's Gallery
42–44 Copperfield Road, London E3 4RR.
**Tel** 020 8983 1771
**Fax** 020 8983 1435
**Opening times** Wed–Sun 12–6 (ring for details).
**Personnel** Director: Robin Klassnik.

### ▶ Matthiesen Fine Art Limited
7/8 Mason's Yard, Duke Street, London SW1Y 6BU.
**Tel** 020 7930 2437
**Fax** 020 7930 1387
**Email** matthiesen@oldmasterslondon.demon.co.uk
**Ws** www.Europeanpaintings.com
**Opening times** Mon–Fri 10–6. By appointment only.
**Nearest Underground** Green Park, Piccadilly.
**Personnel** Director: Patrick Matthiesen.
**Services and Facilities** Art Consultancy.
**Work Stocked and Sold** Pa.
**Price range** £30,000–£5,000,000
For artists see Commercial Gallery Artists.
*Museum quality Italian, French and Spanish Old Master paintings 1330–1848. Specialising in Italian painting in London and French painting in New York. Exhibition catalogues available. In association with Stair Sainty Matthiesen Inc., 22 E. 80th St, New York, NY 10021, USA. Tel (212) 288 1088, fax (212) 628 2449.*
*In association with: Matthiesen Gallery (Japan), Hiromi Kaminishi, Exec. Vice President, N.W. Hill 401, 2–12 Haramachi, Shinjuku-ku, Tokyo 162. Tel: (81) 3-3353 2081.*

### ▶ Maureen Paley Interim Art
21 Herald Street, London E2.
**Tel** 020 7729 4112

### ▶ Mayor Gallery
22a Cork Street, London W1X 1HB.
**Tel** 020 7734 3558
**Fax** 020 7494 1377

### ▶ McDonald Wyckaert
The Georgian Group, 6 Fitzroy Square, London W1P 6DX.
**Tel** 020 7706 3387 or 0410 750 929
**Opening times** Daily 10–9.
**Nearest Underground** Warren Street, Goodge Street.
**Price range** £300–£30,000

### ▶ The McHardy Sculpture Company
Cardamom Building, Shad Thames, London SE1 2YR.
**Tel** 020 7403 7555 **Fax** 020 7378 7300
**Email** nevagi@compuserve.com
**Ws** www.mchardy-sculpture.com
**Opening times** Tue–Sat 11–5, Sun 12–5.
**Nearest Underground** London Bridge, Tower Hill.
**Personnel** Contacts: Agi & Neville Cohen. Polly Bacon. Gemma Gates.
**Services and Facilities** Art Consultancy. Art for Offices. Commissioning Service.
**Work Stocked and Sold** Cer. Dec. Dr. Sc.
**Price range** £150–£10,000
For artists see Commercial Gallery Artists.
*The gallery at Butlers Wharf by Tower Bridge has a continual display of more than 100 pieces including figurative and abstract works from distinguished names and new discoveries. McHardy Sculpture Company can help all those with an interest in sourcing the work of contemporary sculptors at realistic prices. Sculpture for private collections, Home and Office Interiors, Parks, Gardens, Open Spaces, Awards, Gifts, Presentations, Interior & Exterior Design.*

### ▶ The Medici Galleries
7 Grafton Street, London W1S 4EJ.
**Tel** 020 7629 5675
**Fax** 020 7495 2997
**Email** grafton@medici-society.freeserve.co.uk
**Ws** www.medicigalleries.co.uk
**Opening times** Mon–Fri 10–6.
**Nearest Underground** Green Park.
**Personnel** Manager: Jenny Kerr.
**Services and Facilities** Art Consultancy. Art for Offices. Framing. Shop.
**Work Stocked and Sold** Cra. Pa. Pr.
**Price range** £100–£35,000
For artists see Commercial Gallery Artists.
*Offering a rare combination of services, The Medici Galleries have been a Mayfair landmark since 1910. The ground floor gallery has a changing display of original contemporary art and craft, with approximately nine exhibitions a year. Limited edition, reproduction and children's prints are available in the lower gallery, plus a framing service. Three rooms in the lower gallery are devoted to fine art greeting cards, contemporary miniatures, stationery and children's books. A personalised Christmas card service is available from mid-August.*

### ▶ Meghraj Gallery
Meghraj Court, 18 Jockey's Fields, London WC1R 4BW.
**Tel** 020 7831 6881 **Fax** 020 7404 8288

### ▶ Mellow Birds
34 Underwood Street, London N1.
**Tel** 020 7497 0116

### ▶ Mercury Gallery
26 Cork Street, London W1X 1HB.
**Tel** 020 7734 7800 **Fax** 020 7287 9809
**Email** mercury@netcomuk.co.uk
**Ws** www.mercury-gallery.co.uk
**Opening times** Mon–Fri 10–5.30, Sat 10–12.30.
**Nearest Underground** Green Park, Piccadilly.
**Personnel** Director: Gillian Raffles.
**Services and Facilities** Art Consultancy. Art for Offices.
**Work Stocked and Sold** Ab. Cer. Dr. Pa. Pr. Sc.
**Price range** £100–£100,000
For artists see Commercial Gallery Artists.

### ▶ Merrifield Studios
112 Heath Street, Hampstead, London NW3 1AA.
**Tel** 020 7794 0343/020 7431 0794
**Fax** 020 7435 8039
**Work Stocked and Sold** Sc.

### ▶ Messums Fine Art
8 Cork Street, London W1X 1PB.
**Tel** 020 7437 5545
**Fax** 020 7491 3162/020 7734 7018
**Opening times** Mon–Sat 10–4.
**Personnel** Director: David Messum. Michael Child. Carol Tee.
**Work Stocked and Sold** Dr. Pa.

### ▶ Michael Elcke
2 Old Bond Street, London W1X.
**Tel** 020 7495 2687
**Services and Facilities** Framing.

### ▶ Michael Hue-Williams Fine Art
21 Cork Street, First Floor, London W1S 3LZ.
**Tel** 020 7434 1318 **Fax** 020 7434 1321
**Email** mhw@btinternet.com
**Opening times** Mon–Fri 9.30–5.30, Sat 10–1.
**Nearest Underground** Bond St, Piccadilly, Green Park.
**Personnel** Michael Hue-Williams.
**Services and Facilities** Art Consultancy. Art for Offices.
**Work Stocked and Sold** Ab. App. Dec. Dr. Pa. Ph. Pr.
For artists see Commercial Gallery Artists.

### ▶ Mil Arté
98 Mill Lane, West Hampstead, London NW6 1NF.
**Tel** 020 7681 9136
**Fax** 020 7435 1005
**Opening times** Tue–Sat 11–6.30.
**Personnel** Amanda Pointer. Thierry Poizat.
**Work Stocked and Sold** Wd.

### ▶ Millinery Works
85/87 Southgate Road, Islington, London N1 3JS.
**Tel** 020 7359 2019 **Fax** 020 7226 9446
**Personnel** Mr J. Jackson.

### ▶ Milne & Moller
35 Colville Terrace, London W11 2BU.
**Tel** 020 7727 1679
**Personnel** Directors: Chris Moller, Juliet Moller.

### ▶ Mina Renton Fine Art
50 Eresby House, Rutland Gate, London SW7 1BG.
**Tel** 020 7584 1907
**Fax** 020 7584 1907
**Opening times** By appointment only.
**Personnel** Mina Renton.
**Work Stocked and Sold** Pr.

### ▶ Mobile Home
42 Theobalds Road, London WC1.
**Tel** 020 7405 7575

### ▶ Modern African Gallery
102 Park Street, London W1Y.
**Tel** 020 7629 7528
**Services and Facilities** Framing.

### ▶ Modern Art Inc
73 Redchurch Street, London E2.
**Tel** 020 739 2081 **Fax** 020 7729 2017

### ▶ Momtaz Islamic Art
79A Albany Street, Regent's Park, London NW1 4BT.
**Tel** 020 7486 5411, mobile 0973 405 428
**Fax** 020 7487 5250

### ▶ Montpellier Sandelson
5A Cork Street, London W1X 1PB.
**Tel** 020 7439 1001 **Fax** 020 7439 2299

### ▶ Moreton Contemporary Art

CONTEMPORARY ART

40 Moreton Street, London SW1V 2PB.
**Tel** 020 7834 7773/7775 **Fax** 020 7834 7834
**Email** sales@frasco.co.uk
**Ws** www.moretonart.com
**Opening times** Mon–Fri 9.30–6, Sat 12–4.
**Nearest Underground** Pimlico
**Personnel** Director: Lisa Banholzer. Gallery Manager: Sheena McGoran. Frame Workshop Manager: Richard Miller.
**Services and Facilities** Art Consultancy. Art for Offices. Commissioning Service. Disabled Access. Framing. Gallery space for hire.
**Price range** £100–£7,000
*Contemporary paintings, sculpture and graphic works by British and international artists. Gallery artists include Teresa Pemberton, Ross Loveday, Alex Jorgensen, Hsiao-Mei Lin, Paul Rudall, Lydia Bauman, Susan Andreae, Luke Skiffington, Charlotte Cornish, Lee Crew, Alison Neville. Moreton Contemporary Art also operates a comprehensive consultancy service (see listing under Art Consultants).*

### ▶ Morley Gallery
61 Westminster Bridge Road, London SE1 7HT.
**Tel** 020 7450 9226 **Fax** 020 7928 4074
**Opening times** Mon 1–6, Tue, Thu, Fri 10–6, Wed 10–8, closed bank holidays; please contact gallery for details of Sat openings.
**Nearest Underground** Lambeth North, Waterloo.
**Personnel** Exhibitions Organiser: Jane Hartwell.
**Work Stocked and Sold** Cer. Cra. Dr. Pa. Ph. Pr. Sc. Tx.
**Price range** £50–£10,000

### ▶ Nairi Sahakian Contemporary Art
34 Burton Court, Franklin's Row, London SW3 4SZ.
**Tel** 020 7730 0432
**Fax** 020 7831 9489
**Opening times** By appointment only.
**Nearest Underground** Sloane Square.
**Personnel** Director: Nairi Sahakian.
**Services and Facilities** Art Consultancy. Commissioning Service.
**Work Stocked and Sold** Cra. Dr. Pa. Ph. Pr. Sc.
For artists see Commercial Gallery Artists.

### ▶ Neffe-Degandt
32a St George Street, London W1R 9FA.
**Tel** 020 7493 2630, 020 7629 9788
**Fax** 020 7493 1379
**Opening times** Tue–Fri 10–5.30 and by appointment.
For artists see Commercial Gallery Artists.

### ▶ New Academy Gallery and Business Art Galleries
34 Windmill Street, Fitzrovia, London W1T 2JR.
**Tel** 020 7323 4700 **Fax** 020 7436 3059
**Email** gallery@curwengallery.com
**Ws** www.newacademygallery.com
**Opening times** Mon–Fri 10–6 but Thu 10–8, Sat 11–5. Closed Sun and bank holiday weekends.
**Nearest Underground** Goodge St/Tottenham Court Road**Personnel** Directors: John Hutchings, Jill Hutchings. Contact: Pryle Behrman.
**Services and Facilities** Art Consultancy. Art for Offices. Commissioning Service. Framing.
**Work Stocked and Sold** Dr. Pa. Pr. Sc.
**Price range** £20–£20,000
For artists see Commercial Gallery Artists.

*Exhibits and promotes a wide range of contemporary British painting, sculpture, original prints. Regular exhibiting artists include: Barry Atherton, Jo Barry, Clare Bigger, Clive Blackmore, Naomi Blake, Glynn Boyd Harte, John Brokenshire, Clare Chinnery, Jane Corsellis, Alexander Creswell, Peter Dover, Bernard Dunstan RA, Frederick Gore RA, Donald Hamilton Fraser RA, Brenda Hartill, Susan-Jayne Hocking, Sarah Holliday, Andrew Macara, Padraig Macmiadhachain, Anita Mandl, Michèle Noach, Linda Norris, John Piper, Hans Schwarz, Keith Roberts, Zoe Rubens, Richard Walker and Peter Wray. We offer a comprehensive service to businesses including free advice on purchases, a flexible hire scheme and on-site presentations; and undertake commissions (painting of portraits, houses, Christmas cards etc.) for both business and private individuals.*

*Naomi Blake,* Shalom, *bronze, 19 x 14 x 7.5 cm.*

### ▶ New Art Centre
168 Sloane Street, London SW1X.
**Tel** 020 7235 5844
**Services and Facilities** Framing.

### ▶ New Grafton Gallery
49 Church Road, Barnes, London SW13 9HH.
**Tel** 020 8748 8850 **Fax** 020 8748 9818
**Opening times** Tue–Sat 10–5.30.
**Services and Facilities** Art Consultancy. Commissioning Service. Disabled Access. Parking. Valuation.
**Work Stocked and Sold** Dr. Pa.
**Price range** £100–£10,000
For artists see Commercial Gallery Artists.

### ▶ The Northcote Gallery
110 Northcote Road, Battersea, London SW11 6QP.
**Tel** 020 7924 6741

### ▶ The Nunnery
181 Bow Road, London E3.
**Tel** 020 8980 7770

### ▶ Nylon
10 Vyner Street, London E2.
**Tel** 020 8983 5333

### ▶ O'Shea Gallery
120a Mount Street, London W1Y 5HB.
**Tel** 020 7629 1122
**Work Stocked and Sold** Pr.

### ▶ The October Gallery
24 Old Gloucester Street, London WC1N 3AL.
**Tel** 020 7242 7367 **Fax** 020 7405 1851
**Email** octobergallery@compuserve.com
**Ws** www.theoctobergallery.com
**Opening times** Tue–Sat 12.30–5.30.
**Nearest Underground** Holborn/ Russell Square.
**Personnel** Artistic Director: Elisabeth Lalouschek. Director: Chili Hawes.
**Services and Facilities** Art Consultancy. Art for Offices. Bookshop. Café. Craftshop. Friends Society. Gallery space for hire. Workshop Facilities.
**Work Stocked and Sold** Ab. Dr. Pa. Ph. Pr. Sc.
**Price range** £100–£10,000
For artists see Commercial Gallery Artists.
*The October Gallery represents a range of artists from the international avant-garde. The gallery offers an extensive selection of contemporary paintings, drawings, prints, photographs and sculpture by artists from Africa, the Americas, Asia, Europe, Oceania, Australia and the Middle East. Artists include Pablo Amaringo, El Anatsui, Carol Beckwith, LeRoy Clarke, Ira Cohen, Ablade Glover, Emmanuel Taiwo Jegede, Mathias Kauage, Elisabeth Lalouschek, Manuel Mendive, Z. O. Oloruntoba, Bruce Ouobrakpeya, Gérard Quenum, Julieta Rubio, Laila Shawa, Wijdan, Julieu Sinzogan, Twins Seven Seven, Gerald Wilde, Aubrey Williams and Xu Zhong Min. The October Gallery café serves food from around the world and is open at lunch time, Tue–Sat 12.30–2.30. Education programme.*

### ▶ Offer Waterman & Co. Fine Art Ltd
20 Park Walk, London SW10 0AQ.
**Tel** 020 7351 0068 **Fax** 020 7351 2269
**Personnel** Offer Waterman. Karen Jakobsen.

### ▶ Oliver Hoare
Flat 3, 7 Onslow Gardens, London SW7 3LY.
**Tel** 020 7835 1600 **Fax** 020 7373 5787

### ▶ One In The Other
4 Dingley Place, London EC1.
**Tel** 020 7253 7882

### ▶ Orangery
Central Library, Phillimore Walk, London W8 7RX.
**Tel** 020 7361 2295
**Personnel** Marketing Organiser: Mike Volpe. Organiser of Exhibitions: Michael Goggin. Organiser of Exhibitions: Anna Sansick.

### ▶ Oriel Contemporary Art
25 Princess Road, Regents Park, London NW1 8JR.
**Tel** 020 7483 1375 **Fax** 020 7483 1363
**Opening times** Mon–Fri 9–6, Sat & Sun 11–5.
**Personnel** Geoff Evans.
**Work Stocked and Sold** Pa. Pr.

### ▶ The Osborne Studio Gallery
13 Motcomb Street, London SW1X 8LB.
**Tel** 020 7235 9667 **Fax** 020 7235 9668
**Email** osbornestudio.gallery@virgin.net
**Ws** www.osg.uk.com
**Opening times** Mon–Fri 10–6.30, Sun (most) 11–5.30.
**Nearest Underground** Knightsbridge.
**Personnel** Art Director: Geoffrey Hughes. Director: Caroline Talbot-Ponsonby, Christopher Judd. Gallery Assistant: Amanda Daubeney.
**Services and Facilities** Art for Offices. Gallery space for hire.
**Work Stocked and Sold** Dr. Pa. Pr. Sc.
**Price range** £50–£30,000
For artists see Commercial Gallery Artists.
*The Osborne Studio Gallery was set up in 1985 and deals in racing and sporting art. It has become recognised internationally as the leading racing gallery in the United Kingdom. It stocks paintings, bronzes and prints by a wide range of leading contemporary artists, including Hubert De Watrigant, Katie O'Sullivan and Jonathon Trowell. The Osborne Studio Gallery also shows the work of a number of landscape and figurative artists, and regularly holds one-man exhibitions featuring both racing and non-racing art. The gallery first started publishing prints in 1989, and three or four new prints are produced yearly, featuring the work of some of our favourite and most successful artists.*

### ▶ Oxford House Basement Gallery
Derbyshire Street, London E2.
**Tel** 020 7739 9001

### ▶ Paisnel Gallery
22 Mason's Yard, Duke Street, St James's, London SW1Y 6BU.
**Tel** 020 7930 9293
**Fax** 020 7930 7282
**Personnel** Steven Paisnel. Sylvia Paisnel.

### ▶ Park Gallery
26 Connaught Street, London W2 2AF.
**Tel** 020 7262 2588
**Fax** 020 7262 2587

### ▶ Park Walk Gallery
20 Park Walk, London SW10 0AQ.
**Tel** 020 7351 0410

### ▶ Parker Gallery
28 Pimlico Road, Chelsea, London SW1W 8LJ.
**Tel** 020 7730 6768 **Fax** 020 7259 9180
**Work Stocked and Sold** Pr.

### ▶ Partridge Fine Arts
144 New Bond Street, London W1Y.
**Tel** 020 7629 0834
**Services and Facilities** Framing.

### ▶ Paton Gallery
London Fields, 282 Richmond Road, London E8 3QS.
**Tel** 020 8986 3409
**Fax** 020 8986 0811
**Opening times** Tue–Sat 11–6, Sun 12–6.
**Nearest Underground** Bethnal Green.
**Personnel** Director: Graham Paton. Emma Vial.
**Services and Facilities** Art Consultancy. Art for Offices. Commissioning Service. Disabled Access.
**Work Stocked and Sold** Dr. Pa. Sc.
**Price range** £450–£14,000
For artists see Commercial Gallery Artists.

### ▶ Paul Hawkins Gallery
4 Davies Street, London W1Y 1LY.
**Tel** 020 7499 7009
**Fax** 020 7499 2265
**Personnel** Paul Hawkins.

### ▶ Paul Mason Gallery
149 Sloane Street, London SW1X 9BZ.
**Tel** 020 7730 3683/7359
**Personnel** Paul Mason.

### ▶ Paul Smith/R. Newbold Gallery
Paul Smith Press Office, 33 Longacre, London WC2E 9LA.
**Tel** 020 7240 0009/32
**Personnel** Ms Hallie Logan.

### ▶ Percy Miller Gallery
39 Snowfields, London SE1.
**Tel** 020 7207 4578

### ▶ Philip Graham Contemporary Art
9a–11 Bonhill Street, London EC2A.
**Tel** 020 7920 0350
**Services and Facilities** Framing.

### ▶ Photofusion
17a Electric Lane, London SW9.
**Tel** 020 7738 5774

### ▶ Piccadilly Gallery Ltd
43 Dover Street, London W1X 3RE.
**Tel** 020 7629 2875 **Fax** 020 7499 0431
**Email** art@piccadillygall.demon.co.uk
**Ws** www.piccadillygall.demon.co.uk
**Opening times** Mon–Fri 10–5.30, Sat by appointment.
**Nearest Underground** Green Park.
**Personnel** Directors: R. G. Pilkington, Eve Pilkington, Christabel Pool.
**Services and Facilities** Disabled Access.
**Work Stocked and Sold** Dr. Pa.
**Price range** £200–£20,000
For artists see Commercial Gallery Artists.

### ▶ Piers Feetham Gallery
475 Fulham Road, London SW6 1HL.
**Tel** 020 7381 3031 **Fax** 020 7381 3031
**Email** Piersfeethamgallery@hotmail.com
**Opening times** Tue–Fri 10–1, 2–6, Sat 10–1.
**Nearest Underground** Fulham Broadway.
**Personnel** Consultant: Piers Feetham. Director: Caroline Feetham.
**Services and Facilities** Framing. Gallery space for hire. Restoration.
**Work Stocked and Sold** Dr. Pa.
**Price range** £100–£2,000

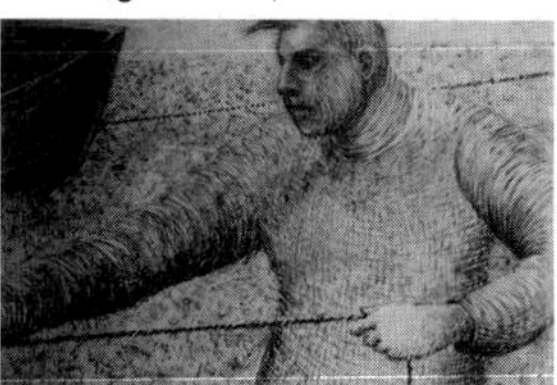

*The gallery holds 10 mixed and solo exhibitions a year by contemporary British artists – with a special emphasis on drawings. The gallery also comprises a long-established and comprehensive framing business, specialising in hand-finished frames, conservation framing, paper conservation, oil restoration and antique frame restoration.*

### ▶ The Pike Gallery
145 St John's Hill, London SW11 1TQ.
**Tel** 020 7223 6741

### ▶ Plantation House
31–35 Fenchurch Street, London EC3M 3DX.
**Tel** 020 7623 2935
**Personnel** Alison Gourlay.

### ▶ Plazzotta Ltd
18 Shoa Road, London W3 7LN.
**Tel** 020 8743 0937
**Email** oconor@plazzotta.co.uk
**Ws** www.plazzotta.co.uk
**Opening times** The office and storeroom are open by appointment.
**Nearest Underground** Sloane Square, Earls Court.
**Personnel** Director: Richard S. O'Conor.
**Services and Facilities** Valuation.
**Work Stocked and Sold** Ab. Sc.
**Price range** £400–£50,000
For artists see Commercial Gallery Artists.

### ▶ Polak Gallery
21 King Street, St James's, London SW1Y 6QY.
**Tel** 020 7839 2871

### ▶ Portal Gallery
43 Dover Street, Piccadilly, London W1X 4NU.
**Tel** 020 7493 0706 **Fax** 020 7493 2667
**Email** portalgallery@btinternet.com
**Ws** www.portal-gallery.com
**Opening times** Mon–Fri 10–5.30, Sat 10–4.
**Nearest Underground** Green Park.
**Personnel** Directors: Lionel Levy, Jess Wilder.
**Services and Facilities** Art Consultancy. Art for Offices. Commissioning Service. Shop.
**Work Stocked and Sold** Pa. Pr.
**Price range** £500–£40,000
For artists see Commercial Gallery Artists.

*James McNaught,* Shining Cascading Hose, *gouache/paper, 21" x 16", 2001.*
*The gallery specialises in idiosyncratic, figurative painting by contemporary British artists. Started in 1959, Portal has long been a venue for the work of quirky and imaginative artists such as John Byrne, Beryl Cook, Haydn Corner, Nick Cudworth, Steve Easby, Jane Lewis, Lizzie Riches and many others. The gallery has eight solo exhibitions each year, theme shows and a permanent exhibition of Portal painters. Prices from £500 upwards.*

### ▶ Portland Gallery
9 Bury Street, St James's, London SW1Y 6AB.
**Tel** 020 7321 0422
**Fax** 020 7321 0230
**Personnel** Tom Hewlett. Nathalie Martin. Ian Geraghty.

### ▶ Posk Gallery

238 King Street, London W6 0RF.
**Tel** 020 8741 1940
**Fax** 020 8746 3798
**Opening times** 11–9.
**Nearest Underground** Ravenscourt Park.
**Personnel** Director: J. Baranowska.
**Services and Facilities** Bar. Bookshop. Café. Disabled Access. Gallery space for hire. Restaurant.
**Work Stocked and Sold** Cer. Cra. Dr. Jew. Pa. Ph. Pr. Sc.
**Price range** £100–£1, 800
For artists see Commercial Gallery Artists.
*The POSK Gallery provides exhibitions of works (all kinds of media) from artists of all nationalities. The price of hiring the gallery is £48.00 plus VAT per week for the members of POSK and £64.00 plus VAT for non-members plus 15% commission from the price of sold exhibits.*
*The POSK Gallery will advertise all exhibitions free of charge in art magazines* Galleries *and* Art Review, *also in papers of the Polish Social and Cultural Association Ltd, and in the Polish Cultural Institute. Artists who wish to exhibit should send a short curriculum vitae and five colour photographs of their work. Exhibitors are solely responsible for printed material, advertising and invitations. Exhibitions changed fortnightly.*

### ▶ Primrose Hill Gallery
81 Regents Park Road, London NW1 8UY.
**Tel** 020 7586 3533
**Personnel** Mr Franks.
**Work Stocked and Sold** Pr.

### ▶ Proud Galleries
5 Buckingham Street, London WC2N 6BS.
**Tel** 020 7839 4942
**Fax** 020 7839 4947

### ▶ Pryory Art
240 Belsize Road, London NW6 4BT.
**Tel** 020 7604 4455
**Opening times** Mon–Fri 10.30–5.30, Sat by appointment.
**Nearest Underground** Kilburn Park/ West Hampstead.
**Personnel** Managing Director: Andy Worth.
**Services and Facilities** Art Consultancy. Art for Offices. Framing. Gallery space for hire.
**Work Stocked and Sold** Cer. Cra. Dr. Jew. Pa. Ph. Pr. Sc. Tx.
**Price range** £200–£2,000
For artists see Commercial Gallery Artists.

### ▶ Purdy Hicks Gallery
65 Hopton Street, Bankside,
London SE1 9GZ.
**Tel** 020 7401 9229
**Fax** 020 7401 9595
**Email** enquiries@purdyhicks.com
**Ws** www.purdyhicks.com
**Opening times** Mon, Tue, Thu, Fri 10–5.30; Wed 10–7; Sat 10–3.
**Nearest Underground** Blackfriars.
**Personnel** Rebecca Hicks. Jayne Payne. Frankie Rossi. Nicola Shane.
**Services and Facilities** Art Consultancy. Disabled Access.
**Work Stocked and Sold** Dr. Pa. Ph. Pr.
**Price range** £200–£30,000
For artists see Commercial Gallery Artists.

### ▶ Pyms Gallery
9 Mount Street, Mayfair, London W1Y 5AD.
**Tel** 020 7629 2020
**Fax** 020 7629 2060
**Opening times** Mon–Fri 10–6 and by appointment.
**Nearest Underground** Green Park, Bond Street.
**Personnel** Alan Hobart. Mary Hobart.
**Work Stocked and Sold** Dr. Pa.
**Price range** £200–£1,000,000
For artists see Commercial Gallery Artists.

### ▶ Quantum Contemporary Art
The Old Imperial Laundry, 71 Warriner Gardens, London SW11 4XW.
**Tel** 020 7498 6868
**Fax** 020 7498 7878
**Work Stocked and Sold** Pa.

### ▶ Rafael Valls Gallery
6 Ryder Street, London SW1Y.
**Tel** 020 7930 0029
**Services and Facilities** Framing.

### ▶ Railings Gallery
5 New Cavendish Street, London W1M 7RP.
**Tel** 020 7935 1114
**Fax** 020 7486 9250
**Personnel** Eric Sander.

### ▶ Rebecca Hossack Gallery

Rh|g

Fitzrovia, 35 Windmill Street, London W1P 1HH.
**Tel** 020 7436 4899
**Fax** 020 7323 3182
**Email** rebecca@r-h-g.co.uk
**Ws** www.r-h-g.co.uk
**Opening times** Mon–Sat 10–6.
**Nearest Underground** Goodge Street.
**Personnel** Director: Rebecca Hossack. Contact: Deneah Stubbs. Amy Rose.
**Services and Facilities** Art Consultancy. Art for Offices. Bookshop. Commissioning Service. Framing. Gallery space for hire. Valuation.
**Work Stocked and Sold** Ab. App. Cer. Cra. Dec. Dr. Fur. Jew. Pa. Ph. Pr. Sc. Tx. Wd.
**Price range** £100–£20,000
For artists see Commercial Gallery Artists.
*The Rebecca Hossack Gallery is one of the most innovative galleries in central London with a reputation for showing top quality non-European art as well as the best of British Contemporary artists. The leading European gallery for Australian Aboriginal art and for the art of the Kalahari Bushmen, the Rebecca Hossack Gallery has a full range of such work – both paintings and prints – always in stock including pieces by Clifford Possum, Jimmy Pike, Gertie Huddlestone, Emily Kngwarreye and Mathias Kauage. Contemporary Scottish artists are also a strong focus of the gallery (Abigail McLellan, Helen Flockhart and Alasdair Wallace). British Contemporary art shown includes painting (figurative and abstract), sculpture, ceramics (Deborah Prosser, Ann Stokes) and furniture (Camilla Meddings). The gallery has opened a new space to expand its exhibition programe of Australian Contemporary art.*

### ▶ Redchurch Galleries (John Hunt Galleries)
47–49 Redchurch Street, London E2 7DJ.
**Tel** 020 7739 7333
**Fax** 020 7739 7333
**Opening times** Tue–Fri 11–5.30.
**Personnel** John Hunt. Anne Bates.
**Work Stocked and Sold** Dr. Pa. Sc.

### ▶ Redfern Gallery
20 Cork Street, Burlington Gardens, London W1X 2HB.
**Tel** 020 7734 1732/0578
**Fax** 020 7494 2908
**Personnel** Director: David Gault. Director: Margaret Thornton. Director: Richard Gault. Director: Richard Selby.
**Work Stocked and Sold** Pr.

### ▶ Reel Poster Gallery
First Floor, 22 Great Marlborough Street, London W1V 1AF.
**Tel** 020 7734 4303
**Fax** 020 7734 4260
**Opening times** Mon–Sat 10.30–6 and by appointment.

### ▶ Rhodes + Mann
37 Hackney Road, London E2.
**Tel** 020 7729 4372

### ▶ Richard Day
173 New Bond Street, London W1Y.
**Tel** 020 7629 2991
**Services and Facilities** Framing.

### ▶ Richard Philip
59 Ledbury Road, London W11 2AA.
**Tel** 020 7727 7915

### ▶ Richard Salmon Ltd
Studio 4, 54 South Edwards Square, London W8 6HW.
**Tel** 020 7602 9494
**Fax** 020 7371 6617

### ▶ Robert Sandelson
5 Cork Street, London W1.
**Tel** 020 7439 1001

### ▶ Rona Gallery
1/2 Weighhouse Street, London W1Y 1YL.
**Tel** 020 7491 3718
**Fax** 020 7491 4171
**Personnel** Stanley Harries.

### ▶ ROSL ARTS, Royal Over-Seas League
Over-Seas House, Park Place, St James's Street, London SW1A 1LR.
**Tel** 020 7408 0214
**Fax** 020 7499 6738**Email** culture@rosl.org.uk
**Ws** www.rosl.org.uk
**Opening times** Daily 10–6.
**Nearest Underground** Green Park.
**Personnel** Director-General: Mr R. F. Newell. Director, ROSL ARTS: Roderick Lakin. Promotions Officer, ROSL ARTS: Elaine Mitchener.
**Services and Facilities** Bar. Café. Lectures. Restaurant.
**Work Stocked and Sold** Dr. Pa. Ph.
**Price range** £100–£5,000
*ROSL OVER-SEAS LEAGUE*
*ROSL ARTS TRAVEL SCHOLARSHIP*
*Since 2000 the ROSL Annual Exhibition has concentrated on five artists from five different Commonwealth countries (or former Commonwealth countries), one from each of the five continents: Africa, the Americas, Asia, Australia and Europe. Countries and regions change each year. Selected artists will receive a travel scholarship to make a study visit to a country other than their country of origin, and will participate in a group exhibition at Over-seas House London and Over-Seas House Edinburgh.*

### ▶ Rowley Gallery Contemporary Arts
115 Kensington Church Street, London W8 7LN.
**Tel** 020 7229 5561, 01420-542 885
**Fax** 020 7229 5561
**Opening times** Mon–Fri 10–6, Sat 11–5.
**Nearest Underground** Notting Hill Gate.
**Personnel** David Kitchen.
**Work Stocked and Sold** Pa.
**Price range** £150–£1,000

### ▶ Royal Exchange Art Gallery
24 Cork St, London W1S 3NJ.
**Tel** 020 7439 6655
**Personnel** Directors: R. B. Hadlee, A. J. Hadlee, A. McCorquodale & I. McCorquodale.

### ▶ Russian Arts Gallery – GZHEL (UK)
257 High Street, Acton, London W3 9BY.
**Tel** 020 8993 9096 **Fax** 020 8993 5989
**Opening times** Mon–Fri 10–5.30.
**Nearest Underground** Acton Town, train: Ealing Broadway.
**Personnel** Directors: Mr Shakil Ahmad, Mr V. M. Loginov. Contact: Miss Asma.
**Services and Facilities** Commissioning Service.
**Work Stocked and Sold** Cer. Pa.
For artists see Commercial Gallery Artists.

### ▶ Ruth Piper
Studio 11, Waterside, 99 Rotherhithe Street, London SE16 4NF.
**Tel** 020 7252 1130
**Work Stocked and Sold** Pa.

### ▶ Sabin Galleries
Campden Lodge, 82 Campden Hill Road, London W8 7AA.
**Tel** 020 7937 0471

### ▶ Sadie Coles HQ
35 Heddon Street, London W1R.
**Tel** 020 7434 2227

### ▶ Sandra Lummis Fine Art
Flat 7, 17 Haslemere Road, London N8 9QP.
**Tel** 020 8340 2293

### ▶ Sarah Myerscough Fine Art
15–16 Brooks Mews, Mayfair, London W1Y 1LF.
**Tel** 020 7495 0069 **Fax** 020 7629 9613
**Email** sarah@myerscough.freeserve.co.uk
**Opening times** Mon–Fri 10–6, Sat 11–2.
**Nearest Underground** Bond Street.
**Personnel** Director: Sarah Myerscough. Consultant: Dan Seymour-Davies.
**Services and Facilities** Art Consultancy. Art for Offices. Commissioning Service. Framing.
**Work Stocked and Sold** App. Cer. Cra. Dr. Gla. Pa. Ph. Pr. Sc. Tx. Wd.
**Price range** £300–£30,000

*The gallery in Brooks Mews*

*Sarah Myerscough Fine Art provides a comprehensive consultancy service based in our West End gallery. We show a mixture of established artists and affordable work of recent graduates all over the country. Every October we host the DLA Art Award, a show of the best graduates nationwide. Our consultancy side caters to both private and corporate clients, so whether you are looking for a couple of paintings for your house, or enough to fill an office we would be happy to source original and high quality work for you.*

### ▶ Scolar Fine Art/Gordon Samuel
35 Bruton Place, London W1J 6NS.
**Tel** 020 7629 4944
**Fax** 020 7629 4494
**Email** gsamuel@cwcom.net
**Ws** www.scolarfineart.com
**Opening times** Mon–Fri 10–5.30.
**Nearest Underground** Green Park /Bond Street
**Personnel** Director: Gordon Samuel.
**Services and Facilities** Art Consultancy. Art for Offices. Bookshop. Valuation.
**Work Stocked and Sold** Dr. Pa. Pr. Sc.
**Price range** £200–£100,000
For artists see Commercial Gallery Artists.
*Modern British, international and contemporary paintings, drawings, sculpture and fine prints. The gallery also specialises in the British colour linocuts of the 1920s and 30s by the artists of the Grosvenor School of Modern Art including Andrews, Flight, Power and Tschudi. Scolar also details in Modern Master prints, broadly from Picasso to Hockney. A number of contemporary artists including Richmond Burton, Jane Dickson, Felicity Powell and Graciela Sacco are represented. Scolar Fine Art will also stock art book publications by Scolar Press, Ashgate and Lund Humphries and Special Editions of Scolar Press publications or artist's monographs containing original prints.*

### ▶ SE1 Gallery
64 Southwark Bridge Road, London SE1.
**Tel** 020 7401 9494

### ▶ Shine
3 Jubilee Place, London.
**Tel** 020 7352 4499

### ▶ Sho Gallery
73 Curtain Road, Shoreditch, London EC2.
**Tel** 020 7729 1590

### ▶ Shoreditch Gallery
5 Hoxton Market, London N1.
**Tel** 020 7733 4229

### ▶ The Showroom
44 Bonner Road, London E2.
**Tel** 020 8983 4115

### ▶ Simmons Gallery
53 Lambs Conduit Street, London WC1N 3NB.
**Tel** 020 7831 2080
**Fax** 020 7831 2090
**Email** art@simmonsgallery.co.uk
**Ws** www.simmonsgallery.co.uk
**Opening times** Mon–Fri 10.30–5.30 or by appointment.
**Nearest Underground** Russell Square or Holborn.
**Personnel** Directors: Howard Simmons, Frances Simmons.
**Services and Facilities** Art Consultancy. Art for Offices. Commissioning Service. Shop. Valuation.
**Work Stocked and Sold** Cer. Dec. Jew. Sc.
**Price range** £5–£5,000
For artists see Commercial Gallery Artists.
*Sculpture, medals and coins – the only specialist gallery for contemporary medals in the UK. Apart from solo and group exhibitions, we always have exciting international work for sale in a relaxed setting. Visitors are warmly encouraged to touch and handle the small sculpture. We also offer a commissioning service.*

### ▶ Simon C. Dickinson Ltd/ James Roundell
58 Jermyn Street, London SW1Y 6LX.
**Tel** 020 7493 0340
**Fax** 020 7493 0796
**Email** info@sdickinson.co.uk
**Opening times** Mon–Fri 10–6.
**Nearest Underground** Green Park, Piccadilly.
**Personnel** Directors: Simon Dickinson, David Ker, James Roundell.
**Services and Facilities** Art Consultancy. Framing. Valuation.
**Work Stocked and Sold** Dr. Pa.
**Price range** From £10,000
*Simon C Dickinson Ltd, incorporating James Roundell, was founded in 1993 by Simon Dickinson, formerly Head of Old Master Pictures at Christie's and by David Ker, a dealer in English pictures. They were subsequently joined by James Roundell, formerly Head of Christie's Impressionist and Modern Department in London. The company provides a discreet alternative to buying and selling works of art at public auction. A substantial stock of important Old Master, Impressionist and Modern paintings is held. Usual curatorial services are offered and substantial funds are available for the purchase of paintings privately.*

### ▶ Simon Capstick-Dale Fine Art
12 Georgian House, 10 Bury Street, St James's, London SW1Y 6AA.
**Tel** 020 7839 4070
**Fax** 020 7839 4077
**Email** simoncdale@aol.com
**Opening times** Mon–Fri 10–6, Sat by appointment.
**Nearest Underground** Green Park.
**Work Stocked and Sold** Dr. Pa. Pr. Sc.
For artists see Commercial Gallery Artists.

### ▶ Sims Reed
43a Duke Street, St James's, London SW1Y 6DD.
**Tel** 020 7493 5660
**Work Stocked and Sold** Pr.

### ▶ Sloane Graphics Ltd
6 Harben Parade, Finchley Road, London NW3.
**Tel** 020 7586 0189
**Work Stocked and Sold** Pa.

### ▶ Sosho
2 Tabernacle Street, London EC2.
**Tel** 020 7920 0701

### ▶ The Special Photographer's Company
21 Kensington Park Road, London W11 2EU.
**Tel** 020 7221 3489
**Fax** 020 7792 9112
**Email** info@specialphoto.co.uk
**Ws** www.specialphoto.co.uk
**Opening times** Mon–Fri 10–6, Sat 11–5.
**Nearest Underground** Notting Hill Gate and Westbourne Grove.
**Personnel** Directors: Catherine Turner, Chris Kewbank.
**Services and Facilities** Art for Offices. Bookshop. Framing. Gallery space for hire. Valuation.
**Work Stocked and Sold** Ph.
**Price range** £80–£2,000
For artists see Commercial Gallery Artists.

### ▶ Spink-Leger
69 Southampton Row, London WC1B 4ET.
**Tel** 020 7563 4000
**Ws** www.spinkandson.co.uk
**Opening times** Mon–Fri 9–5.30, Tue 9–7.30.
**Nearest Underground** Green Park.
**Personnel** Lowell Libson. James Holland-Hibbert.
**Services and Facilities** Art Consultancy. Gallery space for hire. Valuation.
**Work Stocked and Sold** Dr. Pa.

### ▶ Spink-Leger Pictures
13 Old Bond Street, London W1X 3DB.
**Tel** 020 7629 3538/9

### ▶ Spovieri
27 Heddon Street, London W11.
**Tel** 020 7734 2066

### ▶ St James's Fine Arts
72 New Bond Street, London W1Y 9DD.
**Tel** 020 7355 1096 **Fax** 020 7495 3017

### ▶ St James's Prints
15 Piccadilly Arcade, London SW1Y 6NH.
**Tel** 020 7495 6487
**Work Stocked and Sold** Pr.

### ▶ St Martins Gallery
St Martins-in-the-Fields, Trafalgar Square, London WC2N 4JJ.
**Tel** 020 7839 4342 **Fax** 020 7839 5163
**Personnel** Diana Rowe.

### ▶ Standpoint Gallery
45 Coronet Street, London N1 6HD.
**Tel** 020 7729 5292

### ▶ StART Gallery
493 Fulham Palace Road, London SW6.
**Tel** 020 7371 0909

### ▶ Stephanie Hoppen
17 Walton Street, London SW3.
**Tel** 020 7589 3678 **Fax** 020 7581 5744

### ▶ Stephen Friedman Gallery
25–28 Old Burlington Street, London W1X 1LN.
**Tel** 020 7494 1434 **Fax** 020 7494 1431

### ▶ Stephen Lacey Gallery
One Crawford Passage, Ray Street, London EC1 3DP.
**Tel** 020 7837 5507 **Fax** 020 7837 5549

### ▶ Stephen Somerville Ltd
14 Old Bond Street, London W1X 3DB.
**Tel** 020 7493 8363 **Fax** 020 7738 5995

### ▶ Stern Art Dealers
46 Ledbury Road, London W11 2AB.
**Tel** 020 7229 6187 **Fax** 020 7229 7016
**Email** pisaro@global-net.co.uk
**Ws** www.stern-art.com
**Opening times** Mon–Sat 10–6.
**Nearest Underground** Notting Hill Gate.
**Personnel** Director: David Stern.
**Services and Facilities** Art Consultancy. Framing. Restoration. Valuation.
**Work Stocked and Sold** Dr. Pa. Sc.
**Price range** £500–£15,000
For artists see Commercial Gallery Artists.

### ▶ Strategic Art
21 Douglas Street, London SW1P.
**Tel** 020 7416 0173

### ▶ Studio Nine
9 Marylands Road, London W9 2DU.
**Tel** 020 7266 3729
**Fax** 020 7286 2305
**Email** axis@gn.apc.org
**Opening times** By appointment.
**Nearest Underground** Warwick Avenue, train: Paddington.
**Personnel** Directors: Cliff Hanley, Moira Rudolf Hanley.
**Work Stocked and Sold** Pa. Ph. Pr.
For artists see Commercial Gallery Artists.

### ▶ Studio Sienko
57a Lant Street, London SE1 1QN.
**Tel** 020 7403 1353 **Fax** 020 7357 6976
**Opening times** Mon–Fri 11–6 and by appointment.
**Personnel** Director: Olga Sienko-Tutton.

### ▶ Swan Fine Art
120 Islington High Street, London N1.
**Tel** 020 7226 5335, 020 7359 2225

### ▶ T.A.G. Sale Co. Ltd
Ladbroke Hall, 79 Barlby Road, London W10.
**Tel** 020 8932 7210
**Opening times** Daily 10–8.
**Nearest Underground** Holland Park & Notting Hill.
**Work Stocked and Sold** Pa. Pr. Sc.

### ▶ Tablet
The Tabernacle, Powis Square, London W11.
**Tel** 020 7565 7890

### ▶ Tadema Gallery
10 Charlton Place, Camden Passage, London N1 8AJ.
**Tel** 020 7359 1055 **Fax** 020 7359 1055
**Opening times** Wed & Sat 10–5 or by appt.
**Nearest Underground** Angel.
**Personnel** Directors: Sonya Newell-Smith, David Newell-Smith.
**Work Stocked and Sold** Jew. Pa.

### ▶ Talisman Fine Arts
82 Mill Lane, West Hampstead, London NW6 1NL.
**Tel** 020 7794 4266 **Fax** 020 7435 65

### ▶ Tardis
52–56 Turnmill Street, London EC1.
**Tel** 020 7352 4976

### ▶ Tart Gallery
52 Ferndale Road, London N15.
**Tel** 020 8211 0958

### ▶ Taylor Galleries
1 Bolney Gate, London SW7.
**Tel** 020 7581 0253

### ▶ Thackeray Gallery
18 Thackerey Street, Kensington Square, London W8 5ET.
**Tel** 020 7937 5883 **Fax** 020 7937 6965
**Opening times** Tue–Fri 10–6, Sat 10–4.
**Personnel** Gabriella Scott.

### ▶ Thameside Studio
109 Oxo Tower Wharf, Barge House, London SE1.
**Tel** 020 7928 7411

### ▶ Theo Waddington Fine Art
5a Cork Street, London W1X 1PB.
**Tel** 020 7494 1584 **Fax** 020 7287 0926
**Opening times** Tue–Fri 11–6, Sat 11–5, closed Mon.
**Nearest Underground** Green Park/Piccadilly Circus.
**Personnel** Gallery Director: Karol Pawsey.
**Work Stocked and Sold** Pa.

### ▶ Third Floor Art Gallery, Whiteleys
Queensway, London W2 4YN.

### ▶ Thomas Heneage
42 Duke Street, St James's, London SW1Y 6DJ.
**Tel** 020 7930 9223

### ▶ Thompson's Gallery
18 Dover Street, London W1X 3PB.
**Tel** 020 7629 6878
**Fax** 020 7629 6181
**Opening times** Mon–Fri 10–6 or by appointment.
**Personnel** John Thompson. Susan Thompson. Graham Simper. Mathew Hall.
**Work Stocked and Sold** Pa.

### ▶ Thornton Bevan Arts
130 Percy Road, London W12 9QL.
**Tel** 020 8740 8084
**Fax** 020 8740 8084
**Opening times** By appointment Wed–Sun.
**Price range** £40–£3,000

### ▶ Throssells
13 Broad Street, Teddington TW11 8QZ.
**Tel** 020 8943 4248
**Nearest Station** Teddington.
**Personnel** Nola Throssell.
**Services and Facilities** Art Consultancy. Art for Offices. Café. Commissioning Service. Craftshop. Disabled Access. Gallery space for hire. Restaurant. Shop.
**Work Stocked and Sold** Cer. Cra. Fur. Gla. Pa. Pr.
**Price range** £25–£500
For artists see Commercial Gallery Artists.

### ▶ Tian Art
36 Beauchamp Place, London SW3.
**Tel** 020 7823 8088

### ▶ The Timothy Taylor Gallery
1 Bruton Place, London W1.
**Tel** 020 7409 3344
**Personnel** Timothy Taylor.

### ▶ The Tom Blau Gallery
21 Queen Elizabeth Street, London SE1 2PD.
**Tel** 020 7378 1300

### ▶ Tom Tempest Radford
16 Devonshire Row, London EC2M.
**Tel** 020 7377 8004

### ▶ The Tower/James Colman Fine Art
The Tower, 28 Mossbury Road, London SW11 2PB.
**Tel** 020 7924 3860
**Fax** 020 7924 3860
**Personnel** James Colman.

### ▶ Trade Apartment
404–408 Coldharbour Lane, London SW9.
**Tel** 020 7733 8181

### ▶ Tribal Gathering London
1 Westbourne Grove Mews, Notting Hill, London W11 2RU.
**Tel** 020 7221 6650
**Fax** 020 7221 6650
**Opening times** Tue, Fri, Sat. Other days by appointment.
**Personnel** Mr Bryan Reeves.

### ▶ Tricycle Gallery
Tricycle Theatre, 269 Kilburn High Road, London NW6 7JR.
**Tel** 020 7372 6611 **Fax** 020 7328 0795
**Opening times** Mon–Sat 10.30–10.30. Admission free.
**Nearest Underground** Kilburn.
**Services and Facilities** Bar. Café. Disabled Access. Gallery space for hire. Restaurant. Workshop Facilities.
**Work Stocked and Sold** Pa. Ph. Pr.

### ▶ Trowbridge Gallery
555 Kings Road, London SW6.
**Tel** 020 7371 8733

### ▶ Tryon & Swann Gallery
23–24 Cork Street, London W1X 1HB.
**Tel** 020 7634 6961, 020 7734 2256
**Fax** 020 7287 2480
**Personnel** Oliver Swann.

### ▶ TS2k: project space
1 Bernay's Grove, London SW9.
**Tel** 020 7733 2000

### ▶ Victoria Gallery
158 Hermon Hill, London E18 1QH.
**Tel** 020 8989 1195
**Personnel** John Barratt.

### ▶ Victoria Miro London
16 Wharf Road, London N1.
**Tel** 020 7734 5082

### ▶ Vilma Gold
66 Rivington Street, London EC2.
**Tel** 020 7613 1609

### ▶ Vyvyan Robinson & Co.
235 Regent Street, London W1R.
**Tel** 020 7495 6642

### ▶ W.H. Patterson Fine Arts
19 Albemarle Street, London W1X.
**Tel** 020 7629 4119
**Services and Facilities** Framing.

### ▶ Waddington Galleries
11 Cork Street, London W1S 3LT.
**Tel** 020 7851 2200
**Fax** 020 7734 4146
**Email** mail@waddington-galleries.com
**Ws** www.waddington-galleries.com
**Opening times** Mon–Fri 10–5.30, Sat 10.30–1.30 (closed Sat from mid-Jul–Aug).
**Nearest Underground** Green Park.
**Personnel** Directors: Leslie Waddington, Thomas Lighton, Stephen Saunders.
**Work Stocked and Sold** Dr. Pa. Sc.
For artists see Commercial Gallery Artists.
*Exhibitions monthly. Artists represented: The Estate of Josef Albers, Blake, Caulfield, Davenport, Flanagan, Halley, Heron, Milroy, Paladino, Tàpies, Turnbull. Works in stock by: Arp, Avery, Calder, Chamberlain, Chia, Degas, de Kooning, Dubuffet, Ernst, Flavin, Francis, Hepworth, Hockney, Hodgkin, Judd, Klee, Léger, Lichtenstein, Lim, Lipchitz, Magritte, Matisse, Miró, Moore, Nicholson, Picabia, Picasso, Rauschenberg, Samaras, Schnabel, Spencer, Warhol, Wesselmann, Westermann, Yeats. Founded 1966.*

### ▶ The Walk
23 King Edward Walk, London SE1 7PR.
**Tel** 020 7928 3786
**Fax** 020 7261 1541
**Opening times** Mon–Sat 1–6 during exhibitions. Other times by appointment.
**Nearest Underground** Lambeth North, train: Waterloo.
**Personnel** Directors: Ranabir Chanda, Gillian Salmon.
**Services and Facilities** Art Consultancy. Art for Offices. Commissioning Service.
**Work Stocked and Sold** App. Dr. Pa. Ph. Pr. Sc.
**Price range** £150–£7,000
For artists see Commercial Gallery Artists.

### ▶ Walpole Gallery
38 Dover Street, London W1X 3RB.
**Tel** 020 7499 6626

### ▶ Walton Contemporary Art
188 Walton Street, London SW3 2JL.
**Tel** 020 7581 9011
**Fax** 020 7581 0585
**Personnel** Michael Potter.
**Services and Facilities** Art Consultancy.
**Work Stocked and Sold** Pa. Pr. Sc.
**Price range** £100–£5,000

### ▶ Westminster Gallery
Central Hall, Storey's Gate, London SW1 9NH.
**Tel** 020 7222 8010
**Fax** 020 7222 6883
**Email** eets@wch.co.uk
**Ws** www.wch.co.uk
**Opening times** Various
**Personnel** Senior Events Manager: Ms Cathy Williamson. General Manager: Michael Sharp.
**Services and Facilities** Café. Disabled Access. Gallery space for hire. Guided Tours

*Central Hall, Westminster*
*The Westminster Gallery offers an elegant, spacious and versatile exhibition area. The three rooms the gallery occupies can be hired individually or as a whole and are available throughout the year. Lighting, hanging and display facilities are easily managed. The adjacent café is open daily and is very happy to assist with refreshments for your private viewings.*

### ▶ White Cube
44 Duke Street, St James's, London SW1Y 6DD.
**Tel** 020 7930 5373
**Fax** 020 7930 9973
**Opening times** Fri and Sat 12–6 or by appointment.
**Nearest Underground** Piccadilly Circus, Green Park.
**Personnel** Directors: Jay Jopling, Julia Royse. Daniela Gareh.

### ▶ White Cube²
48 Hoxton Square, London N1.
**Tel** 020 7930 5373

### ▶ White Horse Gallery
Upstairs at The White Horse, 1–3 Parson's Green, London SW6 4UL.
**Tel** 020 7736 2115, 07970 810 168
**Fax** 020 7610 6091
**Personnel** Chloe Johnson. Mark Paber.

### ▶ Whitfield Fine Art
180 New Bond Street, London W1Y.
**Tel** 020 7499 3592

### ▶ Whitford Fine Art
6 Duke Street, St James's, London SW1Y 6BN.
**Tel** 020 7930 9332
**Fax** 020 7930 5577
**Email** whitfordfineart@btinternet.com
**Ws** www.artnet.com/whitford.html
**Opening times** 10–6.
**Nearest Underground** Green Park, Piccadilly Circus.
**Personnel** Yvonne Elphick.
**Services and Facilities** Art Consultancy.
**Work Stocked and Sold** Fur. Pa. Sc.
**Price range** £400–£500,000
For artists see Commercial Gallery Artists.
*Whitford Fine Art specialises in 20th-century paintings, sculpture and designer furniture from the sixties.*

### ▶ Wigmore Fine Art
104 Wigmore Street, London W1H 9DR.
**Tel** 020 7224 1962
**Fax** 020 7224 1965
**Opening times** Tue–Fri 11–6, Sat 10–3.
**Personnel** Gallery Contact: Nayia Fagouli.

### ▶ Wilkins & Wilkins
1 Barrett Street, London W1M.
**Tel** 020 7935 9613

### ▶ Will's Art Warehouse
Unit 3, Heathmans Road, Parsons Green, Fulham, London SW6 4TJ.
**Tel** 020 7371 8787
**Fax** 020 7371 0044
**Ws** www.willsart.demon.co.uk
**Opening times** Mon–Thu 10.30–8, Fri–Sun 10.30–6.
**Nearest Underground** Parsons Green.
**Personnel** Director: Will Ramsay.
**Services and Facilities** Art Consultancy. Art for Offices. Commissioning Service. Disabled Access. Gallery space for hire. Parking.
**Work Stocked and Sold** Pa. Pr. Sc.
**Price range** £50–£2,000
For artists see Commercial Gallery Artists.

### ▶ William Thuillier
14 Old Bond Street, London W1X 3DB.
**Tel** 020 7499 0106
**Fax** 020 7233 8965
**Email** thuillart@aol.com
**Ws** www.thuillart.com
**Opening times** 10–6 by appointment.

**Nearest Underground** Green Park.
**Personnel** Proprietor: William Thuillier.
**Services and Facilities** Art Consultancy. Restoration. Valuation.
**Work Stocked and Sold** Pa.
**Price range** £500–£150,000
*Old Master paintings and drawings 1600–1850.*

### ▶ William Weston Gallery
7 Royal Arcade, Albemarle Street, London W1X 4JN.
**Tel** 020 7493 0722
**Work Stocked and Sold** Pr.

### ▶ Williams & Son
2 Grafton Street, London W1X.
**Tel** 020 7493 5751, 020 7493 4985

### ▶ Wilson Stephens Fine Art
11 Cavendish Road, London NW6 7XT.
**Tel** 020 8459 0760 **Fax** 020 8459 0760
**Personnel** Rosanna Wilson Stephens. Katherine Roberts.

### ▶ Wiseman Originals
34 West Square, Lambeth, London SE11 4SP.
**Tel** 020 7587 0747 **Fax** 020 7793 8817/9917
**Email** wisemanoriginals@compuserve.com
**Ws** www.wisemanoriginals.com
**Opening times** Any time by appointment.
**Nearest Underground** Lambeth North.
**Personnel** Director: Caroline Wiseman. Garth Wiseman. Lucia Lindsay.
**Services and Facilities** Art Consultancy. Art for Offices. Commissioning Service. Framing. Valuation.
**Work Stocked and Sold** Dr. Pa. Pr.
**Price range** £300–£30,000
For artists see Commercial Gallery Artists.

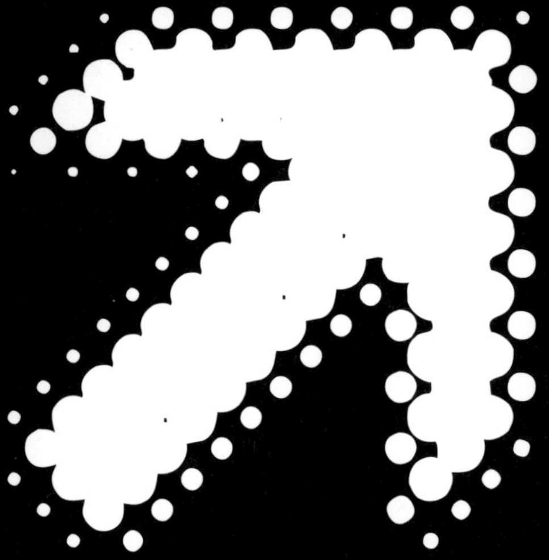

# Additional copies of the Art World Directory. Save more than 20%.

**Use this form to buy additional copies of this edition for just £15.00 plus £2.00 p&p. Simply complete the form below and return it freepost, along with your remittance to Art Review, Art World Directory, Free post, London EC1B 1DE (A photocopy of this page is fine)**

## Art World Directory Additional Copies Order Form.

Please send me ______ additional copy(ies) of the 2002 Art World Directory @ £15.00 plus £2.00 p&p each.*

I enclose my remittance for £ ____________ made payable to Art Review Ltd.

Please debit my ☐ Access ☐ Visa ☐ Amex ☐ Mastercard

Card No: ______________________ Expiry Date ______________

Signature ______________________ Date ______________

Name ______________________ Address ______________________

______________________________________________

______________________ Postcard ______________

Tel ______________________ (in case of queries only)

The postage and packing cost relates to UK orders only, European p&p £3.00, Overseas £6.00.

# London Public Galleries

*All entries in this section are sorted alphabetically by gallery. Where this information has been provided, entries are designated 'P' for public gallery or museum or 'PS' for a public gallery or museum holding selling shows*

NOTES

# Keeping up with the Tates

Little can be done to eclipse the impact that the Tate Modern has had on London in 2000 and 2001, if only because there is barely enough room, let alone enough money, to open another world-class museum in the capital. However, this has not stopped the existing institutions from building, renovating, rehanging and relaunching to keep up with the Tates.

Two latecomers in 2000, the British Museum's Great Court and the Hermitage Rooms at Somerset House, continued their successes into 2001. Meanwhile the National Gallery spruced up the Sainsbury Wing in the summer of 2001 to celebrate the annexe's tenth anniversary and the Victoria and Albert Museum's British Galleries opened in November, adding considerably to their existing 145 galleries.

The Serpentine Gallery went one stage further than the Dulwich Picture Gallery's 2000 Rick Mather arcade and café, with an extravagant, albeit temporary, outdoor marquee designed by Daniel Libeskind. The Barbican Centre underwent more refurbishment in 2001 and both the Wallace Collection and the Geffrye Museum should complete their ongoing programmes of improvements by March 2002.

Looking ahead, the Royal Festival Hall will be the subject of a series of demolitions and extensions, while the Hayward Gallery will be extended to provide a permanent place for the Arts Council's collection.

2001 was another great year for exhibitions in London with 'The Genius of Rome' at the Royal Academy and 'Vermeer and the Delft School', travelling from Washington's to London's National Gallery. An interesting British Art Season launched in Autumn 2001 with exhibitions of Frank Auerbach at the Royal Academy and watercolours by Turner, Gainsborough and Ruskin at the Dulwich Picture Gallery, heralding the November opening of the V&A's British Galleries and, of course, the Tate Britain Centenary Development. The theme continues into 2002 with an exhibition of 1950s British Art at the Barbican.

### ▶ 198 Gallery PS
194–198 Railton Road, Herne Hill, London SE24 0LU.
**Tel** 020 7978 8309 **Fax** 020 7652 1418
**Email** gallery@198gallery.co.uk
**Ws** www.198gallery.co.uk
**Opening times** Mon–Fri 11–5, Sat 12–4.
**Nearest Underground** Train: Herne Hill. Buses 3, 37, 68, 196, 322, 468, P4.
**Personnel** Gallery Manager: Lucy Davies. Exhibitions Coordinator: Asako Yokoya. IT Projects Manager: Kareen Williams.
**Services and Facilities** Art Consultancy. Commissioning Service. Disabled Access. Friends Society. Lectures. Shop. Workshop Facilities.
**Work Stocked and Sold** Cer. Dr. Pa. Ph. Pr. Sc. Tx. Wd.
**Price range** £50–£5,000
For artists see Commercial Gallery Artists.
*198 Gallery, education and training resource. Contemporary art by artists from diverse cultural backgrounds, wide range of media including new technologies. Education centre offers programmes for schools/colleges/training for young people in arts/new technologies, agency for artists in schools/hospitals/public commissions. Eight exhibitions per annum, shop offers original ceramics, jewellery and small sculptures.*

### ▶ Architecture Foundation P
30 Bury Street, London SW1Y.
**Tel** 020 7839 9389

### ▶ The Ark (Museum of Garden History) P
220 Lambeth Road, London SE7 7JY.
**Personnel** Julia Battesby.

### ▶ Artists Gallery (Brent Artists Register)
Willesden Green Library Centre, 95 High Road, London NW10.
**Tel** 020 8937 3417
**Email** artistsgallery@hotmail.com
**Services and Facilities** Art Consultancy. Art for Offices. Commissioning Service.
**Work Stocked and Sold** Pa. Pr. Sc.

### ▶ Bankside Gallery PS
48 Hopton Street, Blackfriars, London SE1 9JH.
**Tel** 020 7928 7521 **Fax** 020 7928 2820
**Email** bankside@freeuk.com
**Opening times** During exhibitions Tue 10–8, Wed–Fri 10–5, Sun 1–5.
**Nearest Underground** Blackfriars, Southwark.
**Personnel** Director: Judy Dixey. Deputy Director: Victoria Weir.
**Services and Facilities** Art for Offices. Bookshop. Commissioning Service. Friends Society. Gallery space for hire. Guided Tours. Shop.
**Work Stocked and Sold** Ab. Dr. Pa. Pr.
**Price range** £40–£4,000
*Bankside Gallery is the home of the Royal Watercolour Society and the Royal Society of Painter-Printmakers. This friendly gallery runs a changing programme of exhibitions of contemporary watercolours and original prints. Members of the two societies are elected by their peers and represent a tradition of excellence reaching back two hundred years. Their work embraces both established and experimental practices and the exhibitions balance these different approaches. Informal 'Artists Perspectives' take place every Tuesday evening during the course of an exhibition. Practical courses and tutorials are held every year by artist members of the two societies. Full details are available from the Gallery. Admission: £3.50, concessions £2. Free admission to Friends.*

### ▶ Barbican Centre PS
Silk Street, London EC2Y 8DS.
**Tel** 020 7382 7105 (weekdays before 5), 020 7638 8891 (box office) **Fax** 020 7628 0364
**Email** jhealy@barbican.org.uk
**Ws** www.barbican.org.uk
**Opening times** Please call for details.
**Nearest Underground** Moorgate, Barbican, St Paul's, Liverpool Street and Bank.
**Personnel** Head of Exhibitions: Carol Brown. Press Officer: Lisa Collins. Marketing Officer: Joanne Healy.
**Services and Facilities** Bar. Bookshop. Café. Disabled Access. Gallery space for hire. Lectures. Parking. Restaurant.
*A variety of paid admission and free spaces showing a diverse and eclectic programme of exhibitions throughout the year including painting, design, material culture, photography and contemporary art.*
*Barbican Art Gallery* *level 3*
*The Curve* *level 0*

### ▶ The Ben Uri Gallery PS
See website for address details
**Tel** 020 8349 5724
**Fax** 020 8346 8489
**Email** benuri@ort.org
**Ws** www.benuri.com
**Opening times** By appointment only.
**Services and Facilities** Art for Offices. Disabled Access. Friends Society. Gallery space for hire. Lectures.
*The Ben Uri, founded in 1915, was awarded museum accreditation in 1995 and has the largest collection of Anglo-Jewish art in the world. Masterpieces by Bombers, Sertler, Solomon, Kramer and Reninsky mixed with European masters such as Ury and Israelis such as Castel and Rubin. Contemporary artists such as Kossof and Auerbach are equally well represented in the Hemmse Collection. Please see website for reviews in detail of the collection.*

### ▶ Bethnal Green Museum of Childhood
Cambridge Heath Road, London E2 9PA.
**Tel** 020 8983 5200, recorded info 020 8980 2415 **Fax** 020 8983 5225
**Email** m.baker@vam.ac.uk
**Ws** www.vam.ac.uk/bgm/welcome.html
**Opening times** Mon–Thu, Sat/Sun 10–5.50. Closed every Fri, May Day bank holiday, 24–26 Dec, 1 Jan.
**Nearest Underground** Bethnal Green.
**Services and Facilities** Café. Guided Tours. Museum Shop.

### ▶ British Museum P
Great Russell Street, London WC1B 3DG.
**Tel** 020 7636 1555
**Opening times** Mon–Sat 10–5, Sun 2.30–6, closed during Christmas, 1 Jan, Good Friday and the early May bank holiday. Admission free.
**Nearest Underground** Holborn, Tottenham Court Road.
**Personnel** Director: Dr Robert G W Anderson, MA, DPhil, FSA.
**Services and Facilities** Bookshop. Café. Lectures. Restaurant. Shop.

### ▶ Camden Arts Centre P
Arkwright Road, London NW3 6DG.
**Tel** 020 7435 2643/5224 **Fax** 020 7794 3371
**Personnel** Gordon Agar.

### ▶ Carlyle's House P
24 Cheyne Row, London SW3 5HL.
**Tel** 020 7352 7087

### ▶ Chalk Farm Gallery P
20 Chalk Farm Road, London NW1 8AG.
**Tel** 020 7267 3300 **Fax** 020 7267 3300
**Email** info@chalk-farm-gallery.co.uk
**Ws** www.chalk-farm-gallery.co.uk
**Opening times** Wed–Mon 10–6, closed Tue.
**Nearest Underground** Chalk Farm.
**Personnel** Geoff Caziox. Sue Gibson.
**Work Stocked and Sold** Cer. Gla. Sc.
**Price range** £50–£500

### ▶ Chisenhale Gallery P
64 Chisenhale Road, London E3 5QZ.
**Tel** 020 8981 4518 **Fax** 020 8980 7169
**Personnel** Curator: Sue Jones. Karen Hopkins.

### ▶ Chiswick House P
Burlington Lane, London W4 2RP.
**Tel** 020 8995 0508 **Fax** 020 8742 3104

### ▶ Clapham Art Gallery
61 Venn Street, London SW4.
**Tel** 020 7720 0955

### ▶ Contemporary Applied Arts PS
2 Percy Street, London W1T 1DD.
**Tel** 020 7436 2344 **Fax** 020 7436 2446
**Ws** www.caa.org.uk
**Opening times** Mon–Sat 10.30–5.30.
**Nearest Underground** Goodge Street/ Tottenham Court Road.
**Personnel** Director: Mary LaTrobe-Bateman. Press: Zoë Parker.
**Services and Facilities** Bookshop. Commissioning Service. Disabled Access. Friends Society. Shop.
**Work Stocked and Sold** Ab. App. Cer. Cra. Fur. Gla. Jew. Tx. Wd.
**Price range** £10–£10,000
For artists see Commercial Gallery Artists.

*Contemporary Applied Arts – outside.*



**Ab** Artists' Books **App** Applied Art **Cer** Ceramics **Cra** Craft **Dec** Decorative **Dr** Drawing **Fur** Furniture

*Contemporary Applied Arts was founded in 1948 as the Crafts Centre of Great Britain for the exhibition and sale of the finest contemporary applied art. Recognised internationally, museums and collectors worldwide visit the gallery to acquire ceramics and glass, both sculptural and functional, jewellery, textiles, metalwork and silver, wood and furniture. CAA's bright double-level gallery in central London holds a programme of exhibitions spotlighting new and established makers. CAA welcomes both individual and corporate commissions.*

### ▶ Courtauld Institute Galleries P
Somerset House, Strand,
London WC2R 0RN.
**Tel** 020 7837 2526
**Fax** 020 7873 2589
**Opening times** Mon–Sat 10–6, Sun 2–6. Admission charge.
**Personnel** Director: John Murdoch.

### ▶ Crafts Council PS
44a Pentonville Road, Islington, London N1 9BY.
**Tel** 020 7278 7700 **Fax** 020 7837 6891
**Ws** www.craftscouncil.org.uk
**Opening times** Free entry. Tue–Sat 11–6, Sun 2–6, closed Mon.
**Nearest Underground** Angel.
**Personnel** Director: Janet Barnes. Director of Exhibitions, Collection and Education: Louise Taylor.
**Services and Facilities** Café. Disabled Access. Lectures. Shop.
*The national centre for the crafts showing five exhibitions a year, including ceramics, textiles, glass, wood, furniture, metal work and jewellery. Reference library. Photostore, the digital picture library for crafts. Gallery shop stocking a wide variety of objects and books.*

### ▶ Crystal Palace Museum P
Anerley Hill, London SE19 2BA.
**Tel** 020 8676 0700

### ▶ Delfina P
50 Bermondsey Street, London SE1 3UD.
**Tel** 020 7357 6600 **Fax** 020 7357 0250
**Personnel** David Gilmour.

### ▶ Design Museum
28 Shad Thames, London SE1 2YD.
**Tel** 020 7403 6933, 020 7940 8790 (recorded info) **Fax** 020 7378 6540
**Email** enquiries@designmuseum.org.uk
**Ws** www.designmuseum.org
**Opening times** Daily 11.30–6. Admission: adults £5.50, students £4.50, concessions £4.00, family £12.00.
**Nearest Underground** London Bridge or Tower Hill.
**Personnel** Communications Manager: Jo Taylor.
**Services and Facilities** Café. Disabled Access. Friends Society. Gallery space for hire. Museum Shop. Shop. Workshop Facilities.
*The Design Museum is an international museum of design and architecture, focusing on 20th- and 21st-century mass products and systems. The exhibition programme includes three major shows a year as well as a number of smaller exhibitions encompassing interiors, fashion, architecture, engineering, technology and graphics.*

### ▶ Dulwich Picture Gallery P
College Road, London SE21 7AD.
**Tel** 020 8693 5254 **Fax** 020 8693 0923
**Opening times** Tue–Fri 10–5, Sat & bank holiday Mon 11–5.
**Nearest Underground** Train: West Dulwich (from Victoria).
**Personnel** Director: Desmond Shawe-Taylor.
**Services and Facilities** Bookshop. Disabled Access. Friends Society. Guided Tours. Lectures. Museum Shop. Parking. Shop.

### ▶ Estorick Collection of Modern Italian Art
Northampton Lodge, 39A Canonbury Square, London N1 2AN.
**Tel** 020 7704 9522 **Fax** 020 7704 9531
**Email** curator@estorickcollection.com
**Ws** www.estorickcollection.com
**Opening times** Wed–Sat 11–6, Sun 12–5.
**Nearest Underground** Highbury & Islington.
**Personnel** Director: Alexandra Noble. Curator: Roberta Cremoncini.
**Services and Facilities** Café. Disabled Access. Friends Society. Guided Tours. Shop.
*The Estorick Collection opened in January 1998 in a handsome, Grade II, Georgian villa showing a permanent collection of early-20th-century Italian art including world famous works by the Futurists, Boccioni, Balla, Carrà, Severini and Russolo. Other artists represented include de Chirico, Modigliani, and Morandi and sculptors Medardo Rosso, Giacomo Manzù and Marino Marini. There is a changing exhibition and education programme. Group and school visits are always welcome, but must book in advance. Art reference library by appointment. Access for wheelchair users on two floors only. Zwemmers gallery shop and Cafe open museum hours.*

### ▶ Federation of British Artists PS
17 Carlton House Terrace, London SW1Y 5BD.
**Tel** 020 7930 6844 **Fax** 020 7839 7830
**Ws** www.mallgalleries.org.uk
**Opening times** Daily 10–5.
**Nearest Underground** Charing Cross/ Piccadilly Circus.
**Personnel** Company Secretary: John Sayers. General Manager: John Oeston.
**Services and Facilities** Art Consultancy. Commissioning Service. Friends Society. Gallery space for hire. Guided Tours. Lectures. Workshop Facilities.
**Work Stocked and Sold** Dr. Pa. Pr. Sc.
**Price range** £200–£20,000
*The Mall Galleries is home to the Federation of British Artists, the umbrella organisation for nine of Britain's leading art societies: Royal Institute in Water Colours (RI), Royal Society of British Artists (RBA), Royal Society of Marine Artists (RSMA), Royal Society of Portrait Painters (RP), Royal Institute of Oil Painters (ROI), New English Art Club (NEAC), Pastel Society (PS), Society of Wildlife Artists (SWLA), Hesketh Hubbard Art Society (HH).*
*Besides the annual exhibitions held by each society, the FBA hosts a varied and exciting programme of exhibitions and events throughout the year. These include The National Print Exhibition which is an open exhibition featuring the work of invited artists, and members of the Royal Society of Painter-Printmakers, together with selected work from the open submission. Lectures, demonstrations and workshops are held throughout the year to complement the exhibitions. In addition, two major art competitions are held at the Mall Galleries: The Singer & Friedlander/ Sunday Times Watercolour Competition and the Laing Painting Competition. Artists' prizes and awards are offered by many of the societies.*
*The FBA also operates a Fine Art and Portrait Commissions and Advisory Service. For details on any of the above, please contact the administrative address. Please see also entry under Gallery Space for Hire and entries under Art Consultants and Art Societies.*

### ▶ Frith Street Gallery P
60 Frith Street, London W1V.
**Tel** 020 7494 1550

### ▶ Geffrye Museum P
Kingsland Road, London E2 8EA.
**Tel** 020 7739 9893 **Fax** 020 7729 5647
**Ws** www.lattimore.co.uk/geffrye
**Personnel** Director: David Dewing. Nancy Loader.

### ▶ Goethe-Institut London P
50 Princes Gate, Exhibition Road, London SW7 2PH.
**Tel** 020 7411 3445 **Fax** 020 7581 0974
**Email** goethe.lon@dial.pipex.com
**Ws** www.goethe.de/gr/lon/enindex.htm
**Opening times** Mon–Fri 10–8, Sat 9.30–12.30. Admission free.
**Nearest Underground** South Kensington.
**Personnel** Head of Exhibitions: Helga Wilderotter-Ikonomou.

### ▶ Goldsmiths' Hall P
Foster Lane, London EC2V 6BN.
**Tel** 020 7606 7010 **Fax** 020 7606 1511

### ▶ Guildhall Art Gallery
Guildhall Yard, London EC2P 2EJ.
**Tel** 020 7606 3030/020 7332 1632
**Fax** 020 7332 3342
**Email** guildhall.artgallery@corpoflondon.gov.uk
**Ws** www.guildhall-art-gallery.org.uk
**Opening times** Mon–Sat 10–5, Sun 12–4.
**Nearest Underground** Bank, St Paul's, Mansion House.
**Personnel** Curator: Vivien Knight. Assistant Curator: Jeremy Johnson. Curatorial Assistant: Naomi Allen.
**Services and Facilities** Art for Offices. Bookshop. Disabled Access. Guided Tours.

*John William Godward (1861–1922),* The Betrothed, *oil on canvas, 17" x 33", 1892.*
*Guildhall Art Gallery recently reopened in a stunning new building in the heart of the City of London. Originally established in 1885, it is home to the Corporation of London's renowned art collection. Among the highlights are: Victorian paintings and sculpture, including famous Pre-Raphaelite works; fascinating views of London*

*and Londoners from the 16th century to the present; John Singleton Copley's enormous painting* The Siege of Gibraltar *which spans two floors of the gallery.*
*Exhibitions: There is a programme of changing exhibitions and the entire gallery is re-hung annually.*

### ▶ Hayward Gallery
Belvedere Road, London SE1 8XZ.
**Tel** 020 7928 3144, box office 7960 4242
**Fax** 020 7401 2664
**Ws** www.haywardgallery.org.uk
**Opening times** 10–6 daily, Tue–Wed 10–8.
**Nearest Underground** Waterloo/ Embankment.
**Personnel** Director: Susan Ferleger Brades.
**Services and Facilities** Bookshop. Café. Disabled Access. Friends Society. Gallery space for hire. Lectures. Parking. Shop.
*Exhibitions of international stature are the hallmark of the Hayward Gallery, with a programme featuring the works of modern masters, thought-provoking historical shows and the most exciting names in contemporary art. Exhibitions for 2002: Paul Klee (January–March 2002), Ansel Adams at 100 (July–September 2002), Douglas Gordon (October 2002–January 2003). Admissions: £7, £5 concessions. Further information on 020 7960 4242.*

### ▶ Hogarth's House Foundation P
Hogarth's House, Hogarth Lane, Great West Road, London W4 2QN.
**Tel** 020 8994 6757/8570 0622
**Fax** 020 8862 7602
**Opening times** Tue–Fri 1–5 (Nov–Mar 1–4); Sat/Sun 1–6 (Nov–Mar 1–5); closed Mon and month of Jan.
**Personnel** Allan Downend.

### ▶ The Horniman Museum and Gardens
100 London Road, Forest Hill, London SE23 3PQ.
**Tel** 020 8699 1872
**Fax** 020 8291 5506
**Email** enquiry@horniman.demon.co.uk
**Ws** www.horniman.demon.co.uk
**Opening times** Mon–Sat 10.30–5.30, Sun 2–5.30 (except over Christmas).
**Nearest Underground** Train: Forest Hill (from London Bridge).
**Personnel** Director: Janet Vitmayer. Director of Finance and Operational Services: Jennifer Beaver.
**Services and Facilities** Café. Disabled Access. Friends Society. Museum Shop. Workshop Facilities.

### ▶ Imperial War Museum
Lambeth Road, London SE1 6HZ.
**Tel** 020 7416 5211 (voicemail)
**Fax** 020 7416 5409
**Email** art@iwm.org.uk
**Ws** www.iwm.org.uk
**Opening times** Mon–Fri 10–5.
**Nearest Underground** Lambeth North, Elephant and Castle.
**Personnel** Director General: Robert Crawford.
**Services and Facilities** Café. Disabled Access. Friends Society. Museum Shop.
*The Museum's art collection is displayed in two galleries on Level D. The permanent collection was re-hung in February 2001 and further changes to the First World War galleries are planned to link with a display at Tate Britain in October 2001. Public access to the reserve collections, posters and War Artists Archive is via the Department of Art Print Room, contact 020 7416 5211 for an appointment. Electronic access to 3000 images via the Museum's website.*

### ▶ Institute of Contemporary Arts P
The Mall, London SW1Y 5AH.
**Tel** 020 7839 6751, 7873 0061, box office 020 7930 3647 **Fax** 020 7873 0051
**Email** lori@ica.co.uk
**Ws** www.illumin.co.uk/ica/
**Opening times** Mon 12–11, Tue–Sat 12–1, Sun 12–11. Gallery Sun–Sat 12–7.30, Fri 12–9.
**Nearest Underground** Charing Cross, Piccadilly Circus.
**Personnel** Alex Hinten. Lars Drinkrow. Lori Mackellar.

### ▶ Jerwood
174 Union Street, London SE1.
**Tel** 020 7654 0171

### ▶ Kensington Palace P
Kensington Gardens, London W8 4PX.
**Tel** 020 7937 7079 **Fax** 020 7376 0198
**Nearest Underground** High Street Kensington, Gloucester Road, Queensway.
**Services and Facilities** Café. Guided Tours. Museum Shop.

### ▶ Kenwood House P
The Iveagh Bequest, Hampstead Lane, London NW3 7JR.
**Tel** 020 7973 3891
**Opening times** Apr–Sep 10–6, Oct–Mar 10–4; closed Christmas Eve, Christmas Day & Good Friday. Open daily.
**Nearest Underground** Archway or Golders Green, then 210 bus to Hampstead Lane.
**Services and Facilities** Bookshop. Friends Society. Guided Tours. Lectures. Parking. Restaurant. Shop.

### ▶ Kingsgate Gallery PS
114 Kingsgate Road, London NW6 2JG.
**Tel** 020 7328 7878
**Fax** 020 7328 7878
**Email** mail@kingsgategallery.org.uk
**Ws** www.kingsgategallery.org.uk
**Opening times** Sat & Sun 12–6 and by appointment.
**Nearest Underground** West Hampstead.
**Personnel** Gallery Director: Stephen Williams. Gallery Assistant: Matthew Poole.
**Services and Facilities** Art Consultancy. Commissioning Service. Framing.
*Contemporary work shown in a split-level space. 2–4-week exhibitions. The exhibition programme is decided at quarterly meetings and is particularly interested in group proposals. It is part of the charitable organisation Kingsgate Workshops Trust.*
*During 2000 Kingsgate took part in the Women In Focus Festival and the Kilburn Festival and also exhibited the work of Amanda Beech, Alison Jones, Matthew Poole, Hermann Pitz, Rosemary Phelps, Peter Lamb, Sally Waterman, Rolfe Kiessling, Melanie Clews and Carol Anderson.*

### ▶ Kufa Gallery PS
26 Westbourne Grove, London W2 5RH.
**Tel** 020 7229 1928 **Fax** 020 7243 8513
**Email** kufa@dircon.co.uk
**Opening times** Tue–Sat 11–5.
**Nearest Underground** Bayswater, Queensway.
**Personnel** Manager: Walid Atiyeh.
**Services and Facilities** Gallery space for hire. Lectures.
**Work Stocked and Sold** Ab. App. Cer. Cra. Dec. Dr. Pa. Ph. Pr. Tx.

### ▶ Lauderdale House, Arts & Education PS
Waterlow Park, Highgate Hill, London N6 5HG.
**Tel** 020 8348 8716 **Fax** 020 8442 9099
**Email** admin@lauderdale.org.uk
**Ws** www.lauderdale.org.uk
**Opening times** Tue–Fri 11–4, Sun 12–5 (check events), Sat (dependent on private bookings).
**Nearest Underground** Archway.
**Personnel** Director: Carolyn Naish. General Manager: Katherine Ives. Arts Education Officer: Loretta Windsor. Bookings Officer: Sarah Tresidder.
**Services and Facilities** Café. Friends Society. Gallery space for hire. Restaurant. Workshop Facilities.
*Old Tudor building from 1580, set in Waterlow Park. Reopened in 1978 by Lauderdale House Society Charity promoting arts and education (registered no. 275502). Approx. 38 exhibitions a year, admission free, varying from fine art, photography, local history, to special exhibitions by local groups, societies and schools. Four gallery spaces for hire as follows – Lower Gallery £310, Upper Gallery £175, Entrance Hall £115, and Long Gallery £300. These prices are for a fortnight (Mon to Mon) and include a Private View evening. Space can be shared among artists, no commission on sales and no selection, but artists must manage show professionally. Limited disabled access.*

### ▶ Leighton House Museum PS
12 Holland Park Road, London W14 8LZ.
**Tel** 020 7602 3316 **Fax** 020 7371 2467
**Opening times** Daily 11–5.30 except Tue, spring/summer bank holiday Mon.
**Nearest Underground** High St Kensington.
**Personnel** Curator: Daniel Robbins. Assistant Curator: Reena Suleman. Lettings Officer: Gina Gillam.
**Services and Facilities** Friends Society. Gallery space for hire. Guided Tours. Lectures. Museum Shop.

### ▶ London Institute Gallery PS
65 Davies Street, London W1K 5DA.
**Tel** 020 7514 8083 **Fax** 020 7514 6131
**Email** gallery@linst.ac.uk
**Opening times** Mon–Fri 10–8.
**Nearest Underground** Bond Street.
**Personnel** Gallery Manager: Lynne Trembath.
**Services and Facilities** Gallery space for hire.
*The London Institute Gallery presents an ambitious programme of exhibitions across a range of art and design disciplines that reflect the diversity of activities taking place within the Institute's five colleges – Camberwell, Central Saint Martins, Chelsea, London College of Fashion and London College of Printing. The*

*Gallery acts as a focal point for the work of the Institute's staff, students and alumni as well as a venue for national and international touring exhibitions.*

### ▶ Lothbury Gallery PS
41 Lothbury, London EC2P 2BP.
**Tel** 020 7726 1642/1643
**Opening times** Mon–Fri 10–4.
**Nearest Underground** Bank, Moorgate, Liverpool Street (train), Cannon Street.
**Personnel** Curator: Rosemary Harris. Assistant: Lynne Richards. Office Administrator: Daksha Patel.

### ▶ Marble Hill House P
(English Heritage), Richmond Road, Twickenham TW1 2NL.
**Tel** 020 8892 5115

### ▶ Milch P
144 Charing Cross Road, London WC2.
**Tel** 020 7379 4338

### ▶ Museum of Installation
175 Deptford High Street, London SE8 3NU.
**Tel** 020 8692 8778 **Fax** 020 8692 8122
**Email** moi@dircon.co.uk
**Ws** www.moi.dircon.co.uk
**Opening times** Tue–Fri 12–5, Sat 2–5.
**Nearest Underground** Deptford.
**Personnel** Directors: Nicola Oxley, Nicolas de Oliveira, Michael Petry. Assistant Director: Jeremy Wood. Administrator: Calan Stanley. Project Assistants: David Howells, Sarah Loriot.
**Services and Facilities** Art Consultancy. Commissioning Service. Guided Tours. Lectures. Workshop Facilities.

### ▶ The Museum of London PS
150 London Wall, London EC2Y 5HN.
**Tel** 020 7600 3699 **Fax** 020 7600 1058
**Email** info@museumoflondon.org.uk
**Ws** www.museumoflondon.org.uk
**Opening times** Mon–Sat 10–5.50, Sun 12–5.50.
**Nearest Underground** St Paul's, Barbican, Moorgate.
**Services and Facilities** Café. Commissioning Service. Disabled Access. Friends Society. Lectures. Museum Shop. Restaurant.

### ▶ Museum of Mankind P
The Ethnography Dept. of the British Museum, Burlington Gardens, London W1.
**Tel** 020 7437 2224
**Opening times** Mon–Sat 10–5, Sun 2.30–6. Closed during Christmas, 1 Jan, Good Friday and the early May bank holiday. Admission free.
**Personnel** Keeper: J B Mack MA, DPhil.
**Services and Facilities** Café.

### ▶ Museum of Women's Art P
Correspondence: 2nd Floor North, 55–63 Goswell Road, London EC1V 7EN.
**Tel** 020 7251 4881 **Fax** 020 7251 4882

### ▶ National Army Museum P
Royal Hospital Road, Chelsea, London SW3 4HT.
**Tel** 020 7730 0717 **Fax** 020 7823 6573
**Email** nam@enterprise.net
**Ws** www.failte.com/nam/
**Opening times** Daily 10–5.30 (closed 1 Jan, Good Friday, May bank holiday, Dec 24–26). Admission free.
**Personnel** Director: Ian G. Robertson MA FMA.
**Services and Facilities** Art Consultancy. Bookshop. Disabled Access. Gallery space for hire. Lectures. Museum Shop.

### ▶ National Gallery P
Trafalgar Square, London WC2N 5DN.
**Tel** 020 7747 2885 **Fax** 020 7930 4764
**Email** information@ng-london.org.uk
**Ws** www.nationalgallery.org.uk
**Opening times** Daily 10–6, Wed 10–9. Closed New Year's Day, Good Friday, 24–26 Dec.
**Nearest Underground** Charing Cross, Leicester Square, Embankment. All buses to Trafalgar Square.
**Personnel** Director: Neil MacGregor.
**Services and Facilities** Bookshop. Café. Disabled Access. Guided Tours. Lectures. Museum Shop. Restaurant. Shop. Workshop Facilities.
*The Collection numbers over 2, 200 works and covers Western European painting from 1260 to 1900, including works by Leonardo, Titian, Rubens, Rembrandt, Turner, Constable, and the Impressionists. Exhibitions and displays; many educational events: quizzes for children, lectures, audiovisuals and guided tours. Micro Gallery computer information room. Gallery Guide Soundtrack (CD audio commentary on the collection).*
*Admission free, except for some major exhibitions.*

### ▶ National Maritime Museum, Queen's House and Old Royal Observatory P
Romney Road, Greenwich, London SE10 9NF.
**Tel** 020 8858 4422 **Fax** 020 8312 6632
**Opening times** Daily 10–5, closed 24–26 Dec.

### ▶ National Portrait Gallery
St Martin's Place, London WC2H 0HE.
**Tel** 020 7306 0055 **Fax** 020 7306 0056
**Ws** www.npg.org.uk
**Opening times** Mon–Wed, Sat/Sun 10–6, Thu/Fri 10–9.
**Nearest Underground** Charing Cross, Leicester Square.
**Personnel** Director: Dr Charles Saumarez Smith.
**Services and Facilities** Bookshop. Café. Disabled Access. Friends Society. Guided Tours. Lectures. Museum Shop. Restaurant. Shop.
*The National Portrait Gallery was founded in 1856 to collect the likenesses of famous British men and women. Today the collection is the most comprehensive of its kind and constitutes a unique record of men and women who created (and are still creating) the history and culture of the nation. The gallery houses over 9,000 works, as well as an immense archive. There are oil paintings, watercolours, drawings, sculptures, caricatures and photographs. The gallery continues to develop its role through changing displays, a programme of temporary exhibitions and an annual portrait competition for young artists.*

### ▶ Orleans House Gallery PS
Riverside, Twickenham TW1 3DJ.
**Tel** 020 8892 0221 **Fax** 020 8744 0501
**Email** r.tranter@richmond.gov.uk
**Ws** www.guidetorichmond.co.uk/orleans.html
**Opening times** Apr–Sep: Tue–Sat 1–5.30, Sun 2–5.30 (Oct–Mar closes at 4.30). Sun & bank holidays 2–5.30.
**Nearest Underground** Train: St Margaret's from Waterloo.
**Personnel** Acting Curator: Rachel Tranter. Assistant Curator: Mark de Novelis.
**Services and Facilities** Craftshop. Disabled Access. Lectures. Parking. Shop. Workshop Facilities.
**Work Stocked and Sold** App. Cer. Cra. Dec. Gla. Jew. Pa. Ph. Pr. Tx.
**Price range** £30–£2,000
*Our exhibitions programme showcases contemporary artists and makers, and draws in loans from art museums across the UK or from Richmond Borough's own collections. We hold 5/6 exhibitions per year, which are created in-house or in partnership with other galleries. The 2001 exhibition programme includes a ground-breaking exhibition on outsider and visionary art, portraits by photographer Anne Purkiss, and historical and contemporary Thames riverside views. In the smaller Stables Gallery, which is open during from April to September, we work exclusively with local interest groups and local artists, to provide an outlet for expression and discussion.*

### ▶ Percival David Foundation P
53 Gordon Square, London WC1H 0PD.
**Tel** 020 7387 3909
**Fax** 020 7383 5163
**Opening times** Mon–Fri 10.30–5, closed weekends and bank holidays.
**Nearest Underground** Russell Square.
**Personnel** Head of Museums: Ms Rosemary E Scott. Assistant Curator: Ms Stacey Pierson.
**Services and Facilities** Friends Society. Guided Tours.

### ▶ The Petrie Museum
University College, Malet Place, London WC1.
**Tel** 020 7679 2884

### ▶ Photographers' Gallery P
5–8 Great Newport Street, London WC2H 7HY.
**Tel** 020 7831 1772 minicom
**Fax** 020 7836 9704
**Opening times** Mon–Sat 11–6.
**Nearest Underground** Leicester Square.
**Personnel** Director: Paul Wombell.

### ▶ Pitshanger Manor Gallery PS
Walpole Park, Mattock Lane, Ealing, London W5 5EQ.
**Tel** 020 8567 1227
**Fax** 020 8567 0595
**Email** pitshanger@ealing.gov.uk
**Ws** www.ealing.gov.uk/pitshanger
**Opening times** Tue–Sat 10–5.
**Nearest Underground** Ealing Broadway (underground & train).
**Personnel** Head of Arts & Cultural Services: Neena Sohal. Arts Development Officer: Helen Walker. Arts & Museums Officers: Carol Swords, Valerie Chang. Arts Project Officer: Reema Ratbod.
**Services and Facilities** Art Consultancy. Disabled Access. Guided Tours. Lectures. Workshop Facilities.
*Pitshanger Manor Gallery is the largest contemporary art gallery in West London, housing 5–6 major contemporary exhibitions every year.*

*Work is drawn from all media by international, national and local artists. The gallery aims to show eclectic, challenging and accessible work, supported by a comprehensive education programme.*

### ▶ Pump House Gallery PS
Battersea Park, London SW11 4NJ.
**Tel** 020 8871 7572 **Fax** 020 7228 9062
**Email** pump_house@lineone.net
**Ws** www.wandsworth.gov.uk/gallery
**Opening times** Nov–Feb: Wed–Sun 11–4; Mar–Oct: Wed–Sun 11–5 (Sat 11–4).
**Nearest Underground** Sloane Square, train: Battersea Park Station (one stop from Victoria or Waterloo). Buses: 19, 39, 44, 45, 137, 170.
**Personnel** Manager: Susie Gray. Gallery Assistant: Katy Culbard. Private Event Coordinator: Catherine Davies.
**Services and Facilities** Café. Museum Shop. Parking. Shop.
**Work Stocked and Sold** Cer. Cra. Dr. Jew. Pa. Ph. Pr. Sc.
**Price range** £50–£5,000
*The Pump House Gallery is situated beside the lakes in Battersea Park, just south of the Thames over Chelsea Bridge. The gallery runs an annual programme of about 10 exhibitions by contemporary artists, which emphasises variety in media and style. 35% commission on sales (+ VAT).*

### ▶ Queen's Gallery P
Buckingham Palace, London SW1A 1AA.
**Tel** 020 7799 2331/020 7839 1377
**Nearest Underground** Victoria.

### ▶ RIBA
66 Portland Place, London W1.
**Tel** 020 7307 3770

### ▶ Royal Academy of Arts PS
Burlington House, Piccadilly, London W1J 0BD.
**Tel** 020 7300 8000 **Fax** 020 7300 8001
**Ws** www.royalacademy.org.uk
**Opening times** Mon–Sun 10–6, Fri 10–10.
**Nearest Underground** Green Park & Piccadilly Circus.
**Personnel** Head of Press & Marketing: Katharine Jones.
**Services and Facilities** Bookshop. Café. Disabled Access. Framing. Friends Society. Guided Tours. Lectures. Museum Shop. Restaurant. Shop.
*Founded in 1768, the Royal Academy is the o ldest arts institution in the UK, governed by its artists members.*
*Its exhibition programme includes the annual Summer Exhibition of work by living artists and internationally acclaimed travelling exhibitions such as Monet in the 20th Century (1999) and The Genius of Rome 1592–1623 (2001).*

### ▶ Saatchi Collection P
98a Boundary Road, London NW8 0RH.
**Tel** 020 7624 8299 **Fax** 020 7624 3798
**Opening times** Thu–Sun 12–6.

### ▶ Serpentine Gallery P
Kensington Gardens, London W2 3XA.
**Tel** 020 7402 6075/0343, 020 7823 9727
**Fax** 020 7402 4103
**Opening times** Daily 10–6 (except during installation of exhibitions). Please telephone for opening times. Admission free.
**Nearest Underground** South Kensington, Lancaster Gate. Buses: 9, 10, 52 (Royal Albert Hall), 12 (Bayswater Road), 94.
**Personnel** Director: Julia Peyton Jones. Administrator: Jackie McNerney.

### ▶ Sir John Soane's Museum P
13 Lincoln's Inn Fields, London WC2A 3BP.
**Tel** 020 7405 2107 **Fax** 020 7831 3957
**Opening times** Tue–Sat 10–5.
**Nearest Underground** Holborn.
**Personnel** Director: Mrs Margaret Richardson.

### ▶ The Sladmore Gallery - 19th and 20th Century Bronze Sculpture. P
32 Bruton Place, Berkeley Square, London W1X 7AA.
**Tel** 020 7499 0365 **Fax** 020 7409 1381
**Opening times** Mon–Fri 10–6, Sat during exhibitions 10–1.
**Nearest Underground** Green Park/Bond St.
**Personnel** Directors: E. F. Horswell, G. Farrell.
**Services and Facilities** Restoration. Valuation.

### ▶ Small Mansion Arts Centre PS
Gunnersbury Park, Popes Lane, Acton, London W3 8IQ.
**Tel** 020 8993 8312
**Opening times** 11–6.
**Nearest Underground** Acton Town.
**Personnel** Maureen Adiloglu.
**Services and Facilities** Disabled Access. Gallery space for hire. Parking.
**Work Stocked and Sold** Dr. Pa. Pr.
**Price range** £50–£5,000

### ▶ South London Gallery
65 Peckham Road, London SE5 8UH.
**Tel** 020 7703 6120, recorded information line 020 7703 9799 **Fax** 020 7252 4730
**Email** mail@southlondonart.com
**Ws** www.southlondonart.co.uk
**Opening times** Tue, Wed & Fri 11–6, Thu 11–7, Sat & Sun 2–6.
**Nearest Underground** Elephant & Castle, then 12 or 171 bus, Oval, then 36 bus.
**Personnel** Director: David Thorp. Curator: Donna Lynas. Press, Marketing & Development: Katharine Burton.
**Services and Facilities** Art for Offices. Friends Society. Gallery space for hire. Lectures.

***South London Gallery – interior, 70 x 30 x 22 ft.***
*The South London Gallery is one of London's foremost contemporary art exhibition spaces, committed to a challenging curatorial programme showing the work of local, national and international living artists. It also holds in storage an extensive collection that extends from work by John Everett Millais and Frederic Leighton to contemporary artists including Anish Kapoor, Tracey Emin and Tom Phillips.*
*In the past decade, exhibitions of work by artists including Gilbert and George, Gavin Turk and Julian Schnabel have established the South London Gallery as an important national and international forum for the extension of the debate around contemporary art. Forthcoming shows include solo exhibitions of work by Bill Woodrow and Ross Sinclair, live art performances, the annual Goldsmiths' exhibition and several group exhibitions.*
*The gallery also provides a range of debates, seminars, talks and performances by artists and key figures in the fields of art journalism, broadcasting and curatorship. Recent speakers at the gallery have included Richard Cork, art critic for* The Times, *artist Julian Schnabel, Gill Hedley, director of the Contemporary Arts Society and Tim Marlow, editor of* Tate Magazine *and television arts presenter.*

### ▶ Southwark Park Arts Projects (incorporating Clare College Mission Church and Cafe Gallery) PS
Southward Park, London SE16 2TY.
**Tel** 020 7266 4665/020 7237 1230/ 020 7232 2170
**Opening times** Wed–Sun 11–5 (summer) or 11–4 (winter), closed Mon/Tue.
**Nearest Underground** Surrey Quays.
**Services and Facilities** Disabled Access. Friends Society. Parking.

### ▶ Strang Print Room P
University College London, London WC1E 6BT.
**Tel** 020 7387 7050 ext 2540
**Fax** 020 7813 2803
**Email** e.chambers@ucl.ac.uk

### ▶ Tate Britain/ Tate Modern Bankside P
Tate Britain, Millbank, London SW1P 4RG.
Tate Modern, South Bank.
**Tel** 020 7887 8008
**Ws** www.tate.org.uk
**Opening times** Tate Britain: Mon–Sun 10–5.50.
Tate Modern: Sun–Thu 10–6, Fri/Sat 10–10.
**Nearest Underground** Tate Britain: Pimlico. Tate Modern: Blackfriars or Southwark.
**Personnel** Director: Nicholas Serota. Press Office, Tate Britain: Ben Luke. Press Office, Tate Britain & Modern: Sioban Ketelaar. Press Office, Tate Modern: Nadine Thompson.
**Services and Facilities** Bookshop. Café. Disabled Access. Friends Society. Guided Tours. Lectures. Museum Shop. Restaurant. Shop.
*The Tate Gallery houses the national collection of British art from the 16th century to the present day, including the Turner Bequest, and the national collection of international modern art.*
*The Tate is a family of galleries comprising: Tate Gallery, London, founded 1897; Tate Gallery Liverpool which opened in 1988; and Tate Gallery St Ives which opened in 1993.*
*The Tate has recently embarked on an exciting and ambitious programme of development and expansion for London in the millennium. Tate Modern opened May 2000, converting the redundant Bankside Power Station situated across the River Thames from St Paul's Cathedral; and a Tate Gallery of British Art at the original London site on Millbank.*

*The Tate Gallery of Modern Art has been designed by the Swiss architects Herzog & de Meuron and houses the Tate Collection of international 20th-century art including major works by some of the most influential artists of this century such as Picasso, Matisse, Dali, Duchamp, Moore, Bacon, Gabo, Giacometti and Warhol.*

### ▶ TWO10 Gallery

The Wellcome Trust, 210 Euston Road, London NW1 2BE.
**Tel** 020 7611 8888 **Fax** 020 7611 8562
**Email** k.arnold@wellcome.ac.uk
**Ws** www.wellcome.ac.uk
**Opening times** Mon–Fri 9–6 (closed weekends and public holidays).
**Nearest Underground** Euston.
**Personnel** Exhibitions Manager: Dr Ken Arnold. Exhibitions Officer: Denna Jones.

### ▶ Victoria and Albert Museum The National Museum of Art and Design

Cromwell Road, South Kensington, London SW7 2RL.
**Tel** 020 7942 2000 **Fax** 020 7942 2266
**Email** infodome@vam.ac.uk
**Ws** www.vam.ac.uk
**Opening times** Daily 10–5.45 (Wed and the last Fri of the month, 10–10). Open every day except 24–26 Dec.
**Nearest Underground** South Kensington.
**Services and Facilities** Bookshop. Café. Craftshop. Disabled Access. Friends Society. Gallery space for hire. Guided Tours. Lectures. Museum Shop. Restaurant. Shop.
*The Victoria and Albert Museum is one of the world's greatest museums of art and design. Seven miles of galleries contain unrivalled collections dating from 3000 BC to the present day. Photography, furniture, fashion, textiles, paintings, silver, glass, ceramics, sculpture, jewellery, books and prints illustrate the artistic life of many different cultures from around the world. In addition, there is an exciting programme of exhibitions, displays, activities and contemporary events. Exhibitions in 2002 include: Italian Terracottas, 14 March–7 July 2002, and Tiaras, 14 March–7 July 2002. The new British Galleries – 15 new galleries unfolding the story of British design from 1500 to 1900 – are a must-see for any visit. Admission is free (some exhibitions may have a separate entrance charge).*

### ▶ Wallace Collection P

Hertford House, Manchester Square, London W1M 6BN.
**Tel** 020 7935 0687 **Fax** 020 7224 2155
**Email** admin@wallcoll.demon.co.uk
**Ws** www.demon.co.uk/heritage/wallace
**Opening times** Mon–Sat 10–5, Sun 2–5.
**Personnel** Director: Rosalind Savill. Joanne Charlton.
**Services and Facilities** Bookshop. Disabled Access. Lectures. Museum Shop. Shop.

### ▶ Westminster Gallery

Central Hall, Storey's Gate, London SW1 9NH.
**Tel** 020 7222 8010 **Fax** 020 7222 6883
**Email** events@wch.co.uk
**Ws** www.wch.co.uk
**Opening times** various
**Personnel** Senior Events Manager: Ms Cathy Williamson. General Manager: Michael Sharp.
**Services and Facilities** Café. Disabled Access. Gallery space for hire. Guided Tours.

*Central Hall, Westminster*
*The Westminster Gallery offers an elegant, spacious and versatile exhibition area. The three rooms the gallery occupies can be hired individually or as a whole and are available throughout the year. Lighting, hanging and display facilities are easily managed. The adjacent café is open daily and is very happy to assist with refreshments for your private viewings.*

### ▶ Whitechapel Art Gallery P

Whitechapel High Street, London E1 7QX.
**Tel** recorded information: 020 7522 7878, other enquiries 020 7522 7888 **Fax** 020 7377 1685
**Opening times** Tue–Sun 11–5 (Wed 11–8), closed Mon.
**Nearest Underground** Aldgate East.
**Personnel** Director: Catherine Lampert.
**Services and Facilities** Disabled Access. Friends Society. Gallery space for hire.

### ▶ William Morris Gallery and Brangwyn Gift P

Lloyd Park, Forrest Road, Walthamstow, London E17 4PP.
**Tel** 020 8527 3782 **Fax** 020 8527 7070
**Email** gallery@lbwf.gov.uk
**Ws** www.lbwf.gov.uk
**Personnel** Norah Gillow.

NOTES

# English Regional Galleries



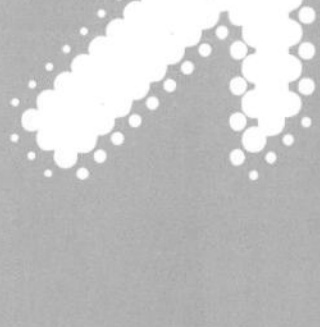

*All entries in this section are sorted by region. Where this information has been provided, entries are designated 'C' for commercial, 'P' for public gallery or museum or 'PS' for a public gallery or museum holding selling shows*

# Beating a path to contemporary art

It is often said that the UK follows cultural trends from the US, but the transatlantic osmosis that has brought us multiplexes and internet cafés has not yet impacted on our regional museums. In the US, funding for regional museums comes from many different sources – private or philanthropic donations, membership schemes, creative merchandising, corporate sponsors and entrance tickets – but practically none from central government. In England, thankfully, many museums have resisted the urge to charge for access, thanks to the bill that allows museums to claim back tax, regardless of whether or not admission is free.

Consequently, the majority of institutions rely on the government for core funding and currently there is not nearly enough to go around, leaving many museums to employ survival tactics. Despite 'cash boosts' of £6–7 million in early 2001 which benefited the Horniman Museum in South London, Manchester's Whitworth Art Gallery and museums in Northampton, Birmingham and Dorset, the shortfall for new developments and refurbishments has been plugged by funds from the National Lottery. The museum building boom in Britain has resulted in some outstanding new venues, from the Lowry in Salford to the New Art Gallery in Walsall, both opened in early 2000.

The Walker Art Gallery in Liverpool is to be reopened in 2002 to coincide with the Liverpool Biennial of contemporary art. Also opening in 2002 is the Baltic Centre for Contemporary Art in Gateshead, proving that the Northeast is not just a location for siting monumental sculptures such as Gormley's *Angel of the North* or David Mach's brick *Train*. A series of ambitious new commissions on the four floors of the converted Baltic flour mills, situated on the banks of the river Tyne, will open to the public on 9 March 2002 and inaugurates a new type of public art space, the 'Art Factory'.

This completes an imaginary line of museums, galleries and other spaces in which to view contemporary art that stretches the length of England, from the very north, with the new Baltic in Gateshead and the Northern Gallery of Contemporary Art in Sunderland, all the way down to the Newlyn Art Gallery and the Tate St Ives at the very southern tip of Cornwall.

# East Midlands

## DERBY

### DERBY

**▶ The Arbor Darkrooms & Gallery** C
Arboretum Lodge, Arboretum Square, Derby DE23 8FN.
**Tel** 01332 299 049
**Personnel** Exhibitions: Colin Wilson. Paula Moss.
**Services and Facilities** Disabled Access.
**Work Stocked and Sold** Ph.

**▶ Art for All**
Derby City General Hospital, Uttoxeter Road, Derby DE22 3NE.
**Tel** 01332 340 131 ext 5910
**Personnel** Director: Frank Walters.

**▶ The Atrium Gallery**
The Derwent Business Centre, Clarke Street, Derby DE1 2BU.
**Personnel** Stuart Mills.

**▶ Derby Museum and Art Gallery** P
The Strand, Derby DE1 1BS.
**Tel** 01332 255 586 **Fax** 01332 255 804
**Personnel** Keeper of Fine Arts and Exhibitions: Maggie Cullen.

**▶ Royal Crown Derby Museum** P
Royal Crown Derby Porcelain Co. Ltd, 194 Osmaston Road, Derby DE3 8JZ.
**Tel** 01332 712800 **Fax** 01332 712899

## DERBYSHIRE

### CHESTERFIELD

**▶ Chesterfield Museum & Art Gallery** P
St Mary's Gate, Chesterfield, S41 7TY.
**Tel** 01246 559727 **Fax** 01246 206667
**Personnel** Anne-Marie Knowles.

**▶ Uno Gallery** C
5 South Street, Chesterfield, S40 1QX.
**Opening times** Mon–Sat 10–5.
**Work Stocked and Sold** Gla. Jew.

### TIDESWELL

**▶ Amber House Gallery** C
High Street, Tideswell SK17 8LD.
**Tel** 01298 872975
**Email** cluckie@amberhousegallery.fsnet.co.uk
**Opening times** 11–6 Sat, Sun, bank holidays. Any time by appointment.
**Personnel** Proprietor/Art Historian: Linda Cluckie.
**Services and Facilities** Art Consultancy. Art for Offices. Commissioning Service. Disabled Access. Framing. Valuation.
**Work Stocked and Sold** Dr. Pa. Ph. Pr. Sc. Tx.
**Price range** £50–£1000
*Set in the heart of the beautiful Peak district, adjacent to Tideswell's main attraction, 'The Cathedral of the Peak.' Solo and theme exhibitions change every six weeks. The third and newly extended gallery room exhibits regularly changing work from over 30 artists both local and nationwide; inc.: Ginette Ashkenazy, David Bowyer, Richard Clare, John Davies, Andrew Heath, Victoria Hill, Emerson Mayes, Donna Nolan, Andrea Ottaviano, Rebecca Rickets and Helen Willey.*

### WIRKSWORTH

**▶ Modern Print Gallery**
25 Market Place, Wirksworth, DE4 4ET.
**Tel** 01629 824525

## LEICESTER

### LEICESTER

**▶ The City Gallery** PS
90 Granby Street, Leicester LE1 1DJ.
**Tel** 0116 254 0595 **Fax** 0116 254 0593
**Opening times** Tue–Fri 11–6, Sat 10–5.
**Nearest Station** Leicester.
**Personnel** Manager: Sylvia Wright.
**Services and Facilities** Art for Offices. Commissioning Service. Craftshop. Disabled Access. Friends Society. Gallery space for hire. Shop. Workshop Facilities.
**Work Stocked and Sold** Cer. Cra. Dr. Gla. Jew. Pa. Ph. Pr. Sc. Tx. Wd.
**Price range** £10–£10,000
For artists see Commercial Gallery Artists.

*Serena Partridge,* Court Dress *(detail).*
*The City Gallery is Leicester's leading contemporary gallery promoting the very best in contemporary art and craft. The gallery aims to provide an opportunity to the general public of all ages and abilities to become involved in the visual arts and crafts through a dynamic and accessible programme of changing exhibitions and events. There are three spaces; the Main Gallery, Craft Gallery and Upstairs Gallery (available to hire at highly competitive prices), as well as a shop which is stocked with a wide range of work by new makers and famous names (on the Craft Council's National List of Craft shops and Galleries). The City Gallery runs an active and popular education programme as well as a touring exhibitions scheme operating in many regional arts venues and neighbourhood centres. The City Gallery is directly managed by Leicester City Council. Admission is free. There is access at street level and a chairlift to the Upstairs Gallery.*

**▶ Gadsby Gallery**
22 Market Place, Leicester LE1 5GF.
**Tel** 0116 262 2410
**Personnel** Peter Gadsby.

**▶ Leicester Museum & Art Gallery/ New Walk Museum & Gallery** P
53 New Walk, Leicester LE1 7EA.

## LEICESTERSHIRE

### ASHBY DE-LA-ZOUCH

**▶ Ferrers Gallery** C
Staunton Harold, Ashby de-la-Zouch, LE6 5RU.
**Tel** 01332 863337
**Opening times** Tue–Sat 11–5. Jan closed weekdays, open Sat & Sun 11–5.
**Personnel** Jayne McKay.
**Work Stocked and Sold** Cer. Cra. Fur. Gla. Jew. Tx. Wd.

### MARKET HARBOROUGH

**▶ Coughton Galleries** C
The Old Manor, Arthingworth, Market Harborough, LE6 8JD.
**Tel** 01858 525436 **Fax** 01858 525535

**▶ The Frank Haynes Gallery**
50 Station Road, Great Bowden, Market Harborough, LE16 7HN.
**Tel** 01858 464862
**Opening times** Thu–Sun 10–5. Admission free.
**Nearest Station** Market Harborough
**Personnel** Frank Haynes.
**Services and Facilities** Framing. Shop.
**Work Stocked and Sold** Cer. Pa.

## NORTHAMPTONSHIRE

### NORTHAMPTON

**▶ Central Museum and Art Gallery** PS
Guildhall Road, Northampton NN1 1DP.
**Tel** 01604 238548 **Fax** 01604 238720
**Opening times** Mon–Sat 10–5, Sun 2–5.
**Nearest Station** Northampton.
**Personnel** Curator: S. Stone.
**Services and Facilities** Bookshop. Disabled Access. Friends Society. Gallery space for hire. Guided Tours. Lectures. Museum Shop.

**▶ Four Seasons Gallery**
39 St Giles Street, Northampton,
**Tel** 01604-32287
**Personnel** Kate Leese.

**▶ Onsight Gallery**
The Roadmender, 1 Lady's Lane, Northampton, NN1 3AH.

**▶ Weston Favell Library**
Weston Favell Shopping Centre, Northampton,
**Tel** 01604 413327
**Personnel** Olivia Spencer.

### TOWCESTER

**▶ Towcester Library**
Richmond Road, Towcester, NN12 7EX.
**Tel** 01327 50794

### WELLINGBOROUGH

**▶ The Gallery**
108 Midland Road, Wellingborough, NN8 1NB.

**Tel** 01933 274215
**Personnel** Exhibitions Organiser: John Black.
**Work Stocked and Sold** Pa.

### ▶ Raunds Library
High Street, Raunds,
Wellingborough, NN9 6HT.
**Tel** 01933 623671

### ▶ Wellingborough Library
Pebble Lane, Wellingborough, NN8 1AS.
**Tel** 01933 225365
**Fax** 01933 44060
**Personnel** Assistant County Librarian: Derrick Bond. Assistant County Librarian: Dominic Jones.

## NOTTINGHAMSHIRE

NEWARK

### ▶ Millgate Museum P
48 Millgate, Newark, NG24 4TS.
**Tel** 01636 79403
**Personnel** M. J. Hall.

### ▶ Pierrepont Gallery
Thoresby Park, near Ollerton, Newark.
**Tel** 01623 822365 **Fax** 01623 822301
**Personnel** Janet McFerrn.

NOTTINGHAM

### ▶ Angel Row Gallery PS
Central Library Building, 3 Angel Row, Nottingham, NG1 6HP.
**Tel** 0115 915 2869 **Fax** 0115 915 2860
**Opening times** Mon–Sat 10–5, Wed 10–7.
**Nearest Station** Nottingham.
**Personnel** Visual Arts and Exhibitions Manager: Deborah Dean.
**Services and Facilities** Bookshop. Disabled Access. Lectures. Shop.
*Situated in central Nottingham, Angel Row Gallery shows an exciting and diverse programme of contemporary visual arts. A large gallery with three exhibition spaces, it promotes regional, national and international artists. An extensive programme of events and activities is organised in conjunction with the exhibitions. The gallery stocks a wide range of art magazines, catalogues, postcards and greetings cards.*

### ▶ Arnold Library
Front Street, Arnold, Nottingham, NG5 7EE.
**Tel** 0115 920 2247

### ▶ Byard Gallery
9 Byard Lane, Nottingham.

### ▶ Djanogly Art Gallery PS
The University of Nottingham Arts Centre, University Park, Nottingham, NG7 2RD.
**Tel** 0115 951 3192 **Fax** 0115 951 3194
**Email** neil.walker@nottingham.ac.uk
**Ws** www.nottingham.ac.uk/artscentre/
**Opening times** Mon–Sat 11–5, Sun & bank holidays 2–5.
**Nearest Station** Nottingham.
**Personnel** Director: Joanne Wright. Exhibitions Officer: Neil Walker. Marketing Officer: Neil Bennison. Exhibitions Secretary: Tracey Isgar.
**Services and Facilities** Café. Craftshop. Disabled Access. Lectures. Parking.
*The Djanogly Art Gallery originates historical and contemporary exhibitions and hosts a wide range of touring shows. Foyer exhibitions and craft cabinets extend the type of work shown. The gallery has an artist in residence – currently French artist, Gerard Renvez – who leads workshops and education programmes in conjunction with the exhibitions.*

### ▶ Future Factory at the Bonington Gallery PS
The Nottingham Trent University, Dryden Street, Nottingham, NG1 4FX.
**Tel** Office 0115 848 6131, Gallery 0115 848 2260 **Fax** 0115 848 6132
**Email** stella.couloutbanis@ntu.ac.uk
**Ws** www.future-factory.org
**Opening times** Mon–Thu 10–5, Fri 10–4, Sat 1–5.
**Nearest Station** Nottingham.
**Personnel** Artistic Director: Robert Ayers. Exhibitions Organiser: Stella Couloutbanis. Gallery Administrator: Jenny Rainforth. Exhibitions Assistant: Raif Killips. Clerical Support: Alicia Clarke.
**Services and Facilities** Art for Offices. Disabled Access. Lectures.
*Situated within the Bonington Building of the University, the gallery is one of the foremost exhibition spaces for contemporary art in the Midlands.*
*The gallery presents a diverse programme of events encompassing both pure and applied contemporary Visual Arts, Crafts, Design, Performance and Dance. Emphasis is placed upon programming work which is innovative and at the forefront of contemporary practice, encouraging the work of younger, emerging artists as well as established practitioners.*

### ▶ The Hart Gallery C
23 Main Street, Linby, Nottingham, NG15 8AE.
**Tel** 0115 963 8707
**Personnel** Directors: John Hart, Katherine Hart.
**Work Stocked and Sold** Cer. Dr. Pa. Pr. Sc.

### ▶ Nottingham Castle Museum & Art Gallery PS
Nottingham, NG1 6EL.
**Tel** 0115 915 3700 (general information)
**Fax** 0115 915 3653
**Opening times** Daily, 10–5 (Nov–Feb: Fri closed). Closed Christmas Day, Boxing Day & New Year's Day.
**Nearest Station** Nottingham.
**Personnel** Director: Michael Williams.
**Services and Facilities** Café. Commissioning Service. Craftshop. Disabled Access. Friends Society. Gallery space for hire. Guided Tours. Lectures. Museum Shop.
**Work Stocked and Sold** Cra. Pa. Ph.
*Founded 1878. A seventeenth century mansion on the site of the original Nottingham Castle, housing a strong collection of fine art from the seventeenth century to the present day. Featuring artists such as Bonington, Rossetti, Laura Knight and Lowry with a unique collection of medieval alabasters. A lively programme of temporary exhibitions of historical and contemporary art, craft and textiles in newly refurbished galleries. Regularly feature work for sale by up and coming painters, photographers and craftmakers and host an annual contemporary art auction. Crafts Council recommended shop selling a wide range of crafts.*

### ▶ Nottingham Playhouse Gallery
Wellington Circus, Nottingham, NG1 5AF.
**Tel** 0115 941 9419
**Personnel** Christabel King.

### ▶ The West End Gallery C
St Mary's Church, High Pavement, The Lace Market, Nottingham, NG1 1HF.
**Tel** 0115 947 2476 **Fax** 0115 947 2476
**Email** stmary@john316.com.
**Opening times** Tue–Sat 9–4.30.
**Nearest Station** Nottingham.
**Personnel** Community Arts Organiser: Ruth Shelton.
**Services and Facilities** Disabled Access. Gallery space for hire. Lectures.
**Work Stocked and Sold** Pa. Ph. Sc.
**Price range** £20–£1,000
For artists see Commercial Gallery Artists.

### ▶ The Yard Gallery PS
Wollaton Park, Nottingham, NG8 2AE.
**Tel** 0115 915 3920 (general enquiries)
**Fax** 0115 915 3932
**Opening times** Winter 11–4, summer 11–5.
**Nearest Station** Nottingham.
**Personnel** Exhibition Coordinator: Jim Waters.
**Services and Facilities** Bookshop. Café. Craftshop. Disabled Access. Guided Tours. Lectures. Parking.

RAVENSHEAD

### ▶ Longdale Gallery
Longdale Craft Centre, Museum and Restaurant, Longdale Lane, Ravenshead, NG15 9AH.
**Tel** 01623 794858
**Personnel** Manager: Janet Purcell.

WORKSOP

### ▶ Harley Gallery C
Welbeck, Worksop, S80 3LW.
**Tel** 01909 501700 **Fax** 01909 488747
**Opening times** Thu–Sun & bank holiday Mon 11.30–5.
**Personnel** Gallery Director: Steve Abbott.
**Work Stocked and Sold** Cer. Fur. Pa. Sc.

## RUTLAND

UPPINGHAM

### ▶ The Goldmark Gallery C
14 Orange Street, Uppingham, LE15 9SQ.
**Tel** 01572 821424
**Fax** 01572 821503
**Email** Mike@mgoldmark.freeserve.co.uk
**Opening times** Daily 9.30–5.30 & Sun afternoons.
**Nearest Station** Kettering/Oakham.
**Personnel** Director: Mike Goldmark. Emma Beanland. Roger Porter.
**Services and Facilities** Art for Offices. Bookshop. Disabled Access. Framing.
**Work Stocked and Sold** Ab. Pa. Pr. Sc.
**Price range** £250–£3,000
For artists see Commercial Gallery Artists.

# Eastern

## BEDFORDSHIRE

BEDFORD

### ▶ The Gatehouse
Foster Hill Road, Bedford, MK41 7TD.
**Tel** 01234-355870
**Personnel** Community Arts Development Officer: Gilly Love.

BIGGLESWADE

### ▶ Fairfield Gallery
Fairfield House, Biggleswade, SG18 0AA.
**Tel** 01767 312176
**Opening times** Thu, Fri, Sat & Sun 10–5. Otherwise by appointment.

BROMHAM

### ▶ Bromham Mill Art Gallery PS
Bromham Mill, Bridge End, Bromham, MK43 8LP.
**Tel** 01234 824330
**Fax** 01234 228531
**Email** wilemans@deed.bedfordshire.gov.uk
**Ws** www.borneo.co.uk/bromham-mill/
**Opening times** Mar–Oct: Wed–Sat 1–5. Sun and bank holidays 10.30–5. Nov–Feb: Sun & New Year's Day 1–5.
Last admission half an hour before closing
**Nearest Station** Midland Road, Bedford
**Services and Facilities** Café. Craftshop. Guided Tours. Parking. Shop. Workshop Facilities. App. Cer. Cra. Dec. Dr. Fur. Gla. Jew. Pa. Ph. Pr. Sc. Tx. Wd.
**Price range** £5–£5,000
*Changing programme of contemporary art and craft work, including national touring exhibitions. Three gallery spaces are used to exhibit 1, 2 or 3 separate shows. At least two of these are textile based. We show exciting new regional and local makers as well as outstanding individuals from further afield. Some photography and visual arts are shown but the gallery specialises in contemporary craft and textiles. Some exhibitions are commissioned by the gallery through a guest curator and include work on loan from national collections. However the majority is for sale. i/free art scheme in operation through East England Arts, offering interest-free credit on purchases between £100 and £1000 with a 10% deposit and repayment over 10 months.*

LANGFORD

### ▶ Loggia Gallery
Lansbury, 51a High Street, Langford, SG18 9RU.

LUTON

### ▶ 33 Arts Centre
33–35 Guildford Street, Luton LU1 2NQ.
**Tel** 01582 419 584
**Fax** 01582 459 401

### ▶ The Gallery, Luton Central Library
St George's Square, Luton, LU1 2NG.
**Tel** 01582 30161 **Fax** 01582 24638

### ▶ Luton Museum and Art Gallery P
Wardown Park, Luton.
**Tel** 01582 746722

SANDY

### ▶ Sculptor's Studio: Thane Studios
10 Vicarage Road, Waresley, Sandy, SG19 3DA.
**Tel** 01767 650444 **Fax** 01767 650444
**Personnel** Laurence Broderick.
**Work Stocked and Sold** Sc.

## CAMBRIDGESHIRE

BOURN

### ▶ Wysing Arts P
Fox Road, Bourn, CB3 7TX.
**Tel** 01954 718881 **Fax** 01954 718500
**Email** info@wysing.demon.co.uk
**Ws** www.wysing.demon.co.uk
**Opening times** 7 days a week. Phone for details.
**Nearest Station** Cambridge/Royston.
**Personnel** Director: Trystan Hawkins.
**Services and Facilities** Commissioning Service. Disabled Access. Gallery space for hire. Guided Tours. Parking. Workshop Facilities.

CAMBRIDGE

### ▶ Broughton House Gallery C
98 King Street, Cambridge, CB1 1LN.
**Tel** 01223 314960 **Fax** 01223 314960
**Email** bhg@dircon.co.uk
**Ws** www.picassomio.com/broughtonhousegallery
**Opening times** Mar–Dec Tue–Sat 10.30–5.30.
**Nearest Station** Cambridge; bus station: Drummer Street.
**Personnel** Director: Rosemary Davidson.
**Services and Facilities** Art Consultancy. Art for Offices. Disabled Access. Friends Society.
**Work Stocked and Sold** Cer. Pa. Pr. Sc. Tx.
**Price range** £25–£1, 500
For artists see Commercial Gallery Artists.
*This modern gallery has been built into the ground floor of an 18th century house, opening onto a walled garden, in the centre of Cambridge. There are monthly exhibitions from March to December, each lasting three weeks (both one-man/woman and theme shows). Contemporary paintings and prints, also sculpture, from British and European, artists. A wide variety of paintings and prints always in stock. The gallery holds the Gwen Raverat archive of wood engravings, of which there is a permanent (changing) exhibition. Friends of the Broughton House Gallery scheme. Consultancy for private and business clients.*

### ▶ Cambridge Darkroom
Dales Brewery, Gwydir Street, Cambridge, CB1 2LJ.
**Tel** 01223 312188 (01223 566725,01223 350725) **Fax** 01223 312188
**Email** darkroom@66cnc.org.uk
**Opening times** Tue–Sun 12–5.

### ▶ Fitzwilliam Museum
Trumpington Street, Cambridge, CB2 1RB.
**Tel** 01223 332900
**Fax** 01223 332923
**Email** fitzmuseum-enquires@lists.com.ac.uk
**Ws** www.fitzmuseum.cam.ac.uk
**Opening times** Tue–Fri 10–5, Wed 10–7, Sat–Sun 12–5.
**Nearest Station** Cambridge.
**Personnel** Director: Duncan Robinson. Education Officer: Frances Sword.
**Services and Facilities** Café. Disabled Access. Friends Society. Guided Tours. Lectures. Museum Shop. Shop.
*Antiquities from Egypt, Greece, Rome, and displays of Roman, Romano-Egyptian, Cypriot and Western Asiatic art; Applied arts including: ceramics, furniture, textiles; coins and medals; manuscripts and rare printed books; paintings, including masterpieces by Titian, Veronese, Brueghel, Rubens, Canaletto, Monet, Renoir, Cézanne; drawings, prints. Events, concerts, gallery talks. Disabled Access, preferably by arrangement. Guided tours Sun 2.30 and by arrangement. The Museum's Courtyard development begins in January 2002 and will continue for approx. 18 months. The Founders Building only will remain open during this time, with variations in the display of the permanent collection. Admission free.*

### ▶ The Gallery
23 High Street, Fen Ditton, Cambridge, CB5 8ST.
**Tel** 012205 5264
**Opening times** By appointment.
**Personnel** Lynne Strover.

### ▶ Julia Heffer Gallery
2 Sussex Street, Cambridge.
**Tel** 01223 367699

### ▶ Kettle's Yard
Castle Street, Cambridge, CB3 0AQ.
**Tel** 01223 352124
**Fax** 01223 324377
**Email** Kettles-Yard-gen@lists.cam.ac.uk
**Opening times** Permanent collection 2–4 daily, closed Mon. Gallery Tue–Sat 12.30–5.30, Sun 2–5.30, closed Mon.
**Personnel** Director: Michael Harrison. Exhibitions: Simon Wallis. Education: Sophie Weeks. Public Relations: Fiona Bond.
**Services and Facilities** Bookshop. Disabled Access. Friends Society. Lectures. Museum Shop. Shop.

### ▶ Lynne Strover Gallery C
23 High Street, Fen Ditton, Cambridge, CB5 8ST.
**Tel** 01223 295264
**Fax** 01223 295264
**Opening times** Tue–Sat 10–5, Sun 12–5. Closed Mon.
**Work Stocked and Sold** Cer. Pa.

ELY

### ▶ The Stained Glass Museum P
North Triforium, Ely Cathedral, Ely, CB7 4DN.
**Tel** 01353 667735
**Fax** 01223 327367
**Opening times** Daily 1 Mar–31 Oct, Mon–Fri 10.30–4, Sat 10.30–4.30, Sun 12–3.
Also open on bank holidays, all school holidays and every weekend.
**Services and Facilities** Bookshop. Guided Tours. Lectures.

HUNTINGDON

### ▶ The Cottage Gallery C

11/12 High Street, Huntingdon, PF18 6TE.
**Tel** 01480 411521
**Fax** 01480 386521
**Opening times** Mon–Sat 9–5.30, Sun 10–4.
**Nearest Station** Huntingdon.
**Personnel** Manageress: Amanda Burrell. Proprietor: John Nind. Art Coordinator: Sarah Rennison.
**Services and Facilities** Art Consultancy. Art for Offices. Commissioning Service. Framing. Gallery space for hire. Lectures. Restoration. Shop. Valuation. Workshop Facilities.
**Work Stocked and Sold** App. Cer. Dec. Dr. Gla. Jew. Pa. Ph. Pr. Sc. Tx. Wd.
**Price range** £20–£10,000
For artists see Commercial Gallery Artists.

PETERBOROUGH

### ▶ Annakin Fine Arts

Owlburn, Church Lane, Helpston, Peterborough.
**Tel** 01733 252555
**Opening times** Daily 10–5.
**Personnel** Graham Kinnaird.

### ▶ Yarrow Gallery

Art Department, Oundle School, Glapthorn Road, Oundle, Peterborough, PE8 4GH.
**Tel** 01832 277170 **Fax** 01832 274034
**Opening times** Mon–Fri 10.30–1 & 2.30–5, Sun 2.30–5.
**Nearest Station** Peterborough.
**Personnel** Director: Roger Page.
**Services and Facilities** Gallery space for hire.

WISBECH

### ▶ Skylark Studios C

Hannath Road, Tydd Gote, Wisbech, PE13 5ND.
**Tel** 01945 420403
**Work Stocked and Sold** Pr.
**Price range** £30–£300

## ESSEX

BRENTWOOD

### ▶ Brandler Galleries C

1 Coptfold Road, Brentwood, CM14 4BN.
**Tel** 01277 222269 **Fax** 01277 222786
**Email** John@Brandler-Galleries.com
**Ws** www.brandler-galleries.com and www.thesaurus.co.uk/brandler
**Opening times** Tues–Sat 10–5.30.
**Nearest Station** Brentwood 400 yds, Shenfield 1 mile.
**Personnel** Director: John Brandler. Linda Rodrigues.
**Services and Facilities** Art Consultancy. Art for Offices. Commissioning Service. Framing. Parking. Restoration. Valuation.
**Work Stocked and Sold** Cer. Dr. Pa. Pr. Sc.
**Price range** £50–£65,000
For artists see Commercial Gallery Artists.

BUCKHURST HILL

### ▶ Reynolds Fine Art C

59 Queens Road, Buckhurst Hill, IG9 5BU.
**Tel** 020 8504 2244
**Opening times** Tue–Sat 10–6.
**Nearest Station** Buckhurst Hill.
**Personnel** Proprietor: Michael R. Reynolds.
**Services and Facilities** Restoration.
**Work Stocked and Sold** Dr. Pa.
**Price range** £150–£5,000
For artists see Commercial Gallery Artists.

CHELMSFORD

### ▶ Chelmsford and Essex Regimental Museums P

Oaklands Park, Moulsham Street, Chelmsford, CM2 9AQ.
**Tel** 01245 353066
**Opening times** Mon–Sat (bank holidays) 10–5, Sun 2–5.
**Personnel** Dr Tony Walentowicz.
**Services and Facilities** Lectures. Parking. Shop.

### ▶ Chelmsford Museum P

Old Cemetry Lodge, 1 Writtle Road, Chelmsford.
**Tel** 01245 281660
**Personnel** Anne Lityers Humprey.

COLCHESTER

### ▶ Chappel Galleries

15 Colchester Road, Chappel, Colchester, CO6 2DE.
**Tel** 01206 240326
**Opening times** Wed–Sun 10–6 or by appointment.
**Personnel** Wladyslaw Mirecki. Edna Mirecka.

### ▶ Dragonfly

The Old Bakery, Fordstreet, Aldham, Colchester, CO6 3PH.
**Tel** 01206 241043
**Opening times** Wed–Sat 10.30–4.30.
**Personnel** Hazel Albarn.

### ▶ Firstsite PS

The Minories art gallery, 74 High Street, Colchester, CO1 1UE.
**Tel** 01206 577067 **Fax** 01206 577161
**Email** info@1stsite.co.uk
**Ws** www.firstsite-online.org.uk
**Opening times** Mon–Sat 10–5 (summer), 10–4 (winter). Thu 10–8, Sun 12–5 (Jul & Aug only).
**Nearest Station** Colchester Mainline & Colchester Town.
**Personnel** Director: Katherine Wood. Education Officer: Sarah Lockwood. Marketing: Michelle Nye-Brown.
**Services and Facilities** Bookshop. Café. Commissioning Service. Friends Society. Guided Tours. Lectures. Shop.
**Work Stocked and Sold** Ab. Pa.
*Firstsite is one of the leading organisations presenting contemporary visual art in the East of England. Based at the Minories art gallery, Firstsite runs a year-round programme of exhibitions ranging from local to international artists. The exhibitions and events cover a wide variety of art forms, from painting, sculpture and crafts to live art and architecture. All exhibitions are accompanied by an exciting and inspiring series of events, talks and workshops for all ages. Visitors also enjoy relaxing in our Garden Café and browsing through the books, cards and magazines in our bookshop. Families are always welcome. Admission is free.*

### ▶ Sir Alfred Munnings Art Museum P

Castle House, Dedham, Colchester, C07 6AZ.
**Tel** 01206 322127 **Fax** 01206 322127
**Opening times** 3 May–4 Oct, Wed, Sun, bank holiday Mon. Also Thu & Sat Aug 2–5.
**Nearest Station** Colchester, Manningtree, Ipswich.
**Personnel** Chairman of Trustees: Mr J. D. Short. Administrator: Mrs C. Woodage.
**Services and Facilities** Disabled Access. Museum Shop. Parking.
**Work Stocked and Sold** Ab. Pr.
For artists see Commercial Gallery Artists.

### ▶ University of Essex Gallery P

Wivenhoe Park, Colchester, CO4 3SQ.
**Tel** 01206 284 100/873 333/872 074
**Fax** 01206 873 598/873 702
**Email** kennj@essex.ac.uk
**Ws** www.essex.ac.uk

GANTS HILL

### ▶ Deece Gallery

58 Highwood Gardens, Gants Hill, IG5 0AB.
**Personnel** Director: Philip See.

HARLOW

### ▶ Addison Wesley Longman

Edinburgh Gate, Harlow, CM20 2JE.
**Tel** 01279 623260
**Opening times** By appointment only.
**Personnel** Chris Brown.

SAFFRON WALDEN

### ▶ Fry Public Art Gallery

Bridge End Gardens, Castle Street, Saffron Walden, CB10 1BD.
**Tel** 01799 513779
**Opening times** 2.30–5.30, Sat, Sun and bank holidays from Easter Sunday–end of Oct.
**Nearest Station** Audley End.
**Personnel** Mr Nigel Weaver.
**Services and Facilities** Disabled Access. Friends Society. Lectures. Museum Shop. Shop.

### ▶ Saffron Walden Museum P

Museum Street, Saffron Walden, CB10 1LL.
**Tel** 01799 22494
**Personnel** Curator: Leonard M. Pole. Assistant Curator: Sheila Jordain.

SOUTHEND-ON-SEA

### ▶ Focal Point Gallery P

Southend Central Library, Victoria Avenue, Southend-on-Sea, SS2 6EX.
**Tel** 01702 612621 ext 207
**Fax** 01702 469241
**Email** sos@dial.pipex.com
**Services and Facilities** Workshop Facilities.

WESTCLIFF-ON-SEA

### ▶ Beecroft Art Gallery PS

Station Road, Westcliff-on-Sea, SS0 7RA.

**Tel** 01702 347 418
**Opening times** Tue–Sat 9.30–5 (closed 1–2).
**Nearest Station** Westcliff (Fenchurch Street line).
**Personnel** Curator: Arthur C Wright AMA. Assistant Keeper of Art: Miss C. Furlong.
**Services and Facilities** Friends Society. Gallery space for hire.

## HERTFORDSHIRE

### BARNET

**▶ Contemporary Ceramics** C
Whalebones, Wood Street,
Barnet, EN5 4BZ.
**Tel** 020 8449 5288
**Personnel** Gaynor Lindsell.

**▶ Old Bull Arts Centre**
68 High Street, Barnet, EN5 5SJ.
**Tel** 020 8449 5189

### HATFIELD

**▶ University of Hertfordshire Galleries** PS
College Lane, Hatfield, AL10 9AB.
**Tel** 01707 285376 **Fax** 01707 285310
**Email** s.moore@herts.ac.uk
**Ws** www.herts.ac.uk/artdes/
**Opening times** Art & Design Gallery Mon–Sat 9.30–5.30.
Margaret Harvey Gallery Wed–Sat 1–5.
**Nearest Station** Hatfield, St Albans.
**Personnel** Exhibitions Officer: Matthew Shaul. Exhibitions Assistant: Sanna Moore.
**Services and Facilities** Café. Commissioning Service. Disabled Access. Gallery space for hire. Lectures. Parking.
**Work Stocked and Sold** Ab. App. Cer. Cra. Dec. Dr. Pa. Ph.
*The Margaret Harvey Gallery at St Albans and the Art & Design Gallery on the Hatfield Campus provide excellent opportunities for both the academic community and the public to enjoy progressive and stimulating exhibitions of art and design from across the whole spectrum of activity. Each gallery has different design characteristics and together they support an extensive exhibition programme based on the work of a range of nationally and internationally recognised artists and makers. The galleries operate a policy which emphasises commitment to a diversity of practice and a desire to support our varied communities of users. Both spaces provide educational activities.*

### HEMEL HEMPSTEAD

**▶ Old Town Hall** PS
High Street, Hemel Hempstead, HP1 3AE.
**Tel** 01442 228095 **Fax** 01442 234072
**Opening times** Mon–Thu 10–3, Fri–Sat 10am–11pm.
**Nearest Station** Hemel Hempstead.
**Personnel** Borough Arts Manager: Sara Railson. Exhibitions: Claire Dolling.
**Services and Facilities** Art for Offices. Bar. Commissioning Service. Craftshop. Gallery space for hire. Parking. Restaurant.
**Work Stocked and Sold** App. Cer. Cra. Dec. Dr. Jew. Pa. Ph. Pr. Sc.
**Price range** £25–£500
For artists see Commercial Gallery Artists.

### HITCHIN

**▶ The Grosvenor Art Gallery**
11 Bridge Street, Hitchin,
**Tel** 01462 33663
**Opening times** Mon–Sat 10–5, closed Wed.
**Personnel** Roger McGowan.

**▶ Hitchin Museum & Art Gallery** P
Paynes Park, Hitchin, SG5 1EQ.
**Tel** 01462 434476
**Personnel** Acting Curator: Alison Taylor.

### LETCHWORTH

**▶ Letchworth Museum and Art Gallery** P
Broadway, Letchworth, SG6 3PF.
**Tel** 01462 685647
**Opening times** Mon–Sat 10–5. Closed Sun and some bank holidays.
**Personnel** Curator: Rosamund Allwood. Senior Curator: John Margoram. Curator: Anna Mercer. Education Officer: Liz Hunter.
**Services and Facilities** Gallery space for hire. Workshop Facilities.

**▶ Vilas Fine Arts** C
8–10 Leys Avenue, Letchworth, SG6 3EU.
**Tel** 01462 677455
**Fax** 01462 677455
**Work Stocked and Sold** Sc.
**Price range** £300–£12,000

### MUCH HADHAM

**▶ The Henry Moore Foundation**
Dane Tree House, Perry Green,
Much Hadham, SG10 6EE.
**Tel** 01279 843333
**Fax** 01279 843647
**Email** curator@henry-moore-fdn.co.uk
**Ws** www.henry-moore-fdn.co.uk/hnt
**Personnel** C. M. Joint.

### SAWBRIDGEWORTH

**▶ The Gowan Gallery** C
3 Bell Street, Sawbridgeworth, CM21 9AR.
**Tel** 01279 600004
**Opening times** Tue–Sat 10–5. Also most Mons – telephone to confirm.
Closed one week Christmas to New Year.
**Personnel** Joanne Gowan.
**Work Stocked and Sold** Cer. Cra. Gla. Jew. Wd.

### ST ALBANS

**▶ Museum of St Albans** P
Hatfield Road, St Albans, AL1 3RR.
**Tel** 01727 56679
**Personnel** Keeper of Natural Sciences: David Curry.

### STEVENAGE

**▶ Boxfield Gallery** PS
Stevenage Arts & Leisure Centre,
Stevenage, SG1 1LZ.
**Tel** 01438 242644
**Fax** 01438 242342
**Email** gordoncraig@stevenage-leisure.co.uk
**Opening times** Mon–Sun 9.30–10.
**Nearest Station** Stevenage mainline.
**Personnel** Visual Arts Officer: William Barnard.
**Services and Facilities** Bar. Café. Craftshop. Disabled Access. Gallery space for hire. Restaurant.
**Work Stocked and Sold** Cer. Dr. Pa. Pr. Sc. Wd.
**Price range** £10–£500
For artists see Commercial Gallery Artists.
*Boxfield Gallery, run by contract to Stevenage Borough Council, runs a varied programme of temporary exhibitions. Duration one month each, about four a year are contemporary shows, the remainder are mixed theme exhibitions. The gallery aims to increase public awareness and appreciation of art in general and to make the art gallery a welcoming and popular place. Gallery space 36 linear metres, height 3 metres. Gallery pays for preview, and hire cost. Also smaller Foyer Gallery which is suitable for water-colourists, photographers and printmakers. Four craft cabinets are avaliable.*

### WARE

**▶ Loft Gallery**
63 Cappell Lane, Stanstead Abbotts,
Ware, SG12 8BX.
**Tel** 01920 870013
**Opening times** By appointment.
**Personnel** Mrs Juliet Hill.

**▶ Trading Places Gallery**
11 New Road, Ware, SG12 7BS.
**Tel** 01920 469620 **Fax** 01920 463003
**Opening times** Main Gallery open Tues 10.30–4.30 or by arrangement.
**Personnel** Director: K. Walden.

### WATFORD

**▶ John Harsfield**
25 Valley Rise, Watford, WD2 7EY.
**Tel** 01923 675671/463123/226642

## LINCOLNSHIRE

### BOSTON

**▶ Blackfriars Art Centre**
Spain Lane, Boston, PE21 6HP.
**Tel** 01205 363108
**Personnel** Susan McCormick.

**▶ The Guildhall Museum** P
South Street, Boston, PE21 6HT.
**Tel** 01205 365954
**Personnel** Andrew Crabtree.

### GAINSBOROUGH

**▶ Gainsborough Old Hall** P
Parnell Street, Gainsborough, DN21 2NB.
**Tel** 01427 612669 **Fax** 01427 612779

### LINCOLN

**▶ Doddington Hall** P
Doddington, Lincoln, LN6 4RU.
**Tel** 01522 694308 **Fax** 01522 682584

**▶ Usher Gallery** PS
Lindum Road, Lincoln, LN2 1NN.
**Tel** 01522 527980 **Fax** 01522 560165



**Ab** Artists' Books **App** Applied Art **Cer** Ceramics **Cra** Craft **Dec** Decorative **Dr** Drawing **Fur** Furniture

**Email** woodr@lincolnshire.gov.uk
**Opening times** Mon–Sat 10–5.30, Sun 2.30–5. Admission charge.
**Nearest Station** Lincoln.
**Personnel** Principal Keeper: Richard H. Wood. Keepers: Rosalyn Thomas, Judith Robinson, Janita Elton. Education Officer: Pauline Roberts.
**Services and Facilities** Café. Disabled Access. Friends Society. Guided Tours. Shop.

### SPALDING

#### ▶ Woodbine Cottage Gallery C
Back Bank, Whaplode Drove,
Spalding, PE12 0TT.
**Tel** 01406 330693
**Fax** 01406 331004
**Email** yorath@woodbinecottagegallery.co.uk
**Ws** www.woodbinecottagegallery.co.uk
**Opening times** Sat, Sun, Mon 10.30–5.30 or by appointment.
**Nearest Station** Spalding or Peterborough.
**Personnel** Artist/Gallery Owner: Liz Yorath. Artist/Gallery Owner: Rowan Yorath.
**Services and Facilities** Art for Offices. Commissioning Service. Parking.
**Work Stocked and Sold** Cer. Dr. Pa. Ph. Pr. Sc.
**Price range** £50–£2,000
For artists see Commercial Gallery Artists.
*Woodbine Cottage Gallery, in a renovated Fenland cottage, is situated in the village of Whaplode Drove, 10 miles from Spalding and 14 miles from Peterborough, in the South Holland area of Lincolnshire. Owned and run by Liz and Rowan Yorath, it was established in 1996. The gallery features changing exhibitions of high quality contemporary art at accessible prices. The wide range of media shown include wood engraving, linocuts, ceramic pottery and sculpture painting and drawing. For details of current and forthcoming exhibitions please telephone, email or view our website. Limited disabled access.*

*Mick Stump,* Cathedral, Florence, *charcoal on paper, 50 x 70 cm, £290.*

### STAMFORD

#### ▶ Torkington Gallery
38 St Peters Street, Stamford, PE9 2PF.
**Tel** 01780 62281
**Personnel** Will Illsley.

## NORFOLK

### AYLSHAM

#### ▶ Red Lion Gallery
Holman House, Market Place,
Aylsham, NR11 6EJ.
**Tel** 0263 732115
**Fax** 0263 732115
**Personnel** Director: Elizabeth Butler.

### DISS

#### ▶ Palgrave Gallery
The Old Rectory, Rose Lane, Palgrave,
Diss, IP22 1AP.
**Tel** 01379 652056
**Personnel** Lesley Elgood.

### GORLESTON ON SEA

#### ▶ Hardies Gallery and Art Shop
205/6 High Street, Gorleston on Sea,
NR31 6RR.
**Tel** 01493 668003
**Opening times** Mon–Sat 9.45–6.
**Personnel** Michael Wide.

### GREAT YARMOUTH

#### ▶ Museums Galleries P
Central Library, Tolhouse Street,
Great Yarmouth, NR30 2SH.
**Tel** 01493 858900/745526
**Fax** 01493 745459

### HOLT

#### ▶ Judy Hines of Holt C
3 Fish Hill, Holt, NR25 6BD.
**Tel** 01263 713000

### HUNSTANTON

#### ▶ Ringstead Gallery
Ringstead, Hunstanton, PE36 5JZ.
**Tel** 01485 525316
**Personnel** Don Greer.

### KING'S LYNN

#### ▶ Deepdale Exhibitions
The Old Plough House, Burnham, Deepdale, near Brancaster, King's Lynn, PE31 8DD.
**Tel** 01485 210801
**Opening times** End Nov–end May daily by appointment including Sun at a time to suit you. End May–end Oct 11–5 including Sun, 11–4 Sat all through Sep–Oct.
**Personnel** Director: I. M. Birtwistle.
**Work Stocked and Sold** Pa.

#### ▶ Galeria Reflexions
56 Norfolk Street, King's Lynn, PE30 1AG.
**Tel** 01553 760766
**Opening times** Tues–Sat 10–5.30.
**Personnel** Derek Wright.

#### ▶ Houghton Hall
Estate Office, Houghton,
King's Lynn, PE31 6UE.
**Tel** 01485 528569
**Personnel** Miss S. Cleaver.

#### ▶ King's Lynn Arts Centre PS
27–29 King Street, King's Lynn, PE30 1HA.
**Tel** 01553 774725 **Fax** 01553 770591
**Opening times** Nov 1–Mar 31, Tue–Sat 11–4. Apr 1–Oct 31, 10–5.
**Personnel** Visual Arts Manager: Liz Falconbridge.
**Services and Facilities** Café. Disabled Access. Gallery space for hire. Restaurant. Workshop Facilities.
**Work Stocked and Sold** App. Cer. Cra. Dec. Dr. Jew. Pa. Sc. Tx. Wd.
**Price range** £10–£5,000

#### ▶ Unit 2 Gallery C
The Rural Workshops, Station Road,
Docking, King's Lynn, PE31 8LT.
**Tel** 01485 518817
**Opening times** Tue–Sun 10–4.
**Nearest Station** King's Lynn.
**Personnel** Director: Tony Eeles.
**Services and Facilities** Craftshop. Disabled Access. Parking.
**Work Stocked and Sold** Cer. Cra. Gla. Jew. Pr. Sc. Tx. Wd.
**Price range** £5–£1,000
For artists see Commercial Gallery Artists.

### MUNDESLEY

#### ▶ St Brannock's Gallery C
7 Cromer Road, Mundesley, NR11 8BE.
**Tel** 01263 722622
**Fax** 01692 650330
**Opening times** Sun/Mon 11–8 or by appointment.
**Nearest Station** North Walsham.
**Personnel** Curator: Jonathan Plumb.
**Services and Facilities** Gallery space for hire. Parking.
**Work Stocked and Sold** Cer. Cra. Dr. Fur. Pa. Pr. Sc. Tx.
**Price range** £150–£400
For artists see Commercial Gallery Artists.

### NORWICH

#### ▶ Frederick Gallery C
The Raveningham Centre, Beccles Road,
Raveningham, Norwich, NR14 6NU.
**Tel** 01508 548688 **Fax** 01508 548958
**Opening times** Mon–Sun 11–5, closed Tue.
**Personnel** Directors: Adrian Woodard, Janet Woodard.
**Services and Facilities** Commissioning Service. Disabled Access. Parking.
**Work Stocked and Sold** Cer. Dr. Pa. Sc. Wd.
**Price range** £25–£3,000
For artists see Commercial Gallery Artists.

#### ▶ The King of Hearts
13–15 Fye Bridge Street, Norwich, NR3 1LJ.
**Tel** 01603 766129
**Personnel** Mike Power.

#### ▶ Mandell's Gallery
Elm Hill, Norwich, NR3 1HN.
**Tel** 01603 629180

#### ▶ Norfolk Museums Service
Norwich, NR1 3JU.
**Tel** 01603 493624
**Fax** 01603 765651

**Ws** www.norfolk.gov.uk/tourism/museums/museums.htm
**Opening times** Mon–Sat 10–5, Sun 2–5.
**Nearest Station** Thorpe, Norwich.
**Personnel** Head of Museums: Vanessa Trevelyan. Keeper of Art: Andrew W. Moore.
**Services and Facilities** Art Consultancy. Art for Offices. Bookshop. Café. Craftshop. Disabled Access. Friends Society. Guided Tours. Lectures. Museum Shop. Shop.

### ▶ Norwich Gallery
Norwich School of Art and Design, St George Street, Norwich, NR3 1BB.
**Tel** 01603 610561 **Fax** 01603 615728
**Opening times** Mon–Sat 10–5.
**Personnel** Curator: Lynda Morris.
**Services and Facilities** Disabled Access. Lectures.

### ▶ Sainsbury Centre for Visual Arts
University of East Anglia, Norwich, NR4 7TJ.
**Tel** 01603 456060 (Galleries),01603 593199 (Enquiries) **Fax** 01603 259401
**Email** scva@uea.ac.uk
**Opening times** Tue–Sun 11–5. Admission £2 (£1 concs.).
**Nearest Station** Norwich.
**Personnel** Director: Nichola Johnson. Head of Admin. & Services: Kate Carreno. Curator of Collections and Exhibitions: Amanda Daly. Head of Education: Dr Veronica Sekules. Head of Conservation & Collection Management: Don Sale.
**Services and Facilities** Art for Offices. Bar. Bookshop. Café. Disabled Access. Friends Society. Guided Tours. Lectures. Museum Shop. Parking. Restaurant. Shop.

### ▶ The Orangery
Blickling Hall Gardens, Norwich.
**Tel** 01603 74077755

#### WELLS-NEXT-THE-SEA

### ▶ Holkham Picture Gallery
The Ancient House, Holkham, Wells-next-the-Sea.
**Opening times** 10–1, 2–5.
**Personnel** Margaret Melicharova.

### ▶ School House Gallery C
Wighton, near Wells-next-the-Sea, NR23 1AL.
**Tel** 01328 820457
**Opening times** 11.30–5.30 inclusive Sat, Sun and bank holidays. Closed Mon.
**Personnel** Director: Diana Cohen.
**Services and Facilities** Parking.
**Work Stocked and Sold** Cer. Dr. Pa. Pr. Sc.
**Price range** £100–£3,000
For artists see Commercial Gallery Artists.

## NORTH LINCOLNSHIRE

#### SCUNTHORPE

### ▶ Normanby Hall Country Park
Normanby, Scunthorpe, DN15 9HU.
**Tel** 01724 720226
**Personnel** Vivienne Morpeth.

### ▶ Scunthorpe Museum & Art Gallery P
Oswald Road, Scunthorpe, DN15 7BD.
**Tel** 01724 843533

### ▶ 20-21 Visual Arts Centre
St John's Church, Church Square, Scunthorpe.
**Tel** 01724 297 070

## SUFFOLK

#### ALDEBURGH

### ▶ Thompson's Gallery
175 High Street, Aldeburgh, IP15 5AN.
**Tel** 01728 453743 **Fax** 01728 452488
**Personnel** John Thompson. Susan Thompson. Graham Simper. Mathew Hall.

#### BURY ST EDMUNDS

### ▶ Bury St Edmund's Art Gallery PS
The Market Cross, Bury St Edmund's IP33 1BT.
**Tel** 01284 762081
**Fax** 01284 75074
**Email** enquiries@burysted-artgall.org
**Ws** www.burysted-artgall.org
**Opening times** Tue–Sat 10.30–5.
**Nearest Station** Bury St Edmund's.
**Personnel** Director: Barbara Taylor. Gallery Manager: Barbara Murray.
**Services and Facilities** Craftshop. Friends Society. Lectures. Shop. Workshop Facilities.
*Housed on the first floor of a magnificent grade one listed Adam building and playing a key role for visual arts in the region, the Gallery presents a changing programme of contemporary fine art and craft exhibitions. Often involving outreach partnerships, the Gallery has built an international reputation for its work in art textiles and a strong position for promoting craft practice It curates exhibitions that tour nationally. Run as an educational charitable trust, the Gallery's mission is to increase public awareness and enjoyment of art. A full programme of events accompanies each exhibition, aimed at all age groups and levels of interest and ability.*

### ▶ Chimney Mill Galleries
Chimney Mill, West Stow, Bury St Edmunds.
**Tel** 01284 778234

### ▶ Manor House Museum P
Honey Hill, Angel Corner, Bury St Edmunds, IP33 1UZ.
**Tel** 01284 757074
**Personnel** Gallery Supervisor: Chris Reeve.

### ▶ Moyses Hall Museum P
Cornhill, Bury St Edmunds.
**Tel** 01284 769834
**Personnel** Assistant Curator: Gareth Jenkins. Museums Liaison Officer: Irene Edwards.

### ▶ Ottewell Art Gallery
50 St Andrew's Street South, Bury St Edmunds, IP33 3PH.
**Tel** 01284 61172
**Opening times** Mon–Sat 9–5.30.
**Personnel** Mrs Denny.

#### CRANSFORD

### ▶ Boundary Gallery
Boundary House, Cransford.
**Tel** 01728 723862

#### HALESWORTH

### ▶ Halesworth Gallery
Steeple End, Halesworth.
**Tel** 01986 872409
**Opening times** Mon–Sat 11–5, Sun 2–5; May–Sep. Admission free.
**Personnel** Gallery Committee & Administrator.

#### IPSWICH

### ▶ First Floor Gallery
M. F. Frames Ltd, 10 St Helens Street, Ipswich.
**Tel** 01473 225544

### ▶ Ipswich Museums & Galleries Christ Church Mansion PS
(including Wolsey Art Gallery), Soane Street, Ipswich IP4 5NB.
**Tel** 01473 253246
**Fax** 01473 210328
**Opening times** Tue–Sat 10–5, Sun 2.30–4.30. Closes at dusk in winter.
**Personnel** Exhibitions Organiser: Rebecca Weaver.
**Services and Facilities** Disabled Access. Friends Society. Gallery space for hire. Lectures. Museum Shop. Shop.

### ▶ John Russell Gallery
4–6 Wherry Lane, Ipswich, IP4 1LG.
**Tel** 01473 212051 **Fax** 01473 212051
**Opening times** Mon–Sat 9.30–5.
**Personnel** Director: Anthony R. Coe.

### ▶ Shelley Priory
Hadleigh, Ipswich.
**Tel** 01206 337220

### ▶ Wolsey Art Gallery & Christchurch Mansion PS
Christchurch Park, (Ipswich Museums and Galleries: Ipswich Borough Council), Ipswich IP4 2BE.
**Tel** 01473 253246 **Fax** 01473 210328
**Email** christchurch.mansion@ipswich.gov.uk
**Opening times** Tue–Sat 10–5, Sun 2.30–4.30 or dusk in winter. Open bank holiday Mon.
**Nearest Station** Ipswich main line.
**Personnel** Exhibitions Officer: Rebecca Weaver.
**Services and Facilities** Art for Offices. Disabled Access. Friends Society. Guided Tours. Lectures. Museum Shop. Workshop Facilities.
*Grade I listed mansion with period rooms from Tudor to Victorian, which houses paintings by Gainsborough, Constable and Suffolk Artists. Incorporating gallery spaces with a lively exhibitions programme: The Wolsey Art Gallery and 'The Room Upstairs'.*

#### NEWMARKET

### ▶ Equus Art Gallery
Sun Lane, Newmarket, CB8 8EW.
**Tel** 01638 660901
**Personnel** Lydia Minahan.

### ▶ The Newmarket Fine Art Gallery
Nell Gwynn Studio,

Palace Street, Newmarket.
**Tel** 94 660065
**Personnel** Judith Leonard.

SAXMUNDHAM

### ▶ Snape Maltings Gallery C
Snape Maltings, near
Saxmundham, IP17 1SR.
**Tel** 01728 688305
**Fax** 01728 688930
**Email** info@snapemaltings.co.uk
**Ws** www.snapemaltings.co.uk
**Opening times** Open every day 10–, except 25–26 Dec.
**Nearest Station** Saxmundham.
**Personnel** Julia Pipe.
**Services and Facilities** Bar. Bookshop. Café. Craftshop. Disabled Access. Gallery space for hire. Parking. Restaurant. Shop.
**Work Stocked and Sold** Ab. Cer. Cra. Dr. Jew. Pa. Pr. Tx.
**Price range** £50–£500
For artists see Commercial Gallery Artists.

*Sylvia Paul,* Spring Flowers, *mixed media. Snape Maltings is a unique group of 19th-century granaries and malt houses beside the River Alde. The Gallery is one of six interesting outlets on the site, and shows original paintings, prints and craft. Additional space available to hire for exhibitions. Also painting and craft courses in summer.*

SOUTHWOLD

### ▶ New Gallery
10 Market Place, Southwold.
**Tel** 01728 724269
**Personnel** Jude Lockie.

SUDBURY

### ▶ Gainsborough's House PS
46 Gainsborough Street, Sudbury, CO10 2EU.
**Tel** 01787 372958 **Fax** 01787 376991
**Email** mail@gainsborough.org
**Ws** www.gainsborough.org
**Opening times** Tue–Sat 10–5, Sun 2–5. (closes at 4 Nov–Mar).
**Nearest Station** Sudbury.
**Personnel** Curator: Hugh Belsey. Assistant Curator: Andrew Hunter.
**Services and Facilities** Friends Society. Guided Tours. Lectures. Museum Shop. Workshop Facilities.
**Work Stocked and Sold** Pr.
**Price range** £50–£200

### ▶ The Phoenix Gallery
97 High Street, Lavenham, Sudbury, CO10 9PZ.
**Tel** 01787 247356
**Opening times** Mon–Fri 10–5.30, Sat 10–6, Sun 2–6.
**Personnel** Noel Oddy.

WOODBRIDGE

### ▶ The Barn Gallery
Mill Lane, Butley, Woodbridge, IP12 3PA.
**Tel** 01394 450843 **Fax** 01394 450843
**Opening times** Open daily 10.30–5.
**Personnel** Director: Graham Hussey.
**Services and Facilities** Café.

### ▶ The Fraser Gallery
62a New Street, Woodbridge, IP12 1DX.
**Tel** 01394 387535
**Personnel** Rosemary Fraser.

# North West

## BOLTON

BOLTON

### ▶ Bolton Museum, Art Gallery and Aquarium P
Le Mans Crescent, Bolton BL1 1SE.
**Tel** 01204 522311 ext 2191
**Fax** 01204 391352
**Opening times** Mon, Tue, Thu, Fri 9.30–5.30, Sat 10–5.
**Personnel** Keeper: Adrian Jenkins. Director: Dr J R A Gray.
**Services and Facilities** Disabled Access. Friends Society. Lectures. Museum Shop. Shop.

## BURY

BURY

### ▶ Bury Art Gallery & Museum PS
Moss Street, Bury BL9 0DR.
**Tel** 0161 253 5878 **Fax** 0161 253 5915
**Email** artgallery@bury.gov.uk
**Ws** www.bury.gov.uk/culture.htm
**Opening times** Tue–Sat 10–5.
**Nearest Station** Bury (Metrolink – Tram).
**Personnel** Curator: Richard Burns.
**Services and Facilities** Disabled Access. Gallery space for hire. Guided Tours. Lectures. Shop.

## CHESHIRE

PRESTBURY

### ▶ Artizana C
The Village, Prestbury, SK10 4DG.
**Tel** 01625 827582 **Fax** 01625 827582
**Opening times** Mon–Sat 10.30–5.30, Sun 2–5.30. (Furniture gallery closed Sun & Mon).
**Personnel** Directors: Jemila Topalian, Ramez Ghazoul.
**Services and Facilities** Commissioning Service.
**Work Stocked and Sold** Cer. Cra. Dec. Fur. Gla. Jew. Sc. Tx. Wd.
For artists see Commercial Gallery Artists.

SANDBACH

### ▶ dukes oak contemporary art gallery C
Dukes Oak, Brereton,
Sandbach, CW11 1SD.
**Tel** 01477 532337
**Opening times** Tue–Fri 10.30–5, Sat & Sun 12.30–4.
**Nearest Station** Crewe.
**Personnel** Director: Ruth Foster.
**Services and Facilities** Art Consultancy. Café. Commissioning Service. Craftshop. Parking. Workshop Facilities.
**Work Stocked and Sold** Cer. Dr. Pa. Pr. Sc. Tx.
For artists see Commercial Gallery Artists.

WARRINGTON

### ▶ Castle Park Arts Centre
off Fountain Lane, Frodsham,
Warrington WA6 6SE.
**Tel** 01928 35832

### ▶ Warrington Museum & Art Gallery P
Bold Street, Warrington, WA1 1JG.
**Tel** 01925 630550/444400
**Personnel** Curator: Alan Leigh. Cherry Gray.

WINSFORD

### ▶ Cheshire Visual Arts
Woodford Lodge, Woodford Lane,
Winsford, CW7 4EH.
**Tel** 01606 557328
**Personnel** Senior Art Advisor: David Firmstone.

### ▶ Woodford Visual Art Centre
Woodford Lane West, Winsford, CW7 4EH.
**Tel** 01606 557328 **Fax** 01606 862113
**Personnel** County Senior Art Adviser: David Firmstone.

## LANCASHIRE

ACCRINGTON

### ▶ Haworth Art Gallery P
Haworth Park, Manchester Road,
Accrington, BB5 2JS.
**Tel** 01254 233782 **Fax** 01254 301954
**Opening times** Open daily 2–5, except Fri.

BLACKBURN

### ▶ Blackburn Museum and Art Gallery P
Museum Street, Blackburn, BB1 7AJ.
**Tel** 01254 667130 **Fax** 01254 680870

### ▶ Lewis Textile Museum P
Exchange Street, Blackburn, BB1 7JN.
**Tel** 01254 667130

### ▶ The Street
Blackburn Central Library,
Town Hall Street,
Blackburn, BB2 1AH.

**Tel** 01254 661221 **Fax** 01254 690539
**Personnel** District Librarian: Mrs N. L. Monks.

### ▶ Witton Country Park Visitor Centre

Preston Old Road, Blackburn, BB2 2TP.
**Tel** 01254 55423
**Personnel** Senior Warden: Robert Wilson.

BLACKPOOL

### ▶ Grundy Art Gallery P

Queen Street, Blackpool, FY1 1PX.
**Tel** 01253 751701
**Fax** 01253 26370
**Opening times** Mon–Sat 10–5. Closed bank holidays.
**Personnel** Curator: Lynn Fade.
**Services and Facilities** Disabled Access. Lectures. Shop.

BURNLEY

### ▶ The Gallery Downstairs

Mid-Pennine Arts Association, Yorke Street, Burnley BB11 1HD.
**Tel** 01282 421986
**Personnel** Sheenagh Mayo.

### ▶ Towneley Hall Art Gallery and Museums P

Burnley BB11 3RQ.
**Tel** 01282 424213 **Fax** 01282 424213
**Opening times** Mon–Fri 10–5, closed Sat, Sun 12–5.
**Personnel** Director: Miss J. Susan Bourne BA, FMA.
**Services and Facilities** Café. Disabled Access. Guided Tours. Lectures. Parking. Shop.

### ▶ Wheatley Lane Library

Wheatley Lane, Burnley, BB12 9QH.
**Tel** 01282 693160
**Personnel** Exhibition Organiser: Shirley Ellis.

CHORLEY

### ▶ Astley Hall Museum and Art Gallery P

Astley Park, Chorley, PR7 1NP.
**Tel** 01257 515555 **Fax** 01257 515556

LANCASTER

### ▶ City Museum P

Market Square, Lancaster, LA1 1HT.
**Tel** 01524 64637 **Fax** 01524 841692

### ▶ Folly Gallery

26 Castle Park, Lancaster.
**Tel** 01524 388550

### ▶ Peter Scott Gallery PS

University of Lancaster, Lancaster, LA1 4YW.
**Tel** 01524 593057 **Fax** 01524 592603
**Email** m.p.gavagan@lancaster.ac.uk
**Ws** www.lancs.ac.uk/users/PETERSCOTT/Scott.htm
**Opening times** Mon–Fri 11–4; late Thu 6–8.30.
**Nearest Station** Lancaster.
**Personnel** Director: Mary Gavagan.
**Services and Facilities** Bar. Disabled Access. Guided Tours. Parking. Restaurant. Shop.
**Work Stocked and Sold** Cer. Dr. Pa. Pr. Sc.

PRESTON

### ▶ Harris Museum & Art Gallery PS

Market Square, Preston, PR1 2PP.
**Tel** 01772 258248 **Fax** 01772 886764
**Email** harris@pbch.demon.co.uk
**Ws** www.preston.gov.uk/museum
**Opening times** Mon–Sat 10–5. Closed on public holidays.
**Nearest Station** Preston.
**Personnel** Head of Arts and Heritage: Alexandra Walker.
**Services and Facilities** Art for Offices. Café. Disabled Access. Framing. Friends Society. Gallery space for hire. Guided Tours. Museum Shop. Shop.

***Cornelia Parker,* A Meteorite Lands in Epping Forest, *1996.***

*Fine art collections mainly British 18th–20th-century paintings, drawings and prints. Includes works by the Devis family, Newsham bequest of 19th-century paintings and sculpture. A collection of British ceramics, glass and costume includes Cedric Houghton bequest of ceramics. A lively and varied programme of temporary exhibitions including contemporary art. Limited blue badge parking only. Lift. Chairlifts to Mezzanine Galleries. Wheelchair Ramp. Refreshments. Guided tours are available and an education service to complement the permanent collection and exhibitions. Entry to all exhibitions is free.*

### ▶ Samlesbury Hall

Preston New Road, Samlesbury, Preston, PR5 0UP.
**Tel** 01254 812010
**Personnel** Exhibition Coordinator: Diana Birnie.

## LIVERPOOL

LIVERPOOL

### ▶ Acorn Gallery

16–18 Newington, Liverpool, L1 4ED
**Tel** 0151 709 5423 **Fax** 0151 709 0759
**Opening times** Mon–Sat 11–5.
**Personnel** Gallery Director: Janine Pinion.

### ▶ Bluecoat Display Centre C

Bluecoat Chambers, School Lane, Liverpool L1 3BX.
**Tel** 0151 709 4014 **Fax** 0151 707 0048
**Opening times** Tue–Sat 10.30–5.
**Personnel** Director: Maureen Lampton.
**Services and Facilities** Shop.
**Work Stocked and Sold** Cer. Cra. Gla. Jew. Tx. Wd.

### ▶ Liverpool University Exhibition

Abercromby Square, PO Box 147, Liverpool, L69 3BX.
**Tel** 0151 794 2000

### ▶ Open Eye Gallery P

28–32 Wood Street, Liverpool, L1 4AQ.
**Tel** 0151 709 9460 **Fax** 0151 709 3059
**Email** info@openeye.u-net.com
**Opening times** Tue–Fri 10.30–5.30, Sat 10.30–5.
**Nearest Station** Liverpool Central.
**Personnel** Director: Paul Mellor. Gallery Manager: Dave Williams. Education Officer: Helen James.
**Services and Facilities** Commissioning Service. Disabled Access. Gallery space for hire.
*Open Eye is an organisation which develops, promotes, enables, celebrates, challenges and contextualises contemporary and historical art practices which use or acknowledge a photographic language or technology for Merseyside and the greater North West region. The aims of the organisation are to: Develop: new artists, existing artists, informal educational programmes, formal educational programmes, training opportunities, bridges to new and existing audiences, curatorial skills and awareness, collaboration. Create: opportunities for new work, exhibitions (external, internal and virtual), technical support services, pathways to facilities. Disseminate: touring exhibitions, publications (both image and text), archived resources, the mission.*

### ▶ Parkingspace Gallery

37 Berry Street, Liverpool.
**Tel** 07779 589846

### ▶ Sudley House

Mossley Hill Road, Aigburth, Liverpool, L18 8BX.
**Tel** 0151 724 3245 **Fax** 0151 478 4190
**Ws** www.nmgm.org.uk
**Opening times** Mon–Sat 10–5, Sun 12–5.
**Nearest Station** Mossley Hill.
**Personnel** Director: Dr David Flemming. Keeper of Art Galleries: Julian Treuherz.
**Services and Facilities** Café. Disabled Access. Friends Society. Lectures. Parking.
*Sudley is undoubtedly one of Merseyside's gems. Situated in the leafy suburb of Mossley Hill, it was the home of George Holt (1825–1896), a founder of Lamport and Holt Shipping line. On display is a fine collection of late 18th and 19th century British paintings including two of Turner's most ambitious and dazzling works. There are superb paintings by Gainsborough, Bonnington and the Pre-Raphaelites and a group of 19th century sculptures ranging from Neoclassical marbles to decorative bronzes.*

### ▶ Tate Liverpool

Albert Dock, Liverpool L3 4BB.
**Tel** 0151 702 7400 **Fax** 0151 702 7401
**Email** liverpoolinfo@tate.org.uk
**Ws** www.tate.org.uk
**Opening times** Tue–Sun 10–5.50, closed Mon, except bank holidays. Also closed 24–26, 31 Dec, 1–2 Jan.

**Nearest Station** Lime Street.
**Personnel** Director: Lewis Biggs.
**Services and Facilities** Bar. Bookshop. Café. Disabled Access. Friends Society. Guided Tours. Lectures. Parking. Restaurant. Shop. Workshop.

### ▶ University of Liverpool Art Gallery PS
3 Abercromby Square, Liverpool L69 7WY.
**Tel** 0151 794 2348 **Fax** 0151 794 2343
**Email** artgall@liv.ac.uk
**Opening times** Mon–Fri 12–4. Closed weekends, bank holidays and Aug.
**Nearest Station** Lime Street.
**Personnel** Curator: Ann Compton. Assistant Curator: Matthew H. Clough. Secretary: Carole Clarke.
**Services and Facilities** Café. Lectures. Museum Shop.
*The art gallery displays a selection of the finest works of art belonging to the University of Liverpool. Among the highlights are a representative group of English watercolours, paintings by Joseph Wright of Derby and J. M. W. Turner, rare oil paintings by the wildlife artist J. J. Audubon, a fine selection of early English porcelain, stained glass cartoons by Edward Burne-Jones, portraits by August John, sculpture by John Foley and Lord Leighton and important works by leading twentieth century artists, including Sir Jacob Epstein, Lucian Freud and Dame Elizabeth Frink. The collection has grown up over the last hundred years through the generosity of local benefactors, supplemented more recently by purchases. These gifts and acquisitions of paintings, watercolours, sculpture, medals, silver, ceramics, furniture and textiles are both a fine collection of British art and an integral part of the University's history since its foundation in 1881. The presentation of the Art Gallery complements the elegant Georgian terrace house it occupies in Abercromby Square. A fine selection of clocks, furniture, carpets and tapestries lends a domestic atmosphere to this charming gallery. Only a small part of the University's substantial collection is on display in the Art Gallery; a tour of art around the Precinct is available from the Curator. Postcards and publications are on sale at the entrance to the Art Gallery. Coffee and light refreshments are available in Staff House next door to the Art Gallery at 4–5 Abercromby Square. Free lunchtime gallery talks are organised in term time, please telephone for details.*

### ▶ Walker Art Gallery PS
William Brown Street, Liverpool, L3 8EL.
**Tel** 0151 478 4199 **Fax** 0151 478 4190
**Ws** www.nmgm.org.uk
**Opening times** Mon–Sat 10–5, Sun 12–5.
**Nearest Station** Lime Street.
**Personnel** Director: Richard Foster. Keeper of Art Galleries: Julian Treuherz.
**Services and Facilities** Art Consultancy. Café. Disabled Access. Friends Society. Guided Tours. Lectures. Parking. Shop.

## MANCHESTER

MANCHESTER

### ▶ Bankley Studios Gallery
Bankley Street, Manchester.
**Tel** 0161 2564143

### ▶ Beech Road Gallery
70 Beech Road, Chorlton, Manchester M21.
**Tel** 0161 881 4912

### ▶ Castlefield Gallery
5 Campfield Avenue Arcade, Manchester.
**Tel** 0161 832 8034

### ▶ Chinese Arts Centre
39–43 Edge Street, Manchester M1 4FD.
**Tel** 0161 8327271
**Personnel** Exhibition Officer: Joanna Tong.

### ▶ Colin Jellicoe Gallery C
82 Portland Street, Manchester M1 4QX.
**Tel** 0161 236 2716
**Opening times** Tue–Fri 11–5, Sat 1–5.
**Nearest Station** Piccadilly, Oxford Road.
**Personnel** Directors: Colin Jellicoe, Alan Behar.
**Services and Facilities** Framing. Gallery space for hire.
**Work Stocked and Sold** Dr. Pa. Pr.
**Price range** £50–£450
For artists see Commercial Gallery Artists.

### ▶ Cornerhouse PS
70 Oxford Street, Manchester M1 5NH.
**Tel** 0161 228 7621 **Fax** 0161 236 7323
**Opening times** Tue–Sat 11–6, Sun 2–6.
**Nearest Station** Oxford Road.
**Personnel** Exhibitions Director: Paul Bayley.
**Services and Facilities** Bar. Bookshop. Café. Disabled Access. Guided Tours. Lectures.

### ▶ The Gallery Manchester's Art House C
131 Portland Street, Manchester M1 4PY.
**Tel** 0161 237 3551 **Fax** 0161 228 3621
**Email** elaine@manchesterarthouse.com
**Ws** www.manchesterarhouse.com
**Opening times** Mon–Fri 10–5, Sat 10–4, Sun closed.
**Nearest Station** Oxford Road/Piccadilly.
**Personnel** Proprietor: Elaine Mather. Manager: Zoë Ainscough. Manager: Claire Livingstone.
**Services and Facilities** Art Consultancy. Art for Offices. Commissioning Service. Disabled Access. Framing. Friends Society. Gallery space for hire. Restoration. Valuation.
**Work Stocked and Sold** Ab. App. Cer. Cra. Dec. Dr. Fur. Gla. Jew. Pa. Pr. Sc. Tx.
**Price range** £10–£10,000
For artists see Commercial Gallery Artists.

*Guy Portelli,* Dragonfly, *bronze ltd ed 1/10, 50" x 29" x 36", 2001, £4,100.*

*The Gallery Manchester's Art House opened on Portland Street in 1993 and is the largest private Fine Art Gallery outside of London. The Gallery's prestige has grown through hard work and dedication by the owner Elaine Mather and her talented staff Zoë Ainscough and Claire Livingstone.*
*The Gallery specialises in British contemporary Art and has helped to raise the profile of many young contemporary artists, not least Neil Canning and Caroline Bailey. It has launched the work of Arthur Berry, Kristen Baggaley, Peter Brown, and Mark Halsey. The Gallery has received awards from MCCI, Addleshaw Sons & Latham and Newsco, and was nominated for the first ABSA awards in 1999.*

### ▶ Manchester Central Library
St Peter's Square, Manchester M2 5PD.
**Tel** 0161 234 1900
**Personnel** Exhibitions Officer: Bill Nuttall.

### ▶ Manchester City Art Gallery PS
Mosley Street/Princess Street, Manchester M2 3JL.
**Tel** 0161 236 5244 **Fax** 0161 236 7369
**Email** cityart@mcr1.poptel.org.uk
**Ws** www.u-net.com/set/mcag/cag.html
**Opening times** Mon 11–5.30, Tue–Sat 10–5.30, Sun 2–5.30. Free admission.
**Nearest Station** Piccadilly, Oxford Road.
**Personnel** Director: Virginia Tandy. Press Officer: Kate Farmery. Senior Keeper, Exhibitions: Howard Smith. Senior Keeper, Collections: Lesley Jackson.
**Services and Facilities** Café. Friends Society. Gallery space for hire. Guided Tours. Lectures. Shop.
**Work Stocked and Sold** Cer. Fur. Pa. Sc.

### ▶ The Museum of Science & Industry in Manchester P
Liverpool Road, Castlefield, Manchester M3 4FP.
**Tel** 0161 832 2244 **Fax** 0161 833 2184
**Email** market@mussci.u-net.com
**Ws** www.edes.co.uk/mussci
**Opening times** 10–5.
**Personnel** Director: Dr J Patrick Greene OBE BSc FMA.

### ▶ Object 57 C
57 Thomas St, Northern Quarter, Manchester, M4 1NA.
**Tel** 0161 833 3377 **Fax** 0161 833 3773
**Email** mail@object57.co.uk
**Ws** www.object57.co.uk
**Opening times** 12–7 Thu–Sat, or by appointment.
**Nearest Station** Piccadilly.
**Personnel** Director: Trevor Johnson. Director: Michelle Lamon-Johnson.
**Services and Facilities** Art Consultancy. Art for Offices. Commissioning Service. Gallery space for hire.
**Work Stocked and Sold** Ab. App. Dr. Fur. Pa. Ph. Pr. Tx.
**Price range** £50–£5000
For artists see Commercial Gallery Artists.
*Object57 is an independent commercial gallery space based in the Northern Quarter of Manchester city centre.*
*Presenting fine and commercial art for viewing and sales, including painting, photography, graphics, illustration, 3D and new media. Exhibiting internationally established living artists and*

*collaborators alongside up-and-coming new talent from around Manchester and the North West. Mixed and solo shows. Object57 directors have over 20 years' experience with visual communication industries, and provide art and design consultancy. A comprehensive register of artists available to work on both private and commercial commissions is available by appointment.*

### ▶ Philips Contemporary Art C
37 Ducie Street, Piccadilly, Manchester.
**Tel** 0161 236 2707
**Opening times** By appointment.
**Personnel** Director: David Powell.
**Work Stocked and Sold** Pa.

### ▶ Rainmaker Gallery Of Contemporary Native American Indian Art C
41 Lapwing Lane, West Didsbury, Manchester M20 2NT.
**Tel** 0161 4480 1495 **Fax** 0161 4480 1495
**Opening times** Mon–Sat 10–6.
**Personnel** Mark Jacobs.
**Work Stocked and Sold** Pa.

### ▶ Tib Lane Gallery C
14a Tib Lane, Manchester M2 4JA.
**Tel** 0161 834 6928
**Opening times** Open during exhibitions 11–2, 3–5, Sat 11–1; closed Sun.
**Personnel** Director: J. M. Green.
**Services and Facilities** Art Consultancy. Art for Offices. Commissioning Service. Framing. Restoration. Valuation.
**Work Stocked and Sold** Dr. Pa. Sc.
**Price range** £100–£10,000
For artists see Commercial Gallery Artists.
*Founded in 1959, Tib Lane Gallery continues to exhibit British, mainly figurative 20th-century paintings, watercolours, drawings etc. and some sculpture, particularly bronzes by Adrian Sorrell. Solo and mixed exhibitions between September and the end of June each year show the work of well-established artists (Frink, Sutherland, Herman, Valette, Vaughan etc.) as well as that by many artists whose work is less widely known. Conservation and Framing.*

*Adrian Sorrell,* Hare, *bronze, height 19", 2001.*

### ▶ Via Communications
9 Market Buildings, Thomas Street, Northern Quarter, Manchester M4 1EU.
**Personnel** Michelle Lamon.

### ▶ The Whitworth Art Gallery
University of Manchester, Oxford Road, Manchester M15 6ER.
**Tel** 0161 275 7450 **Fax** 0161 275 7451
**Opening times** Mon–Sat 10–5, Sun 2–5. Free admission.
**Nearest Station** Oxford Road.
**Personnel** Director: Alistair Smith. Marketing Officer: Emma Parsons.
**Services and Facilities** Bookshop. Disabled Access. Friends Society. Guided Tours. Lectures. Parking. Restaurant. Shop.

## OLDHAM

OLDHAM

### ▶ Oldham Art Gallery P
Union Street, Oldham OL1 1DN.
**Tel** 0161 911 4653/4650
**Fax** 0161 627 1025
**Personnel** Senior Art Gallery Officer: Tessa Gudgeon. Catherine Gibson.

### ▶ Saddleworth Museum and Art Gallery P
High Street, Uppermill, Oldham OL3 6HS.
**Tel** 01457 874093/870336
**Opening times** Mon–Sat 10–5, Sun 12–5.
**Personnel** Voluntary Gallery Manager: Peter Fox.

## ROCHDALE

ROCHDALE

### ▶ Rochdale Art Gallery P
Esplanade Arts & Heritage Centre, Esplanade, Rochdale, OL16 1AQ.
**Tel** 01706 342154 **Fax** 01706 342154
**Personnel** Arts & Exhibitions Officer: Jill Morgan. Assistant Arts & Exhibitions Officer: Maud Sulter.

## SALFORD

SALFORD

### ▶ Chapman Gallery
University of Salford, The Crescent, Salford, M5 4WT.
**Tel** 0161 745 5000 ext 3219
**Personnel** Arts Administrator: Janice Webster.

### ▶The Lowry
Pier 8, Salford Quays, Manchester M5 2AZ.
**Tel** 0161 876 2035
**Fax** 0161 876 2001

### ▶ Salford Museum & Art Gallery PS
Peel Park, The Crescent, Salford M5 4WU.
**Tel** 0161 736 2649
**Fax** 0161 745 9490
**Opening times** Mon–Fri 10–4.45, Sat & Sun 1–5. Admission Free.
**Nearest Station** Salford Crescent.
**Services and Facilities** Café. Disabled Access. Friends Society. Gallery space for hire. Museum Shop. Parking.
For artists see Commercial Gallery Artists.

### ▶ Viewpoint Photography Gallery
Fire Station Square, The Crescent, Salford M5 4NZ.
**Tel** 0161 737 1040/0161 736 9448
**Fax** 0161 737 1091
**Opening times** Weekdays 9.30–5, Sun 2–5.
**Personnel** Viewpoint Art Base Manager: Jan Johnston. Marketing Assistant, Education & Leisure Directorate: Gavin Burns.

## SEFTON

SOUTHPORT

### ▶ Atkinson Art Gallery
Lord Street, Southport, PR8 1DH.
**Tel** 01704 533133 Ext. 2111
**Fax** 0151 934 2107
**Personnel** Keeper of Art Galleries and Museums: Anthony K. Wray.

## ST HELENS

ST HELENS

### ▶ St Helens Museum & Art Gallery P
College Street, St Helens, WA10 1TW.
**Tel** 01744 616614, 24061 ext 2961
**Personnel** Museum Officer: Kevin Moore.

## STOCKPORT

STOCKPORT

### ▶ Stockport Art Gallery PS
Wellington Road South, Stockport SK3 8AB.
**Tel** 0161 474 4453 **Fax** 0161 480 4960
**Email** stockport.art.gallery@stockport.gov.uk
**Opening times** Mon–Fri 11–5, Sat 10–5, closed Wed/Sun.
**Nearest Station** Stockport.
**Personnel** Senior Officer: Mr J. Sculley. Exhibitions Officer: Mr A. Firth. Outreach: Mr M. Bloom.
**Services and Facilities** Art for Offices. Craftshop. Disabled Access. Gallery space for hire.
**Work Stocked and Sold** App. Cer. Cra. Dec. Dr. Gla. Jew. Pa.
**Price range** £5–£2000
*Changing exhibitions of contemporary art, photography and craft with an emphasis on complementary events and practical workshops for children and adults, lectures etc. 'Artlink' – loan and purchase scheme for contemporary works of art. Small permanent collection of 19th- and 20th-century British paintings.*

## TAMESIDE

STALYBRIDGE

### ▶ Astley Cheetham Art Gallery PS
Trinity Street, Stalybridge, SK15 2BN.
**Tel** 0161 338 2708

**Opening times** Mon–Fri 1–7.30, Thu closed, Sat 9–4.
**Nearest Station** Stalybridge.
**Personnel** Director: Dr Alan Wilson.
**Services and Facilities** Friends Society. Gallery space for hire. Lectures. Museum Shop.
**Work Stocked and Sold** Ab. App. Cra. Dr. Pa. Pr.
**Price range** £10–£200

## WIGAN

LEIGH

### ▶ Turnpike Gallery PS

Civic Square, Leigh WN7 1EB.
**Tel** 01942 404469 **Fax** 01942 404447
**Email** turnpikegallery@wiganmbc.gov.uk
**Ws** www.wiganmbc.gov.uk
**Opening times** Mon, Thu, Fri 9.30–5.30, Tue 10–5.30, Wed 9.30–5, Sat 10–3. Closed Sun and bank holidays.
**Nearest Station** Atherton.
**Personnel** Gallery Officer: Kerri Moogan. Visual Arts Outreach Officer: Martyn Lucas.
**Services and Facilities** Disabled Access. Guided Tours. Lectures. Parking. Workshop Facilities.
*The Turnpike Gallery is a modern purpose-built gallery 3,200 sq ft in size, situated on the first floor of the Turnpike Centre. The contemporary exhibitions programme reflects the broad variety of current visual arts practice by regional, national and international artists. Each exhibition is accompanied by education events for general public, schools, colleges and other groups. Outreach activities for the public are organised throughout the year. The gallery also accommodates an artist in residence. Free admission.*

## WIRRAL

BIRKENHEAD

### ▶ Blackthorn Galleries C

2a Price Street, Hamilton Quarter, Birkenhead, CH41 6JN.
**Tel** 0151 649 0099
**Fax** 0151 649 0088
**Email** ogilvie@galleries.u-net.com
**Ws** www.galleries.u-net.com
**Opening times** Mon–Fri 9.30–5.30, Sat 10–5.
**Nearest Station** Hamilton Square (Mersey Rail).
**Personnel** Director (MD): Iain Ogilvie. Arts Director: Chris Wells.
**Services and Facilities** Art for Offices. Craftshop. Gallery space for hire. Shop. Workshop Facilities.
**Work Stocked and Sold** Cer. Gla. Jew. Pa. Ph. Pr. Sc.
**Price range** £15–£2, 500
For artists see Commercial Gallery Artists.

### ▶ Williamson Art Gallery and Museum P

Slatey Road, Birkenhead, L43 4UE.
**Tel** 0151 652 4177
**Fax** 0151 670 0253
**Opening times** Tue–Sat 10–5.
**Personnel** Curator: Colin Simpson.

HESWALL

### ▶ Dee Fine Arts

182 Telegraph Road, Heswall, L60 0AJ.
**Tel** 0151 342 6657
**Personnel** Deidre Waite.

PORT SUNLIGHT

### ▶ Lady Lever Art Gallery

Lower Road, Port Sunlight, CH62 4EQ.
**Tel** 0151 478 4136 **Fax** 0151 478 4140
**Ws** www.nmgm.org.uk
**Opening times** Mon–Sat 10–5, Sun 12–5.
**Nearest Station** Bebington.
**Personnel** Director: Dr David Flemming. Keeper of Art Galleries: Julian Treuherz.
**Services and Facilities** Café. Disabled Access. Friends Society. Guided Tours. Parking. Shop.
*Opened in 1922. The gallery was founded and built by philanthropist and soap manufacturer William Hesketh Lever, later the first Viscount Leverhulme, and houses his personal collection of works of art. These include Pre-Raphaelites, 18th- and 19th-century paintings, 18th-century furniture, Chinese ceramics, Wedgwood, sculpture, embroideries and tapestries. The Lady Lever Art Gallery is named in memory of Lever's wife and forms the centre piece of the garden village Lever built for his workforce. Of special note is a series of superb carved or inlaid cabinets, some by Chippendale and paintings by Reynolds, Wilson, Sargent, Burne-Jones and Leighton.*

# Northern

## CUMBRIA

ALSTON

### ▶ Gossipgate Gallery C

The Butts, Alston, CA9 3JU.
**Tel** 01434 381806
**Opening times** 10–5 daily including Sun Easter–Oct and winter weekends. Winter weekdays – telephone for details (closed 4 Jan–mid-Feb).
**Personnel** Proprietor: Sonia Kempsey.
**Services and Facilities** Art Consultancy. Café. Craftshop. Disabled Access. Friends Society. Parking. Shop.
**Work Stocked and Sold** Cer. Cra. Gla. Jew. Pa. Pr. Sc. Tx. Wd.
**Price range** £0.25–£500
For artists see Commercial Gallery Artists.

AMBLESIDE

### ▶ Dexterity C

Kelsick Road, Ambleside, LA22 0BZ.
**Tel** 015394 34045
**Opening times** 7 days 9.30–6, not 25–26 Dec.
**Nearest Station** Windermere.
**Personnel** Directors: Gillean Bell, Roger Bell.
**Services and Facilities** Art for Offices. Commissioning Service. Craftshop. Disabled Access. Framing.
**Work Stocked and Sold** Ab. Cer. Cra. Gla. Jew. Pa. Pr. Sc. Wd.
**Price range** £5–£500
For artists see Commercial Gallery Artists.

BOWNESS-ON-WINDERMERE

### ▶ Blackwell – The Arts & Crafts House PS

Bowness-On-Windermere, LA23 3JR.
**Tel** 015394 46139 **Fax** 015394 88486
**Email** info@blackwell.org.uk
**Ws** www.blackwell.org.uk
**Opening times** Open 7 days a week mid-Feb to Christmas, 10–5 (reduced hours in winter). Admission: adult £4.50, child/student £2.50, family £12.00.
**Personnel** PA to the Director: Julia Wells. Education Assistant: Kate Morgan. Marketing Assistant: Greg Hall. Registrar: Harvey Wilkinson. Curator: Ulrike Weiss. Director: Edward King.
**Services and Facilities** Bookshop. Café. Disabled Access. Friends Society. Guided Tours. Parking.

***Stained glass in bedroom, Blackwell House.***
*Blackwell is the largest and most important surviving Arts & Crafts house by the architect M. H. Baillie Scott. Built in 1900, it sits in an elevated position overlooking Lake Windermere and the Coniston Fells. Inspired by Lakeland flora and fauna, Baillie Scott designed every last detail of this treasure trove of the Arts and Crafts Movement, as can be seen in the symphony of art noveau stained glass, oak panelling, intricate plasterwork and fanciful metalwork. Recently restored, it now houses a collection of furniture, sculpture, ceramics, glass and metalwork as well as changing exhibitions of the highest quality sculpture, crafts and applied arts.*

CARLISLE

### ▶ Tullie House Museum & Art Gallery PS

Castle Street, Carlisle, CA3 8TP.
**Tel** 01228 534781
**Fax** 01228 810249
**Email** mickn@carlisle-city.gov.uk
**Opening times** Mon–Sat 10–5, Sun 12–5.
**Personnel** Arts Development Manager: Mick North. Director: Joanne Orr.
**Services and Facilities** Bar. Café. Disabled Access. Friends Society. Gallery space for hire. Lectures. Museum Shop. Restaurant. Shop. Workshop Facilities.
*Cumbria's largest museum and gallery complex. Continuous programme of contemporary visual arts and crafts. Exhibitions also drawn from the Fine and Decorative Art collections of 19th- and 20th-*

*century British art including the Bottomley Bequest of Pre-Raphaelites and an outstanding collection of porcelain from the major English factories. Lecture theatre and restaurant available for evening hire. Grounds and gardens.*

### COCKERMOUTH

**▶ Castlegate House**
Cockermouth, CA13 9HA.
**Tel** 01900 822149
**Personnel** Chris Wadsworth.

### CONISTON

**▶ Brantwood** P
Brantwood, Coniston, LA21 8AD.
**Tel** 015394 41396 **Fax** 015394 41263
**Personnel** Manager: Howard Hull.

### EGREMONT

**▶ Lowes Court Gallery**
12 Main Street, Egremont, CA22 2DW.
**Tel** 01946 820693
**Personnel** Jane Haywood.

### KENDAL

**▶ Abbot Hall Art Gallery** PS
Kendal, LA9 5AL.
**Tel** 01539 722464 **Fax** 01539 722494
**Email** info@abbothall.org.uk
**Ws** www.abbothall.org.uk
**Opening times** Open 7 days a week mid-Feb–20 Dec 2002, 10.30–5, 10.30–4 in winter. Admission: adult £3 (concessions available).
**Nearest Station** Oxenholme, the Lake District.
**Personnel** Director: Mr Edward King. Deputy Director & Head of Education: Cherrie Trelogan. Head of Finance & Administration: Beryl Tulley. Registrar: Harvey Wilkinson. Assistant Curator: Hannah Neale. Marketing Assistant: Greg Hall.
**Services and Facilities** Bookshop. Café. Commissioning Service. Disabled Access. Friends Society. Guided Tours. Lectures. Museum Shop. Parking. Shop.
*One of Britain's finest small independent art galleries, Abbot Hall is a wonderful place in which to see and enjoy art in the elegantly proportioned Georgian rooms. Permanent collection includes work by George Romney and the growing watercolour collection contains important Lake District scenes by Ruskin and Turner. The 20th century is represented by, amongst others, Ben Nicholson, Lucien Freud, Stanley Spencer and Kurt Schwitters. Abbot Hall has a high quality temporary exhibition programme which in recent years has seen successful shows by Lucien Freud, Bridget Riley and Paula Rego.*

*Abbot Hall exterior*

**▶ Brewery Arts Centre**
Warehouse Gallery, 122a Highgate, Kendal, LA9 4HE.
**Tel** 01539 725133 **Fax** 01539 730257
**Personnel** Visual Arts Officer: Ms Lene Bragger.

**▶ Oddfellows Gallery**
Highgate, Kendal.
**Tel** 01539 734669
**Personnel** Christian Thurston.

### KESWICK

**▶ Keswick Museum & Art Gallery** P
Fitz Park, Station Road, Keswick, CA12 4NF.
**Tel** 017687 73263
**Personnel** Hazel Davison.

**▶ Thornthwaite Gallery**
Thornthwaite, Keswick, CA12.
**Tel** 017687 78248

### PENRITH

**▶ Beck Stone Art Gallery**
Graystoke Gill, Penrith, CA11 0UQ.
**Tel** 017684 83601

**▶ Laburnum Ceramics Gallery**
Yanwath, near Penrith, CA10 2LF.
**Tel/Fax** 01768 864842
**Email** laburnum@kencomp.net
**Ws** www.laburnumceramics.co.uk
**Personnel** Owner: Viv Rumbold. Owner/Manager: Arne Rumbold. Assistant & Sales: Jan Bartle.
**Opening times** Tue–Sat 10–4, and bank holidays.
**Nearest Station** Penrith
**Work Stocked and Sold** App. Cer. Cra. Dec. Gla. Jew. Pa. Sc. Tx. Wd.
**Services and Facilities** Art Consultancy, Art for Offices, Commissioning, Craftshop, Disabled access, Guided Tours, Lectures, Parking, Restoration, Shop.
**Price range** £2–£1500
*Small rural specialist gallery devoted to contemporary studio ceramics, pottery and glass (few textiles, wood and jewellery). Cottage garden with pond and sculptures. High quality one-off works carefully selected by collector owners. 100 artists-designers from Great Britain and eight EU and other European countries. Exhibition programme of 5–6 shows, all self-originated, running from March to early January.*

### WHITEHAVEN

**▶ The Harbour Gallery**
The Beacon, Whitehaven.
**Tel** 01946 592302
**Opening times** Tue–Sun 10–4.30.

**▶ Whitehaven Museum & Art Gallery** P
Civic Hall, Lowther Street, Whitehaven.
**Tel** 01946 3111307 **Fax** 01946 693373
**Personnel** Curator: Harry Fancy.

### WORKINGTON

**▶ Carnegie Arts Centre**
Finkle Street, Workington, CA14 2B.
**Tel** 01900 602122 **Fax** 01900 604351
**Personnel** Director: Paul Sherwin.

## DURHAM

### BARNARD CASTLE

**▶ The Bowes Museum** C
Barnard Castle, DL12 8NP.
**Tel** 0183 369 0606 **Fax** 0183 637 163
**Email** info@bowesmuseum.org.uk
**Ws** bowesmuseum.org.uk
**Opening times** Daily 11–5.
**Nearest Station** Darlington.
**Personnel** Marketing: Ms Anne Allen.
**Services and Facilities** Art Consultancy. Café. Disabled Access. Friends Society. Gallery space for hire. Guided Tours. Lectures. Museum Shop. Parking. Restaurant. Restoration.
*Situated in the elegant Georgian market town of Barnard Castle in Teesdale, The Bowes Museum is a magnificent French chateau housing a nationally important collection of fine and decorative art including paintings by Boudin, Canaletto, El Greco, Goya and Tiepolo. It is famous for a life-sized silver swan automaton and has a busy programme of events and exhibitions. Exhibition of sugar sculpture in 2002. Touring exhibitions bring contemporary art. There are monthly craft markets and regular concerts, outdoor and indoor theatre, family fun days and an education and outreach programme.*

*The Bowes Museum, 2001*

**▶ Castle Gallery**
Witham Hall, Horsemarket, Barnard Castle, DL12.
**Personnel** Secretary: Mrs J. McLean.

### DARLINGTON

**▶ Darlington Art Gallery** P
Crown Street, Darlington, DL1 1ND.
**Tel** 01325 462034/469858
**Fax** 013225 381556
**Personnel** Divisional Manager: Peter White.

### DURHAM

**▶ Durham Art Gallery** PS
Aykley Heads, Durham, DH1 5TU.

**Tel** 0191 384 2214 **Fax** 0191 386 1770
**Email** durham.gallery@durham.gov.uk
**Ws** www.durham.gov.uk
**Opening times** Tue–Sat 10–5, Sun 2–5. Closed Mon.
**Nearest Station** Durham (5 mins walk).
**Personnel** Arts Development Manager: Post vacant. Art Gallery Assistant: Dennis Hardingham.
**Services and Facilities** Café. Disabled Access. Framing. Friends Society. Gallery space for hire. Museum Shop. Parking. Shop.

### ▶ Durham University Oriental Museum PS
Elvet Hill, Durham, DH1 3TH.
**Tel** 0191 374 7911 **Fax** 0191 374 7911
**Email** oriental.museum@durham.ac.uk
**Ws** www.dur.ac.uk/
**Opening times** Weekdays 10–5. Weekends 12–5.
**Nearest Station** Durham
**Personnel** Curator: Lindy Brewster. Deputy Curator: Karen Exell. Education Officer: Edith Nicholson. Secretary: Gloria Juniper.
**Services and Facilities** Bookshop. Café. Disabled Access. Friends Society. Guided Tours. Lectures. Museum Shop. Parking. Shop.

*Sung dynasty 12th–13th century,* Meiping (flower vase), *Malcolm MacDonald Collection, Acc. No. 1969 (M)253.*
*The Oriental Museum is a major resource for anyone in the North East who is interested in the visual arts. Its collections range from ancient Egypt to modern Japan and the major cultures of the Orient are well represented. The Museum runs a programme of lectures, day-schools and other events. Details from the Oriental Museum. Following a six-month period of Lottery-funded refurbishment, the Oriental Museum has reopened with a new Chinese Gallery focusing on 20th-century China, arts and crafts, the Imperial court, and the Silk Route. The museum has improved access, two cafés and a shop.*

## HARTLEPOOL

HARTLEPOOL

### ▶ Gray Art Gallery and Museum P
Clarence Road, Hartlepool TS24 8BT.
**Tel** 01429 266522

### ▶ Hartlepool Art Gallery P
Church Square, Hartlepool TS24 8EQ.
**Tel** 01429 869706 **Fax** 01429 523408

## MIDDLESBROUGH

MIDDLESBROUGH

### ▶ Cleveland Craft Centre C
57 Gilkes Street, Middlesbrough TS1 5EL.
**Tel** 01642 262376/226351
**Fax** 01642 226351
**Opening times** Tue–Sat 10–5.
**Personnel** Jeanette Harbron.
**Services and Facilities** Disabled Access. Lectures. Parking. Workshop Facilities.
**Work Stocked and Sold** Cer. Cra. Gla. Jew. Tx. Wd.

### ▶ Dorman Museum P
Linthorpe Road, Middlesbrough TS5 6LA.
**Tel** 01642 813781 **Fax** 01642 813781
**Personnel** Curator: Hilary Wade.

### ▶ Middlesbrough Art Gallery P
320 Linthorpe Road, Middlesbrough TS1 4AW.
**Tel** 01642 247445
**Fax** 01642 813781
**Opening times** Tue 10–5, Wed–Sat 10–6. Closed Sun & Mon except bank holidays.
**Personnel** Assistant Curator: Alison Lloyd.

## NEWCASTLE-UPON-TYNE

GATESHEAD

### ▶ Baltic Centre for Contemporary Art
Opens 9 March 2002.
Contact Gateshead Quays Visual Centre, St Mary's Church, Oakwellgate, Gateshead.
**Tel** 0191 478 1810.
**Email** Emmart@balticmill.com

### ▶ Design Works
William Street, Gateshead, NE10 OPJ.
**Tel** 0191 495 0066
**Personnel** Robin Bell.

### ▶ The Gallery, Gateshead Central Library
Prince Consort Road, Gateshead, NE8 4LN.
**Tel** 0191 477 3478
**Fax** 0191 477 7454
**Email** gateslib.demon.co.uk
**Ws** www.wamses.unn.ac.uk
**Opening times** Mon–Fri 9–7, Wed 9–5, Sat 9–1.
**Services and Facilities** Art Consultancy. Bar. Commissioning Service. Disabled Access. Parking. Workshop Facilities.

NEWCASTLE-UPON-TYNE

### ▶ Browns
First Floor, 15 Acorn Road, Jesmond, Newcastle-upon-Tyne NE2 2DJ.
**Tel** 0191 281 1315
**Opening times** Tue–Sat 10.30–5. Admission free.
**Personnel** Gallery Proprietor: Maureen Morgan.
**Services and Facilities** Café. Framing. Gallery space for hire. Restaurant.

### ▶ Chameleon Gallery
Milburn House, Dean Street, Newcastle-upon-Tyne NE1 1PQ.
**Tel** 0191 232 2819
**Personnel** Anne Collier.

### ▶ Corrymella Scott Gallery C
5 Tankerville Terrace, Jesmond, Newcastle-upon-Tyne NE2 3AH.
**Tel** 0191 281 8284, 0191 401 7513
**Fax** 0191 281 5434
**Email** corrymella@corrymella.co.uk charles.scott@corrymella.co.uk
**Ws** www.corrymella.co.uk
**Opening times** Daily 12–6.
**Personnel** Charles Scott.
**Services and Facilities** Art Consultancy. Art for Offices. Commissioning Service. Valuation.
**Work Stocked and Sold** Cer. Gla. Pa. Sc. Tx.
For artists see Commercial Gallery Artists.
*Specialising in British and Scottish contemporary paintings and sculpture.*

### ▶ Gallagher & Turner C
Units 3&4, St Thomas Street Workshops, St Thomas Street, Newcastle-upon-Tyne NE1 4LE.
**Tel** 0191 232 4895 **Fax** 0191 230 3013
**Personnel** Clare Turner.

### ▶ Gulbenkian Gallery
c/o 72 Moor Road North, Newcastle-upon-Tyne NE3 1AB.
**Personnel** Paula Stephenson.

### ▶ Hatton Gallery PS
Newcastle University, Newcastle-upon-Tyne NE1 7RU.
**Tel** 0191 222 6057 **Fax** 0191 222 6057
**Opening times** Mon–Fri 10–5.30, Sat 10–4.30.
**Personnel** Director: Andrew Burton.
**Services and Facilities** Bookshop. Friends Society. Gallery space for hire. Guided Tours. Lectures.

### ▶ Laing Art Gallery
Higham Place, Newcastle-upon-Tyne.
**Tel** 0191 232 7734

### ▶ Newcastle Arts Centre
67–69 Westgate Road, Newcastle-upon-Tyne NE1 1SG.
**Tel** 0191 261 5618
**Personnel** Mike Tilley.

### ▶ Side Gallery
5/9 Side, Newcastle-upon-Tyne NE1 3JE.
**Tel** 0191 232 2000
**Personnel** Richard Grassick.

### ▶ The University Gallery PS
University of Northumbria, Sandyford Road, Newcastle-upon-Tyne NE1 8ST.
**Tel** 0191 227 4424
**Fax** 0191 227 4718
**Email** mara-helen.wood@unn.ac.uk
**Opening times** Mon–Thu 10–5, Fri–Sat 10–4. Closed Sun and bank holidays.
**Personnel** Director: Mara-Helen Wood.
**Services and Facilities** Bookshop. Lectures.
**Work Stocked and Sold** Dr. Pa.
**Price range** £50–£5,000
For artists see Commercial Gallery Artists.

## NORTH TYNESIDE

### NORTH SHIELDS

**▶ Globe Gallery**
97 Howard Street, North Shields, NE30 1NA.
**Tel** 0191 259 2614
**Personnel** Ms Rashida Davison.

### WALLSEND

**▶ AdHoc Gallery** PS
Buddle Arts Centre, 258b Station Road, Wallsend, NE28 8RH.
**Tel** 0191 200 7132
**Fax** 0191 200 7142
**Email** the.buddle@northtyneside.gov.uk
**Ws** www.northtynesidearts.org.uk
**Opening times** Tue–Thu 1–5, Fri 10–5, Sat 2–5.
**Nearest Station** Train: Newcastle. Metro: Wallsend.
**Personnel** Curator: Mike Campbell.
**Services and Facilities** Bar. Commissioning Service. Disabled Access. Parking. Workshop Facilities.
**Work Stocked and Sold**
*AdHoc Gallery is located in the Buddle Arts Centre, North Tyneside's community arts and creative industries resource. The gallery has 46.5 meters linear hanging space and programmes a range of exhibitions. Main emphasis on professional artists from the Northern region; other shows by schools, community groups and the voluntary visual arts sector. Also occasional temporary installations and commissions. AdHoc Gallery and the Buddle Arts Centre are managed by North Tyneside Arts. Exhibitions policy available on request.*

## NORTHUMBERLAND

### ALNWICK

**▶ Bondgate Gallery** P
22 Narrowgate, Alnwick, NE66 3JG.
**Tel** 01665 576450
**Personnel** Exhibition Secretary: Peter Andrews.

**▶ The Chatton Gallery** C
Church House, New Road, Chatton, Alnwick, NE66 5PU.
**Tel** 01668 215494
**Personnel** Robert Turnbull.
**Work Stocked and Sold** Pa. Sc.

### BELFORD

**▶ Norselands Gallery** C
The Old School, Warenford, Belford, NE70 7HY.
**Tel** 01668 213465
**Opening times** Winter: 9–5. Summer: 9–9. Closed two weeks over Christmas/New Year.
**Nearest Station** Berwick-Upon-Tweed.
**Personnel** Directors: Barrie Rawlinson, Veronica Rawlinson.
**Services and Facilities** Café. Craftshop. Disabled Access. Parking. Workshop Facilities.
**Work Stocked and Sold** Cer. Cra. Dr. Gla. Pa. Pr.
**Price range** £15–£250
For artists see Commercial Gallery Artists.

### BERWICK UPON TWEED

**▶ Berwick Upon Tweed Borough Museum and Art Gallery** P
The Clock Block, Berwick Barracks, Ravensdowne, Berwick Upon Tweed, TD15 1DQ.
**Tel** 01289 330933 (Curator),01289 330044 (Council) **Fax** 01289 330540 (Council)

**▶ Sallyport Gallery**
48 Bridge Street, Berwick Upon Tweed, TD15 1AQ.

**▶ Three Feathers Gallery**
83c Mary Gate, Berwick Upon Tweed, TD15 1BA.
**Tel** 01289 307642
**Personnel** Brian Martin.

### CRAMLINGTON

**▶ Forum Gallery**
Cramlington Library, Forum Way, Civic Precinct, Cramlington.
**Tel** 0167 071 4371
**Personnel** Cultural Development Officer: Helen Payne.

### HEXHAM

**▶ Moot Hall**
Market Place, Hexham.

**▶ Queens Hall Art Centre**
Beaumont Street, Hexham, NE46 3LS.
**Tel** 01434 606787/8 **Fax** 01434 606043
**Personnel** Director: Peter Cutchie.

### ROTHBURY

**▶ Coquet Dale Arts Centre**
Front Street, Rothbury, NE65 7TZ.
**Tel** 01669 621557

**▶ Rothbury Library and Art Gallery**
Front Street, Rothbury. **Tel** 01669 620428.

**▶ Smith & Watson Stained Glass**
The Rothbury Gallery, Townfoot, Rothbury, NE65 7SL.
**Tel** 01669 621156
**Personnel** Dawn Smith.

### STAMFORDHAM

**▶ Stamfordham Gallery**
23 North Side, Stamfordham.

### WARKWORTH

**▶ Dial Gallery** C
5 Dial Place, Warkworth, NE65 0UR.
**Tel** 01665 710822
**Opening times** Tue–Sun 10–5.30, closed Mon.
**Personnel** Owner: Janice Charlton.
**Work Stocked and Sold** Cer. Cra. Gla. Jew. Tx. Wd.

## REDCAR AND CLEVELAND

### GUISBOROUGH

**▶ Art Screen Prints**
7a Chaloner Street, Guisborough, TS14 6QD.
**Tel** 01287 637527
**Work Stocked and Sold** Pr.

**▶ Walton Galleries**
Walton Terrace, Guisborough, TS14 6QG.
**Tel** 01287 638639
**Personnel** Director: Terry Wealleans.

### REDCAR

**▶ Kirkleatham Old Hall Museum** P
Kirkleatham Village, Redcar, TS10 5NW.
**Tel** 01642 479500
**Personnel** Curator: Philip Philo.

## SOUTH TYNESIDE

### JARROW

**▶ Bede Gallery**
Springwell Park, Butchersbridge Road, Jarrow, NE32 5QA.
**Tel** 0191 489 1807/420 0585
**Fax** 0191 420 0585
**Personnel** Director: Vince Rea.

### SOUTH SHIELDS

**▶ South Shields Museum & Art Gallery** P
Ocean Road, South Shields, NE33 2AU.
**Tel** 0191 456 8740
**Personnel** Curator: Mr J. Wilks.

## STOCKTON ON TEES

### BILLINGHAM

**▶ Billingham Art Gallery** P
Queensway, Billingham, TS23 2LN.
**Tel** 01642 397590 **Fax** 01642 397590

### STOCKTON ON TEES

**▶ Dovecot Arts Centre**
Dovecot Street, Stockton on Tees TS18 1LL.
**Tel** 01642 611625
**Personnel** Paul Mellor.

**▶ Preston Hall Museum** P
Yarm Road, Stockton on Tees TS18 3RH.
**Tel** 01642 791424
**Personnel** Curator: Julian Herbert.

## SUNDERLAND

### SUNDERLAND

**▶ Northern Gallery for Contemporary Art (NGCA)** PS
City Library and Arts Centre, 28–30 Fawcett Street, Sunderland SR1 1RE.
**Tel** 0191 514 1235 **Fax** 0191 514 8444
**Email** ele.carpenter@edcom.sunderland.gov.uk
**Ws** www.ngca.co.uk
**Opening times** Mon/Wed 9.30–7.30, Tue/Thu/Fri 9.30–5, Sat 9.30–4. Closed Sun, bank holidays.
**Nearest Station** Sunderland, 20 minutes from Newcastle.
**Personnel** Principal Curator: Ele Carpenter.
**Services and Facilities** Craftshop. Disabled

Access. Friends Society. Guided Tours. Lectures.
**Work Stocked and Sold** Cer. Cra. Dec. Gla. Jew. Pr. Sc. Tx. Wd.
**Price range** £5–£500
*Located on the top floor of the City Library and Arts Centre, 2 minutes' walk from Sunderland train station, NGCA presents internationally significant contemporary art. Year-round programme of exhibitions and events. Telephone for details.*

### ▶ Sunderland Museum & Art Gallery P
Fine and Applied Arts, Borough Road, Sunderland SR1 1PP.
**Tel** 0191 565 0723 **Fax** 0191 510 0675
**Personnel** Principal Keeper: Juliet Horsley.

WASHINGTON

### ▶ Arts Centre PS
Biddick Lane, Fatfield, District 7, Washington, NE38 8AB.
**Tel** 0191 219 3455 **Fax** 0191 219 3466
**Opening times** Mon–Sat 9–7.30.
**Personnel** Manager: Marie Kirbyshaw.
**Services and Facilities** Bar. Café. Craftshop. Disabled Access. Parking. Shop. Workshop Facilities.
**Work Stocked and Sold** Cer. Cra. Dec. Gla. Jew.
**Price range** £3–£75
For artists see Commercial Gallery Artists.

### ▶ Sun Arts
Biddick Farm, Fat Field, Washington, NE38 8AB.

# South East

## BRIGHTON & HOVE

BRIGHTON

### ▶ Barlow Collection of Chinese Art P
University Library, University of Sussex, Falmer, Brighton, BN1 9QE.
**Tel** 01273 606755
**Personnel** Curator: Prof. Craig Clunas.

### ▶ Brighton Museum and Art Gallery PS
Church Street, Brighton, BN1 1UE.
**Tel** 01273 603005/202900/290900
**Fax** 01273 779108
**Opening times** Mon, Tue, Thu–Sat 10–5, Sun 2–5.
**Personnel** Head of Libraries and Museums: Jessica Rutherford. Exhibitions Section: Nicola Coleby, Helen Grundy.
**Services and Facilities** Café. Friends Society. Guided Tours. Lectures. Museum Shop. Shop.

### ▶ First Light
3 Nile Street, Brighton, BN1 1HW.
**Tel** 01273 327344

### ▶ Gardner Centre Gallery C
University of Sussex, Falmer, Brighton, BN1 9RA.
**Tel** 01273 685447 **Fax** 01273 678551
**Opening times** Mon–Sat 11–5 and during theatre performances.
**Personnel** General Manager: Norma Binnie.

### ▶ Hugo Barclay C
7 East Street, Brighton, BN1 1HP.
**Tel** 01273 321694 **Fax** 01273 725959
**Email** hbarclay@cix.compulink.co.uk
**Opening times** Mon–Sat 10–1, 2–5.30.
**Personnel** Director: Hugo Barclay.
**Work Stocked and Sold** Cer. Gla. Jew. Wd.

### ▶ Phoenix Gallery
10–14 Waterloo Place, Brighton, BN2 2NB.
**Tel** 01273 603700
**Opening times** Mon–Sat 11–6, Sun 12–4.

### ▶ Preston Manor P
Preston Park, Brighton, BN1 6SD.
**Tel** 01273 292770

### ▶ Royal Pavilion P
Pavilion Buildings, Brighton, BN1 1EE.
**Tel** 01273 290900 **Fax** 01273 292871
**Opening times** Mon, Tues, Wed, Fri & Sat 10–5, Sun 2–5, closed all day Thu.
**Services and Facilities** Disabled Access.

### ▶ University of Brighton Gallery
Grand Parade, Brighton, BN2 2JU.
**Tel** 01273 643012 **Fax** 01273 643128
**Opening times** Mon–Fri 10–6.
**Personnel** Exhibitions Manager: Colin Matthews.

### ▶ White Gallery C
86/87 Western Rd, Hove, Brighton BN3 1JB.
**Tel** 01273 774 870 **Fax** 01273 748 475
**Email** artists@whitegallery.co.uk
**Ws** www.whitegallery.co.uk
**Opening times** Mon closed, Tue–Sat 10–6, Sun 11–4.
**Nearest Station** Brighton.
**Personnel** Director: Simon Owers. Director: Tim Owers. Ceramics Curator: Tina Davies. Jewellery Curator: Heidi Smith.
**Services and Facilities** Art Consultancy. Art for Offices. Commissioning Service.
**Work Stocked and Sold** App. Cer. Cra. Gla. Jew. Pa. Ph. Pr. Sc. Wd.
**Price range** £50–£6,000
*The White Gallery is an independent commercial gallery committed to promoting and presenting the best of contemporary art and craft in the South East. It is one of the few galleries outside London to consistently show non-figurative painters and one of the few places to see ceramics, glass and jewellery by known makers in a gallery setting. The White Gallery shows affordable works of art for the home and office.*

### ▶ Window Gallery, Fine Art and Framing C
59 Ship Street, Brighton, BN1 1AE.
**Tel** 01273 726190
**Opening times** Mon–Sat 10–5.30, bank holidays & Sun 1–5 (summer), 12–4 (winter).
**Nearest Station** Brighton.
**Personnel** Owner: Carole-Anne White.
**Services and Facilities** Art for Offices. Disabled Access. Framing.
**Work Stocked and Sold** Cer. Gla. Pa. Pr. Sc.
**Price range** £3–£6,000
For artists see Commercial Gallery Artists.

HOVE

### ▶ Hove Museum & Art Gallery P
19 New Church Road, Hove, BN3 4AB.
**Tel** 01273 290200 **Fax** 01273 292827
**Opening times** Tue–Fri 10–5, Sat 10–4, Sun 2–5, Mon closed.
**Personnel** Curator: Timothy Wilcox.

## EAST SUSSEX

BEXHILL-ON-SEA

### ▶ De La Warr Pavilion PS
The Marina, Bexhill-on-Sea, TN40 1DP.
**Tel** 01424 787900 **Fax** 01424 787940
**Email** dlwp@rother.gov.uk
**Ws** www.dlwp.com
**Opening times** Summer 10am–11pm. Winter 10–6.
**Nearest Station** Bexhill-on-Sea
**Personnel** Manager: Alan Haydon. Visual Arts Coordinator: Celia Davies. Marketing Manager: Tina Stiles.
**Services and Facilities** Bar. Café. Disabled Access. Friends Society. Guided Tours. Lectures. Parking. Restaurant.
*One of the world's best examples of modernist architecture, this Grade 1 listed building dominates the Bexhill seafront. Opened in 1935, the Pavilion offers a wide range of facilities and is a renowned centre of visual and performing arts. The gallery shows exhibitions of modern art, architecture and design. The 1000-seat theatre offers music, opera, drama and dance as well as children's shows, talks and exhibitions. The café/bar and balcony have superb sea views and in summer, the sun terrace is alive with open-air entertainments. Wheelchair access to all floors. Free admission to building.*

DITCHLING

### ▶ Ditchling Gallery
30 High Street, Ditchling, BN6 8TA.

EASTBOURNE

### ▶ Towner Art Gallery and Local Museum PS
Manor Gardens, High Street, Old Town, Eastbourne, BN20 8BB.
**Tel** 01323 417961 (admin) & 411688 (info service) **Fax** 01323 648182
**Email** townergallery@eastbourne.gov.uk
**Opening times** Tue–Sat 12–5, Sun & bank holiday Mon 2–5. Close at 4 Nov–Mar. Closed Mon, Good Friday, 24–27 Dec & New Year's Day.
**Personnel** Curator (Visual Arts): Matthew Rowe. Arts Administrator: Sarah Blessington.
**Services and Facilities** Disabled Access. Friends Society. Gallery space for hire. Guided Tours. Lectures. Shop.

HASSOCKS

### ▶ Ditchling Museum P
Church Lane, Ditchling, Hassocks, BN6 8TB.
**Tel** 01273 844744
**Opening times** Daily 11–5, Sun 2–5 (Apr–Oct); Sat 11–4.30, Sun 2–4.30 (Nov–Mar).
**Personnel** Curator: Hilary Bourne. Janel Cragg.

HASTINGS

### ▶ Hastings Museum and Art Gallery P

Johns Place, Cambridge Road,
Hastings, TN38 1ET.
**Tel** 01424 721202/781155
**Fax** 01424 781165
**Opening times** Mon–Fri 10–5, Sat 10–1, 2–5, Sun 3–5.
**Personnel** Director: Victoria Williams.

### ▶ Riviera Gallery

6 Pelham Arcade, Hastings, TN34 3AE.
**Tel** 01424 427088
**Opening times** Summer 10–6, Winter 11–5.
**Personnel** Coordinator: Vanessa Cunnew.

LEWES

### ▶ Firle Place

Lewes, BN8 6LP.
**Tel** 01273 858188

### ▶ Star Gallery C

Castle Ditch Lane, Lewes, BN7 1YJ.
**Tel** 01273 480218 **Fax** 01273 488241
**Opening times** Mon–Sat 10.30–5.30, closed Sun and bank holidays.
**Nearest Station** Lewes. Close to the castle and railway station, just off the High Street.
**Personnel** Director: Patricia Cooper.
**Services and Facilities** Disabled Access. Framing. Gallery space for hire. Restoration. Workshop Facilities.
**Work Stocked and Sold** Cer. Cra. Dr. Gla. Pa. Pr. Sc.
**Price range** £50–£5,000
For artists see Commercial Gallery Artists.

### ▶ The Workshop C

164 The High Street, Lewes, BN7 1XU.
**Tel** 01273 474207
**Opening times** Mon–Sat 9–5.30.
**Work Stocked and Sold** Jew.

RYE

### ▶ Rye Art Gallery C

Stormont Studio, Ockman Lane,
Rye, TN31 7JY.
**Tel** 01797 223218 **Fax** 01797 225376
**Opening times** Daily 10.30–5.
**Nearest Station** Rye.
**Personnel** Eric Money.
**Services and Facilities** Workshop Facilities.
**Work Stocked and Sold** Ab. Cer. Cra. Dr. Fur. Gla. Jew. Pa. Ph. Pr. Sc. Tx.
For artists see Commercial Gallery Artists.

## KENT

CANTERBURY

### ▶ The Herbert Read Gallery

KIAD at Canterbury, New Dover Road,
Canterbury, CT1 3AN.
**Tel** 01227 769371 ext 240 **Fax** 01227 451320
**Opening times** Mon–Fri 10–5.
**Personnel** Exhibitions Officer: Christine Gist.

### ▶ Nevill Gallery C

43 St Peter's Street, Canterbury, CT1 2BG.
**Tel** 01227 765291
**Fax** 01227 76291
**Email** inquiries@nevillgallery.com
**Ws** www.nevillgallery.com
**Opening times** Mon–Sat 10–5.
**Nearest Station** Canterbury.
**Services and Facilities** Art Consultancy. Commissioning Service. Framing. Restoration. Valuation. Workshop Facilities.
**Work Stocked and Sold** Pa. Pr. Sc.
**Price range** £11–£10,000
For artists see Commercial Gallery Artists.

### ▶ Royal Museum & Art Gallery P

High Street, Canterbury, CT1 2JE.
**Tel** 01227 452747
**Opening times** Mon–Sat 10–5.
**Personnel** Curator: Kenneth Reedie.

CHALLOCK

### ▶ Staveli Gallery

Forrest Office, Bucks St,
Challock, TN25 4AR.
**Tel** 01233 740040
**Opening times** Mon–Sat 10–5.
**Personnel** Director: Sandra Drew.

FOLKESTONE

### ▶ Folkestone Museum P

2 Grace Hill, Folkestone, CT20 1HD.
**Tel** 01303 850123
**Fax** 01303 242907

### ▶ Metropole Galleries PS

The Leas, Folkestone, CT20 2LS.
**Tel** 01303 255070
**Fax** 01303 244706
**Opening times** Apr–Oct: Mon–Sat 10–5, Sun 2.30–5. Nov–Mar: Tue-Sat 10–4, Sun 2.30–5.
**Personnel** Director: Nick Ewbank.
**Services and Facilities** Friends Society. Lectures. Parking.
**Work Stocked and Sold**
*Ten major exhibitions per year with an emphasis on contemporary painting, photography and sculpture (admission free). The Arts Centre programmes include a Children's Festival (April), Kent Literature Festival (September), Classical Concert Series, community arts and initiatives to support local artists.*

GILLINGHAM

### ▶ Gillingham Library Gallery

High Street, Gillingham, ME7 1BG.
**Tel** 01634 281066
**Fax** 01634 855814
**Personnel** Group Manager: Mrs V. Mawhinney.

### ▶ Space Frame Gallery C

Gillingham Adult Education Centre, Green Street, Gillingham, ME7 1XA.
**Tel** 01634 856439
**Personnel** Nicholett Goff. Rebecca Thomas.

HERNE BAY

### ▶ Herne Bay Museum and Art Gallery

William Street, Herne Bay.
**Tel** 01227 367 368

MAIDSTONE

### ▶ Bearsted Gallery

The Green, Bearsted, Maidstone, ME14 4DN.
**Tel** 01622 744130
**Personnel** Media Services Officer: Philip Schofield.

### ▶ Graham Clarke C

White Cottage, Green Lane, Boughton Monchelsea, Maidstone, ME17 4LF.
**Tel** 01622 743938 **Fax** 01622 747229
**Email** info@grahamclarke.co.uk
**Ws** www.grahamclarke.co.uk
**Opening times** Open by appointment.
**Nearest Station** Maidstone East.
**Personnel** Wendy Clarke. Dawn Masters.
**Services and Facilities** Disabled Access.
**Work Stocked and Sold** Ab. Dr. Pa. Pr.
**Price range** £50–£2, 500
For artists see Commercial Gallery Artists.
*Graham Clarke's 'Up The Garden Studio' is open by appointment. Graham Clarke, the artist, writer and humorist, one of Britain's most popular and best-selling printmakers, has created some 500 images of English rural life and history, and of the Englishman's view of Europe. He has been widely exhibited in Britain and abroad, examples of his work being held by royal, public and private collections in addition to those hanging on the walls of homes all over the world. His original etchings which are produced entirely by hand using traditional processes in strictly limited editions are available together with his watercolours, books, and greetings cards. Price lists and illustrations of recent images will be sent on request.*

### ▶ Maidstone Library Gallery

St Faith's Street, Maidstone, ME14 1LH.
**Tel** 01622 752344 **Fax** 01622 754980
**Opening times** Mon & Wed 9.30–7, Tue, Fri & Sat 9.30–5.30, Thu 10–5.30.
**Personnel** Dinah Pyatt. Arts Promotions Officer: Jenny Bowmer.

RAINHAM

### ▶ Christopher Turner C

4 Caledonian Court, Rainham, ME8 0DG.
**Tel** 01634 231465 **Fax** 01634 231465
**Work Stocked and Sold** Dr. Pa.

RAMSGATE

### ▶ Addington Street Studio & Gallery

49 Addington Street, Ramsgate, CT11 9JJ.
**Tel** 084 359 7405

### ▶ Ramsgate Library Gallery

Guildford Lawn, Ramsgate, CT11 9AY.
**Tel** 01843 593532 **Fax** 01843 293015
**Opening times** Mon–Thu 9.30–6, Fri 9.30–7, Sat 9.30–5.
**Personnel** Director: Sheena Watson.
**Services and Facilities** Lectures.

ROCHESTER

### ▶ Medway Towns Galleries PS

c/o Head of Arts, Civic Centre, Strood,
Rochester, ME20 4AW.

**Tel** 01634 727777
**Opening times** Phone for details.
**Services and Facilities** Disabled Access. Lectures.

SEVENOAKS

### ▶ Bank Street Gallery
3–5 Bank Street, Sevenoaks, TN13 1UW.
**Tel** 01732 458063
**Opening times** Mon–Sat 9.30–5.30.
**Personnel** Exhibitions Organiser: Fay Leighton.

### ▶ Sevenoaks Library Gallery
Buckhurst Lane, Sevenoaks, TN13 1LQ.
**Tel** 01732 453118/452384
**Fax** 01732 742682
**Opening times** Mon–Wed & Fri 9.30–5.30, Thu 9.30–8, Sat 9–5.
**Personnel** Arts and Heritage Officer: Amber Baylis.

TUNBRIDGE WELLS

### ▶ Fairfax Gallery C
23 The Pantiles, Tunbridge Wells, TN2 5TD.
**Tel** 01892 525525 **Fax** 01892 525525
**Opening times** Tue–Sat 10–6, Sun 11–4.
**Personnel** Directors: Andrew Scrutton, Lucy Scrutton, Tonia Bates.
**Services and Facilities** Art for Offices.
**Work Stocked and Sold** Cer. Dr. Pa. Sc.
For artists see Commercial Gallery Artists.

### ▶ Nicholas Bowlby
9 Castle Street, Tunbridge Wells, TN1 1XJ.
**Tel** 01892 510880
**Fax** 01892 510880
**Personnel** Nicholas Bowlby. Rosalind Bowlby. Jane McNeile.

### ▶ Squeaky Door
1 The Pantiles, Tunbridge Wells, TN2 5TD.
**Tel** 01892 518024
**Opening times** Mon–Sat 10–5.30, Sun 2–5.
**Personnel** Director: Dave Nicklin.

### ▶ Trinity Gallery PS
Church Road, Tunbridge Wells, TN1 1JP.
**Tel** 01892 678670
**Fax** 01892 678680
**Opening times** Daily 10–3.
**Nearest Station** Tunbridge Wells.
**Personnel** Visual Arts Officer: Emma Sandor.
**Services and Facilities** Art for Offices. Bar. Café. Commissioning Service. Craftshop. Disabled Access. Friends Society. Gallery space for hire. Lectures. Free parking. Restaurant. Shop. Workshop Facilities.
**Work Stocked and Sold** Cer. Cra. Dr. Gla. Jew. Pa. Ph. Pr. Sc. Tx. Wd.
**Price range** £50–£5,000
For artists see Commercial Gallery Artists.
*Trinity is dedicated to an engaging exhibition programme of diverse, innovative and high quality contemporary art in all media. There are two exhibition spaces, the main gallery exhibits work by both established artists and a new generation of promising younger artists. The smaller café gallery supports our commitment to education and outreach, displaying work by local schools, recent graduates, community workshops and collaborations with young curators. The gallery is part of an active arts centre with a varied programme of performances and cultural evenings.*

### ▶ Tunbridge Wells Museum and Art Gallery PS
Civic Centre, Mount Pleasant, Tunbridge Wells, TN1 1JN.
**Tel** 01892 554171
**Fax** 01892 534227
**Ws** www.tunbridgewells.gov.uk/museum
**Opening times** Mon–Sat 9.30–5. Admission free.
**Nearest Station** Tunbridge Wells.
**Personnel** Museum Manager: Dr M. L. J. Rowlands.
**Services and Facilities** Disabled Access. Friends Society. Gallery space for hire. Museum Shop. Shop.
**Work Stocked and Sold** App. Cer. Cra. Dec. Dr. Pa. Ph. Sc.
**Price range** £5–£5,000
*The Art Gallery holds around 20 exhibitions each year. These include the work of contemporary artists and craftsmen, touring exhibitions from national galleries, and the museum's works by Henry Peach Robinson, the Dodd Family, Pamela McDowell, Kenneth Pengelly, and the Ashton bequest of Victorian oil paintings.*

WHITSTABLE

### ▶ Whitstable Museum & Art Gallery P
Oxford Street, Whitstable, CT5 1DB.
**Tel** 01227 276998 **Fax** 01227 772379
**Opening times** Daily 10.30–1, 2–4; Wed & Sun closed.
**Personnel** Museum Development Officer: Amanda Giffard.

## SURREY

CHOBHAM

### ▶ The Bank Gallery C
73–75 High Street, Chobham, GU24 8AF.
**Tel** 01276 857369
**Opening times** Tue–Sat 10–5.
**Personnel** Proprietor: Elaine Coles.
**Work Stocked and Sold** Cer. Cra. Gla. Jew. Tx. Wd.

EAST MOLESEY

### ▶ The Molesey Gallery C
46 Walton Road, East Molesey, KT8 0DQ.
**Opening times** Thu, Fri & Sat 10–5 or by appointment.
**Personnel** Proprietor: Sue Palmer. Proprietor: Michael Palmer.
**Work Stocked and Sold** Pr.

FARNHAM

### ▶ CCA Galleries C
13 Lion and Lamb Yard, West Street, Farnham, GU9 7LL.
**Tel** 01252 722231 **Fax** 01252 733336
**Email** farnham@ccagalleries.com
**Ws** www.ccagalleries.com
**Opening times** Mon–Sat 9–5.30.
**Nearest Station** Farnham
**Personnel** Gallery Manager: Susan Kirkman.
**Services and Facilities** Framing.
**Work Stocked and Sold** Cer. Gla. Jew. Pa. Pr. Sc. Wd.
**Price range** £50–£5,000
For artists see Commercial Gallery Artists.
*For over 25 years, CCA Galleries has been one of Europe's leading publishers and galleries specialising in contemporary limited edition hand painted silkscreen prints and etchings. Our aim today is to seek out and bring to the attention of collectors the best prints available by both new and more established famous painters and printmakers.*

### ▶ Farnham Maltings Gallery
Bridge Square, Farnham, GU9 7QR.
**Tel** 01252 713637 **Fax** 01252 718177
**Opening times** Tue–Fri 10–4, Sat 10–1, closed Mon & Sun.
**Personnel** Visual Arts Officer: Christine Barker.
**Services and Facilities** Art Consultancy. Art for Offices. Bar. Disabled Access. Gallery space for hire. Lectures. Parking. Restaurant. Workshop Facilities.

### ▶ Foyer Gallery/ James Hockey Gallery PS
Surrey University College Institute of Art and Design, Falkner Road, Farnham, GU9 7DS.
**Tel** 01252 892668/01252 892646
**Fax** 01252 892667
**Email** ckapteijn@surrart.ac.uk
**Ws** www.surrart.ac.uk
**Opening times** Mon–Fri 10–5, Sat 10–4.
**Nearest Station** Farnham.
**Personnel** Galleries Coordinator: Christine Kapteijn.
**Services and Facilities** Art Consultancy. Disabled Access. Guided Tours. Lectures. Parking. Restaurant.
*The Foyer Gallery and James Hockey Gallery are operated as public galleries. They are committed to the accessibility of the visual arts to all, including those with special needs. The galleries show a wide range of exhibitions, including art, craft, design and related media, both from Britain and from abroad. They aim to promote work of lasting importance, which will contribute to the public and professional debate. Many of the educational events organised in conjunction with the exhibitions programme, are open to a broad and inclusive range of visitors, fostering the audience and arts professional of the future.*

### ▶ New Ashgate Gallery C
Wagon Yard, Lower Church Lane, Downing Street, Farnham, GU9 7PS.
**Tel** 01252 713208 **Fax** 01252 737398
**Email** gallery@newashgate.co.uk
**Ws** www.newashgate.com
**Opening times** Mon–Sat 10–5.
**Nearest Station** Farnham.
**Personnel** Director: Susan Szabanowicz. Manager: Joanne Barber. Gallery Assistant: Melissa Vaughan. Stratford Sales Development Officer: Annabel Wingfield.
**Services and Facilities** Art Consultancy. Art for Offices. Commissioning Service. Craftshop. Disabled Access. Framing. Friends Society. Lectures. Parking. Restoration. Shop.
**Work Stocked and Sold** App. Cer. Cra. Dr.

Fur. Gla. Jew. Pa. Pr. Sc. Tx. Wd.
**Price range** £30–£5,000
For artists see Commercial Gallery Artists.
*The gallery exhibits work by well-established professional contemporary artists and crafts people, whilst also promoting emerging younger talents. Monthly changing exhibitions, and a large stock of paintings, prints, sculpture, ceramics, jewellery, glass, wood and textiles.*

GODALMING

### ▶ Godalming Museum P
109a High Street, Godalming, GU7 1AQ.
**Tel** 01483 426510
**Opening times** Summer 10–5, winter 10–4.
**Personnel** Mr M. M. Gordon-Chairm. Museum Assistant: Jill Benson.

GOMSHALL

### ▶ Gomshall Gallery PS
Station Road, Gomshall, GU5 9LB.
**Tel** 01483 203795
**Fax** 01483 203282
**Opening times** Mon–Sat 10–5.30.
**Nearest Station** Gomshall (Guildford/Dorking).
**Services and Facilities** Craftshop. Parking. Shop.
**Work Stocked and Sold** Cer. Cra. Dec. Fur. Gla. Pa. Wd.
**Price range** £20–£1, 500
For artists see Commercial Gallery Artists.

GUILDFORD

### ▶ Guildford House Gallery
155 High Street, Guildford, GU1 3AJ.
**Tel** 01483 444740
**Fax** 01483 444742
**Opening times** Tue–Sat 10–4.45.
**Personnel** Curator: Iris Rhodes.

### ▶ Jonleigh Gallery
The Street, Wonersh, Guildford, GU5 0PF.
**Tel** 01483 893177

KINGSTON UPON THAMES

### ▶ The Stanley Picker Gallery for the Arts P
Kingston University, Middle Mill Island, Knights Park, Kingston upon Thames, KT1 2QJ.
**Tel** 020 8547 8074
**Fax** 020 8547 8068
**Ws** www.jpegdesign.co.uk
**Opening times** Mon–Fri 9.30–5.30, Sat 10–11.45.
**Nearest Station** Kingston.

LEATHERHEAD

### ▶ Studio Art House C
16 Church Road, Leatherhead, KT22 8AY.
**Tel** 01372 377173
**Work Stocked and Sold** Dr. Pa.

NEW MALDEN

### ▶ Gallery Focus C
Unit 2 Apex Tower, 9 High Street, New Malden, KT3 3DQ.
**Tel** 020 8336 0761/8942 9914
**Fax** 020 8336 2674
**Opening times** Mon–Sat 11–6.
**Nearest Station** New Malden.
**Personnel** Shane Waltener. Christine Kim.

REIGATE

### ▶ Bourne Gallery C
31–33 Lesbourne Road, Reigate, RH2 7JS.
**Tel** 01737 241614
**Fax** 01737 223291
**Email** bournegallery@aol.com
**Ws** www.bournegallery.com
**Opening times** Tue–Sat 10–5. Closed Mon & lunch 1–2.
**Nearest Station** Redhill
**Personnel** Directors: John Robertson, Ian Read, Linda Read.
**Services and Facilities** Art Consultancy. Art for Offices. Commissioning Service. Restoration. Shop. Valuation.
**Work Stocked and Sold** Dr. Pa. Sc.
**Price range** £150–£50,000
For artists see Commercial Gallery Artists.
*30,000 paintings... that's how many Victorian and traditional pictures we have sold in the past 30 years. A remarkable achievement for a gallery tucked away in a quiet side street of a market town. Today, we continue to stock original works priced from under £200 to over £20,000. If you are looking for a particular artist or would like to join us for a glass of champagne at our next exhibition please write for our brochure now or call in (phone for directions).*

RICHMOND

### ▶ Piano Nobile C
26 Richmond Hill, Richmond, TW10 6QX.
**Tel** 020 8940 2435
**Personnel** Dr Robert Travers. Nigel Manton. Alison Hill.

VIRGINIA WATER

### ▶ The Gallery C
13 Station Approach, Virginia Water, GU25 4DP.
**Tel** 01344 844460
**Fax** 01344 844785
**Email** Carpathian@btinternet.com
**Ws** www1.btwebworld.com/carpathian/
**Opening times** Wed–Fri 10.30–3.30, Sat 10–6 or later, Sun 12–6.
**Nearest Station** Virginia Water.
**Personnel** Directors: Bryan Forbes, Richard Dolinski, Andrew Dolinski, Peter Nagy, Nanette Forbes.
**Services and Facilities** Art for Offices. Bookshop. Commissioning Service. Disabled Access. Framing. Gallery space for hire. Parking. Restoration. Shop. Workshop Facilities.
**Work Stocked and Sold** Ab. Cer. Dec. Dr. Gla. Pa. Ph. Pr. Sc.
**Price range** £50–£6,000
For artists see Commercial Gallery Artists.

WEST BYFLEET

### ▶ T. P. I. Gallery
32 Station Approach, West Byfleet, KT14 6NF.
**Tel** 01932 351733
**Fax** 01932 341472
**Personnel** Mrs B. Sacoor.

WEYBRIDGE

### ▶ Edward Cross Gallery
128 Oatlands Drive, Weybridge, KT13 9HL.

## WEST SUSSEX

ARUNDEL

### ▶ Trinity Art Gallery
18B Tarrant Street, Arundel, BN18 9DJ.
**Tel** 01903 883689
**Fax** 01903 884309
**Personnel** Philip Richardson.

BILLINGSHURST

### ▶ Lanards Gallery C
Okehurst Lane, Billingshurst, RH14 9HR.
**Tel** 01403 782692
**Personnel** Mr Sims. Mrs Sims.

CHICHESTER

### ▶ Pallant House Gallery Trust
9 North Pallant, Chichester, PO19 1TJ.
**Tel** 01243 774557
**Fax** 01243 536038
**Opening times** Tue–Sat 10–5.15 (last admissions 4.45).
**Personnel** Curator: Louise Johnson.

HAYWARDS HEATH

### ▶ Ashdown Gallery C
49–53 Sussex Road, Haywards Heath.
**Tel** 01444 412827

HORSHAM

### ▶ Caufold Gallery C
Caufold, Horsham, RH
**Tel** 01403 864237

MIDHURST

### ▶ Peter's Barn Gallery C
South Ambersham, near Midhurst, West Sussex GU29 0BX.
**Tel** 01798 861388
**Fax** 01798 861581
**Email** peters.barn@ic24.net
**Ws** www.petersbarngallery.co.uk
**Opening times** Apr–Dec: Tue–Fri 2–6 and Sat, Sun and holidays 11–6. By appointment Jan–Mar.
**Nearest Station** Chichester, Petersfield, Pulborough, Haslemere – then taxi or bus.
**Personnel** Directors: Gabrielle & Annabel.
**Services and Facilities** Commissioning Service. Disabled Access. Parking.
**Work Stocked and Sold** Ab. App. Cer. Cra. Dr. Gla. Jew. Pa. Pr. Sc. Wd.
**Price range** £10–£9,000
For artists see Commercial Gallery Artists.
*Widely acknowledged as one of the most enchanting garden galleries in the South. Peter's Barn shows work by known, established and up and coming artists.*
*Set in a wild wooded water garden, this little*

*gallery makes full use of the beautiful garden space giving artists the opportunity to exhibit their work in an outside environment. The varied exhibitions change monthly. From the A272 – 3 miles east of Midhurst and 3 miles west of Petworth, take road opposite the Half Way Bridge Inn and follow the brown gallery signs.*

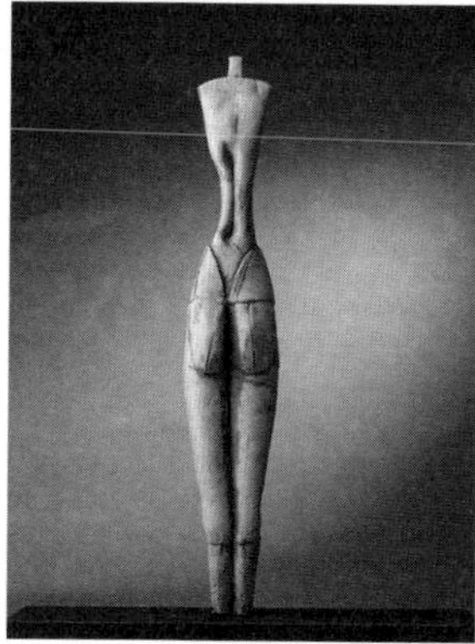

*Mo Jupp,* After Modigliani, *Sep 2000.*

WORTHING

### ▶ Worthing Museum & Art Gallery P
Chapel Road, Worthing, BN11 1HP.
**Tel** 01903 236552 ext 2526
**Fax** 01903 236552
**Opening times** Daily 10–6 (Apr–Sep), 10–5 (Oct–Mar), Sun closed.
**Personnel** Assistant Curator: Laura Woolley.

# South West

## BATH & NORTH EAST SOMERSET

BATH

### ▶ Adam Gallery C
13 John Street, Bath, BA1 2JL.
**Tel** 01225 480406 **Fax** 01225 480406
**Email** enquiries@adamgallery.com
**Ws** www.adamgallery.com
**Opening times** Mon–Sat 9.30–5.30.
**Personnel** Directors: Paul Dye, Philip Dye. Vanessa Wells, James McDonagh.
**Services and Facilities** Art Consultancy. Art for Offices. Framing. Restoration. Valuation.
**Work Stocked and Sold** Dr. Pa. Pr. Sc.
**Price range** £500–£50,000
For artists see Commercial Gallery Artists.

### ▶ American Museum in Britain P
Claverton Manor, Bath, BA2 7BD.
**Tel** 01225 460503
**Fax** 01225 480726
**Opening times** Late Mar to early Nov 2–5 every day (except Mon).
**Personnel** Director: William McNaught. Curator: Judith Elsdon.
**Services and Facilities** Café. Shop.

### ▶ Anthony Hepworth Fine Art Gallery
Ivy House, Cavendish Road, Sion Hill, Bath, BA1 2UE.
**Tel** 01225 442917 **Fax** 01225 442917
**Opening times** Tue–Sat 10–5.
**Personnel** Proprietor: Anthony Hepworth. Proprietor: Rose Hepworth. Paul Stolper.

### ▶ Beaux Arts C
12/13 York Street, Bath, BA1 1NG.
**Tel** 01225 464850
**Fax** 01225 422256
**Email** beauxart@netcomuk.co.uk
**Opening times** Mon–Sat 10–5.
**Nearest Station** Bath Spa.
**Personnel** Directors: Anna-Liza Singh.
**Services and Facilities** Art Consultancy. Art for Offices. Commissioning Service.
**Work Stocked and Sold** Cer. Dr. Pa. Pr. Sc.
**Price range** £50–£10,000
For artists see Commercial Gallery Artists.
*Beaux Arts is the longest established commercial gallery in Bath and is the sister gallery to Beaux Arts in Cork St, London. The gallery specialises in work of major 20th-century painters, sculptors and studio ceramicists. Beaux Arts has a programme of eight annual exhibitions, plus a Summer Exhibition renowned nationally for showcasing emerging new talent. Established artists include Michael Ayrton, John Bellany, Lynn Chadwick, Mary Fedden, Dame Elisabeth Frink, Josef Herman, John Piper and the St Ives School. Beaux Arts exhibits leading ceramists including the work of Emmanuel Cooper, Bernard Leach, John Maltby, Nicholas Arroyave-Portela, Robin Welch and Takeshi Yasuda.*

### ▶ Facade C
5–8 Saville Row, Bath, BA1.
**Tel** 01225 723636
**Work Stocked and Sold** Pa.

### ▶ Hitchcock's C
10 Chapel Row, Bath, BA1 1HN.
**Tel** 01225 330646
**Opening times** Mon–Sat 10–5.30. Closed bank holidays. Open last two Suns before Christmas.
**Personnel** Fleur Hitchcock.
**Work Stocked and Sold** Cra. Gla. Jew. Tx.

### ▶ The Holburne Museum of Art PS
Great Pulteney Street, Bath, BA2 4DB.
**Tel** 01225 466669
**Fax** 01225 333121
**Email** holburne@bath.ac.uk
**Ws** www.bath.ac.uk/holburne
**Opening times** Feb–6 Dec, 11–5 weekdays, Sun 2–5.30 (including bank holidays). Group bookings by appointment.
**Nearest Station** Bath Spa.
**Personnel** Director: Christopher Woodwood. Education Officer: Cleo Witt. Marketing & Publicity Officer: Sue Lucy. Curator of Decorative Art: Lisa White.
**Services and Facilities** Art Consultancy. Bookshop. Café. Disabled Access. Friends Society. Gallery space for hire. Guided Tours.Lectures. Museum Shop. Parking. Restaurant. Shop. Workshop Facilities.

*Thomas Gainsborough,* The Byam Family, *oil on canvas, 9' x 9', 1762. The largest Gainsborough painting in England.*
*The superb art collections in this famous 18th century building were formed by Sir William Holburne. Widely known for his silver, he also collected paintings, Italian bronzes such as the famous Susini owned by Louis XIV, maiolica, porcelain, glass, furniture and portrait miniatures. The picture gallery contains work by Turner Guardi and Stubbs plus portraits of Bath society by Thomas Gainsborough, including* The Byam Family *– on view to the public for the first time. Bath connections are represented by Angelica Kauffman's portrait of Henrietta Laura Pulteney, Hone's miniature of Beau Nash and Joseph Plura's 1752 marble masterpiece, made in Bath, depicting Diana and Endymion. Major temporary art exhibitions complement the displays.*

### ▶ Hotbath Gallery
City of Bath College, Avon Street, Bath.
**Tel** 01225 328673

### ▶ Kelston Fine Arts C
Kelston House, College Road, Lansdown, Bath, BA1 5RY.
**Tel** 01225 424224
**Personnel** Mrs S. Howell.
**Work Stocked and Sold** Pr.

### ▶ Larkhall Fine Art C
9 Cambridge Mews, Bath, BA1 6QE.
**Tel** 01225 329030
**Work Stocked and Sold** Pr.

### ▶ Museum of East Asian Art P
12 Bennett Street, Bath, BA1 2QL.
**Tel** 01225 464640 **Fax** 01225 461718
**Personnel** Tsara Boatman.

### ▶ Peter Hayes Contemporary Art
2 Cleveland Bridge, Bath, BA1 5DH.
**Tel** 01225 466215
**Opening times** Mon–Sat 10–4.
**Personnel** Exhibition Organiser: Peter Hayes. Exhibition Organiser: Joanne Hayes.

### ▶ Rooksmoor Gallery
31 Brock Street, Bath, BA1 2LN.
**Tel** 01225 420495
**Personnel** Connie Herring.

### ▶ Rostra Gallery C
5 George Street, Bath, BA1 2EH.
**Tel** 01225 448121 **Fax** 01225 447421

**Opening times** Mon–Sat 9–5.30.
**Personnel** Owner: Ms Connie Herring.
Manager: Ms Trudy Galvin. Mr Daniel Guld.
**Work Stocked and Sold** Cer. Gla. Jew. Pr.
**Price range** Up to £1,000

### ▶ Six Chapel Row Contemporary Art

Six Chapel Row, Bath, BA1 1HN.
**Tel** 01225 337900
**Fax** 01225 336577
**Opening times** Mon–Sat 10–5.30.
**Personnel** Josie Reed.

### ▶ St James's Gallery, C

9b Margaret's Buildings, Bath, BA1 2LP.
**Tel** 01225 319197
**Opening times** Mon–Sat 10–5.30.
**Personnel** Ron Sloman.
**Work Stocked and Sold** Cer. Cra. Jew. Pa. Pr. Wd.
For artists see Commercial Gallery Artists.

### ▶ Trimbridge Galleries

2 Trimbridge, Bath, BA1 1HD.
**Tel** 01225 466390
**Personnel** Mrs J. Anderson.

### ▶ Victoria Art Gallery P

Bridge Street, Pulteney Bridge, Bath, BA2 4AT.
**Tel** 01225 477772 **Fax** 01225 477231
**Opening times** Mon–Fri 10–5.30, Sat 10–5. Closed Sun and bank holidays.
**Personnel** Victoria Barwell. Jonathon Benneton.
**Services and Facilities** Disabled Access. Friends Society. Lectures. Workshop Facilities.

## BRISTOL

BRISTOL

### ▶ 3D Gallery

13 Perry Road, Bristol BS1 5BG.
**Tel** 0117 929 1363
**Opening times** Tue–Sat 11–5.30.
**Personnel** Owner: Annette Guck.

### ▶ Alexander Gallery C

122 Whiteladies Road, Clifton, Bristol BS8 2RP.
**Tel** 0117 973 4692 **Fax** 0117 940 6991

### ▶ Arnolfini Gallery PS

16 Narrow Quay, Bristol BS1 4QA.
**Tel** 0117 929 9191 **Fax** 0117 925 3876
**Email** publicity@arnolfini.demon.co.uk
**Ws** www.arnolfini.demon.co.uk
**Opening times** Mon–Sat 10–7, Thu 10–9, Sun 12–7.
**Nearest Station** Bristol Temple Meads.
**Personnel** Director: Caroline Collier. Deputy Director: Helen Pearson. Senior Curator: Catsou Roberts.
**Services and Facilities** Specialist Art Bookshop. Café/Bar. Disabled Access. Friends Society. Guided Tours. Lectures.
*Arnolfini is one of Europe's leading centres for the contemporary arts with a national and international reputation for presenting new and innovative work in the visual arts, performance, film and music. Approx. eight exhibitions are mounted annually. Arnolfini welcomes over 450,000 visitors a year. For a full list of Arnolfini publications please contact the Exhibitions Coordinator at Arnolfini. Arnolfini will be closing for refurbishment during 2002. Please phone ahead to confirm details.*

### ▶ Bristol Museum and Art Gallery P

Queen's Road, Bristol BS8 1RL.
**Tel** 0117 922 3571 **Fax** 0117 922 2047
**Opening times** Daily 10–5.
**Personnel** Martin Miller. Collections Manager: Alison Hems.

### ▶ Guild Gallery C

68 Park Street, Bristol BS1 5JY.
**Tel** 0117 926 5548 **Fax** 0117 925 5659
**Opening times** Mon–Sat 9.30–5 except Sun and bank holidays.
**Nearest Station** Temple Meads, Bristol.
**Personnel** Gallery Organiser: John Stops.
**Services and Facilities** Café. Craftshop. Gallery space for hire. Restaurant. Shop.
**Work Stocked and Sold** App. Cer. Cra. Dr. Jew. Pa. Ph. Pr. Sc. Tx. Wd.
**Price range** £100–£1,000
*A large and well-lit gallery on the second floor of the Bristol Guild of Applied Art. It is rented by exhibitors and no commission is charged on sales. There are monthly exhibitions by mainly, but not exclusively, West Country artists and craftspeople, individually or in small groups. There is now a small gallery next to our craft dept. which holds occasional exhibitions by craftsmen.*

### ▶ Michael Stewart Galleries

24 The Mall, Clifton, Bristol BS8 4DS.
**Tel** 0272 706265 **Fax** 0272 706268
**Opening times** Mon–Sat 10–5.30, Sun 12–3.

### ▶ Michael Wright Fine Art

Holloway House, 14 New Road, Pill Bristol BS20 0AD.

### ▶ Parkview Fine Paintings C

24 The Mall, Clifton, Bristol BS8 4DS.
**Tel** 0117 970 6265 **Fax** 0117 970 6268
**Ws** www.ourworld.compuserve.com/homepages/parkviewpaintings
**Personnel** Justin Gardener.
**Work Stocked and Sold** Pa.

### ▶ Royal West of England Academy PS

Queen's Road, Clifton, Bristol BS8 1PS.
**Tel** 0117 973 5129 **Fax** 0117 923 7874
**Opening times** Mon–Sat 10–5.30, Sun 2–5 during exhibitions.
**Nearest Station** Bristol Temple Meads
**Personnel** Secretary: Rachael Fear. Administrator: Diana Franklin. Education & Marketing: Clare Wood.
**Services and Facilities** Bookshop. Craftshop. Disabled Access. Friends Society. Gallery space for hire. Guided Tours. Lectures. Shop.
**Work Stocked and Sold** Pa. Pr. Sc.
*The RWA has been self-supporting for over 150 years, possessing an outstanding Grade II* listed building, galleries and permanent collection. An established venue for the fine arts, embracing an artistic awareness of the widest nature, and showing exhibitions, mainly by practising artists, which represent a 'broad church'. Open Autumn Exhibition held annually. Open Print, Sculpture and Painting Exhibitions triennially. Regular exhibitions of Academicians' work. Two student bursaries awarded annually. Galleries may be hired for evening functions. Friend's Association organises lectures, visits and holidays. Coffee available during exhibitions. Major building refurbishment currently in progress, as a result of appeal launched in 1998.*

### ▶ Royal West of England Academy C

Queen's Road, Clifton, Bristol BS8 1PX.
**Tel** 0117 973 5129 **Fax** 0117 923 7874
**Opening times** Mon–Sat 9–5.30, Sun 2–5.
**Nearest Station** Bristol Temple Meads.
**Personnel** Academy Secretary: Rachel Fear. Administrator: Di Franklin. Marketing and Education: Clare Wood.
**Services and Facilities** Disabled Access. Friends Society. Gallery space for hire. Lectures. Shop.
**Work Stocked and Sold** Pa. Pr. Sc.
**Price range** £30–£25,000

### ▶ Sir William Russell Flint Gallery

Broad Street, Wrington, Bristol BS18 7LA.
**Tel** 0117 940 5440

## CORNWALL

CAMELFORD

### ▶ North Cornwall Museum & Gallery P

The Clease, Camelford.
**Tel** 01840 212954
**Personnel** Sally Holden.

FALMOUTH

### ▶ Falmouth Art Gallery PS

Municipal Buildings, The Moor, Falmouth, TR11 2RT.
**Tel** 01326 313863 **Fax** 01326 312662
**Email** falag@uknetworks.co.uk
**Opening times** Mon–Sat 10–5. Closed bank holidays.
**Nearest Station** Penmere (Falmouth) from Truro.
**Personnel** Curator: Catherine Wallace. Assistants: Alex Hooper, Shelley Brett.
**Services and Facilities** Bookshop. Craftshop. Disabled Access. Guided Tours. Lectures. Museum Shop. Shop.
**Work Stocked and Sold** Ab. Cer. Cra. Dr. Jew. Pa. Pr. Sc.
**Price range** £5–£10,000
For artists see Commercial Gallery Artists.

### ▶ Falmouth Arts Centre

24 Church Street, Falmouth, TR11 3EG.
**Tel** 01326 314566 **Fax** 01326 211078
**Opening times** Daily 10–5.
**Personnel** Administrator: Mr M. Carver.

HELSTON

### ▶ Creftow Gallery C

6 Church Street, Helston, TR13 8TE.
**Tel** 01326 572848
**Opening times** Mon–Sat 10–5.
**Services and Facilities** Craftshop.
**Work Stocked and Sold** Cer. Cra. Dec. Dr. Jew. Pa. Ph. Pr. Sc. Tx. Wd.

**Price range** £5–£1,000
For artists see Commercial Gallery Artists.

### ▶ Mullion Gallery
Nansmellyon Road, Mullion, Helston, TR12 7DQ.
**Tel** 01326 241170
**Opening times** Summer: daily 10–1, 2.30–5.30. Winter: Wed–Sat 10–1, 2.30–5.30.
**Personnel** Agnes Lewis.

## MARAZION

### ▶ Avalon Art C
West End, Marazion, TR17 0EL.
**Tel** 01736 710161/711968
**Opening times** Tue–Sat 10.30–1.30 and 2–5 Oct–Apr. Open 7 days a week in summer.
**Personnel** Sally Scott. Lucie Bray.
**Services and Facilities** Disabled Access.
**Work Stocked and Sold** Ab. Cer. Cra. Jew. Pa. Pr. Sc. Wd.
**Price range** £5–£1, 500
For artists see Commercial Gallery Artists.

## MORVAH

### ▶ Yew Tree Gallery C
Keigwin Farmhouse, Morvah, near Penzance, TR19 7TS.
**Tel** 01736 786425
**Opening times** During exhibitions only 10.30–5.30, Sun 2–5, closed Mon. Other times by appointment.
**Services and Facilities** Art for Offices. Commissioning Service. Framing. Parking.
**Work Stocked and Sold** Cer. Cra. Fur. Gla. Jew. Pa. Tx. Wd.

## NEWLYN

### ▶ Badcocks Gallery
Badcocks Block, The Strand, Newlyn, Penzance, Cornwall, TR18 5HW.
**Tel** 01736 366159

## PENZANCE

### ▶ Market Garden Gallery
1 Bread Street,, Penzance.
**Tel** 01736 810 193

### ▶ The Bakehouse Gallery C
Old Bakehouse Lane, Chapel Street, Penzance,
**Tel** 01736 332223, 369979
**Opening times** Mon–Sat 10–5.
**Personnel** Brenda Gibbard.

### ▶ Newlyn Art Gallery PS
New Road, Newlyn, Penzance, TR18 5PZ.
**Tel** 01736 363715
**Fax** 01736 331578
**Opening times** Mon–Sat 10–5.
**Nearest Station** Penzance.
**Personnel** Director: Emily Ash. Shop Manager: Blair Todd.
**Services and Facilities** Bookshop. Craftshop. Disabled Access. Friends Society. Lectures. Shop. Workshop Facilities.
**Work Stocked and Sold** Ab. App. Cer. Cra. Dec. Dr. Jew. Pa. Ph. Pr. Sc. Tx. Wd.
**Price range** £3–£3,000
For artists see Commercial Gallery Artists.

### ▶ Round House Gallery
Sennen Cove, Land's End, Penzance, TR19 7DF.
**Tel** 01736 871859
**Opening times** Mon–Sat 10–6, Sun 12–6, Jun–Aug only.
**Personnel** Mrs Jones. P. A. Coxon.

### ▶ Shears Fine Art
58 Chapel Street, Penzance, TR18 4AW.
**Tel** 01736 50501

### ▶ Tony Sanders Penzance Gallery
14 Chapel Street, Penzance, TR18 4AW.
**Tel** 01736 66620

### ▶ Victoria Studios
Morrab Road, Penzance.
**Tel** 01736 62228
**Opening times** Throughout the year, opening times vary.
**Personnel** Director: Colin Scott.

## ST IVES

### ▶ Barbara Hepworth Museum P
Barnoon Hill, St Ives.
**Tel** 01736 796226
**Services and Facilities** Workshop Facilities.

### ▶ Judi Emmanuel
30 Fore Street, St Ives, TR26 1HE.
**Tel** 01736 797303/798448
**Personnel** Owner: Judi Emmanuel.

### ▶ Mosaic Gallery
8 St Andrews Street, St Ives, TR26 1AH.
**Tel** 01736 793459
**Opening times** Mon–Sat 10–5.
**Personnel** Owner: Mr A. Hill.

### ▶ The New Millennium Gallery
Street-An-Pol, St Ives, TR26 2DS.
**Tel** 01736 793121
**Personnel** Michael Holloway.

### ▶ Penhaven Gallery
4 St Peters Street, St Ives.
**Tel** 01736 798147
**Opening times** Every evening until 10pm from Whitsun. Aug: Mon–Sun 10.30–5.30. Otherwise most afternoons. Telephone to confirm.
**Personnel** Owner: David Beer.

### ▶ Penwith Galleries PS
Back Road West, St Ives, TR26 1NL.
**Tel** 01736 795579
**Opening times** Tue–Sat 10–1, 2.30–5. Admission: 50p.
**Nearest Station** St Ives.
**Personnel** Director: Kathleen Watkins.
**Services and Facilities** Art for Offices. Bookshop. Commissioning Service. Friends Society. Shop. Workshop Facilities.
**Work Stocked and Sold** Ab. App. Cer. Cra. Dec. Dr. Jew. Pa. Pr. Sc. Wd.
For artists see Commercial Gallery Artists.
*The Penwith Society was founded in 1949 by a group of notable contemporary artists in St Ives and its seasonal exhibitions became a national showing place for contemporary work. The Society has an elected membership, limited to 50, and an unlimited associated membership. Its aims are to encourage practising artists and craftsmen in Cornwall and foster public interest in the arts. The gallery has charity status. It is a unique complex of buildings including public galleries, print workshop, bookshop, artists' studios and workshops. Continuous exhibitions of paintings, sculpture and ceramics throughout the year.*

### ▶ Picture House Galleries C
Island Square, St Ives, TR26 1NT.
**Tel** 01736 794423
**Opening times** Mon–Sun 10.30–5.
**Personnel** Roger Gadwallader.
**Services and Facilities** Framing.
**Work Stocked and Sold** Cer. Gla. Pa. Pr.
For artists see Commercial Gallery Artists.

### ▶ Plumbline Gallery C
2 Barnoon Hill, St Ives, TR26 1AD.
**Tel** 01736 797771
**Opening times** Mon–Sat 10.30–1, 2–6. Open to 9pm in the summer.
**Personnel** Owner: Arthur Hancox.
**Work Stocked and Sold** Pr.

### ▶ Porthmeor Gallery
Porthmeor Road, St Ives, TR26 1NP.
**Tel** 01736 798412
**Opening times** Mon–Sat 10.30–5.30.
**Personnel** Partner: Richard Ayling.

### ▶ Salthouse Gallery
Norway Square, St Ives, TR26 1NA.
**Tel** 01736 795003
**Opening times** Sep–Jul: Mon–Sat 10.30–6; Aug: Mon–Sat 10.30–10.
**Personnel** Director: Bob Devereux.

### ▶ Sims Gallery
22 Fore Street, St Ives, TR26 1HE.
**Tel** 01736 797148 **Fax** 01736 797148
**Opening times** Mon–Sat 10–5 or by appointment.
**Personnel** Owner: Mr Leon Sudderby.

### ▶ Tate Gallery St Ives
Porthmeor Beach, St Ives, TR26 1TG.
**Tel** 01736 796226
**Fax** 01736 794480
**Ws** www.tate.org.uk
**Opening times** Apr–Sep: Mon–Sun 10.30–5.30. Oct–Mar: Tue–Sun 10.30–5.30. Closed 24–26 Dec.
**Nearest Station** St Erth for St Ives.
**Personnel** Gallery Coordinator: Richard Perkins. Press & Information: Ina Cole. Education: Susan Lamb. Works of Art Officer: Andrew Dalton. Curator: Susan Daniel-McElroy.
**Services and Facilities** Bookshop. Café. Disabled Access. Friends Society. Guided Tours. Lectures. Museum Shop. Restaurant. Shop. Workshop Facilities.
*Tate St Ives opened in 1993 and presents changing displays of 20th-century art from the Tate Gallery Collection, focusing on the post-war modern movement St Ives is so famous for. Key artists represented in the collection include Ben Nicholson, Barbara Hepworth, Naum Gabo, John Wells, Patrick Heron and Terry Frost. The displays are complemented by exhibitions which explore the diversity of*

*working methods in art today. Exhibitions: to 3 Mar, Sandra Blow; 16 Mar–May, Ian Hamilton Finlay, Simon Starling; Jun–Aug, Richard Long, Naum Gabo; Sep–Nov, Digital Season. The Barbara Hepworth Museum and Sculpture Garden in St Ives is managed by Tate St Ives.*

### ▶ Wills Lane Gallery
Wills Lane, St Ives, TR26 1AF.
**Tel** 01736 795723
**Opening times** Mon–Sun 10–4.
**Personnel** Director: Mr Henry Gilbert.

#### TRURO

### ▶ The Gallery Portscatho
Portscatho, near St Mawes, Truro TR2 5HQ.
**Tel** 01872 580719
**Fax** 01872 580719
**Opening times** Mon–Tue, Thu–Sat 10–12, 2–5.30; and by appointment.
**Personnel** Exhibition Organiser: Christopher Insoll.

### ▶ Royal Cornwall Museum P
River Street, Truro TR1 2SJ.
**Tel** 01872 72205
**Opening times** Mon–Sat 10–5 all year round, except bank holidays.
**Personnel** Director: Caroline Dudley BA FMA. Curator of Art Exhibitions: Tamsin Daniel.
**Services and Facilities** Bookshop. Craftshop. Disabled Access. Friends Society. Guided Tours. Lectures. Restaurant.
**Work Stocked and Sold** Ab. Cer. Cra. Ph.

## DEVON

#### BIDEFORD

### ▶ Cooper Gallery C
Cooper Street, Bideford, EX39 2DA.
**Tel** 01237 477370 **Fax** 01237 423415
**Personnel** Mrs Jennifer Bruce.
**Work Stocked and Sold** Pr.

#### BUCKFASTLEIGH

### ▶ Buckfast Abbey P
Buckfastleigh, TQ11 0EE.
**Tel** 01364 642519 **Fax** 01364 643891

#### BUDLEIGH SALTERTON

### ▶ Brook Gallery C
Fore Street, Budleigh Salterton, EX9 6NH.
**Tel** 01395 443003 **Fax** 01395 446490

### ▶ Otterton Mill Gallery C
Budleigh Salterton, EX9 7HG.
**Tel** 01395 568521 **Fax** 01395 568521
**Opening times** 10.30–5.30 daily mid-Mar–end Oct, 11–4 daily Nov–mid-Mar.
**Nearest Station** Exmouth.
**Personnel** Director: Desna Greenhow.
**Services and Facilities** Bookshop. Café. Craftshop. Framing. Gallery space for hire. Parking. Workshop Facilities.
**Work Stocked and Sold** Cer. Cra. Fur. Jew. Pa. Ph. Pr. Sc. Tx. Wd.
**Price range** £10–£1,500
For artists see Commercial Gallery Artists.

#### DARTMOUTH

### ▶ Facets C
14 Broadstone, Dartmouth, TQ6 9NR.
**Tel** 01803 833534
**Fax** 01803 833144
**Opening times** Mon–Sat 10–5.30. Sun by appointment.
**Personnel** Norman Dilley.
**Services and Facilities** Commissioning Service.
**Work Stocked and Sold** Jew.

### ▶ Simon Drew Gallery C
13 Foss Street, Dartmouth, TQ6 9DR.
**Tel** 01803 832832 **Fax** 01803 833040
**Opening times** Mon–Sat 9–5. Winter closed Wed pm.
**Work Stocked and Sold** Cer. Cra. Pa.

#### EXETER

### ▶ Boatyard Studios
76 Haven Road, St Thomas, Exeter, EX2 8DP.
**Tel** 01392 218704
**Personnel** Kim O'Laighrin.

### ▶ Gordon Hepworth Gallery
Hayne Farm, Sandowne Lane, Newton St Cyres, Exeter, EX5 5DE.
**Tel** 01392 851351
**Opening times** Wed–Sat 10.30–3.30 and by appointment.
**Personnel** Director: Gordon Hepworth.

### ▶ Laurel Keeley Gallery
4 St David's Hill, Exeter.
**Tel** 01392 428128
**Opening times** Mon–Fri 11–5, Sat 10–5.
**Personnel** Gallery Organiser: David Skilton.

### ▶ The Look C
53 Queen Street, Exeter,
**Tel** 01392 219855
**Opening times** Mon–Sat 9.15–5.30.
**Nearest Station** Exeter Central.
**Personnel** Proprietor: Jeff Goodwin.
**Work Stocked and Sold** Cer. Cra. Dr. Fur. Gla. Pa. Ph. Sc. Tx. Wd.
**Price range** £50–£500
For artists see Commercial Gallery Artists.

### ▶ Off-Site
former Maritime Museum,
60 Haven Road, Exeter.
**Tel** 01392 431786

### ▶ Royal Albert Memorial Museum & Art Gallery PS
Queen Street, Exeter EX4 3RX.
**Tel** 01392 265858
**Fax** 01392 421252
**Email** ramm-events@exeter.gov.uk
**Ws** www.exeter.gov.uk
**Opening times** Mon–Sat 10–5.
**Nearest Station** Exeter Central.
**Personnel** Head of Museums: Katherine Chant. Exhibitions Administrator: Fay Squire. Curator of Decorative Art: John Madin. Assistant Curator of Art: Caroline Worthington. Press & Events Officer: Ruth Randall.
**Services and Facilities** Café. Friends Society. Lectures. Museum Shop. Shop.

### ▶ Spacex Gallery
45 Preston Street, Exeter EX1 1DF.
**Tel** 01392 431786
**Opening times** Tue–Sat 10–5.
**Personnel** Director: Deborah Wood. Alex Farquahson.

### ▶ Vincent Gallery C
15 Magdalen Road, Exeter EX2 4TA.
**Tel** 01392 430082
**Opening times** Tue–Fri 10–1, 2.15–5.30, Sat 10–1.
**Work Stocked and Sold** Cer. Cra.

#### PLYMOUTH

### ▶ Atlantic Gallery C
Armada Centre, Plymouth,
**Tel** 01752 221600 **Fax** 01752 779108
**Opening times** 9.30–4. Closed Wed & Sun.
**Nearest Station** North Road, Plymouth.
**Personnel** Director: Paul Somerville.
**Services and Facilities** Commissioning Service. Disabled Access. Parking.
**Work Stocked and Sold** Cer. Dr. Gla. Pa. Sc.
**Price range** £100–£1,000
For artists see Commercial Gallery Artists

### ▶ Plymouth Arts Centre PS
38 Looe Street, Plymouth, PL4 0EB.
**Tel** 01752 206114 **Fax** 01752 206118
**Opening times** Mon 10–5, Tue–Sat 10–8, Sun 5.30–7.30. Group bookings by appointment.
**Nearest Station** Plymouth.
**Personnel** Jeremy Davies. Curator: Miranda Gardiner. House Manager: Stefan Aloszko.
**Services and Facilities** Bookshop. Café. Restaurant. Shop.
**Work Stocked and Sold** Cer. Dr. Pa. Ph. Pr. Sc. Tx.
**Price range** £20–£3, 500

### ▶ Plymouth City Museum & Art Gallery P
Drake Circus, Plymouth PL4 8AJ.
**Tel** 01752 264878 **Fax** 01752 264959
**Opening times** Tue–Fri 10–5.30, Sat & bank holidays 10–5.
**Personnel** Mark Sandema.
**Services and Facilities** Bookshop. Disabled Access. Friends Society. Gallery space for hire. Guided Tours. Lectures. Shop. Workshop Facilities.

### ▶ White Lane Gallery C
1 White Lane, The Barbican, Plymouth PL1 2LP.
**Tel** 01752 221450
**Opening times** Mon 12–4, Tue–Sat 10–5.
**Personnel** Director: Francis Mallett.
**Work Stocked and Sold** Pr.

#### SEATON

### ▶ Marine House at Beer
Fore Street, Beer, Seaton, BS12 3EF.
**Tel** 01297 625257 **Fax** 01297 625493
**Personnel** Michael Lambert.

#### TIVERTON

### ▶ Angel Gallery
1 Angel Terrace, Tiverton, EX16 6PD.

**Tel** 01994 254778
**Opening times** Mon–Thu 10–5, Fri/Sat 10–10.
**Personnel** Proprietor: Carola Buhse.

TORRINGTON

### ▶ Plough Gallery
Plough Arts Centre, The High Street, Torrington, EX38 8HQ.
**Tel** 01805 622552 **Fax** 01805 624624
**Personnel** Tanya Elliott. Visual Arts Coordinator: Peter Stiles.

TOTNES

### ▶ High Cross House
Dartington Hall, Totnes, TQ9 6ED.
**Tel** 01803 864114 **Fax** 01803 867057
**Opening times** Mid-Feb–mid-Nov: Tue–Fri 10.30–4.30, Sat/Sun 2–4.

### ▶ Marshall Arts Gallery
3 Warland, The Plains, Totnes, TQ9 5EL.
**Tel** 01803 863533
**Opening times** Mon–Sat 10–1; closed Sat & Thu pm. Winter closed Mon & Thu.

### ▶ Seymour Gallery
10 High Street, Totnes, TQ9 5RY.
**Tel** 01803 864200
**Opening times** Tue–Sat 10.30–4.30.
**Personnel** Owner: Shirley Seymour.

WINKLEIGH

### ▶ Square Gallery C
Fore Street, Winkleigh, EX19 8HQ.
**Tel** 01837 83145
**Opening times** 10–5 Tue, Thu, Fri & Sat, 10–2 Wed. Closed Sun and Mon.
**Personnel** Director: Sarah Flower.
**Services and Facilities** Art for Offices. Parking.
**Work Stocked and Sold** Cer. Cra. Dr. Jew. Pa. Ph. Pr. Sc.
For artists see Commercial Gallery Artists.

## DORSET

ABBOTSBURY

### ▶ Abbotsbury Studios C
11a Rodden Row, Abbotsbury, DT3 4JL.
**Tel** 01305 871876
**Opening times** Thu–Sat 1.30–5 or by appointment.
**Nearest Station** Dorchester South.
**Personnel** Artist: John Skinner.
**Services and Facilities** Art for Offices. Commissioning Service. Gallery space for hire. Workshop Facilities.
**Work Stocked and Sold** Dr. Pa.
**Price range** £100–£8,000
For artists see Commercial Gallery Artists.

BRIDPORT

### ▶ Bridport Arts Centre
South Street, Bridport, DT6 3NR.
**Tel** 01308 424204

### ▶ Bridport Museum P
South Street, Bridport, DT6 3NR.
**Tel** 01308 422116
**Fax** 01308 420659

DORCHESTER

### ▶ The Gallery Dorchester C
20 Durngate Street, Dorchester DT1 1JP.
**Tel** 01305 267408 **Fax** 01305 257926
**Email** john.pearson1@virgin.net.uk
**Opening times** Mon–Sat, 10–5.
**Nearest Station** Dorchester South & Dorchester West.
**Personnel** Directors: Susie Pearson, John Pearson.
**Services and Facilities** Disabled Access. Framing. Restoration.
**Work Stocked and Sold** Dr. Pa. Pr. Sc.
**Price range** £100–£2,000
For artists see Commercial Gallery Artists.

### ▶ Gallery Gilbert C
48 High West Street, Dorchester, DT1 1UT.
**Tel** 01305 263740
**Opening times** Tue–Sat 10–5.
**Personnel** Directors: Frances Gilbert, Stephanie Gilbert.
**Work Stocked and Sold** Cer. Cra. Dr. Pa. Pr. Sc.
For artists see Commercial Gallery Artists.

### ▶ Thomas Henry Fine Art C
The Old Warehouse, Durngate Street, Dorchester, DT1 1JP.
**Tel** 01305 250388

LYME REGIS

### ▶ David Hibberd Fine Art
The Town Mill, Mill Lane, Lyme Regis, DT7 3PU.
**Tel** 01297 443446
**Personnel** David Hibberd.

PORTLAND

### ▶ Artworks Gallery C
133 Chiswell, Portland, DT5 1AP.
**Tel** 01305 826191
**Opening times** Tue/Wed 8.30–6, Thu/Fri 8.30–8, Sat 8.30–3.30 and by appointment.
**Nearest Station** Weymouth.
**Personnel** Manager: Suzanne Yates.
**Services and Facilities** Art for Offices. Commissioning Service. Disabled Access. Framing. Parking.
**Work Stocked and Sold** Dr. Pa. Ph. Pr. Sc.
**Price range** £60–£2,000
For artists see Commercial Gallery Artists.

SHERBORNE

### ▶ Alpha House Gallery C
South Street, Sherborne, DT9 3LU.
**Tel** 01935 814944/850511
**Fax** 01935 816717
**Opening times** Tue–Sat 10–5 and by appointment.
**Personnel** Director: Tim Boon.
**Work Stocked and Sold** Cer. Gla. Pa. Sc.

SWANAGE

### ▶ Alpha Gallery C
21A Commercial Road, Swanage, BH19 1DF.
**Tel** 01929 423692
**Email** gallery@art-alpha.co.uk
**Ws** www.art-alpha.co.uk
**Opening times** Tue–Sat 10–5.
**Nearest Station** Wareham
**Personnel** Owners: Jill Mirza, Nick Harris.
**Services and Facilities** Art for Offices. Commissioning Service. Disabled Access. Parking.
**Work Stocked and Sold** Pa.
**Price range** £50–£5,000
For artists see Commercial Gallery Artists.
*We are a contemporary art business specialising in exhibiting and selling paintings by a small group of established artists, whose work is always available from the gallery.*
*Our list of artists includes Bonnie Brown, Nick Harris, Jim Hunter, Peter Joyce, Jill Mirza, David Potter, Virginia Tuszynska. We reguarly participate in national art fairs. The Alpha Gallery offers various additional services, such as handling the commissioning of paintings from our artists. We also provide a comprehensive paintings rental scheme. We are situated in a small cul-de-sac in the centre of Swanage, a delightful coastal resort in Dorset.*

*Jill Mirza,* Below the Acropolis, Evening – No 2, *acrylic on canvas, 51 x 71 cm, 2000, £850.*

### ▶ White Yard Studio
3 Arcade Terrace, Swanage, BH19 1DE.
**Tel** 01929 426621/426578
**Personnel** Bonnie Brown.

## GLOUCESTERSHIRE

CHALFORD

### ▶ Gallery Pangolin C
Unit 9, Chalford Industrial Estate, Chalford, GL6 8NT.
**Tel** 01453 886527 **Fax** 01453 731499
**Opening times** Opening hours by appt.
**Nearest Station** Stroud.
**Personnel** Jane Buck. Claude Koenig.
**Services and Facilities** Art Consultancy. Art for Offices. Commissioning Service. Parking. Restoration. Valuation.
**Work Stocked and Sold** Dr. Sc.
For artists see Commercial Gallery Artists.

CHELTENHAM

### ▶ Cheltenham Art Gallery & Museum PS
Clarence Street, Cheltenham, GL50 3JT.
**Tel** 01242 237431 **Fax** 01242 262334
**Email** ArtGallery@cheltenham.gov.uk

**Ws** www.cheltenhammuseum.org.uk
**Opening times** Mon–Sat 10–5.20, Sun 2–4.20. Closed Easter Sunday and bank holidays.
**Nearest Station** Cheltenham.
**Personnel** Head of Art Gallery & Museum: George Breeze. Information Officer: Anna Stanway.
**Services and Facilities** Bookshop. Café. Disabled Access. Friends Society. Guided Tours. Lectures. Museum Shop. Shop.
*A world-famous, nationally Designated collection relating to the Arts and Crafts Movement, including fine furniture and exquisite metalwork made by Cotswold craftsmen – inspired by William Morris. Rare Chinese and English pottery. 300 years of painting by Dutch and British artists. Also discover the town's history – Britain's most complete Regency town, and archaeological treasures from the neighbouring Cotswolds. Special exhibitions throughout the year.*

### ▶ Jonathan Poole C
Compton Cassey Gallery, near Withington, Cheltenham, GL54 4DE.
**Tel** 01242 890224
**Fax** 01242 890479
**Email** jonathanpoole@comptoncassey.demon.co.uk
**Ws** www.jonathanpoole.co.uk
**Opening times** By appointment.
**Personnel** Jonathan Poole. Selina Rutherston. Amy Cameron.
**Services and Facilities** Art Consultancy. Art for Offices. Gallery space for hire. Valuation.
**Work Stocked and Sold** Dr. Pa. Pr. Sc.
**Price range** £50–£15,000
For artists see Commercial Gallery Artists.
*European representatives for John Lennon and Miles Davis Estates. Exhibition organisers with venues in Europe and the Middle East. Contemporary sculpture and paintings by Jonathan Poole and Bobby Pilsnier. And many other artists.*

### ▶ Manor House Gallery
16 Royal Parade, Bayshill Road, Cheltenham, GL50 3AY.
**Tel** 01242 228330
**Fax** 01242 228328
**Personnel** Geoff Hassell.

### ▶ The Northleach Gallery
The Green, Northleach, Cheltenham, GL54 3EX.
**Tel** 01451 860519

### ▶ Sui Generis C
The Barley Barn, Southern Lane, Southam, Cheltenham, GL52 3PB.
**Tel** 01242 252610
**Fax** 01242 252950
**Email** penny@suigeneris.freeserve.co.uk
**Opening times** Wed–Sun 10–6.
**Nearest Station** Cheltenham Spa.
**Personnel** Proprietor/Gallery Coordinator: Penny Chandler.
**Services and Facilities** Art for Offices. Commissioning Service. Disabled Access. Parking.
**Work Stocked and Sold** App. Cer. Cra. Dec. Dr. Fur. Gla. Jew. Pa. Ph. Sc. Tx. Wd.
**Price range** £20–£4,000
For artists see Commercial Gallery Artists.

## CIRENCESTER

### ▶ Brewery Arts Centre C
Brewery Court, Cirencester, GL7 1JH.
**Tel** 01285 657181 **Fax** 01285 644060
**Opening times** Mon–Sat 10–5.
**Services and Facilities** Commissioning Service. Craftshop. Framing. Restaurant. Restoration.
**Work Stocked and Sold** Cer. Cra. Gla. Jew. Pa. Pr. Sc. Tx. Wd.

## GLOUCESTER

### ▶ Gloucester City Museum & Art Gallery P
Brunswick Road, Gloucester, GL1 1HP.
**Tel** 01452 524131 **Fax** 01452 410898
**Personnel** John Rhodes.

### ▶ Guildhall Arts Centre
23 Eastgate Street, Gloucester, GL1 1NS.
**Tel** 01452 505089
**Opening times** Tue–Sat 10–8, Sun 4.30–8.
**Personnel** Administrative Officer: Mel Rann.

### ▶ Robert Opie Collection Museum of Advertising and Packaging P
Albert Warehouse, Gloucester Docks, Gloucester, GL1 2EH (until end Oct 2001).
**Tel** 01452 302309 **Fax** 01452 308507

## LECHLADE

### ▶ Filkins Gallery & Studio
Cross Tree, Filkins, Lechlade, GL7 3JL.
**Tel** 01367 850385 (evenings)
**Opening times** Mar–Oct 10.30–5, Nov–Feb 10.30–4 Mon–Sat.

### ▶ Kelmscott Manor P
Kelmscott, Lechlade, GL7 3HJ.
**Tel** 01367 252486 **Fax** 01367 253754

## NAILSWORTH

### ▶ Hand Prints & Watercolour Gallery
3 Bridge Street, Nailsworth, GL6 0AA.
**Tel** 01453 834967
**Opening times** Mon–Fri 10–1, 2–5; Sat 10.30–1, 2–5.
**Personnel** Alex Hargreaves.

## PAINSWICK

### ▶ Nina Zborowska C
Damsels Mill, Paradise, Painswick, GL6 6UD.
**Tel** 01452 812460 **Fax** 01452 812912
**Opening times** Daily 11–5 during exhibitions, otherwise by appointment.
**Personnel** Director: Nina Zborowska.
**Work Stocked and Sold** Dr. Pa. Sc.

## STOW-ON-THE-WOLD

### ▶ Fosse Gallery
The Square, Stow-on-the-Wold, GL54 1AF.
**Tel** 01451 831319
**Personnel** Mr O'Farrell.

### ▶ John Blockley Gallery C
Church Street, Stow-on-the-Wold.
**Tel** 01451 832564 **Fax** 01451 832564
**Nearest Station** Moreton-in-Marsh.
**Work Stocked and Sold** Pa.
**Price range** £450–£3,000

### ▶ The John Davies Gallery C
Church Street, Stow-on-the-Wold, GL54 1BB.
**Tel** 01451 831698 **Fax** 01451 832477
**Email** daviesart@aol.com
**Ws** www.The-John-Davies-Gallery.co.uk
**Opening times** Mon–Sat 9.30–1.30, 2.30–5.30.
**Nearest Station** Moreton-in-Marsh.
**Personnel** Proprietor: John Davies. Assistant: Jeffrey Garrington. Assistant: Tony Retallack.
**Services and Facilities** Restoration. Valuation.
**Work Stocked and Sold** Cer. Dr. Pa. Sc.
For artists see Commercial Gallery Artists.
*Established 1977. A fresh, spacious and welcoming gallery. Greatly extended during 1999, it now comprises nine linked exhibition spaces on two floors. There is an established mailing list, and some six or seven catalogues are circulated in the year advertising one-man shows, as well as mixed or themed exhibitions. The gallery deals in late-19th-century and early-20th-century period work, and contemporary painting and sculpture. By arrangement, appropriate work may be brought to clients or taken on approval.*
*Valuation of clients' own work is undertaken as well as cleaning and restoration. This is always done on the basis of an acceptable estimate.*

### ▶ Traffords C
Digbeth Street, Stow-on-the-Wold, GL54 1BN.
**Tel** 01451 830424
**Opening times** Mon–Sat 9–6, Sun 10–4.
**Work Stocked and Sold** Cer. Cra. Gla. Jew. Tx. Wd.

## STROUD

### ▶ Stroud House Gallery
Station Road, Stroud, GL5 3AP.

# NORTH SOMERSET

## WESTON-SUPER-MARE

### ▶ Hans Price Gallery
Weston-super-Mare College, Creative Arts and Design, Knightstone Road, Weston-super-Mare, BS23 2AL.
**Opening times** Term time only – Mon & Fri 9.30–4.30, Tue–Thu 9.30–7.30. Closed weekends and during college vacations.
**Personnel** Ruth Kelly.

### ▶ The Time Machine
North Somerset Museum Service, Burlington Street, Weston-super-Mare, BS23 1PR.
**Tel** 01934 621028 **Fax** 01934 612526
**Opening times** 7 days a week 10–5 (Nov–Feb 10–4).

# SOMERSET

## FROME

### ▶ The Black Swan Guild
2 Bridge Street, Frome, BA11 1BB.
**Tel** 01373 473980
**Opening times** Mon–Sat 10–5.

**Personnel** Anne O'Dwyer.
**Work Stocked and Sold** Jew. Pa. Pr. Sc. Tx.

MONTACUTE

### ▶ National Trust Montacute House P

Montacute, TA15 6XP.
**Tel** 01935 823289 **Fax** 01935 823289

TAUNTON

### ▶ Brewhouse Theatre & Arts Centre C

Coal Orchard, Taunton, TA1 1JL.
**Tel** 01823 274608 **Fax** 01823 323116
**Opening times** Mon 12.15–5.30, Tue–Sat 10–5.30. Performance evenings till 9.30.
**Personnel** Arts Assistant: Kim Hoar.
**Services and Facilities** Bar. Café. Disabled Access. Gallery space for hire. Lectures. Parking. Restaurant. Workshop Facilities.
**Work Stocked and Sold** Dr. Pa.
**Price range** £5–£1,000
For artists see Commercial Gallery Artists.

### ▶ Byram Gallery

Somerset College of Art & Technology, Wellington Road, Taunton, TA1 5AX.
**Tel** 01823 283403
**Opening times** Mon–Fri 10–6.
**Personnel** Head of Art Department: Bill Wier.

WEDMORE

### ▶ The Studio Gallery

Poolbridge, Blackford, Wedmore, BS28 4PD.
**Tel** 01934 713380 **Fax** 01934 712511
**Personnel** David Sawtell.

WELLS

### ▶ Sadler Street Gallery C

7a Sadler Street, Wells, BA5 2RR.
**Tel** 01749 670220
**Opening times** Tue–Sat 10–5.30.
**Work Stocked and Sold** Pa.

### ▶ Wells Museum P

8 Cathedral Green, Wells, BA5 2UE.
**Tel** 01749 673477 **Fax** 01749 676013
**Opening times** Easter to 31 Oct 10–5.30, Nov to Easter 11–4 Wed–Sun.
**Personnel** Administrator: Mr Howard Gillian.

## SOUTH GLOUCESTERSHIRE

CHIPPING SODBURY

### ▶ Carousel Gallery

21a High Street, Chipping Sodbury, BS17 6AE.
**Tel** 01454 312622

# Southern

## BERKSHIRE

BRACKNELL

### ▶ South Hill Park Arts Centre PS

Bracknell, RG12 7PA.
**Tel** 01344 427272 **Fax** 01344 411427
**Email** visual.art@southhillpark.org.uk
**Opening times** Bracknell Gallery: Wed–Fri 1–5 & 7–9.30, Sat 1–10, Sun 1–5. Mansion House: Mon–Sat 9–11pm, Sun & bank holidays 12–10.30.
**Nearest Station** Bracknell.
**Personnel** Visual Arts Coordinator: Lucie May.
**Services and Facilities** Bar. Café. Disabled Access. Gallery space for hire. Parking. Restaurant. Workshop Facilities.
**Work Stocked and Sold** Cer. Cra. Jew. Pa. Ph. Sc.

COOKHAM

### ▶ Stanley Spencer Gallery

Kings Hall, High Street, Cookham, SL6 9SJ.
**Tel** 01628 471885
**Fax** 01628 520537
**Email** diana.benson@ntlworld.com
**Ws** www.stanleyspencer.org
**Opening times** Easter–Oct daily 10.30–5.30. Nov–Easter weekends and bank holidays 11–5.
**Nearest Station** Cookham.
**Personnel** Chairman: Mr R. Hurley.
**Services and Facilities** Bookshop. Disabled Access. Friends Society. Guided Tours. Lectures. Museum Shop. Shop.
*The gallery's important collection includes a fine group of early religious paintings:* The Betrayal *(1914),* The Last Supper *(1920),* St Veronica Unmasking Christ *(1921), and* Christ Overturning the Money Changers' Table *(1921).*
*The theme of the gallery's Summer Exhibition (13 Apr–31 Oct 2001) will be 'Spencer's River and Regatta Scenes' which will include* Turk's Boatyard, Cookham *(1930),* View from Cookham Bridge *(1936),* Listening from Punts *(1955), and* Dinner on the Hotel Lawn *(1956–7). Admission: adults £1, concessions 50p, children free.*

ETON

### ▶ Contemporary Fine Art Gallery & Sculpture Park C

31 High Street, Eton, SL4 6AX.
**Tel** 01753 854315, after 7pm 01753 830731
**Fax** 01753 620390
**Email** Mail@CFAG.co.uk
**Ws** www.CFAG.co.uk
**Opening times** Daily 9–5.
**Personnel** Nicholas Bayldon-Pritchard. Elizabeth Bayldon-Pritchard. Tuss Ingram.
**Work Stocked and Sold** Pa. Sc.

MAIDENHEAD

### ▶ Royal Borough Collection P

c/o Royal Borough of Windsor and Maidenhead, Town Hall, St Ives Road, Maidenhead, SL6 1QS.
**Tel** 01628 798888
**Opening times** Open 1 day per month by appointment.

NEWBURY

### ▶ New Greenham Arts

113 Lindenmuth Way, New Greenham Park, Newbury.
**Tel** 01635 38105

READING

### ▶ Modern Artists Gallery C

High Street, Whitchurch on Thames, near Pangbourne, Reading RG8 7EX.
**Tel** 0118 984 5893 **Fax** 0118 984 4874
**Email** info@mod-art.demon.co.uk
**Opening times** Wed–Sat 10–5.30, some Sun – always phone the gallery first for details before setting out.
**Services and Facilities** Art Consultancy. Art for Offices. Commissioning Service. Gallery space for hire.
**Work Stocked and Sold** Cer. Fur. Pa. Sc.
For artists see Commercial Gallery Artists.

*Katriona Bryson,* Dogs with Moon, *bronze, 28 x 23 cm, £1200.*
*Contemporary paintings – abstract, landscape and figurative; sculpture, ceramics and furniture. Mixed exhibitions and individual shows by new and established artists. Established artists include: Paul Kessling, Kathryn Thomas, Nick Schlee, David Armitage, Helen Williams, Carol Daw, Katriona Bryson and Edla Griffiths.*

### ▶ Museum of Reading

Blagrave Street, Reading, RG1 1QH.
**Tel** 0118 939 9800/9898 **Fax** 0118 939 9881
**Email** info@readingmuseum.org
**Ws** www.readingmuseum.org
**Opening times** All year: please phone.
**Nearest Station** Reading.
**Services and Facilities** Art for Offices. Bar. Bookshop. Café. Craftshop. Disabled Access. Friends Society. Gallery space for hire. Guided Tours. Museum Shop. Shop.

### ▶ Openhand Openspace

571 Oxford Road, Reading.
**Tel** 0119 9597752

### ▶ Rising Sun Institute

30 Silver Street, Reading, RG1 2ST.
**Tel** 01734 866788
**Personnel** Larry Watson.

WINDSOR

### ▶ Century Gallery Datchet

The Shop on the Green, Datchet, Windsor, SL3 9JH.
**Tel** 01753 581284

### ▶ Eton Applied Arts C

81 High Street, Windsor, SL4 6AF.
**Tel** 01753 860771
**Opening times** Mon–Sat 10.30–6, Sun 11–4. Closed Wed.
**Services and Facilities** Workshop Facilities.
**Work Stocked and Sold** Cer. Cra. Gla. Jew. Tx. Wd.

### ▶ The Pembroke Gallery C
15A The Arches, Goswell Hill,
Windsor, SL4 1RH.
**Tel** 01753 868844 **Fax** 01344 876546
**Opening times** Tue–Sat 10–5.
**Personnel** Margaret Hill.
**Work Stocked and Sold** Fur. Pa. Sc.

### ▶ Windsor Arts Centre
The Old Court, St Leonard's Road, Windsor, SL4 3DB.
**Tel** 01753 859421

## BOURNEMOUTH

BOURNEMOUTH

### ▶ Riddetts of Bournemouth
26 Richmond Hill, Bournemouth BH2 6EJ.
**Tel** 01202 555686
**Personnel** Mr K. A. Harris.

### ▶ Russell-Cotes Art Gallery and Museum PS
East Cliff, Bournemouth BH1 3AA.
**Tel** 01202 451800
**Fax** 01202 451851
**Email** enquiries@russell-cotes.demon.co.uk
**Opening times** Tue–Sun 10–5.
**Personnel** Senior Arts Officer: Victoria Pirie. Visual Arts Officer: Mark Bills.
**Services and Facilities** Art Consultancy. Art for Offices. Café. Commissioning Service. Disabled Access. Friends Society. Guided Tours. Lectures. Museum Shop. Workshop Facilities.

### ▶ TZB Southbourne Gallery C
2 Carbery Row, (Southbourne Road),
Bournemouth BH6 3QR.
**Tel** 01202 426967
**Opening times** Wed, Thu, Fri 10–12.30, 2–4.30; Sat 10–12.30.
**Nearest Station** Bournemouth.
**Personnel** Owner: Teresa Zwounska-Brzeski.
**Services and Facilities** Commissioning Service. Disabled Access.
Gallery space for hire.
**Work Stocked and Sold** Pa. Sc.
For artists see Commercial Gallery Artists.

## BUCKINGHAMSHIRE

AYLESBURY

### ▶ Buckinghamshire Art Gallery County Museum PS
Church Street, Aylesbury, HP20 2QP.
**Tel** 01296 331441 **Fax** 01296 334884
**Email** prussell@buckscc.gov.uk
**Opening times** Mon–Sat 10–5, Sun 2–5.
**Nearest Station** Aylesbury.
**Personnel** Head of Museum Service: Oliver Green. Exhibitions Officer: Suzanne Anderegg.
**Services and Facilities** Café. Disabled Access. Friends Society. Guided Tours. Lectures. Museum Shop. Workshop Facilities.

### ▶ Discerning Collections, The Gallery C
Baldways Close, Wingrave,
Aylesbury, HP22 4PB.
**Tel** 01296 681471
**Fax** 01296 682869
**Email** discerningcollections@btinternet.com
**Opening times** Fri 3–8, Sat & Sun 11–5; other times by appointment.
**Nearest Station** Leighton Buzzard (from Euston), Aylesbury (from Marylebone).
**Work Stocked and Sold** Pa. Pr. Sc.
**Price range** £55–£3,000

### ▶ Queens Park Arts Centre Gallery
Queens Park Road, Aylesbury, HP21 7RT.
**Tel** 01296 243325
**Personnel** Mr M. D. Thackwray. Mr Peter Riley.

### ▶ Waddesdon Manor – The Rothschild Collection
Waddesdon, Aylesbury, HP18 0JH.
**Tel** Recorded message: 01296 651211, Booking Office: 01296 651226 **Fax** 01296 651142
**Opening times** Gardens, Aviary, Restaurant and Shops: Wed 3 Mar–Fri 24 Dec, Wed–Sun & bank holiday Mon 10–5. House (including Wine Cellars): Thu 1 Apr–Sun 31 Oct, Thu–Sun, bank holiday Mon & Wed in Jul–Aug 11–4. (Recommended last admission 2.30.) Bachelors' Wing open Thu & Fri, & Wed in Jul & Aug 11–4 (access cannot be guaranteed).
**Services and Facilities** Disabled Access. Guided Tours. Lectures. Museum Shop. Parking. Restaurant. Shop.

MARLOW

### ▶ David Messum Fine Art
Lordswood, Marlow, SL7 2QS.

MILTON KEYNES

### ▶ Milton Keynes Gallery P
900 Midsummer Boulevard, Central Milton Keynes, MK9 3QA.
**Tel** +44 0(1908) 676 900
**Fax** +44 0(1908) 558 308
**Email** mkgallery@mtgc.co.uk
**Ws** www.mkweb.co.uk/mkg
**Nearest Station** 20 mins walk from Milton Keynes Central railway station
**Personnel** Director: Stephen Snoddy.
**Services and Facilities** Bookshop. Disabled Access. Friends Society. Gallery space for hire. Guided Tours. Lectures. Shop. Workshop Facilities.
*The Gallery opened in October 1999 providing the city and the region with an exciting new venue for the presentation of contemporary visual art. Eight to ten exhibitions are held each year, ranging from modern and contemporary art to aspects of design, architecture and popular culture. MK G aims to bring new art to audiences and supports its exhibitions with a lively education events programme for people of all ages. Admission is free.*

### ▶ Stantonbury Gallery
Stantonbury Campus, Milton Keynes.
**Tel** 01908 605536

WINGRAVE

### ▶ The Gallery
2 Baldways Close, Wingrave, HP22 4PB.
**Tel** 01296 681471
**Fax** 01296 682869
**Personnel** Helen Coxhead. Mike Coxhead.

## HAMPSHIRE

ALRESFORD

### ▶ Alresford Gallery C
36 West Street, Alresford, SO24 9AU.
**Tel** 01962 735286 **Fax** 01962 735295
**Opening times** Tue–Sat 10–5. Closed 1–1.30.
**Nearest Station** Winchester.
**Personnel** Director: Brian Knowler RI.
**Services and Facilities** Art Consultancy. Art for Offices. Commissioning Service.
**Work Stocked and Sold** Cer. Dr. Pa. Sc.
**Price range** £100–£10,000
For artists see Commercial Gallery Artists.

ALTON

### ▶ Allen Gallery C
(Hampshire County Museums Service),
10–12 Church Street, Alton, GU34 2BW.
**Tel** 01420 82802
**Opening times** Tue–Sat 10–5. Admission free.
**Work Stocked and Sold** Pa.

ANDOVER

### ▶ Andover Museum P
(Hampshire County Museums Service),
6 Church Close, Andover, SP10 1DP.
**Tel** 01264 366283

BASINGSTOKE

### ▶ Willis Museum and Art Gallery P
Market Place, Basingstoke, RG21 1QD.
**Tel** 01256 465902

CHRISTCHURCH

### ▶ Red House Museum and Art Gallery P
(Hampshire County Museums Service),
Quay Road, Christchurch, BH23 1BU.
**Tel** 01202 482860

EASTLEIGH

### ▶ Eastleigh Museum P
25 High Street, Eastleigh, SO5 5LF.
**Tel** 023 80643026
**Personnel** Sue Franklin.

GOSPORT

### ▶ Gosport Museum P
Walpole Road, Gosport, PO12 1LQ.
**Tel** 023 92588035

HAVANT

### ▶ Havant Museum P
East Street, Havant, PO9 1BS.
**Tel** 023 92451155
**Personnel** Sue Franklin.

**▶ Old Town Hall Arts Centre**
East Street, Havant.

LYMINGTON

**▶ ArtSway** C
Station Road, Sway, Lymington, SO41 6BA.
**Tel** 01590 682260
**Opening times** Wed–Sun 12–4.

NEW ALRESFORD

**▶ Hitchcocks**
11 East Street, New Alresford.
**Tel** 01962 734762

PETERSFIELD

**▶ Academy Arts Centre** C
Winton Road, Petersfield, GU32 3HA.
**Tel** 01730 261624 **Fax** 01730 231499
**Email** nixy@compuserve.com
**Opening times** Mon–Sat 9–5.30.
**Nearest Station** Petersfield.
**Personnel** Gallery Director: Nick Yellop. Art Centre Manager: Geoff Harris.
**Services and Facilities** Art for Offices. Bookshop. Commissioning Service. Framing. Gallery space for hire. Parking. Shop. Workshop Facilities.

PORTSMOUTH

**▶ Aspex Gallery**
27 Brougham Road, Southsea, Portsmouth, PO5 4PA.
**Tel** 023 92812121

**▶ Mountbatten Gallery**
Guildhall Square, Portsmouth, PO1 2AD.
**Tel** 023 92827261

**▶ Portsmouth City Museum and Records Office** P
Museum Road, Portsmouth, PO1 2LJ.
**Tel** 023 9282 7261
**Email** xpcclsde@hants.gov.uk
**Ws** www.xpcclsde@hants.gov.uk
**Opening times** Daily 10–5.30. Last ticket 5. Closed 24–26 Dec. Free admission.
**Services and Facilities** Bookshop. Disabled Access. Friends Society. Lectures. Museum Shop. Parking. Shop.

RINGWOOD

**▶ Bettles Gallery** C
80 Christchurch Road, Ringwood, BH24 1DR.
**Tel** 01425 470410 **Fax** 01425 479002
**Opening times** Tue–Fri 10–5, Sat 10–1.
**Personnel** Directors: Gill Bettle, Roger Bettle.
**Services and Facilities** Commissioning Service. Parking.
**Work Stocked and Sold** Cer. Jew. Pa.
**Price range** £10–£1,000
For artists see Commercial Gallery Artists.

SELBOURNE

**▶ Courtyard Gallery** C
The Plestor, High Street, Selbourne, GU34 3JQ.
**Tel** 01420 511334
**Fax** 01420 346822
**Opening times** Mon–Sat 10–4 or by appointment.
**Personnel** Christina Lee.
**Work Stocked and Sold** Cer. Pa. Sc.

SOUTHSEA

**▶ The Red Gallery** C
98 Marmion Road, Southsea, PO5 2BB.
**Tel** 023 92793924
**Opening times** Thu–Sun 10.30–6.
**Work Stocked and Sold** Cer. Sc.

STOCKBRIDGE

**▶ Wykeham Galleries**
High Street, Stockbridge, SO20 6HE.
**Tel** 01264 810364 **Fax** 01264 810182

WINCHESTER

**▶ Guildhall Gallery**
The Broadway, Winchester.
**Tel** 01962 840222

**▶ Maltby Contemporary Art**
3a Minster Street, Winchester, SO23 9HA.
**Tel** 01962 877601
**Email** info@maltbyart.fsnet.co.uk
**Ws** www.maltbyart.fsnet.co.uk

**▶ The Winchester Gallery**
Park Avenue, Winchester, SO23 8DL.
**Tel** 01962 852500

## ISLE OF WIGHT

NEWPORT

**▶ The Quay Arts Centre**
Sea Street, Newport, PO30 5BD.
**Tel** 01983 528825

**▶ Seely Gallery**
Lord Louis Library, Newport, PO30 1LL.
**Tel** 01983 527655

RYDE

**▶ Ryde Library Gallery**
George Street, Ryde, PO33 2JE.
**Tel** 01983 62170

## OXFORDSHIRE

BAMPTON

**▶ Bampton Arts Centre**
(West Oxfordshire Arts Association), Town Hall, Bampton.
**Tel** 01993 850137

BANBURY

**▶ Banbury Museum** P
8 Horsefair, Banbury, OX16 0AA.
**Tel** 01295 259855

BURFORD

**▶ Brian Sinfield Gallery** C
150 High Street, Burford, OX18 4QU.
**Tel** 01993 824464/830886
**Fax** 01993 830707/824525
**Email** brian@sinfieldg.freeserve.co.uk
**Opening times** Tue–Sat 9.30–1, 2–5.30. Mon by appointment.
**Nearest Station** Charlbury.
**Personnel** Brian Sinfield. Ingrid Levrincova.
**Work Stocked and Sold** Pa. Sc.
**Price range** £400–£15,000
For artists see Commercial Gallery Artists.

CHIPPING NORTON

**▶ Manor House Gallery** C
West Street, Chipping Norton, OX7 5LH.
**Tel** 01608 642620
**Fax** 01608 642240
**Opening times** Weekdays 10–4.30, Sun by appointment.
**Work Stocked and Sold** Pa.

**▶ Merriscourt Gallery** C
Merriscourt Farm, Sarsden, Chipping Norton, OX7 6QX.
**Tel** 01608 658989 **Fax** 01608 659734
**Email** merriscourtpaintings@btinternet.com
**Ws** www.merriscourt.com
**Opening times** Tue–Sun 11–6. Closed Mon.
**Nearest Station** Kingham.
**Personnel** Partner: Nick Clements.
**Services and Facilities** Disabled Access. Parking.
**Work Stocked and Sold** Cer. Dr. Pa. Pr.
**Price range** £150–£4,000
For artists see Commercial Gallery Artists.

**▶ The Theatre Gallery**
2 Spring Street, Chipping Norton, OX7 4NL.
**Tel** 01608 2349

GORING-ON-THAMES

**▶ Goring Mill Gallery** C
Lock Approach, Goring-on-Thames, RG8 9AD.
**Tel** 01491 875030
**Fax** 01491 872519
**Opening times** Apr–Dec: Wed–Fri 10–4, Sat, Sun & bank holidays 10–5. Jan–Mar: Wed–Sun 10–4.
**Nearest Station** Goring and Streatley.
**Personnel** Ron Bridle.
**Services and Facilities** Art for Offices. Commissioning Service. Craftshop. Framing. Gallery space for hire.
**Work Stocked and Sold** Cer. Cra. Dec. Dr. Gla. Pa. Sc. Wd.
**Price range** £50–£1,000
For artists see Commercial Gallery Artists.
*Original art and craftwork in a beautiful riverside setting. Part of a picturesque and historic Water Mill, recorded in the Domesday Book and painted by Turner, Goring Mill Gallery specialises in original work of only the most talented regional artists and craftspeople. Over 500 paintings, ceramics, sculptures and other craftworks by over forty selected professional and recreational artists. Most two-dimensional work is 'representational' art with an emphasis on atmospheric landscapes and riverscapes of the Thames Valley and surrounding countryside. Sensible prices. Services offered include a commissioning service (portraits of people, animals and houses), craftwork commissions and bespoke framing.*

HENLEY-ON-THAMES

### ▶ Barn Galleries C
Aston, Henley-on-Thames, RG9 3DX.
**Tel** 01491 577786 **Fax** 01491 577786
**Opening times** May–Jun: 10–5
or by appointment.
**Nearest Station** Henley-on-Thames.
**Personnel** Director: Bridget Fraser.
**Services and Facilities** Art Consultancy. Art for Offices. Disabled Access. Parking.
**Work Stocked and Sold** Cer. Pa. Sc. Tx. Wd.
**Price range** £200–£15,000
For artists see Commercial Gallery Artists.

### ▶ Bohun Gallery C
15 Reading Road,
Henley-on-Thames, RG9 1AB.
**Tel** 01491 576228 **Fax** 01491 576228
**Opening times** Mon–Sat 9.30–5.30 (closed Wed).
**Nearest Station** Henley.
**Personnel** Director: Patricia Jordan Evans.
**Services and Facilities** Art for Offices. Commissioning Service.
**Work Stocked and Sold** Pa. Pr. Sc.
For artists see Commercial Gallery Artists.

### ▶ Luxters Fine Art
Old Luxters, Hamleden,
Henley-on-Thames, RG9 6JW.
**Tel** 01491 638816
**Personnel** David J. Ealand.

### ▶ River and Rowing Museum
Mill Meadows, Henley-on-Thames, RG9 1BF.
**Tel** 01491 415600

OXFORD

### ▶ Ashmolean Museum of Art and Archaeology
Beaumont Street, Oxford, OX1 2PH.
**Tel** 01865 278000
**Fax** 01865 278018
**Email** jonathan.moffett@ashmus.ox.ac.uk
**Ws** www.ashmol.ox.ac.uk/
**Opening times** Tue–Sat 10–5, Sun 2–5. Admission free.
**Nearest Station** Oxford.
**Personnel** Director: Dr Christopher Brown.
**Services and Facilities** Bookshop. Café. Disabled Access. Friends Society. Guided Tours. Lectures. Museum Shop. Shop.
**Work Stocked and Sold** Pr.

### ▶ Brampton Arts Centre
West Oxfordshire Arts Association,
Town Hall, Brampton, Oxford.
**Tel** 01993 850 137

### ▶ Christ Church Picture Gallery PS
Christ Church, Oxford, OX1 1DP.
**Tel** 01865 276172 **Fax** 01865 202429
**Email** dennis.harrington@christ-church.ox.ac.uk
**Ws** www.chch.ox.ac.uk
**Opening times** Mon–Fri 10.30–1 and 2–4.30, Sun 1–4.30, Easter to end Sep open until 5.30 every day. Free on Mon.
**Personnel** Assistant Curator: Christopher Baker. Exhibitions Officer: Brigid Cleaver.
**Services and Facilities** Guided Tours. Museum Shop.
*Collection of Old Master paintings and drawings displayed in a modern gallery. Quattrocento Masters; works by Tintoretto, Veronese, the Carracci, Frans Hals and Van Dyck. Changing displays in the print room of works selected from over 2000 Old Master drawings and prints. Special temporary exhibitions. Guided tours each Thursday 2.15–3 and by advance request.*

### ▶ Museum of Modern Art P
30 Pembroke Street, Oxford OX1 1BP.
**Tel** 01865 722733
**Fax** 01865 722573
**Email** info@moma.demon.co.uk
**Ws** www.moma.org.uk
**Opening times** Tue–Sun 11–6, Thu 11–9. Closed Mon.
**Nearest Station** Oxford.
**Personnel** Director: Andrew Nairne. Curator: Rob Bowman. Curator: Astrid Bowron.
**Services and Facilities** Bookshop. Café. Disabled Access. Friends Society. Guided Tours. Lectures. Shop. Workshop Facilities.
*MOMA Oxford is one of the leading UK centres for modern and contemporary art, specialising in showing work not previously seen in Britain. MOMA's pioneering programme covers painting, sculpture, photography, film, video and installation by British and international artists. MOMA has a comprehensive education programme for schools and colleges, children and adults. Events include talks, workshops, guided tours and holiday activities. To find out more about exhibitions, you can join the mailing list or become a Friend of MOMA. Please call 01865 722733 for details.*
*MOMA closes during exhibition installation; please check details before visiting.*

### ▶ Museum of Oxford P
St Aldates, Oxford.
**Tel** 01865 815539

### ▶ Oxford Gallery C
23 High Street, Oxford, OX1 4AH.
**Tel** 01865 242731
**Opening times** Mon–Sat 10–5.
**Personnel** Directors: Kristina Mason, Deborah Elliott, Valerie Stewart, Lindsay Hoole.
**Work Stocked and Sold** App. Cer. Cra. Gla. Jew. Pr. Tx. Wd.

### ▶ Stables Gallery
Green College, Woodstock Road,
Oxford, OX2 6HG.
**Tel** 01865 274770

### ▶ Wiseman Gallery C
40/41 South Parade, Summertown,
Oxford, OX2 7JL.
**Tel** 01865 515123
**Opening times** Mon & Wed 10–4, Tue, Thu–Sat 10–6.
**Nearest Station** Oxford.
**Personnel** Director: Sarah-Jane Wiseman.
**Services and Facilities** Art for Offices. Commissioning Service. Framing.
**Work Stocked and Sold** Cer. Dr. Gla. Jew. Pa. Pr. Sc.
**Price range** £35–£5,000
For artists see Commercial Gallery Artists.

WALLINGFORD

### ▶ Wallingford Arts Centre
Kinecroft, Goldsmith Lane, Wallingford.
**Tel** 01753 859336

WOODSTOCK

### ▶ Objet D'Art
1 Market Place, Woodstock, OX20 1SY.
**Tel** 01993 811819
**Work Stocked and Sold** Pa.

## POOLE

POOLE

### ▶ Poole Arts Centre PS
Seldown Gallery, Kingland Road, Poole BH15 1UG.
**Tel** 01202 665334
**Opening times** 10–5.
**Nearest Station** Poole.
**Personnel** Programme Director: Alistair Wilkinson.
**Services and Facilities** Bar. Café. Gallery space for hire. Restaurant.

### ▶ Waterfront Museum P
High Street, Old Town, Poole BH15 1BW.
**Tel** 01202 683138

## SOUTHAMPTON

SOUTHAMPTON

### ▶ Beatrice Royal Contemporary Art and Craft C
Nightingale Avenue, Eastleigh, Hampshire SO50 9JJ.
**Tel** 023 8061 0592 **Fax** 023 8065 0566
**Email** info@beatriceroyal.com
**Ws** www.beatriceroyal.com
**Opening times** 11–5 every day.
**Nearest Station** Eastleigh, Southampton Parkway.
**Personnel** Managing Director: Margaret Woodhead. Art Curator: Elizabeth Hodgson. Craft Curator: Davina Thompson.
**Services and Facilities** Art Consultancy. Art for Offices. Café. Commissioning Service. Craftshop. Disabled Access. Framing. Friends Society. Gallery space for hire. Guided Tours. Lectures. Parking. Workshop Facilities.
**Work Stocked and Sold** Ab. App. Cer. Cra. Dec. Dr. Fur. Gla. Jew. Pa. Ph. Pr. Sc. Tx. Wd.
**Price range** £50–£10,000
For artists see Commercial Gallery Artists.
*The largest purpose-built outlet in the country for contemporary art and craft. Changing exhibitions of paintings, prints, sculpture and all craft media.*
- *Biggest gallery*
- *Best choice*
- *Friendliest welcome*

### ▶ The First Gallery
1 Burnham Chase, Bitterne,
Southampton S018 5DG.
**Tel** 023 80462723
**Personnel** Hilda Clarke.

### ▶ John Hansard Gallery
University of Southampton, Southampton.
**Tel** 02380 592158

### ▶ On Line Gallery C
76 Bedford Place, Southampton SO15 2DF.
**Tel** 023 80330660
**Fax** 023 80330660
**Opening times** Tue–Sat 10–5.
**Personnel** Directors: Alan Jones, Jan Krir.
**Services and Facilities** Art Consultancy.
**Work Stocked and Sold** Cer. Cra. Sc.

## SWINDON

SWINDON

### ▶ Swindon Museum & Art Gallery P
Bath Road, Swindon SN1 4BA.
**Tel** 01793 466556
**Fax** 01793 484141
**Ws** swindon.gov.uk
**Opening times** Mon–Sat 10–5, Sun 2–5.
**Nearest Station** Swindon
**Personnel** Curator/Manager: Isobel Thompson. Art Gallery Officer: Rosalyn Thomas. Marketing Officer: Alison Bouce.
**Services and Facilities** Disabled Access (limited). Friends Society. Guided Tours. Lectures. Museum Shop. Shop.
*Situated in an elegant early-19th-century house, Swindon's oldest museum contains a variety of displays on the history, archaeology and geology of Swindon and the surrounding area. Adjoining the museum, the Art Gallery houses an outstanding collection of 20th-century British art, a selection of which is generally on display. Due to selective purchasing programme, the collection now boasts one of the most wide ranging and high quality experiences of British 20th-century art outside London. It consists of works on canvas, watercolours and drawings, prints and photographs.*
*There is also a small collection of sculpture as well as a significant collection of studio pottery. Artists in the collection include: Terry Frost, Howard Hodgkin, Gwen and Augustus John, Maggi Hambing, W. R. Sickert, Ivon Hitchins, Christopher Le Brun and Lisa Milroy.*

## WILTSHIRE

CALNE

### ▶ Bowood House
Calne, SN11 0LZ.
**Tel** 01249 812102
**Personnel** Jane Meadows.

DEVIZES

### ▶ The Gallery
Handel House, Sidmouth Street, Devizes, SN8 1JQ.
**Tel** 01672 52860

### ▶ Garton & Co. C
Roundway House, Devizes, SN10 2EG.
**Tel** 01380 729624
**Personnel** Robin Garton.
**Work Stocked and Sold** Pr.

LACOCK

### ▶ Fox Talbot Museum of Photography C
Lacock, Chippenham SN15 2LG.
**Tel** 01249 730 459
**Fax** 01249 730 501
**Email** museum@fox-talbot.prestel.co.uk
**Ws** www.fox-talbot.org.uk/foxtalbot
**Opening times** Mar–Oct: weekends 11–4. Nov–Feb: 11–5 every day.
**Nearest Station** Chippenham
**Personnel** Curator: Mr M. W. Gray. Administrator: N. Stevens. Deputy Administrator: L. Padfield.
**Services and Facilities** Bookshop. Disabled Access. Lectures. Museum Shop. Parking.
**Work Stocked and Sold** Ph. Pr.
**Price range** £5–£100
*A permanent exhibition on the ground floor commemorates the achievements of William Henry Fox Talbot, photographic pioneer and inventor of the negative/positive process. All Talbot's important research work was carried out at Lacock Abbey, his Wiltshire home for 50 years. The Upper Gallery normally shows three exhibitions per year by contemporary and 19th-century master photographers.*
*The exhibitions scheduled for 2002 are Tim McMillan's new work 'Lundy Island Installation' and 'Sleep', Apr–Jul; 'Object as Image', five photographers, Jul–Oct; and 'A Moments Space', Oct–Mar. Admission charge (NT members free).*

MARLBOROUGH

### ▶ Bajazzo Gallery
8 St Martins, Marlborough, SN8 1AR.
**Tel** 01672 512860

### ▶ Katharine House Gallery C
The Parade, Marlborough, SN8 1NE.
**Tel** 01672 514040
**Opening times** Mon–Sat 10–5.30.
**Nearest Station** Swindon.
**Personnel** Director: Christopher Gange.
**Services and Facilities** Bookshop.
**Work Stocked and Sold** Ab. Dr. Pa. Pr.
**Price range** £75–£2,000
For artists see Commercial Gallery Artists.

### ▶ Marlborough Studio Art Gallery
4 Hughenden Yard, High Street, Marlborough, SN8 1LT.
**Tel** 01672 514848
**Opening times** Daily 10–1 & 2–5.
**Personnel** Proprietor: Andy Le Poidevin.
**Services and Facilities** Art for Offices. Commissioning Service. Craftshop.

SALISBURY

### ▶ Margaret Turner Gallery
15 St Ann's Street, Salisbury, SP1 2DP.
**Tel** 01722 333501

### ▶ The Wykeham Gallery C
High St, Dockbridge SO20 6HE.
**Tel** 01264 810364
**Email** jerramgal@aol.com
**Opening times** Tue–Sat.
**Nearest Station** Salisbury (main line)
**Services and Facilities** Art Consultancy. Art for Offices. Commissioning Service. Restoration.
**Work Stocked and Sold** Dr. Pa. Sc.
**Price range** £75–£10,000
For artists see Commercial Gallery Artists.

# West Midlands

## BIRMINGHAM

BIRMINGHAM

### ▶ Aston Hall P
Trinity Road, Aston, Birmingham B6 6JD.
**Tel** 0121 327 0062 **Fax** 0121 327 7162

### ▶ B16
Unit 4, Old Union Mill, Grosvenor Street, Birmingham.
**Tel** 0121 6436040

### ▶ The Barber Institute of Fine Arts
The University of Birmingham, Edgbaston, Birmingham B15 2TS.
**Tel** 0121 414 7333 **Fax** 0121 414 3370
**Email** info@barber.org.uk
**Ws** www.barber.org.uk
**Opening times** Mon–Sat 10–5, Sun 2–5.
**Nearest Station** New Street (Main line), University (Cross City line).
**Personnel** Director: Professor Richard Verdi. Senior Curator: Paul Spencer-Longhurst. Administrator: Sophie Wilson. Marketing & Press: Matt O'Callaghan.
**Services and Facilities** Disabled Access. Friends Society. Guided Tours. Lectures. Museum Shop. Parking.
**Work Stocked and Sold** Pa.
*One of the finest small picture galleries in the world housing an outstanding collection of old master and modern paintings including masterpieces by Bellini, Rubens, Poussin, Murillo, Gainsborough, Rossetti, Whistler and Magritte. Among the Impressionist pictures are major works by Manet, Monet, Renoir, Degas, Gauguin and Van Gogh. The Institute regularly holds concerts, lectures and recitals – all of which are open to the public. It is also available for hire for seminars, receptions, concerts and private views.*

### ▶ Birmingham Museum and Art Gallery, including the Gas Hall Exhibition Gallery PS
Chamberlain Square, Birmingham B3 3DH.
**Tel** 0121 303 2834/1966
**Fax** 0121 303 1394
**Email** bmag-enquiries@birmingham.gov.uk
**Ws** www.bmag.co.uk
**Opening times** Mon–Thu & Sat 10–5, Fri 10.30–5, Sun 12.30–5.
**Nearest Station** Birmingham New Street, Birmingham Snow Hill
**Personnel** Marketing & PR Officer: Carmel Girling.
**Services and Facilities** Café. Disabled Access. Friends Society. Gallery space for hire. Guided Tours. Museum Shop. Restaurant.
*A spectacular Victorian building housing one of the world's finest collections of Pre-Raphaelite paintings. Older schools are represented by Dutch, Italian and French artists and other works from the 14th century to the present day. The museum has displays of ceramics and fine silver, and a new sculpture gallery. Other sections include Greek and Roman antiquities, objects from the Near East, Mexico and Peru. The Edwardian tea room offers a varied menu in elegant surroundings.*

*2001/02 offers a varied exhibition programme, including: Living Proof – to 6 Jan 2002; Japan 2001 – to Mar 2002; Carborundum – 9 Feb to 12 May 2002; Minoans and Mycenaeans – to summer 2002. Opening in late 2001 – Water Hall Modern Art Gallery.*

### ▶ The Bond Gallery
Design & Studio Centre, The Bond Warehouse, 180–182 Fazeley Street, Birmingham B5 5SP.
**Tel** 0121 753 2065
**Personnel** Mark Renn.

### ▶ Carleton Gallery
91 Vivian Road, Harborne, Birmingham B17 0DR.
**Tel** 0121 427 2487
**Personnel** David Dunnett.

### ▶ Danford Collection of West African Art and Artefacts P
Centre for West African Studies, University of Birmingham, Birmingham B15 2TT.
**Tel** 0121 414 5128 **Fax** 0121 414 3228

### ▶ Goate Gallery
57 Stephenson Street, New Street, Birmingham B2 4JH.
**Tel** 0121 643 2624
**Personnel** Director: Peter Kandhola.

### ▶ Helios Gallery
25 Valentine Road, Kings Heath, Birmingham B14 7AN.
**Tel** 0121 444 1585
**Personnel** Proprietor: John Palmer.

### ▶ Ikon Gallery P
1 Oozells Square, Brindeyplace, Birmingham B1 2HS.
**Tel** 0121 248 0708 **Fax** 0121 248 0709
**Ws** www.ikon-gallery.co.uk
**Personnel** Marketing Manager: Matthew O'Callaghan.

### ▶ mac (Midlands Arts Centre) PS
Cannon Hill Park, Birmingham B12 9HQ.
**Tel** 0121 440 3838
**Fax** 0121 446 4372
**Email** judy.dames@mac-birmingham.org.uk
**Ws** www.birminghamarts.org.uk
**Opening times** Daily 9am–11pm.
**Personnel** Exhibition Programmer: Judy Dames.
**Services and Facilities** Bar. Bookshop. Café. Disabled Access. Guided Tours. Lectures. Parking. Restaurant. Shop. Workshop Facilities.
*30 exhibitions a year, of which 15 originated and 15 touring. Two stewarded galleries plus three public spaces, with 194 lin. m. hanging space and 300 sq. m. floor space. Shows contemporary fine art, craft and photography from both artists of known stature and those in the early stages of a promising career. Visited by 13,000 people a week. Extensive programme of live performance, cinema, education and exhibitions. Has bar, restaurant and bookshop and set in a large park. Only one space does not have disabled access. Applications from individual artists and touring organisations welcomed. mac is funded by Birmingham City Council and West Midlands Arts.*

### ▶ The Mine Fine Art Gallery
24 Temple Street, Birmingham B2 5DB.
**Tel** 0121 643 8424
**Personnel** Manager: Phil Harris.

### ▶ Number Nine The Gallery C
9 Brindley Place, Birmingham B1 2JA.
**Tel** 07970 142703/0121 643 9099
**Fax** 0121 643 9199
**Ws** www.No9thegallery.com
**Opening times** Tue–Sat 11–8, Sun 11–5 or by appointment.
**Nearest Station** Birmingham New Street.
**Personnel** Directors: Lee Benson, Adrian Burr.
**Services and Facilities** Art Consultancy. Art for Offices. Commissioning Service. Disabled Access. Framing. Gallery space for hire. Valuation.
**Work Stocked and Sold** Cer. Dr. Gla. Jew. Pa. Pr. Sc. Wd.
**Price range** £300–£20,000
For artists see Commercial Gallery Artists.
*The contemporary art gallery in Birmingham selling art, glass ceramics and sculpture.*

### ▶ Warstone & Turner Fine Art C
67 Warstone Lane, Hockley, Birmingham B18 6NG.
**Personnel** Steve Turner.

## COVENTRY

#### COVENTRY

### ▶ Herbert Art Gallery and Museum PS
Jordan Well, Coventry CV1 5QP.
**Tel** 024 76832381/832386; Minicom: 024 832340 **Fax** 024 76832410
**Email** coventry.museums@dial.pipex.com
**Ws** www.coventry.org/coventrymuseums
**Opening times** Mon–Sat 10–5.30, Sun 12–5.
**Nearest Station** Coventry.
**Personnel** Exhibitions & Events Officer: Rosie Addenbrooke. Senior Keeper, Visual Arts: Ron Clarke.
**Services and Facilities** Café. Disabled Access. Friends Society. Gallery space for hire. Lectures. Museum Shop.

### ▶ Mead Gallery, Warwick Arts Centre
University of Warwick, Coventry CV4 7AL
**Tel** 024 7622589 **Fax** 024 76523883
**Opening times** Mon–Sat 12–9.
**Personnel** Curator: Sarah Shalgosky.
**Services and Facilities** Bar. Bookshop. Disabled Access. Parking. Restaurant.

## DERBYSHIRE

#### DUDLEY

### ▶ Dudley Museum and Art Gallery P
St James's Road, Dudley DY1 1HU.
**Tel** 01384 815575 **Fax** 01384 815576

#### KINGSWINFORD

### ▶ Broadfield House Glass Museum P
Compton Drive, Kingswinford, DY6 9QA.
**Tel** 01384 812745
**Personnel** Roger Dodsworth.

## HEREFORD & WORCESTER

#### BEWDLEY

### ▶ Bewdley Museum P
The Shambles, Load Street, Bewdley, DY12 2AE.
**Tel** 01299 403573
**Personnel** Museums Officer: Carol Bowsher.

#### BROADWAY

### ▶ Anderson Gallery C
96 Upper High Street, Broadway, WR12 7AJ.
**Tel** 01386 858086 **Fax** 01386 858086
**Opening times** Open Daily. Please telephone to confirm hours.
**Personnel** Proprietor: Ronald Anderson.
**Services and Facilities** Art Consultancy. Art for Offices. Commissioning Service. Restoration. Valuation.
**Work Stocked and Sold** Cer. Cra. Dec. Dr. Fur. Gla. Jew. Pa. Sc. Wd.
**Price range** £30–£30,000
For artists see Commercial Gallery Artists.

#### BROMSGROVE

### ▶ The Jinney Ring Craft Centre C
Old House Farm, Hanbury, Bromsgrove, B60 4BU.
**Tel** 01527 821272 **Fax** 01527 821869
**Opening times** Tue–Sat 10.30–5, Sun 11.30–5.30. Free admission. Open all year.
**Nearest Station** Droitwich.
**Personnel** Owner/Partner: Richard Greatwood.
**Services and Facilities** Café. Commissioning Service. Craftshop. Disabled Access. Framing. Parking. Restaurant. Shop. Workshop Facilities.
**Work Stocked and Sold** Cer. Cra. Fur. Gla. Jew. Pa. Pr. Sc. Tx. Wd.
**Price range** £5–£1,000
For artists see Commercial Gallery Artists.
*Take a step back in time and absorb the charming rural surroundings of The Jinney Ring Craft Centre. Beautiful old timbered barns have been lovingly restored by Richard and Jenny Greatwood and now house twelve individual Craft Studios, British Craft Gallery – with craft from all over the UK, Farmhouse Kitchen Gift Shop and a Clothes Dept, Pine and Painted Furniture.*

#### CRADLEY

### ▶ The Lower Nupend Gallery C
near Malvern, Cradley, WR13 5NP.
**Tel** 01886 880500/334 **Fax** 01886 880848
**Opening times** Daily 10–6.

#### GREAT MALVERN

### ▶ Malvern Art Gallery
Malvern Library, Graham Road, Great Malvern, WR14 2HW.

**Tel** 016845 61223
**Personnel** Librarian: Keith Barber.

HAY-ON-WYE

### ▶ Brook Street Pottery C
Brook Street, Hay-on-Wye, Hereford, HR3 5BQ.
**Tel** 01497 821026
**Opening times** Mon–Sat 10.30–5, Sun 12–4.30. Closed Tue.
**Work Stocked and Sold** Cra. Tx.

HEREFORD

### ▶ Hatton Art Gallery
Churchill House Museum,
3 Venns Lane, Hereford.
**Tel** 01432 267409 **Fax** 01432 342492
**Opening times** Apr–Sep: Mon closed, Tue–Sun 2–5. Oct to end Mar: Sun and Mon closed, Tue–Sat 2–5. Open 2–5 bank holidays.
**Personnel** Curator: Miss A. E. Sandford BA, AMA.
**Services and Facilities** Disabled Access. Guided Tours. Lectures. Parking. Shop.

### ▶ Hereford City Museum and Art Gallery P
Broad Street, Hereford, HR4 9AU.
**Tel** 01432 364691 **Fax** 01432 342492

### ▶ John McKeller C
23 Church Street, Hereford, HR1 2LR.
**Tel** 01432 354460
**Opening times** Mon–Sat 9.30–5.30.
**Work Stocked and Sold** Jew.

### ▶ Mappa Mundi and Chained Library P
5 College Cloisters, Cathedral Close, Hereford, HR1 2NG.
**Tel** 01432 359880 **Fax** 01432 355929

### ▶ Meridian Contemporary Arts C
13 High Town, Hay-on-Wye, Hereford, HR3 5AE.
**Tel** 01497 821633
**Opening times** Wed–Sat 10–5, Sun 2–5.
**Personnel** Proprietor: Anthea Britnell. Proprietor: Tony Britnell.
**Work Stocked and Sold** App. Cer. Jew.

### ▶ Tidal Wave Gallery C
3 Bridge Street, Hereford, HR4 9DF.
**Tel** 01432 352365
**Fax** 01432 270680
**Opening times** Mon–Sat 9.30–5.30.
**Nearest Station** Hereford.
**Personnel** Rick Guest. Gillie Guest. John Hogg. Toby Armitage.
**Services and Facilities** Art Consultancy. Art for Offices. Disabled Access. Restoration. Shop.
**Work Stocked and Sold** Dr. Pa. Pr.
**Price range** £50–£5,000
For artists see Commercial Gallery Artists.

KIDDERMINSTER

### ▶ Hereford & Worcester County Museum P
Hartlebury Castle, Hartlebury, Kidderminster, DY11 7XZ.
**Tel** 01299 250416
**Personnel** County Museums Officer: Robin Hill.

LEOMINSTER

### ▶ Lion Gallery C
15b Broad Street, Leominster, HR6 8BT.
**Tel** 01568 614644
**Ws** www.cogent-comms.co.uk/lion.htm
**Opening times** Mon–Sat 10–5.
**Nearest Station** Leominster.
**Personnel** Chairman: Blake Mackinnon. Administrator: Rozie Keogh. Publicity Officer: Chris Noble.
**Services and Facilities** Commissioning Service. Craftshop. Disabled Access. Framing.
**Work Stocked and Sold** Ab. App. Cer. Cra. Dr. Fur. Gla. Jew. Pa. Ph. Pr. Sc. Tx. Wd.
**Price range** £5–£2,000
For artists see Commercial Gallery Artists.

### ▶ Old Chapel Gallery C
East Street, Pembridge, near Leominster, Hereford, HR6 9HB.
**Tel** 01544 388842
**Opening times** Mon–Sat 10–5.30, Sun 2–5.30.
**Work Stocked and Sold** Cer. Cra. Fur. Gla. Jew. Tx.

OMBERSLEY

### ▶ Ombersley Gallery C
Church Terrace, near Droitwich, Ombersley, WR9 0EP.
**Tel** 01905 620655
**Opening times** Tue–Sat 10–5.
**Services and Facilities** Parking. Restaurant.
**Work Stocked and Sold** Cer. Gla. Jew. Wd.

WORCESTER

### ▶ City Museum & Art Gallery P
Foregate Street, Worcester.
**Tel** 01905 25371

### ▶ Regent Galleries C
22 Reindeer Court, Worcester, WR1 2DS.
**Tel** 01905 21300

### ▶ Worcester City Art Gallery & Museum P
Foregate Street, Worcester, WR1 1DT.
**Tel** 01905 25371
**Personnel** Art & Exhibitions Officer: Bridget Crump.
**Services and Facilities** Workshop Facilities.

## SANDWELL

WEDNESBURY

### ▶ Wednesbury Museum & Art Gallery P
Holyhead Road, Wednesbury, WS10 7DF.
**Tel** 0121 556 0683
**Fax** 0121 505 1625
**Personnel** Rosie Crook.

## SHROPSHIRE

BISHOPS CASTLE

### ▶ Longhouse Gallery
25 The High Street, Bishops Castle.
**Tel** 01588 638147
**Personnel** Dawn Mcbarnet.
**Work Stocked and Sold** Ab.

BRIDGNORTH

### ▶ Clode Gallery
New Market Building, Listley Street, Bridgnorth, WV16 4AW.
**Tel** 01746 768338 **Fax** 01746 768481

ELLESMERE

### ▶ Ellesmere Arts Centre
Ellesmere College, Ellesmere, SY12 9AB.
**Tel** 01691 622828

LUDLOW

### ▶ Feathers Gallery
20 The Bull Ring, Ludlow, SY8 1AA.
**Tel** 01584 875390
**Personnel** Proprietor: Giles Gourlay.

### ▶ Silk Top Hat Gallery
4 Quality Square, Ludlow, SY8 1AR.
**Tel** 01584 875363
**Personnel** Proprietor: Jill Howorth.

SHREWSBURY

### ▶ Artifex C
Porch House, Swan Hill, Shrewsbury, SY1 1NQ.
**Tel** 01743 241031
**Opening times** Tue–Sat 10–5.30.
**Work Stocked and Sold** Cer. Cra. Fur. Gla. Jew. Wd.

### ▶ Gateway Galleries Gateway Education & Arts Centre
Chester Street, Shrewsbury, SY1 1NB.
**Tel** 01743 55159
**Personnel** Rosemary Hurst.

TELFORD

### ▶ Elton Gallery
Ironbridge Gorge Museum, Coalbrookedale, Telford, TF8 7DG.
**Tel** 01952 433522
**Personnel** Curator of Art: David De Haan.

### ▶ The Gallery
Spout Farm House, Telford Town Park, Telford.
**Tel** 01952 290240
**Personnel** Helen Papasodaro.

## STAFFORDSHIRE

BURTON-UPON-TRENT

### ▶ Brewhouse
Union Street, Burton-upon-Trent, DE14 1EB.
**Tel** 01283 67720
**Personnel** Director: Maureen Milgram.

### ▶ Round House Gallery C
38 High Street, Tutbury, Burton-upon-Trent, DE13 9LS.
**Tel** 01238 814964
**Opening times** Mon–Sat 11–5. Closed Wed and Sun. Please telephone to check winter and bank holiday opening times.
**Personnel** Owner/Proprietor: Leah Evans.

Owner/Proprietor: Phillip Evans.
**Work Stocked and Sold** Cer. Cra. Gla.

LEEK

### ▶ Leek Art Gallery
Nicholson Institute, Stockwell Street, Leek, ST13 6HQ.
**Tel** 01538 399181
**Personnel** Arts Development Officer: Karen Bell.

NEWCASTLE-UNDER-LYME

### ▶ Hood & Broomfield Fine Art
29 Albert Street, Newcastle-under-Lyme, ST5 1JP.
**Tel** 01782 626859
**Personnel** Partner: John Hood. Partner: Gordon Broomfield.

### ▶ Newcastle-Under-Lyme Museum & Art Gallery P
Brampton Park, Newcastle-under-Lyme, ST5 0QP.
**Tel** 01782 619705
**Personnel** Curator: Miranda Goodby.

STAFFORD

### ▶ The Shire Hall Gallery P
Market Square, Stafford, ST16 2LD.
**Tel** 01785 278345 **Fax** 01785 278327
**Opening times** Tue–Sat 10–5. Admission free.
**Personnel** Director: Hilary Foxley. Jackie Bradbury.
**Services and Facilities** Craftshop. Disabled Access. Friends Society. Workshop Facilities.
**Work Stocked and Sold** Cer. Cra. Gla. Jew. Tx. Wd.

### ▶ Shugborough
Ancestral home of the Earls of Milford, Stafford, ST17 0XB.
**Tel** 01889 881388

## STOKE-ON-TRENT

STOKE-ON-TRENT

### ▶ City Museum and Art Gallery, Stoke on Trent P
Bethesda Street, Hanley, Stoke-on-Trent ST1 3DW.
**Tel** 01782 232323 **Fax** 01782 205033
**Opening times** Mon–Sat 10–5, Sun 2–5.
**Personnel** Director of Leisure and Cultural Services: P. Vigurs MA FMA.
**Services and Facilities** Bar. Bookshop. Café. Museum Shop. Restaurant. Shop. Workshop Facilities.

### ▶ The Potteries Museum & Art Gallery
Bethesda Street, Stoke on Trent.
**Tel** 01782 232323

## WALSALL

WALSALL

### ▶ The New Art Gallery Walsall P
Gallery Square, Walsall WS2 8LG.
**Tel** 01922 654400 **Fax** 01922 654401
**Opening times** Tue–Fri 10–5, Sun 2–5.
**Personnel** Rebecca McLaughlin.
**Services and Facilities** Disabled Access. Guided Tours. Lectures.
*Lively and friendly gallery with diverse programme of contemporary art exhibitions and events, innovative education projects and the stunning Garman Ryan collection with its extraordinary range of works from Rembrandt to Van Gogh, Constable to Freud and works from Africa, Asia, ancient Greece and Rome, along with one of the most comprehensive collections of the work of sculptor Sir Jacob Epstein.*

## WARWICKSHIRE

ALCESTER

### ▶ Coughton Court P
Alcester, B49 5JA.
**Tel** 01789 400777, Visitor info: 01789 762435
**Fax** 01789 765544

LEAMINGTON SPA

### ▶ Leamington Spa Art Gallery and Museum P
Avenue Road, Leamington Spa, CV31 3PP.
**Tel** 01926 426559 **Fax** 01926 317867
**Personnel** G. C. Macfarquhar.

RUGBY

### ▶ Rugby Art Gallery & Museum P
Little Elborow St, Rugby, CV21 3BZ.
**Tel** 01788 533 201 **Fax** 01788 533 204
**Email** rugbyartgallery&museum@rugby.gov.uk
**Ws** www.rugbygalleryandmuseum.org.uk
**Opening times** Tue and Thu 10–8, Wed and Fri 10–5, Sat 10–4, Sun and bank holidays 1–5, Mon closed.
**Nearest Station** Rugby
**Personnel** Museums & Galleries Manager: Wendy Parry. Exhibitions Officer: Nikki Grange.
*Explore the treasures of history and art. Temporary exhibition programme of high quality, national and local art and craft both originated by the Art Gallery and hired in from other venues. Home of the Rugby Collection of 20th and 21st Century British Art, regularly shown in the Art Gallery. Home to the Tripontium Collection of Roman Artefacts from an important Roman settlement just outside Rugby. Social History Gallery showing Rugby's history throughout the past two centuries. We offer a lively programme of talks and workshops and welcome school parties and groups.*

STRATFORD-UPON-AVON

### ▶ Montpellier Gallery C
8 Chapel Street, Stratford-upon-Avon, CV37 3EP.
**Tel** 01789 261161 **Fax** 01789 261161
**Opening times** Mon–Sat 9.30–5.30.
**Personnel** Proprietor: Peter Burridge.
**Services and Facilities** Art Consultancy. Art for Offices. Commissioning Service. Craftshop. Disabled Access. Framing.
**Work Stocked and Sold** Cer. Cra. Gla. Jew. Pa. Pr. Sc. Wd.
**Price range** £20–£1, 500

WARWICK

### ▶ Church Street Gallery
5 Church Street, Warwick, CV34 4AB.
**Personnel** Proprietor: T. G. Jones.

### ▶ Mason Watts Fine Art
60 Smith Street, Warwick, CV34 4HU.
**Personnel** Proprietor: Mrs Mason Watts.

## WEST MIDLANDS

HENLEY-IN-ARDEN

### ▶ The Gallery Upstairs/ Torquil Pottery C
81 High Street, Henley-in-Arden, Solihull, B95 5AT.
**Tel** 01564 792174 **Fax** 01564 792174
**Opening times** Mon–Sat 10–6.
**Work Stocked and Sold** Cer. Cra. Pa. Sc.

## WOLVERHAMPTON

WOLVERHAMPTON

### ▶ Bilston Craft Gallery and Museum PS
Mount Pleasant, Bilston, Wolverhampton WV14 7LU.
**Tel** 01902 552507 **Fax** 01902 552504
**Opening times** Tue–Fri 10–4, Sat 11–4, closed Mon & Sun.
**Nearest Station** Wolverhampton, Coseley. Bilston Metro.
**Personnel** Arts & Craft Coordinator: Pauline Thomas. Assistant Craft Development Officer: Angela Corbyn.
**Services and Facilities** Commissioning Service. Craftshop. Disabled Access. Lectures.
**Work Stocked and Sold** Cer. Cra. Gla. Jew. Tx.
**Price range** £10–£200
For artists see Commercial Gallery Artists.

### ▶ Light House Media Centre
The Chubb Buildings, Fryer Street, Wolverhampton WV1 1HT.
**Tel** 01902 716055
**Personnel** Frank Challenger.

### ▶ Wolverhampton Art Gallery PS
Lichfield Street, Wolverhampton WV1 1DU.
**Tel** 01902 552055
**Fax** 01902 552053
**Email** info.wag@dial.pipex.com
**Ws** www.wolverhampton.org.uk
**Opening times** Mon–Sat 10–5. Free entry.
**Nearest Station** Wolverhampton.
**Personnel** Head of Arts & Museums: Nicholas Dodd BA AMA. Marketing Officer: Helen Large. Senior Curator, Visual Arts: Marguerite Nugent. Collections Manager: Philippa Tinsley.
**Services and Facilities** Café. Commissioning Service. Craftshop. Disabled Access. Friends Society. Lectures. Museum Shop. Shop. Workshop Facilities.
**Work Stocked and Sold** Cer. Cra. Gla. Jew.
**Price range** £10–£100
*Wolverhampton's award winning art gallery houses one of the largest collections of contemporary art in the region together with one of the best public collections of Pop Art featuring works by Andy Warhol, Peter Blake and Roy*



**Ab** Artists' Books **App** Applied Art **Cer** Ceramics **Cra** Craft **Dec** Decorative **Dr** Drawing **Fur** Furniture

*Lichtenstein. Redeveloped in 2001, the Gallery now includes the Creation Digital Art Centre and the Makers Dozen artist workshops. The 2002 exhibition programme includes 'SEA' 9 Feb–13 Apr, a themed show which looks to the sea as a symbol of fear, beauty and the sublime; 'Mythical Echoes' 27 Apr–15 Jun featuring the surreal sculptures and installations of Steve West; and 'Collect' 13 Jul–14 Sep which looks at the world of art collecting and features work by Joan Miro, John Piper and Lucie Rie.*

## Yorkshire & Humberside

### BRADFORD

BRADFORD

**▶ Bradford Art Galleries and Museums** P
Headquarters, Cartwright Hall, Lister Park, Bradford BD9 4NS.
**Tel** 01274 493313 **Fax** 01274 481045

**▶ Cartwright Hall Art Gallery** PS
(Bradford Metropolitan Council), Lister Park, Bradford BD9 4NS.
**Tel** 01274 493313 **Fax** 01274 481045
**Opening times** Tue–Sat 10–5, Sun 1–5. Closed Mondays except bank holidays.
**Nearest Station** Frizinghall/Bradford.
**Personnel** City Arts, Museums and Libraries Officer: P. Lawson.
**Services and Facilities** Café. Disabled Access. Friends Society. Lectures. Museum Shop. Parking.

**▶ The Colour Museum** PS
Perkin House, PO Box 244, 1 Providence Street, Bradford BD1 2PW.
**Tel** 01274 390955
**Fax** 01274 392888
**Opening times** Tue–Fri 2–5, Sat 10–4. Open to pre-booked parties on Tue–Fri mornings. Admission: adults £1.50, concessions £1, family group £3.75.
**Nearest Station** Forster Square.
**Personnel** Curator: Sarah Burge.
**Services and Facilities** Disabled Access. Gallery space for hire. Lectures. Museum Shop. Workshop Facilities.

**▶ South Square Gallery** C
Thornton Road, Bradford BD13 3LD.
**Tel** 01274 834747
**Opening times** Daily 12–4 except Mon.
**Work Stocked and Sold** Pa.

KEIGHLEY

**▶ Bronte Parsonage Museum** P
Haworth, Keighley, BD22 8DR.
**Tel** 01535 642323
**Fax** 01535 647131
**Opening times** Open daily Apr–Sep 10–5, Oct–Mar 11–4.30. Closed 8 Jan–3 Feb and 24–27 Dec.
**Personnel** Curator: Rachel Terry.

**▶ Cliffe Castle Art Museum**
Spring Gardens Lane, Keighley, BD20 6LH.
**Tel** 01535 618 230

### CALDERDALE

HALIFAX

**▶ Piece Hall Art Gallery** PS
The Piece Hall, Halifax, HX1 1RE.
**Tel** 01422 358087
**Fax** 01422 349310
**Email** karen.belshaw@calderdale.gov.uk
**Ws** www.calderdale.gov.uk
**Opening times** Tue–Sun and bank holidays 10–5.
**Nearest Station** Halifax
**Personnel** Exhibitions Officer: Karen Belshaw. Art Education Officer: Sarah Thornton.
**Services and Facilities** Commissioning Service. Disabled Access. Gallery space for hire. Museum Shop. Workshop Facilities.
*The Art Gallery is situated in the historic Piece Hall. It has an exciting programme of exhibitions, including art and craft shows by local artists as well as by internationally renown artists.*

TODMORDEN

**▶ Todmorden Fine Art**
27 Water Street, Todmorden, OL14 5AB.
**Tel** 01706 814723
**Personnel** Dave Gurning.

### DONCASTER

DONCASTER

**▶ Doncaster Museum and Art Gallery** P
Chequer Road, Doncaster DN1 2AE.
**Tel** 01302 734222/734293
**Fax** 01302 735409

### EAST RIDING OF YORKSHIRE

BEVERLEY

**▶ Beverley Art Gallery & Museum** P
Champney Road, Beverley, HU17 9BQ.
**Tel** 01482 883903/884956
**Opening times** Wed–Fri 10–5, Sat & Sun 10–12.30 & 1.30–5. Admission free.

BRIDLINGTON

**▶ Sewerby Hall Art Gallery and Museum (Museum of East Yorkshire)** P
Sewerby Hall, Bridlington, YO15 1EA.
**Tel** 01262 677874 **Fax** 01262 674265
**Email** museum@sewerby.demon.co.uk

### HULL

HULL

**▶ Red Gallery**
19 Osbourne Street, Hull.
**Tel** 01482 348333

**▶ University of Hull Art Collection** PS
University of Hull, Cottingham Road, Hull HU6 7RX.
**Tel** 01482 465192/465035
**Fax** 01482 465192
**Email** j.g.bernasconi@hist.hull.ac.uk
**Ws** www.hull.ac.uk/history/art/arthome.htm
**Opening times** Mon–Fri 2–4, Wed 12.30–4 (except public holidays).
**Personnel** Director: John G. Bernasconi.
**Services and Facilities** Disabled Access. Friends Society. Lectures.
*The Hull University Art Collection specialises in paintings, sculpture, drawings and prints produced in Britain 1890–1940. It includes works by Beardsley, Sickert, Steer, Lucien Pissarro, Augustus John, Stanley Spencer, Wyndham Lewis and Ben Nicholson, as well as sculpture by Epstein, Gill, Gaudier-Brzeska and Henry Moore. The Camden Town Group and Bloomsbury artists are particularly well represented. Also on display are the Thompson Collections of Chinese ceramics on long-term loan. Regular loan exhibitions are shown.*

### HUMBERSIDE

KINGSTON UPON HULL

**▶ Ferens Art Gallery** PS
Queen Victoria Square, Kingston Upon Hull, HU1 3RA.
**Tel** 01482 613902 **Fax** 01482 613710
**Ws** www.hullcc.gov.uk/museums
**Opening times** Mon–Sat 10–5, Sun 1.30–4.30.
**Nearest Station** Hull.
**Personnel** Head of Art: Ann Bukantas.
**Services and Facilities** Café. Disabled Access. Friends Society. Lectures. Shop.

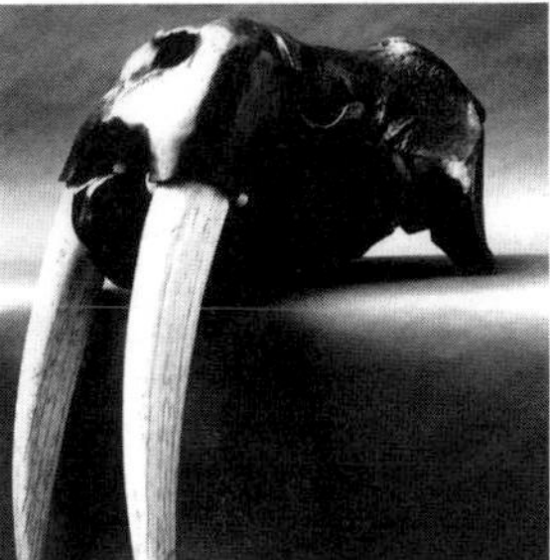

*Steve Dilworth,* Walrus Skull, *bronze, walrus tusks & marble, 90 x 35 x 50 cm, 1997.*
*The gallery houses a permanent collection of old master paintings from the 17th century onwards, with an emphasis on Dutch and Flemish artists, portraits, marine paintings, 19th- and 20th-century watercolours, and 20th-century art to the present day. There is a varied programme of exhibitions throughout the year, ranging across all media from paintings and drawing to installations, sculpture, craft, photography, video and the electronic image. The gallery also has a purpose built performance space and runs a full programme of events and educational activities.*

### KIRKLEES

BATLEY

**▶ Batley Art Gallery**
Market Place, Batley, WF17 5DA.
**Tel** 01924 326090
**Fax** 01924 326308
**Opening times** Mon, Wed, Fri 10–5, Tue 10–1,

Thu 10–5, Sat 10–4, Sun closed.
**Personnel** Helen Robinson.

DEWSBURY

### ▶ Dewsbury Exhibition Gallery
Wellington Road, Dewsbury, WF13.
**Tel** 0113 233 6107
**Personnel** Jane Speller.

HUDDERSFIELD

### ▶ The Ark C
113 North Road, Kirkburton, Huddersfield, HD8 0RL.
**Tel** 01484 605055
**Opening times** Tue–Sat 10–5.
**Services and Facilities** Commissioning Service.
**Work Stocked and Sold** Cra. Gla. Jew. Tx. Wd.

MIRFIELD

### ▶ Eastthorpe Gallery
Huddersfield Road, Mirfield, WF14 8AT.
**Tel** 01924 497646
**Opening times** Tue–Fri 1–5, Sat 10–5.
**Personnel** Liz Hammond.
**Services and Facilities** Disabled Access. Parking. Workshop Facilities.

## LEEDS

ABERFORD

### ▶ Lotherton Hall
(Leeds City Art Galleries), Aberford, LS25 3EB.
**Tel** 0113 281 3259 **Fax** 0113 281 2100
**Opening times** Easter–31 Oct: Tue–Sat 10–5, Sun 1–5. 1 Nov–31 Dec, Mar: Tue–Sat 10–4, Sun 12–4. Closed Mon, except bank holidays, Jan, Feb.
**Personnel** Curator: Andy White. Supervisor: Harry Fisher.
**Services and Facilities** Café. Friends Society. Guided Tours. Shop.

LEEDS

### ▶ Abbey House Museum P
Abbey Road, Leeds LS5 3EH.
**Tel** 01532 755821
**Opening times** Summer: Mon–Sat 10–6, Sun 2–6. Winter: Mon–Sat 10–5, Sun 2–5. Closed Christmas Day, Boxing Day and New Year's Day.
**Personnel** Curator: Mr P. Larkin. Mrs J. Bridgwater.

### ▶ Art.Co, Contemporary Fine Art
No. 1 Meanwood Close, Leeds LS7 2JF.
**Tel** 0113 262 0056 **Fax** 0113 262 8388
**Opening times** Mon–Fri 9–5, Sat 10–3.
**Personnel** Simon Hester.
**Work Stocked and Sold** Pa. Pr. Sc.
**Price range** £50–£3,000

### ▶ City Art Gallery PS
The Headrow, Leeds LS1 3AA.
**Tel** 0113 2478248 **Fax** 0113 2449689
**Ws** www.leeds.gov.uk
**Opening times** Mon–Sat 10–5 (Wed 10–8), Sun 1–5.
**Nearest Station** Leeds City.
**Personnel** Senior Curator: Corrine Miller. Curator: Exhibitions: Nigel Walsh. Education Officer: Amanda Philips. Director (Leeds Museums & Galleries): Evelyn Silber.
**Services and Facilities** Bookshop. Disabled Access. Friends Society. Gallery space for hire. Lectures. Restaurant. Shop. Workshop Facilities.
*The gallery in the centre of Leeds houses one of the most significant collections of 20th-century British art in the country. Other notable features include a splendid Victorian gallery, fine collection of early English watercolours and notable examples of late-19th-century French painting. The Henry Moore Sculpture Gallery houses an outstanding selection of modern British sculpture, while the Henry Moore Institute contains an archive, library, and further exhibition space. There is also a wide-ranging temporary exhibition programme, an active and engaging educational service, and a picture loan scheme. Visitors can also enjoy morning coffee or lunch in the Gallery Café and visit the Craft and Design Centre. Disabled Access: ramped access to front door and craft shop; 50% of Gallery accessible; ETB standard met in one toilet.*

### ▶ The Henry Moore Institute
74 The Headrow, Leeds LS1 3AA.
**Tel** 0113 234 3158 (information line)
**Fax** 0113 246 1481
**Email** hmi@henry-moore.ac.uk
**Ws** www.henry-moore-fdn.co.uk
**Opening times** Daily 10–5.30, Wed 10–9. Admission free. Closed bank holidays.
**Nearest Station** Leeds City.
**Personnel** Assistant Administrator: Catherine Aldred.
**Services and Facilities** Disabled Access. Guided Tours. Lectures. Shop.
*The Henry Moore Institute, formerly a neglected group of early Victorian merchants' offices, has been transformed into a unique building devoted to the exhibition, study and promotion of sculpture. Situated in the heart of Leeds, the Institute houses four sculpture galleries for temporary exhibitions, also a sculpture reference library, archive and slide library. The Institute organises talks, seminars and lectures. Please call our information line for further details.*

### ▶ Leeds Metropolitan University Gallery PS
Woodhouse Lane, Leeds LS1 3HE.
**Tel** 0113 283 3130 **Fax** 0113 283 5999
**Email** m.innes@lmu.ac.uk
**Ws** www.lmu.ac.uk/arts
**Opening times** Mon–Sat 11–5, Wed 11–7.
**Personnel** Gallery Development Officers: Claire Slattery, Moira Innes.
**Services and Facilities** Bar. Disabled Access. Lectures. Workshop Facilities.
*Leeds Metropolitan University Gallery is one of the major contemporary arts venues in the city of Leeds.*

### ▶ The Pavillion Photography Centre
235 Woodhouse Lane, Leeds LS2 3AP.
**Tel** 0113 275 1347

### ▶ Terrace Gallery PS
Harewood House Trust, Moor House, Harewood, Leeds LS17 9LQ.
**Tel** 0113 218 1016 **Fax** 0113 218 1002
**Email** philipa.hht@virgin.net
**Ws** www.harewood.org
**Opening times** 2 Apr–29 Oct: daily 11–5, last admission 4.45.
**Nearest Station** Leeds, Harrogate.
**Personnel** Visual Arts Coordinator: Philippa Brough.
**Services and Facilities** Bookshop. Café. Disabled Access. Guided Tours. Lectures. Parking. Shop.

### ▶ University Gallery Leeds PS
Parkinson Building, Woodhouse Lane, Leeds LS2 9JT.
**Tel** 0113 233 2777
**Email** H. M. Diaper@leeds.ac.uk
**Ws** www.leeds.ac.uk/library/gall/exhibs.html
**Opening times** Exhibitions Mon–Fri 10–5.
**Nearest Station** Leeds City.
**Personnel** Keeper: Dr Hilary Diaper.
**Services and Facilities** Disabled Access. Friends Society.
*Selected displays from the University's permanent collection of British 19th- and 20th-century art, together with a changing programme of exhibitions during each academic year, covering a wide range of historic and contemporary works in a variety of media. Wheelchair access at north end of Parkinson Building.*

WETHERBY

### ▶ Green Frog Gallery C
2 Church Street, Wetherby, LS22 6LP.
**Tel** 01937 586411 **Fax** 01937 586411
**Opening times** Tue–Sat 8.30–5.30.
**Nearest Station** York.
**Personnel** James Jones.
**Work Stocked and Sold** Pa. Sc.
**Price range** £60–£1,000

## NORTH YORKSHIRE

CASTLETON

### ▶ Montage Studio Gallery C
12 Church Street, Castleton, YO21 2EQ.
**Tel** 01287 660159
**Fax** 01947 841295, 01287 660159
**Email** montage.gallery@onyxnqt.co.uk
**Ws** www.montage-gallery.co.uk
**Opening times** Tue–Sat 10–5, Sun 2–5, Mon closed.
**Nearest Station** Castleton.
**Personnel** Director: Jean Freer.
**Services and Facilities** Framing. Workshop Facilities.

**Work Stocked and Sold** App. Cer. Dr. Gla. Jew. Pa. Ph. Sc. Wd.
**Price range** £20–£2,000
For artists see Commercial Gallery Artists.

HARROGATE

### ▶ Anstey Galleries C
33 Swan Road, Harrogate, HG1 2SA.
**Tel** 01423 500102 **Fax** 01423 500102
**Opening times** Tue–Sat 10–4. Closed Mon.
**Work Stocked and Sold** Cer. Sc.

### ▶ Chantry House Gallery C
Ripley, Harrogate, HG3 3AY.
**Tel** 01423 771011
**Opening times** Apr–Sep: Tue–Sat 10–5, Sun 12–5. Oct–Mar: Wed–Sat 10–4, Sun 12–4.
**Personnel** Directors: Terry Logan, Georgina Logan.
**Services and Facilities** Art Consultancy. Art for Offices. Commissioning Service. Disabled Access. Framing.
**Work Stocked and Sold** Dr. Pa. Pr.
**Price range** £10–£1,000
For artists see Commercial Gallery Artists.

### ▶ Harrogate Museums and Arts P
Royal Pump Room Museum, Crown Place, Harrogate, HG1 2RY.
**Tel** 01423 503340 **Fax** 01423 840026
**Email** LG12@harrogate.gov.uk

### ▶ Mercer Art Gallery
Swan Road, Harrogate, HG1 2SA.
**Tel** 01423 503340 **Fax** 01423 840026
**Email** lg31@harrogate.gov.uk
**Opening times** Tue–Sat 10–5, Sun 2–5, closed Mon except bank holidays.
**Personnel** Director: Mary Kershaw. Visual Arts Officer: Karen Southworth.
**Services and Facilities** Disabled Access. Friends Society. Lectures. Restoration. Workshop Facilities.

### ▶ Ripley Castle P
Ripley, Harrogate, HG3 3AY.
**Tel** 01423 770152 **Fax** 01423 771745

### ▶ Studio Gallery
23 Cold Bath Road, Harrogate, HG2 0NL.
**Tel** 01423 523284 **Fax** 01423 523284
**Opening times** Tue–Sat 10–5 (closed Sun & Mon), or by appointment.
**Work Stocked and Sold** Cer. Gla. Pa. Pr. Sc.

HELMSLEY

### ▶ Look Gallery C
20 Castlegate, Helmsley, YO62 5AB.
**Tel** 01439 770545
**Opening times** Mon–Sat 10.30–5, Sun 2–5.
**Personnel** Director: Nicholas Coombes.
**Work Stocked and Sold** Cer. Gla. Pa. Sc.
**Price range** £100–£1,000
For artists see Commercial Gallery Artists.

KNARESBOROUGH

### ▶ Gordon Reece Gallery C
Finkle Street, Knaresborough, HG5 8AA.
**Tel** 01423 866219 **Fax** 01423 868165
**Email** info@gordonreecegalleries.com
**Ws** www.gordonreecegalleries.com
**Opening times** Daily 10.30–5, closed Sun and Mon.
**Nearest Station** Knaresborough.
**Personnel** Director: Gordon Reece. Manager: Rachel Williams.
**Services and Facilities** Art Consultancy. Art for Offices. Bookshop. Lectures.
**Work Stocked and Sold** Cer. Fur. Jew. Sc. Tx. Wd.
**Price range** £50–£5,000
*Specialists in tribal, ethnic, folk arts, primitive and oriental antiques. The Gallery presents selling exhibitions alongside permanent collections of Indian and African art, furniture, nomadic rugs, jewellery, sculpture, ceramics and architectural antiques. For details of our gallery in London, please see London Commercial Galleries listing.*

*Himalayan mask depicting Garuda.*

### ▶ Old Courthouse Museum P
Castle Grounds, Knaresborough.
**Tel** 01423 503340 **Fax** 01423 840026

RICHMOND

### ▶ Richmondshire Museum P
Ryder's Wynd, Richmond, DL10 4JA.
**Tel** 01748 825611
**Personnel** Honorary Secretary: Mr D. Squires.

SCARBOROUGH

### ▶ Crescent Arts Workshop P
The Crescent, Scarborough, YO11 2PW.
**Tel** 01723 351461
**Personnel** Exhibitions Officer: Suzanne Cole. Workshop Information: Helen Berry.

SETTLE

### ▶ Linton Court Gallery C
Duke Street, Settle, BD24 9DW.
**Tel** 01729 822695
**Opening times** Please phone for information about exhibitions and opening times.
**Nearest Station** Settle.
**Personnel** Director: Ann Carr.
**Work Stocked and Sold** Cer. Dr. Pa. Pr.
**Price range** £100–£3,000
For artists see Commercial Gallery Artists.
*The Gallery started in 1980 and is in a 200-year-old converted hay loft. During the year there are a wide variety of exhibitions showing work of young as well as nationally known contemporary artists. Ceramics and original prints are always available.*

THIRSK

### ▶ Sion Hill Hall Museum P
Kirby Wiske, Thirsk, YO7 4EU.
**Tel** 01845 587206
**Personnel** Curator: Mrs S. M. Gadsby.

### ▶ Zillah Bell Contemporary Art
15 Kirkgate, Thirsk, YO7 1PQ.

WHITBY

### ▶ Sutcliffe Gallery
1 Flowergate, Whitby, YO21 3BA.
**Tel** 01947 602239
**Personnel** Managing Director: Bill Eglon Shaw.

## ROTHERHAM

ROTHERHAM

### ▶ Art Gallery P
Rotherham Arts Centre, Walker Place, Rotherham S65 1JH.
**Tel** 01709 382121 ext 3624
**Fax** 01709 823650

## SHEFFIELD

SHEFFIELD

### ▶ City Museum and Mappin Art Gallery P
Weston Park, Western Bank, Sheffield S10 2TP.
**Tel** 0114 2768588 **Fax** 0114 2750957
**Opening times** Tue–Sat 10–5, Sun 11–5, closed Mon.
**Personnel** Curator of Contemporary Art: Julie Milne.
**Services and Facilities** Café. Disabled Access. Friends Society. Museum Shop. Shop. Workshop Facilities.

### ▶ Cupola Gallery C
178a Middlewood Road, Sheffield S6 1TD.
**Tel** 0114 285 2665 **Fax** 0114 285 2665
**Email** cupola@globalnet.co.uk
**Ws** www.cupolagallery.co.uk
**Opening times** Mon–Sat 10–6.30, Sun by appointment. Please ring for details of late night opening.
**Nearest Station** Sheffield. Tram direct from station to gallery.
**Personnel** Manager: Lesley Smailes. Managing Director: Karen Sherwood.
**Services and Facilities** Art Consultancy. Art for Offices. Commissioning Service. Craftshop. Disabled Access (limited). Framing. Lectures. Parking. Restoration. Shop. Valuation.
**Work Stocked and Sold** Cer. Cra. Fur. Gla. Jew. Pa. Ph. Pr. Sc. Tx. Wd.
**Price range** £10–£2,000
For artists see Commercial Gallery Artists.
*Established in 1991, Cupola is very lively and friendly, with a reputation for quality exhibitions*

*and innovation. The gallery shows a collection of constantly evolving quality contemporary work and plays host to a breathless turnover of gallery exhibitions. New artists and makers feature extensively in Cupola, together with the more established. We operate the Artloan interest free credit system and offer free chocolate cake on Saturdays. We also offer a quality bespoke framing service where friendly and helpful staff are happy to offer advice when required. The framing of originals is a speciality. Cupola also operates an extensive commissioning service. If you want something we haven't got we guarantee we can find you an artist who can make it. Everything from small private commissions involving jewellery or furniture or paintings, for example, to large scale public artworks or murals!*

### ▶ Graves Art Gallery P
Surrey Street, Sheffield S1 1XZ.
**Tel** 0114 273 5158 **Fax** 0114 273 4705
**Opening times** Mon–Sat 10–5. Closed Sundays.
**Nearest Station** Sheffield.
**Personnel** Curator of Visual Art: Anne Goodchild.
**Services and Facilities** Café. Friends Society. Lectures. Museum Shop. Shop.

### ▶ Ruskin Gallery P
101 Norfolk Street, Sheffield S1 2JE.
**Tel** 0114 203 9416 **Fax** 0114 203 9417
**Opening times** Mon–Sat 10–5, closed Sun.
**Personnel** Principal Keeper: Camilla Hampshire.
**Services and Facilities** Friends Society. Gallery space for hire. Museum Shop. Shop.

### ▶ Site Gallery
1 Brown Street, Sheffield.
**Tel** 0114 2812077

### ▶ Untitled Photographic Gallery & Workshop
1 Brown Street, Sheffield S1 2BS.
**Tel** 01742 725947
**Personnel** Administrator: Ms J. Woods.

## WAKEFIELD

WAKEFIELD

### ▶ Wakefield Art Gallery P
Wentworth Terrace, Wakefield WF1 3QW.
**Tel** 01924 305796 **Fax** 01924 305770
**Email** avella@wakefield.gov.uk
**Opening times** Tue–Sat 10.30–4.30, Sun 2–4. Admission free.
**Nearest Station** Wakefield, Westgate.
**Personnel** Keeper of Art: Antonino Vella.
**Services and Facilities** Friends Society. Lectures. Museum Shop.
*The gallery houses an important collection of modern British art, with fine work by locally born international renowned artists Henry Moore and Barbara Hepworth. The gallery also has major work from earlier periods and other European schools. In the summer months there is a 'Secret Garden Trail' which combines art activities with the exploration of the natural environment. Other events and workshops take place on a regular basis. Temporary exhibitions are held throughout the year. There is no ramped access.*

## WEST YORKSHIRE

HALIFAX

### ▶ The Dean Clough Galleries C
Halifax, HX3 5AX.
**Tel** 01422 250250
**Fax** 01422 341148
**Email** linda@design-dimension.co.uk
**Ws** www.DeanClough.com
**Opening times** Every day 10–5.
**Nearest Station** Halifax.
**Personnel** Director: Roger Standen. Arts Coordinator: Chris Taylor. Galleries Curator: Doug Binder.
**Services and Facilities** Art Consultancy. Art for Offices. Bar. Bookshop. Café. Craftshop. Disabled Access. Framing. Friends Society. Gallery space for hire. Guided Tours. Lectures. Museum Shop. Parking. Restaurant. Shop. Valuation. Workshop Facilities.
**Work Stocked and Sold** Ab. App. Cer. Cra. Dec. Dr. Fur. Gla. Jew. Pa. Ph. Pr. Sc. Tx. Wd.
**Price range** £5–£3,000
For artists see Commercial Gallery Artists.

HUDDERSFIELD

### ▶ Lupton Square Gallery C
1 & 2 Lupton Square (off Westgate), Honley, Huddersfield, HD7 2AA.
**Tel** 01484 666144
**Fax** 01484 661221
**Email** geoff@luptonsquaregallery.co.uk
**Ws** www.luptonsquaregallery.co.uk
**Opening times** Fri, Sat, Sun and bank holidays 10–5, or by appointment.
**Nearest Station** Huddersfield.
**Personnel** Geoffrey S. Harrop.
**Services and Facilities** Art for Offices. Commissioning Service. Framing. Parking. Shop.
**Work Stocked and Sold** Cer. Pa. Pr. Sc.
**Price range** £15–£2,000
For artists see Commercial Gallery Artists.

## YORK

YORK

### ▶ Castle Howard
York YO6 7DA.
**Tel** 01653 648333

### ▶ Kentmere House Gallery C
53 Scarcroft Hill, York YO2 1DF.
**Tel** 01904 656507
**Fax** 01904 433949
**Opening times** Every Thu evening 6–9, first weekend of every month, each day 11–5, and any other time by appointment.
**Personnel** Director: Ann Petherick.
**Services and Facilities** Art Consultancy. Art for Offices. Commissioning Service. Framing. Parking.
**Work Stocked and Sold** Cer. Pa. Pr.
**Price range** £50–£3,000
For artists see Commercial Gallery Artists.

### ▶ Pyramid Gallery C
43 Stonegate, York YO1 2AW.
**Tel** 01904 641187
**Opening times** Mon–Sat 10–5, Sun in peak season 11–4.
**Personnel** Anne Dawson.
**Services and Facilities** Shop.
**Work Stocked and Sold** Cra. Gla. Jew. Pr. Tx. Wd.

### ▶ Robert Feather Jewellery Gallery C
10 Gillygate, York YO3 7EQ.
**Tel** 01904 632025
**Opening times** Mon–Sat 9.30–5.30.
**Work Stocked and Sold** Cra. Jew.

### ▶ York City Art Gallery PS
Exhibition Square, York YO1 7EW.
**Tel** 01904 551861 **Fax** 01904 551866
**Email** art.gallery@york.gov.uk
**Ws** www.york.gov.uk/heritage/museums/art
**Opening times** Daily 10–5.
**Nearest Station** York (main line)
**Personnel** Exhibitions & Publicity Officer: Lara Goodband.
**Services and Facilities** Bookshop. Craftshop. Disabled Access. Friends Society. Gallery space for hire. Guided Tours. Museum Shop. Shop. Workshop Facilities.

***Barbara Hepworth,*** **Surgeon Waiting,** ***1948–9.***
*York City Art Gallery is remarkable for the range and quality of its collections, which are of local, national and international importance. The gallery provides a survey of most developments in Western European painting over the last six centuries, from early Italian gold-ground panels to the art of the present day. It is unique amongst the countries smaller regional galleries. There is also a collection of watercolours, drawings and prints largely devoted to topographical views of York. A special feature of the gallery is its collection of pioneer studio pottery generally regarded as the finest of its kind.*



**Ab** Artists' Books **App** Applied Art **Cer** Ceramics **Cra** Craft **Dec** Decorative **Dr** Drawing **Fur** Furniture

# Scottish Galleries

*Where this information has been provided, entries are designated 'C' for commercial, 'P' for public gallery or museum or 'PS' for a public gallery or museum holding selling shows*

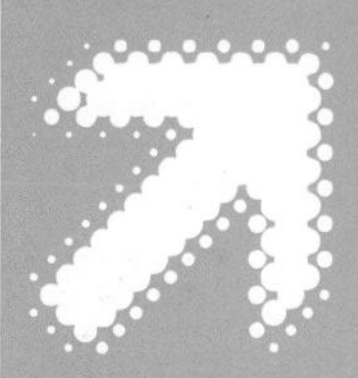

NOTES

# Scotland

One exhibition in Scotland jumps out of the advance publicity for 2002, not only as a certain crowd-puller, but as a symbol for the current state of the Scottish art scene. Douglas Gordon, winner of the 1996 Turner Prize, will have his first major solo exhibition on home turf (well, Edinburgh will never be home to a Glaswegian, but it's close enough) in August at the Scottish National Gallery of Modern Art.

Gordon's success has catapulted Scottish art, and especially the Glasgow art scene, to an international standing second only to London's, but the fact that Gordon and others (most notably, Christine Borland) have been represented by London galleries has long been seen as a sign of a malaise within the commercial sector in Scotland. Yes, there are some fine, established galleries in both Glasgow and Edinburgh, but the conceptual and lens-based work from the past decade or so has largely been overlooked.

In 2001, however, some new ventures began to suggest that the Scottish art scene is flourishing in different and significant directions. Doggerfisher, set up by former art critic Susanna Beaumont, is a vital new addition to Edinburgh's lively but conservative commercial gallery scene, selling work by highly rated younger artists such as Jonathon Owen and Janice McNab. In the non-commercial sector, some of the most exciting developments have been outside of the central belt: Dundee Contemporary Arts continues with its bold, compelling programme, while the artist-run space Generator, also in Dundee, shows work by emerging artists and new curators.

But for gallery-goers, the really good news is that Scotland's leading galleries will all once again be open in 2002, following the reopening of Glasgow's Tramway and CCA after major redevelopment at different points in 2001. To these – with DCA, the National Galleries of Scotland in Edinburgh and the city's Fruitmarket Gallery – we look for further agenda-setting exhibitions. To the smaller commercial galleries, we look for more in the way of risk-taking in the future, more commitment to showing and selling work that doesn't have to hang in some lovely frame over the mantelpiece. A final thought: there was much talk during the Edinburgh Festival 2001 about the place of the visual arts during the annual festival jamboree. Not part of the festival proper, it has been left to individual galleries to come up with a programme for the world's largest arts festival. A Biennale was being mooted in some quarters, as a means of formalising and prioritising the art offerings in Edinburgh. If Venice can do it, why not Scotland, with the galleries, and home-grown talent, to sustain it?

Elisabeth Mahoney

## ABERDEEN

### ABERDEEN

**▶ Aberdeen Art Gallery and Museum** P
Schoolhill, Aberdeen AB9 1FQ.
**Tel** 01224 523700 **Fax** 01224 632133
**Opening times** Mon–Sat 10–5, Thu 1–8, Sun 2–5.
**Services and Facilities** Art for Offices. Café. Disabled Access. Friends Society. Museum Shop. Shop.

**▶ Aberdeen Arts Centre** P
33 King Street, Aberdeen AB2 3AA.
**Tel** 01224 635208

**▶ Gallery Heinzel** C
21 Spa Street, Aberdeen AB1 1PU.
**Tel** 01224 625629 **Fax** 01224 625629
**Email** boagart@zetnet.co.uk
**Personnel** Chris Heinzel.

**▶ Grays School of Art** P
Faculty of Design, The Robert Gordon University, Garthdee Road, Aberdeen AB9 2QD.
**Tel** 01224 263506/263600

**▶ Hoddo Arts Trust**
The Hale, Hoddo Estate, Tarves, Aberdeen AB41 0ER.
**Tel** 01651 851770

**▶ The Lemon Tree** C
5 West North Street, Aberdeen AB2 3AT.
**Tel** 01224 642230

**▶ Peacock Printmakers Gallery** C
21 Castle Street, Aberdeen AB1 1AJ.
**Tel** 01224 627094/639539
**Personnel** Colin Greenslade.
**Work Stocked and Sold** Pr.

**▶ The Rendezvous Gallery** C
100 Forest Avenue, Aberdeen AB15 6TL.
**Tel** 01224 323247

**▶ Vital Spark Gallery** C
45 Rosemount Viaduct, Aberdeen, AB25 1NQ.
**Tel** 01224 658584 **Fax** 01224 658583
**Work Stocked and Sold** Pa.

## ABERDEENSHIRE

### ALFORD

**▶ Syllavethy Gallery** C
Montgarrie, Alford, AB33 8AQ.
**Tel** 019755 62273 **Fax** 019755 63173

### BALLATER

**▶ McEwan Gallery**
Glengarden, Ballater, AB35 5UB.
**Tel** 013397 55429 **Fax** 013397 55995
**Email** rhodmcewan@easynet.co.uk

### BANFF

**▶ Warehouse Gallery**
7 Quayside, Banff Harbour, Banff, AB45 1HQ.
**Tel** 01261 818048

### ELLON

**▶ Tolquhon Gallery** C
Tolquhon, Tarves, Ellon AB41 0LP.
**Tel** 01651 842343

### MACDUFF

**▶ Macduff Arts Centre**
c/o Aberdeenshire Council, 1 Church Street, Macduff, AB44 1UR.
**Tel** 01261 813384

### STONEHAVEN

**▶ Riverside Gallery**
28 David Street, Stonehaven, AB39 2AL.
**Tel** 01569 763931

### STRATHDON

**▶ The Lost Gallery** C
Strathdon, AB36 8UJ.
**Tel** 019756 51287 **Fax** 019756 51287
**Personnel** Peter Goodfellow.

## ANGUS

### FORFAR

**▶ The Meffan Museum and Art Gallery, Forfar** P
20 West High Street, Forfar, Angus DD8 1BB.
**Tel** 01307 464 123

## ARGYLL AND BUTE

### HELENSBURGH

**▶ The Hill House** P
Upper Colquhoun Street, Helensburgh, G84 9AJ.
**Tel** 01436 673900 **Fax** 01436 674685

## DUMFRIES & GALLOWAY

### DUMFRIES

**▶ Gracefield Arts Centre**
28 Edinburgh Road, Dumfries, DG1 1JQ.
**Tel** 01387 262084 **Fax** 01387 60453
**Opening times** Tue–Sat 10–5, Sun 12–5 (summer only).
**Services and Facilities** Bar. Craftshop. Disabled Access. Friends Society. Lectures. Parking. Restaurant. Workshop Facilities.

**▶ Ottersburn Gallery** C
2A Nith Avenue, Dumfries, DG1 1EF.
**Tel** 01387 254860
**Opening times** Tue–Sat 10–6.
**Services and Facilities** Framing.
**Work Stocked and Sold** Pa.

**▶ Robert Burns Centre** P
c/o Dumfries Museum, The Observatory, Dumfries, DG2 7SW.
**Tel** 01387 253374

### KIRKCUDBRIGHT

**▶ Castle Douglas Art Gallery**
Council Offices, Kirkcudbright, DG6 4JG.
**Tel** 01557 331643

**▶ Tolbooth Art Centre**
c/o Council Offices, Kirkcudbright, DG6 4JG.
**Tel** 01557 331643

### STRANRAER

**▶ Stranraer Museum** P
55 George Street, Stranraer, DG9 7JP.
**Tel** 01776 705088

## DUNDEE

### DUNDEE

**▶ University of Dundee Exhibitions** PS
Duncan of Jordanstone College of Art and Design, 13 Perth Road, Dundee DD1 4HT.
**Tel** 01382 345330
**Fax** 01382 345192
**Email** djcexhib@dundee.ac.uk
**Ws** www.exhibitions.dundee.ac.uk
**Opening times** Mon–Fri 9.30–8.30, Sat 9.30–4.30. Closed Sun.
**Nearest Station** Dundee.
**Personnel** Curator of Exhibitions: Deirdre MacKenna. Exhibitions Project Coordinator: Sarah M. Cordwell. Exhibitions Technician: Alex Wallace.
**Services and Facilities** Disabled Access. Friends Society. Guided Tours. Lectures. Parking. Restaurant.

**▶ Dundee Art Galleries and Museums** P
Albert Square, Dundee.
**Tel** 01382 223141

## EAST AYRSHIRE

### CUMNOCK

**▶ Baird Institute** P
East Ayrshire Council, 3 Lugar Street, Cumnock, KA18 1AD.
**Tel** 01290 421701

### KILMARNOCK

**▶ Dean Castle**
c/o Kilmarnock & Londoun, District Museums, Dick Institute, Kilmarnock, KA1 3BU.
**Tel** 01563 26401

**▶ Dick Institute** PS
Elmbank Avenue, Kilmarnock KA1 3BU.
**Tel** 01563 526401
**Fax** 01563 529661
**Opening times** Mon–Fri 10–8, Wed & Sat 10–5, closed Sun.
**Nearest Station** Kilmarnock.
**Services and Facilities** Craftshop. Disabled Access. Museum Shop. Parking. Shop. Workshop Facilities.

## EAST DUNBARTONSHIRE

### KIRKINTILLOCH

**▶ Auld Kirk Museum** P
c/o East Dumbartonshire Museum, Auld Kirk Museum, The Cross, Kirkintilloch, G66 1AB.
**Tel** 0141 775 1185

## EAST LOTHIAN

GULLANE

### ▶ Norrie Toch Studios
St Peters, Main Street, Gullane, EH31 2AA.
**Tel** 01620 842039

HADDINGTON

### ▶ Peter Potter Gallery C
10 The Sands, Haddington, EH41 3EY.
**Tel** 01620 822080
**Opening times** Mon–Sat, 10–4.30.
**Services and Facilities** Café. Craftshop. Friends Society.
**Work Stocked and Sold** Cer. Cra. Gla. Jew. Pa. Pr. Wd.
**Price range** £5–£1,000
For artists see Commercial Gallery Artists.

## EDINBURGH

EDINBURGH

### ▶ Bellevue Gallery C
4 Bellevue Crescent, Edinburgh EH3 6ND.
**Tel** 0131 557 1663
**Fax** 0131 557 1663
**Opening times** Wed–Sun 12–6 and by appointment.
**Work Stocked and Sold** Pa.

### ▶ Bourne Fine Art C
4 Dundas Street, Edinburgh EH3 6HZ.
**Tel** 0131 557 4050 **Fax** 0131 557 8382
**Personnel** Fiona Drennan.

### ▶ Calton Gallery C
10 Royal Terrace, Edinburgh EH7 5AB.
**Tel** 0131 556 1010 **Fax** 0131 558 1150
**Opening times** Mon–Fri 10–6, Sat 10–1.
**Personnel** Dealers: Andrew and Sarah Whitfield. Assistant Gallery Manager: Jane Borthwick.
**Work Stocked and Sold** Pa. Sc.

### ▶ Cameo Cinema
38 Home Street, Tolcross, Edinburgh EH3 9LZ.
**Tel** 0131 228 4141

### ▶ City Art Centre P
2 Market Street, Edinburgh EH1 1DE.
**Tel** 0131 529 3993 **Fax** 0131 529 3977
**Opening times** Mon–Sat 10–5, Sun during the Festival 2–5.
**Personnel** Keeper, Fine Art Collections: Ian O'Riordan.
**Services and Facilities** Bar. Café. Disabled Access. Friends Society. Lectures. Shop.

### ▶ Danish Cultural Institute P
3 Doune Terrace, Edinburgh EH3 6DY.
**Tel** 0131 225 7189 **Fax** 0131 220 6162
**Email** dci.dancult@dancult.demon.co.uk
**Ws** www.dancult.demon.co.uk
**Opening times** Mon–Fri 10–5.
**Personnel** Director: Mette Bligaard.
*Exhibitions of Danish paintings, prints, photography and craft.*

### ▶ Dean Gallery
Belford Road, Edinburgh EH4 3DS
**Tel** 0131 624 6200 **Fax** 0131 623 7126
**Email** enquiries@natgalscot.ac.uk
**Ws** www.natgalscot.ac.uk
**Opening times** Mon–Sat 10–5, Sun 12–5.
**Nearest Station** Edinburgh Haymarket.
**Personnel** Director, Dean Gallery: Richard Calvocoressi. Director-General, National Galleries of Scotland: Timothy Clifford.
**Services and Facilities** Friends Society. Lectures.
*Situated across the road from the Scottish National Gallery of Modern Art, the Dean Gallery houses the Gallery of Modern Art's extensive collections of Dada and Surrealism. In 1994, Edinburgh-born sculptor Sir Eduardo Paolozzi offered a large body of his work to the National Galleries of Scotland. This collection of prints, drawings, plaster, maquettes, moulds and the contents of his studio is now housed in the Dean Gallery. The Gallery also accommodates a remarkable library and archive of artists' books, catalogues and manuscripts relating in particular to the Dada and Surrealist movements, but also to 20th-century art as a whole.*

### ▶ doggerfisher
11 Gayfield Square, Edinburgh.
**Tel** 0131 5587110

### ▶ The Dundas Street Gallery C
6a Dundas Street, Edinburgh EH3 6HZ.
**Tel** 0131 557 4050 **Fax** 0131 557 8382
**Personnel** Fiona Robertson.

### ▶ Eastern General Hospital (East and Midlothian Unit Art Fund)
Seafield Street, Edinburgh EH6 7LN.
**Tel** 0131 536 7000

### ▶ Edinburgh Gallery
18a Dundas Street, Edinburgh EH3 6HZ.
**Tel** 0131 557 5227

### ▶ Edinburgh Printmakers C
23 Union Street, Edinburgh EH1 3LR.
**Tel** 0131 557 2479 **Fax** 0131 558 8418
**Email** printmakers@ednet.co.uk
**Opening times** Tue–Sat 10–6.
**Personnel** Director: Robert Adam.
**Services and Facilities** Art Consultancy. Art for Offices. Framing. Workshop Facilities.
**Work Stocked and Sold** Pr.

### ▶ Edinburgh Sculpture Workshop C
25 Hawthornvale, Newhaven, Edinburgh EH6 4JT.
**Tel** 0131 551 4490 **Fax** 0131 551 4491

### ▶ ESU Gallery
23 Atholl Crescent, Edinburgh EH3 8HQ.
**Tel** 0131 229 1528

### ▶ Firth Gallery C
35 William Street, Edinburgh EH3 7LW.
**Tel** 0131 225 2196 **Fax** 0131 225 2196
**Personnel** Jamie Alexander.

### ▶ French Institute
13 Randolph Crescent, Edinburgh EH3 7TT.
**Tel** 0131 225 5366

### ▶ Fruitmarket Gallery P
45 Market Street, Edinburgh EH1 1DF.
**Tel** 0131 225 2383 **Fax** 0131 220 3130
**Personnel** Susan Mclain. Trevor Cromie.

### ▶ Hanover Fine Arts C
22A Dundas Street, Edinburgh EH3 6JN.
**Tel** 0131 556 2181 **Fax** 0131 556 2181
**Opening times** Tue–Fri 10.30–6; Sat 10–4, Jan–Dec.
**Nearest Station** Waverley.
**Personnel** Proprietor: Richard Ireland.
**Services and Facilities** Framing. Restoration.
**Work Stocked and Sold** Cer. Cra. Dr. Gla. Jew. Pa. Pr. Sc. Tx. Wd.
**Price range** £7–£1, 800
For artists see Commercial Gallery Artists.
*Independent owner-run commercial gallery situated in Dundas Street, right at the heart of the New Town galleries. The present policy of exhibitions (11 per year) features some established Scottish contemporary artists along with lesser-known ones, but concentrating on good quality accessible work at affordable prices. The majority of artists live or work in Scotland, but a number come from abroad, inc. Belgium, Brazil, China, Germany, India, Russia, Ukraine and the USA. Works exhibited include: oils, watercolours, original prints, ceramics, wood and stone sculpture, jewellery, wooden boxes, tiles, textiles and original/printed cards.*

### ▶ Ingleby Gallery C
6 Carlton Terrace, Edinburgh EH7 5DD.
**Tel** 0131 556 4441 **Fax** 0131 556 4454
**Email** mail@inglebygallery.com
**Ws** www.inglebygallery.com
**Opening times** Wed–Sat 10–5 and by appointment at all other times.
**Nearest Station** 10 minutes from Waverley.
**Personnel** Richard & Florence Ingleby. Caroline Broadhurst.
**Services and Facilities** Art Consultancy. Art for Offices. Disabled Access.
**Work Stocked and Sold** Cer. Pa. Ph. Pr. Sc.
**Price range** £50–£100,000
For artists see Commercial Gallery Artists.
*The Ingleby Gallery opened in 1998 on the ground floor of a Georgian house overlooking the Palace of Holyrood and the site of the new Scottish Parliament. We specialise in 20th century British art and particularly in living painters, sculptors and photographers. Recent and forthcoming exhibitions include: Jeffrey Blondes, Thomas Joshua Cooper, Andy Goldsworthy, Howard Hodgkin, Callum Innes, Sean Scully, Alison Watt and Emily Young. We are also the major distributor of printed work by Ian Hamilton Finlay.*

### ▶ Instituto Italiano di Cultura
82 Nicholson Street, Edinburgh EH8 9EW.
**Tel** 0131 668 2232

### ▶ Inverleith House
Royal Botanic Gardens, Edinburgh.
**Tel** 0131 2482983

### ▶ John Stephens Fine Art C
2A St Vincent Street, Edinburgh.
**Tel** 0131 557 6474

### ▶ Kingfisher Gallery C
5 Northumberland Street, North West Lane, Edinburgh EH3 6JL.
**Tel** 0131 557 5454 **Fax** 0131 557 5454
**Opening times** Tue–Sat 11–4.30 or by appointment.
**Personnel** Director: Lena McGregor. Director: Ronnie McGregor. Manager: Loura Brooks.
**Services and Facilities** Art Consultancy. Art for Offices. Disabled Access.
**Work Stocked and Sold** Cer. Cra. Gla. Jew. Pa. Pr. Sc.
**Price range** £150–£10,000
For artists see Commercial Gallery Artists.

### ▶ The Leith Gallery
65 The Shore, Edinburgh EH6 6RA.
**Tel** 0131 553 5255 **Fax** 0131 553 5655

### ▶ Lothian Fine Art
155 Dalry Road, Edinburgh EH11 2EA.
**Tel** 0131 337 2055

### ▶ Malcolm Innes Gallery C
4 Dundas Street, Edinburgh EH3 6HZ.
**Tel** 0131 558 9544/5 **Fax** 0131 558 9525
**Personnel** Managing Director: Malcolm Innes. Deputy Managing Director: A. R. B. Wood. Director: Sarah Stewart. Director: P. C. S. Allfrey.

### ▶ Museum of Scotland
Chambers Street, Edinburgh EH1 1JF.
**Tel** 0131 247 4422, Textphone: 0131 247 4027
**Fax** 0131 220 4819
**Ws** www.nms.ac.uk
**Opening times** Mon–Sat 10–5, Sun 12–5, Tue 10–8. Admission is free although there may be a small charge for some exhibitions.
**Nearest Station** Waverley.
**Personnel** Head of Public Affairs: Mary Bryden. Press Manager: Susan Gray.
**Services and Facilities** Café. Disabled Access. Friends Society. Gallery space for hire. Guided Tours. Lectures. Museum Shop. Restaurant.

*NMS Photography,* Museum of Scotland.
*The Museum of Scotland is a striking new landmark in Edinburgh's historic Old Town and has been described as the finest Scottish building of the twentieth century. The museum presents for the first time the history of Scotland – its land, its people and their achievements – through the rich national collections. It houses more than 10,000 of the nation's most precious artefacts, as well as everyday objects which throw light on life in Scotland through the ages.*

### ▶ National Gallery of Scotland
The Mound, Edinburgh EH2 2EL.
**Tel** 0131 624 6200 **Fax** 0131 220 0917
**Email** enquiries@natgalscot.ac.uk
**Ws** www.natgalscot.ac.uk
**Opening times** Mon–Sat 10–5, Sun 12–5.
**Nearest Station** Edinburgh Waverley.
**Personnel** Director-General, National Galleries of Scotland: Timothy Clifford. Director, National Gallery of Scotland: Michael Clarke.
**Services and Facilities** Bookshop. Disabled Access. Friends Society. Gallery space for hire. Lectures. Museum Shop. Shop.
*The National Gallery of Scotland, is situated in the heart of Edinburgh, on The Mound, between the ancient Old Town and the Georgian New Town. It is home to Scotland's greatest collection of European paintings and sculpture from the Renaissance to Post-Impressionism, and is one of the very finest galleries of its size in the world. The collection of watercolours, prints and drawings boasts some twenty thousand items, and is particularly rich in Italian and Netherlandish drawings. The gallery also has a comprehensive collection of Scottish art, representing all the major names, including Ramsay, Raeburn, McTaggart and Wilkie.*

### ▶ National Library of Scotland P
George IV Bridge, Edinburgh EH1 1EW.
**Tel** 0131 226 4531

### ▶ Netherbrow Art Centre
43–45 High Street, Edinburgh EH1 1SR.
**Tel** 0131 556 9579

### ▶ Open Eye Gallery C
75/79 Cumberland Street, Edinburgh EH3 6RD.
**Tel** 0131 557 1020 **Fax** 0131 557 1020
**Email** open.eye@virgin.net
**Ws** www.openeyegallery.co.uk
**Opening times** Mon–Fri 10–6, Sat 10–4.
**Nearest Station** Waverley, Edinburgh.
**Personnel** Directors: Thomas & Pamela Wilson. Michelle Norman. Lizzie Crook.
**Services and Facilities** Art Consultancy. Art for Offices. Commissioning Service. Disabled Access. Framing. Restoration. Valuation.
**Work Stocked and Sold** Cer. Cra. Dr. Gla. Jew. Pa. Pr. Sc. Wd.
**Price range** £20–£20,000
For artists see Commercial Gallery Artists.
*The Open Eye Gallery situated in the heart of Edinburgh's Historic Georgian New Town, equidistant between the Gallery of Modern Art and The National Gallery of Scotland. An ambitious programme of 15 exhibitions per year is organised, covering both contemporary and fine art, ranging from the work of the young contemporary to that of the established school. In addition to paintings the gallery specialises in early-20th-century prints, sculpture and contemporary crafts including ceramics, glass, wood and jewellery.*

### ▶ Portfolio Gallery PS
43 Candlemaker Row, Edinburgh EH1 2QB.
**Tel** 0131 220 1911
**Fax** 0131 226 4287
**Email** portfolio@ednet.co.uk
**Ws** www.ednet.co.uk/-portfolio
**Opening times** Tue–Sat 12–5.30.
**Personnel** Director: Gloria Chalmers.
**Services and Facilities** Commissioning Service. Gallery space for hire. Lectures.
**Work Stocked and Sold** Ph.
**Price range** £150–£5,000

### ▶ Royal Incorporation of Architects in Scotland Gallery
15 Rutland Square, Edinburgh EH1 2BE.
**Tel** 0131 229 7545

### ▶ Royal Museum P
Chambers Street, Edinburgh EH1 1JF.
**Tel** 0131 247 4219, Textphone: 0131 247 4027
**Fax** 0131 220 4819
**Ws** www.nms.ac.uk
**Opening times** Mon–Sat 10–5, Sun 12–5, Tue 10–8. Admission is free although there may be a charge for some special exhibitions.
**Nearest Station** Waverley.
**Personnel** Head of Public Affairs: Mary Bryden. Press Manager: Susan Gray.
**Services and Facilities** Café. Disabled Access. Friends Society. Gallery space for hire. Guided Tours. Lectures. Museum Shop. Restaurant.
*A magnificent Victorian building distinguished by its soaring, glass-topped roof which floods the main Hall with natural light. The Royal Museum houses outstanding international collections of decorative arts, science and industry, archaeology and the natural world. Some exhibits are millions of years old, others less than a decade. Together they reflect the diversity of life on earth, and the ingenuity of humankind.*

*NMS Photography,* Main Hall, Royal Museum.

### ▶ Royal Scottish Academy PS
17 Waterloo Place, Edinburgh EH1 3BG.
**Tel** 0131 558 7097 **Fax** 0131 557 6417
**Ws** www.royalscottishacademy.org
**Opening times** During exhibitions: Mon–Sat 10–5, Sun 2–5.
**Nearest Station** Waverley.
**Personnel** Administrative Secretary: Bruce Laidlaw. Asst. Admin. Sec.: Margaret Wilson. Public Relations: Wendy Jones.
**Services and Facilities** Art for Offices. Disabled Access. Friends Society. Shop.

*Aileen Bannatyne,* Delta Tree, *oil, 2000.*

*Founded in 1826. The Royal Scottish Academy is widely acknowledged as one of the foremost promoters of contemporary art in Scotland, covering the disciplines of painting, sculpture, architecture and printmaking. The Annual Exhibition is a key event in the Scottish Arts calendar. In addition, the RSA plays an important educational role with its unique Students' Exhibition together with awards and travelling scholarships.*
*The RSA Galleries at The Mound, Edinburgh closed in the Spring of 2001 for major rebuilding and refurbishment which is part of the National Galleries of Scotland 'Playfair Project'. The reopening date is scheduled for mid-2003.*
*For details of locations of Royal Scottish Academy exhibitions, consult website.*

### ▶ Scottish Gallery (Aitken Dott Ltd) C

16 Dundas Street, Edinburgh EH3 6HZ.
**Tel** 0131 558 1200 **Fax** 0131 558 3900
**Email** mail@scottish-gallery.co.uk
**Ws** www.scottish-gallery.co.uk
**Opening times** Mon–Fri 10–6, Sat 10–4.
**Nearest Station** Edinburgh Waverley.
**Personnel** Gallery Administrator: Ruth Lock.
**Services and Facilities** Art Consultancy. Commissioning Service. Craftshop. Valuation.
**Work Stocked and Sold** App. Cer. Cra. Dr. Gla. Jew. Pa. Pr. Sc. Tx. Wd.
**Price range** £20–£20,000
For artists see Commercial Gallery Artists.

*Elizabeth Blackadder,* Two Small Purple Irises, *watercolour, 18" x 13".*

*The Scottish Gallery, founded in 1842, specialises in 20th-century and contemporary Scottish art. The gallery has had close relationships with all the major Scottish painters of this century – The Scottish Colourists, 'The Edinburgh School' – Gillies, Redpath, MacTaggart, etc. and others such as Joan Eardley. Recently we have held major shows by Blackadder, Houston, Morrison, Bryce, Redfern, Fraser, Earl Haig, Rae, Crowe, Dees and Edwards.*
*An exciting and varied monthly exhibition programme is supplemented by extensive stocks of paintings. In addition we have the most prestigious selection of British crafts in Scotland.*

### ▶ Scottish National Gallery of Modern Art

Belford Road, Edinburgh EH4 3DR.
**Tel** 0131 624 6200 **Fax** 0131 343 2802
**Email** gmainfo@natgalscot.ac.uk
**Ws** www.natgalscot.ac.uk
**Opening times** Mon–Sat 10–5, Sun 12–5.
**Nearest Station** Edinburgh Haymarket.
**Personnel** Director, SNGMA: Richard Calvocoressi. Director-General, National Galleries of Scotland: Timothy Clifford.
**Services and Facilities** Bookshop. Café. Disabled Access. Friends Society. Gallery space for hire. Lectures. Museum Shop. Parking. Shop.
*Set in beautiful leafy grounds, the Scottish National Gallery of Modern Art lies to the west of the city centre in a handsome neoclassical building. The gallery has bright, spacious rooms, and its extensive grounds provide the perfect setting for sculptures by Henry Moore, Barbara Hepworth, Anthony Caro and others. The collection includes major works by Vuillard, Matisse, Kirchner, Picasso, Magritte, Dali and Ernst. The gallery also houses an unrivalled collection of 20th-century Scottish art, including work by Charles Rennie Mackintosh, the Scottish Colourists, and members of the Edinburgh School, such as Gillies, Redpath, MacTaggart and Philipson.*

### ▶ Scottish National Portrait Gallery

1 Queen Street, Edinburgh EH2 1JD.
**Tel** 0131 624 6200 **Fax** 0131 558 3691
**Email** pginfo@natgalscot.ac.uk
**Ws** www.natgalscot.ac.uk
**Opening times** Mon–Sat 10–5, Sun 12–5.
**Nearest Station** Edinburgh Waverley.
**Personnel** Director, Scottish National Portrait Gallery: James Holloway. Director-General, National Galleries of Scotland: Timothy Clifford.
**Services and Facilities** Bookshop. Café. Disabled Access. Friends Society. Gallery space for hire. Lectures. Museum Shop. Shop.
*A unique visual history of Scotland told through the portraits of those who shaped it, from the 16th century to the present. Includes such luminaries as Mary Queen of Scots, Robert Burns and Sir Walter Scott, right up to Jimmy Shand and Sean Connery. Also houses the National Photography Collection with regular photography exhibitions. The Print Room and Reference Archive are open by arrangement at the Gallery front desk, Mon–Fri 10–12 and 2–4.30.*

### ▶ Stills Gallery

23 Cockburn Street, Edinburgh EH1 1BP.
**Tel** 0131 225 9876

### ▶ Talbot Rice Gallery PS

University of Edinburgh, Old College, South Bridge, Edinburgh EH8 9YL.
**Tel** 0131 650 2210 2085 **Fax** 0131 650 2213
**Email** val.fiddes@ed.ac.uk
**Opening times** Tue–Sat 10–5.
**Personnel** Valerie Fiddes.
**Services and Facilities** Bookshop. Disabled Access (limited). Friends Society. Lectures.
**Work Stocked and Sold** Pa.
**Price range** £500–£25,000
*A university gallery which houses a permanent collection of old master paintings and bronzes, as well as operating a busy temporary exhibition programme. There is an experimental programme in the Round Room. Founded in the 1970s, the gallery's commitment to the visual arts in Scotland is to provide a platform for more mature (mainly Scottish) artists to mount major solo exhibitions. Exhibitions of work from Europe and elsewhere are also shown. Education programme.*

### ▶ Torrance Gallery C

36 Dundas Street, Edinburgh EH3 6JN.
**Tel** 0131 556 6366
**Personnel** Partners: Florence, Brian and Joanne Torrance.

### ▶ Vincent Kosman Fine Art C

8 Burgess Terrace, Newington, Edinburgh EH9 2BD.
**Tel** 0131 662 9990
**Fax** 0131 662 9990
**Opening times** By appointment.
**Nearest Station** Central Edinburgh.
**Personnel** Louise Kosman.
**Services and Facilities** Art Consultancy. Commissioning Service. Valuation.
**Work Stocked and Sold** Dr. Pa. Sc.
**Price range** £500–£50,000
For artists see Commercial Gallery Artists.

## FALKIRK

#### FALKIRK

### ▶ Callender House P

Callender Park, Falkirk.
**Tel** 01324 503770

## FIFE

#### ANSTRUTHER

### ▶ Kellie Castle P

by Pittenweem, Anstruther, KY10 2RF.
**Tel** 01333 720271 **Fax** 01333 720326

#### CARDENDEN

### ▶ Arts in Fife

Fife Council, Tower Block, ASDARC, Woodend Road, Cardenden, KY5 0NE.
**Tel** 01592 414714/414727

#### DUNFERMLINE

### ▶ Dunfermline Museum P

The Small Gallery, Viewfield Terrace, Dunfermline, KY12 7HY.
**Tel** 01383 721814

#### GLENROTHES

### ▶ Corridor Gallery

Fife Institute, Viewfield Road, Glenrothes, KY6 2RB.
**Tel** 01592 415700

#### KIRKCALDY

### ▶ Kirkcaldy Museum & Art Gallery P

War Memorial Gardens, Kirkcaldy, KY1 1YG.
**Tel** 01592 412860 **Fax** 01592 412870

LEVEN

### ▶ Loomshop Gallery
126 Main Street, Lower Largo, Leven, KY8 6BP.
**Tel** 01333 320330

ST ANDREWS

### ▶ Crawford Arts Centre PS
93 North Street, St Andrews, KY16 9AL.
**Tel** 01334 474610 **Fax** 01334 479880
**Opening times** Mon–Sat 10–5, Sun 2–5.
**Nearest Station** Leuchars.
**Personnel** Director: Diana Sykes. Exhibitions Officer: Susan Davis. Gallery Assistant: Lucy Portchmouth.
**Services and Facilities** Craftshop. Disabled Access. Friends Society. Guided Tours. Lectures. Shop. Workshop Facilities.
**Work Stocked and Sold** App. Cer. Cra. Dr. Jew. Pa. Ph. Pr. Sc. Tx. Wd.
**Price range** £5–£1, 500

## GLASGOW

GLASGOW

### ▶ 90s Gallery
12 Otago Street, Kelvinbridge, Glasgow G12 8HJ.
**Tel** 041 339 3158

### ▶ Art Exposure Gallery C
19 Parnie Street, Glasgow G1 5RJ.
**Tel** 0141 552 7779
**Opening times** Mon–Sat 11–6 or by appointment.
**Nearest Station** Glasgow Central/Queen Street.
**Personnel** Directors: John Heuston, Frances Lowrie.
**Services and Facilities** Art Consultancy. Art for Offices. Commissioning Service. Disabled Access.
**Work Stocked and Sold** Cer. Dr. Jew. Pa. Pr. Sc.
For artists see Commercial Gallery Artists.

### ▶ Artbank
24 Cleveden Road, Glasgow, G12 0PX.
**Tel** 0141 334 6180

### ▶ The Burrell Collection P
2060 Pollokshaws Road, Pollock Country Park, Glasgow G43 1AT.
**Tel** 0141 649 7151 **Fax** 0141 636 0086
**Opening times** Mon, Wed–Sat 10–5, Sun 11–5, closed Tue.
**Nearest Station** Pollokshaws West.
**Personnel** Director: Julian Spalding.
**Services and Facilities** Bar. Café. Disabled Access. Friends Society. Guided Tours. Lectures. Museum Shop. Parking. Restaurant.
**Work Stocked and Sold** App. Cer. Cra. Dec. Dr. Gla. Jew. Ph. Pr.
**Price range** £5–£100

### ▶ Collins Gallery PS
University of Strathclyde, 22 Richmond Street, Glasgow G1 1XQ.
**Tel** 0141 548 2558 **Fax** 0141 552 4053
**Email** collinsgallery@strath.ac.uk
**Opening times** Mon–Fri 10–5, Sat 12–4. Closed public holidays and during exhibition changeovers.
**Nearest Station** Queen Street.
**Personnel** Curator: Laura Hamilton.
**Services and Facilities** Café. Disabled Access. Friends Society. Gallery space for hire. Guided Tours. Lectures. Parking. Shop. Workshop Facilities.
**Work Stocked and Sold**
*Monthly programme of temporary exhibitions ranging from contemporary Fine and Applied Art, Photography and Design, and multi-media installations to social history. Most exhibitions are complemented by educational workshops, videos, performances or lectures. Plus activities for special needs' groups. Permanent collection: Historic and contemporary Fine Art and Scientific Instruments.*

*Alison Harper,* Voluptua, *etching, 56 x 45 cm, 1998.*

### ▶ Compass Gallery
178 West Regent Street, Glasgow G2 4RL.
**Tel** 0141 221 6370 **Fax** 0141 248 1322
**Opening times** Mon–Sat: 10–5.30.
**Personnel** Cyril Gerber.

### ▶ Cyril Gerber Fine Art C
148 West Regent Street, Glasgow G2 2RQ.
**Tel** 0141 221 3095 **Fax** 0141 248 1322
**Opening times** Mon–Sat 9.30–5.30.
**Personnel** Cyril Gerber. Jill Gerber. Stephanie Hand.
For artists see Commercial Gallery Artists.

### ▶ Ewan Mundy Fine Art
211 West George Street, Glasgow G2 2LW.
**Tel** 0141 248 9755 **Fax** 0141 248 9744
**Personnel** Ewan Mundy. Carol Mundy.

### ▶ Fossil Grove P
Victoria Park, Glasgow G14 1BN.
**Tel** 0141 950 1448/287 2000
**Opening times** Open daily 12–5 Easter to end of Sep.

### ▶ Gallery of Modern Art P
Queen Street, Glasgow G1 3AZ.
**Tel** 0141 229 1996
**Fax** 0141 204 5316
**Opening times** Mon, Wed–Sat 10–5, Sun 11–5, closed Tue.
**Nearest Station** Queen Street.
**Personnel** Director: Julian Spalding.
**Services and Facilities** Café. Disabled Access. Friends Society. Museum Shop.
**Work Stocked and Sold** App. Cra. Dr. Jew. Ph.
**Price range** £5–£100

### ▶ Gatehouse Gallery C
Rouken Glen Road, Giffnock, Glasgow G46 7UG.
**Tel** 0141 620 0235
**Opening times** Mon–Fri 1.30–6, closed Tue, Sat–Sun 12.30–5.30.

### ▶ Glasgow Print Studio Gallery C
22 King Street, Glasgow G1 5QP.
**Tel** 0141 552 0704/1394 **Fax** 0141 552 2919
**Email** gallery@gpsart.co.uk
**Ws** www.gpsart.co.uk
**Opening times** Tues–Sat 10–5.30.
**Nearest Station** Glasgow Central /Queen Street.
**Personnel** Administrator: Carolyn Nicoll. Director: John Mackechnie. Gallery Assistant: Karen Bauld. Development Manager: Leona Stewart.
**Services and Facilities** Art Consultancy. Art for Offices. Bookshop. Disabled Access. Framing. Shop. Workshop Facilities.
**Work Stocked and Sold** Ab. App. Cer. Cra. Gla. Jew. Pr.
**Price range** £25–£2,000
For artists see Commercial Gallery Artists.

*John Byrne,* The American Boy, *screenprint, 65" x 30", 2000, £1250 + VAT.*
*Non-profit gallery of charitable status. Highly acclaimed for its beautiful exhibition space, the gallery hosts monthly exhibitions of original prints, paintings and sculpture by local, national and international artists.*
*The gallery also organises exhibitions of original prints by Glasgow Print Studio artists in Britain and abroad, including New York, Berlin, Munich, Moscow, Los Angeles and Iceland.*

### ▶ Glasgow Tourist Board
39 St Vincent Place, Glasgow G1 2ER.
**Tel** 0141 204 4480

### ▶ Hunterian Art Gallery P
University of Glasgow, 82 Hillhead Street, Glasgow G12 8QQ.
**Tel** 0141 330 5431
**Fax** 0141 330 3618
**Email** syoung@museum.gla.ac.uk
**Ws** www.hunterian.gla.ac.uk
**Opening times** Mon–Sat 9.30–5, (Mackintosh House closed 12.30–1.30).
**Nearest Station** Partick (rail), Hillhead (underground).
**Personnel** Secretary: Sheena Young.
**Services and Facilities** Bookshop. Disabled Access. Gallery space for hire. Shop.
**Work Stocked and Sold**

*This award-winning gallery houses the University of Glasgow's outstanding art collections. In the Main Gallery there are paintings by Rembrandt, Stubbs and Chardin, 18th-century British portraits, some fine Scottish 19th- and 20th-century paintings, and the Estate of the American painter J. M. Whistler, making this the largest display of his works anywhere. The Mackintosh House comprises the principal rooms from the Glasgow home of the architect Charles Rennie Mackintosh, with changing displays of his work in the Gallery above the House. Contemporary sculpture is displayed in The Sculpture Courtyard and there are temporary exhibitions from the print collection.*

### ▶ The Kelly Gallery
118 Douglas Street, Glasgow G2 4ET.
**Tel** 0141 248 6386
*(See Gallery Space for Hire)*

### ▶ Kelvingrove Art Gallery and Museum P
Kelvingrove, Glasgow G3 8AG.
**Tel** 0141 221 9600/287 2000
**Fax** 0141 305 2690/287 2690

### ▶ Lillie Art Gallery PS
Station Road, Milngavie, Glasgow G62 8BZ.
**Tel** 0141 578 8847 **Fax** 0141 570 0244
**Opening times** Tue–Fri 10–1 and 2–5, Sat–Sun 2–5.
**Nearest Station** Milngavie.
**Personnel** Curator: Hildegarde Berwick.
**Services and Facilities** Disabled Access. Lectures. Museum Shop. Parking.
*Collection of 20th-century Scottish paintings including the Scottish Colourists, local artists William and Mary Armour and an extensive collection of Joan Eardley drawings. Temporary exhibition programme of fine and applied art, also exhibitions from the collection.*

### ▶ Lloyd Jerome Gallery C
At The Dental Practice,
200 Bath Street, Glasgow G2 4HG.
**Tel** 0141 331 0722 **Fax** 0131 331 0733
**Personnel** Lloyd Jerome.

### ▶ McLellan Galleries P
270 Sauchiehall Street, Glasgow G2 3EH.
**Tel** 0141 331 1854 **Fax** 0141 332 9957
**Opening times** Opening dates depend upon exhibition schedule. Please call to check.
**Nearest Station** Queen Street.
**Personnel** Director: Julian Spalding.
**Services and Facilities** Disabled Access. Museum Shop.
**Work Stocked and Sold** Cra.
**Price range** £3–£60

### ▶ Michael Main Gallery
32 Gibson Street, Kelvinbridge, Glasgow G12 8NX.
**Tel** 0141 334 8858 **Fax** 0141 339 2819

### ▶ Mitchell Library P
North Street, Glasgow G3 7DN.
**Tel** 0141 305 2803

### ▶ Pollok House P
2060 Pollokshaws Road, Pollok Country Park, Glasgow G43 1AT.
**Tel** 0141 616 6410 **Fax** 0141 616 6521
**Opening times** From Easter weekend to last Sep weekend: Mon, Wed–Sat 10–5, Sun 11–5, closed Tue. Winter: 11–4, admission free.
**Nearest Station** Pollokshaws West.
**Personnel** Director: Julian Spalding.
**Services and Facilities** Café. Disabled Access. Friends Society. Lectures. Museum Shop. Parking. Shop.
**Work Stocked and Sold** App. Cer. Dec. Dr. Gla. Jew. Ph. Sc.
**Price range** £5–£50

### ▶ Project Ability Centre for Developmental Arts/ Trongate Studios PS
18 Albion Street, Glasgow G1 1LH.
**Tel** 0141 552 2822
**Fax** 0141 552 3490
**Email** info@project-ability-co.uk
**Ws** www.project-ability.co.uk
**Opening times** Mon–Fri 10–5.
**Nearest Station** Glasgow Queen Street.
**Personnel** Artistic Director: Elisabeth Gibson. General Manager: Anne Knowles.
**Services and Facilities** Art for Offices. Disabled Access. Workshop Facilities.
**Work Stocked and Sold** Cer. Pa. Pr. Tx.
**Price range** £30–£300
*At the Centre for Developmental Arts and the Trongate Studios in the centre of Glasgow, Project Ability provides space where disabled people participate in an artist-led workshop programme and people with mental health problems have access to studio spaces. There are facilities and equipment for ceramics, digital art, sculpture, print-making, painting, textiles, film-making, animation and photography. A varied programme of temporary exhibitions in the two gallery spaces at 18 Albion Street is open to the public throughout the year. It provides a showcase for people using the workshops and studios, and the best of national and international disabled artists.*

### ▶ Provand's Lordship P
3 Castle Street, Glasgow G4 0RB.
**Tel** 0141 552 8819
**Opening times** Mon, Wed–Sat 10–5, Sun 11–5, closed Tue.
**Nearest Station** Queen Street.
**Personnel** Director: Julian Spalding.
**Services and Facilities** Museum Shop.

### ▶ Roger Billcliffe Fine Art C
134 Blythswood Street, Glasgow G2 4EL.
**Tel** 0141 332 4027 **Fax** 0141 332 6573
**Email** roger@rbfa.demon.co.uk
**Opening times** Mon–Fri 9.30–5.30, Sat 10–1.
**Personnel** Roger Billcliffe. Lynn D. Park. Michael Corsar.
**Services and Facilities** Art Consultancy. Disabled Access. Valuation.
**Work Stocked and Sold** App. Cer. Cra. Gla. Jew. Pa. Sc. Wd.
**Price range** £30–£25,000
For artists see Commercial Gallery Artists.

### ▶ Rowan Gallery C
36 Main Street, Drymen, Glasgow G63 0BG.
**Tel** 01360 660996

### ▶ Royal Glasgow Institute of the Fine Arts
5 Oswald Street, Glasgow G1 4QR.
**Tel** 0141 248 7411 **Fax** 0141 221 0417
**Personnel** R. C. Liddle. Nancy McLardy. Mrs Lesley Nicholl.
**Services and Facilities** Lectures.

### ▶ Rutherglen Museum P
King Street, Rutherglen, Glasgow G73 1DQ.
**Tel** 0141 647 0837
*The history of the former Royal Burgh.*

### ▶ Springburn Museum P
Atlas Square, Ayr Street, Glasgow G21 4BW.
**Tel** 0141 557 1405
**Opening times** Mon–Fri 10.30–5, Sat 10–4.30, Sun & holidays 2–5.

### ▶ St Mungo Museum of Religious Life and Art P
2 Castle Street, Glasgow G4 0RH.
**Tel** 0141 553 2557 **Fax** 0141 552 4744
**Opening times** Mon–Sat 10–5, Sun 1–5, closed Tue.
**Nearest Station** Queen Street.
**Personnel** Director: Julian Spalding.
**Services and Facilities** Disabled Access. Friends Society. Guided Tours. Lectures. Museum Shop. Parking. Restaurant.
**Work Stocked and Sold** Dec. Dr. Gla. Jew. Pa.
**Price range** £5–£50

### ▶ Strathclyde Arts Centre
12 Washington Street, Glasgow G12 8PD.
**Tel** 0141 221 4526

### ▶ Street Level Photography Gallery and Workshop C
26 King Street, Glasgow G1 5QP.
**Tel** 0141 552 2151
**Fax** 0141 552 2323
**Opening times** Mon–Sat 10–5.30. Admission free.
**Personnel** Malcolm Dickson.
**Services and Facilities** Bookshop. Commissioning Service. Disabled Access. Friends Society. Lectures. Workshop Facilities.

### ▶ T. Garner Gallery
4 Parnie Street, Glasgow G1 5LR.
**Tel** 0141 552 4585
**Opening times** Closed Mon.
**Personnel** Todd Garner.

### ▶ T & R Annan & Sons Ltd
The Annan Gallery, 164 Woodlands Road, Glasgow G3 6LL.
**Tel** 0141 332 0028

### ▶ William Hardie Gallery C
15a Blythswood Square, Glasgow G2 2BG.
**Tel** 0141 221 6780 **Fax** 0141 248 6237
**Personnel** William Hardie. Fiona Robertson.

## HIGHLAND

CAITHNESS

### ▶ Lyth Arts Centre
by Wick, Caithness, KW1 4UD.
**Tel** 01955 641270

INVERNESS

### ▶ Highland Arts
Inverness Museum & Art Gallery, Castle Wynd, Inverness, IV2 3ED.
**Tel** 01463 237114 **Fax** 01463 225293
**Personnel** Cathy Shankland. Trevor Avery.

### ▶ Inverness Museum & Art Gallery P
Castle Wynd, Inverness, IV2 3ED.
**Tel** 01463 237114
**Opening times** Mon–Sat 9–5.
**Services and Facilities** Bookshop. Craftshop. Disabled Access. Gallery space for hire. Lectures. Restaurant.

### ▶ Iona Gallery
c/o Inverness Museum and Art Gallery, Castle Wynd, Inverness, IV2 3EB.
**Tel** 01463 237114

### ▶ Rhue Studio C
Rhue, Ullapool, IV26 2TJ.
**Tel** 01854 612460 **Fax** 01854 612460
**Email** 100531.1317@compuserve.com
**Personnel** Flick Hawkins. Steve Campbell.
**Work Stocked and Sold** Pa.

### ▶ Scottish Fine Arts Group
57 Church Street, Inverness, IV1 1DR.
**Tel** 01463 243575 (antique paintings) or 01808 521268 (contemporary art)
**Personnel** Antique paintings: Ken Hardeman. Contemporary art: Peter Tovell.

## INVERCLYDE

GREENOCK

### ▶ McLean Museum and Art Gallery P
15 Kelly Street, Greenock, PA16 8JX.
**Tel** 01475 723741
**Personnel** Valerie Boa.

## ISLE OF SKYE

DUNVEGAN

### ▶ Orbost Gallery C
Dunvegan, IV55 8ZB.
**Tel** 01470 521207
**Opening times** Apr–Oct: 10–6. By appointment outside these months.
**Services and Facilities** Disabled Access. Framing. Parking. Restoration.
**Work Stocked and Sold** App. Pa. Pr.
**Price range** £30–£950
For artists see Commercial Gallery Artists.

PORTREE

### ▶ An Tuireann Arts Centre
Struan Road, Portree, IV15 9ES.
**Tel** 01478 613306
**Personnel** Director: Nora Campbell.

WATERNISH

### ▶ Artizania
Captains House, Stein, Waternish, IV55 8GA.
**Tel** 01470 592361

## KINGDOM OF FIFE

### ▶ Art on the Links Gallery C
Old Course Hotel, Golf Resort and Spa, St Andrews KY16 9SP.
**Tel** +44 (0) 1334 474 371
**Fax** + 44 (0) 1334 477 668
**Email** artonthelinks@oldcoursehotel.co.uk
**Ws** www.oldcoursehotel.co.uk
**Opening times** Usually 24 hours, 7 days a week – please call hotel to check viewing times
**Work Stocked and Sold** Jew. Pa. Ph. Pr.
**Price range** £500–£10,000
For artists see Commercial Gallery Artists.
*Art on the Links is located within the stunning setting of the Old Course Hotel, Golf Resort & Spa which itself sits alongside the most famous golf course in the world, the Old Course. Ideal also for video art and sculpture, the gallery offers a continuously changing series of paintings and photographic exhibitions from galleries, artists and private collections.*

## MIDLOTHIAN

LOANHEAD

### ▶ Dalkeith Arts Centre P
Midlothian Council, Library HQ, 2 Clerk Street, Loanhead, EH20 9DR.
**Tel** 0131 440 2210/0131 663 6986

## MORAY

ELGIN

### ▶ Elgin Museum P
1 High Street, Elgin, IV30 1EQ.
**Tel** 01343 543675

## NORTH AYRSHIRE

IRVINE

### ▶ The Vennel Gallery PS
10 Glasgow Vennel, Irvine, KA12 0BD.
**Tel** 01294 275059 **Fax** 01294 275059
**Email** vennel@globalnet.co.uk
**Ws** www.northayrshiremuseums.org.uk
**Opening times** Open all year Mon, Tue, Thu, Fri, Sat 10–1 & 2–5.
**Nearest Station** Irvine.
**Personnel** Museums Curator: Martin Bellamy. Museum Officer: John Gray.
**Services and Facilities** Craftshop. Disabled Access. Museum Shop. Workshop Facilities.
*The gallery has a varied programme of exhibitions. Exhibitions tend to concentrate on contemporary Scottish fine and applied art but also include some historical shows and artists from outside Scotland. The gallery is situated in a restored 18th century street, and includes the Heckling Shop where Robert Burns worked.*

## NORTH LANARKSHIRE

COATBRIDGE

### ▶ Ironworks Gallery
Summerlee Heritage Trust, West Canal Street, Coatbridge, ML5 1QD.
**Tel** 01236 431261 **Fax** 01236 440429
**Opening times** Daily 10–5.
**Services and Facilities** Disabled Access. Museum Shop. Parking. Restoration. Shop.

## ORKNEY ISLANDS

KIRKWALL

### ▶ Taukerness House Museum P
Broad Street, Kirkwall, KW15 1DH.
**Tel** 01865 3191

STROMNESS

### ▶ Pier Arts Centre P
Victoria Street, Stromness, KW16 3AA.
**Tel** 01856 850209

## PERTH AND KINROSS

CRIEFF

### ▶ Strathearn Gallery and Pottery C
32 West High Street, Crieff, PH7 4DL.
**Tel** 01764 656100
**Email** info@strathearn-gallery.com
**Ws** www.strathearn-gallery.com
**Opening times** Mon–Sat 10–5, Sun 1–5.
**Nearest Station** Perth.
**Personnel** Directors: Edith Maguire, Owen Maguire. Contact: Fiona Maguire.
**Services and Facilities** Commissioning Service. Disabled Access.
**Work Stocked and Sold** App. Cer. Cra. Dr. Fur. Gla. Jew. Pa. Ph. Pr. Sc. Wd.
**Price range** £15–£1,000
For artists see Commercial Gallery Artists.
*Opened in March 1994, one of five Scottish galleries selected for quality by the Craft Council. We exhibit work by artists and craftspeople based in Scotland. Our annual graduates show is selected from Glasgow, Edinburgh, Dundee and Aberdeen Colleges of Art to encourage and promote new emerging talent. The Strathearn Pottery which is located in the basement of the gallery, opened in December 1995, and is run by John Maguire. You can be assured of a warm welcome in the bright and friendly atmosphere of our family-run gallery.*

DUNKELD

### ▶ Atholl Gallery C
6 Atholl Street, Dunkeld, PH8 0AR.
**Tel** 01350 728855 **Fax** 01577 840636
**Opening times** Mar–Oct: Mon–Sat 11–5.

Dec–Jan: Wed, Fri–Sun 11–4.
**Personnel** Proprietor: Edward Mackay.
**Services and Facilities** Commissioning Service. Craftshop. Disabled Access. Framing. Gallery space for hire. Valuation.
**Work Stocked and Sold** Cer. Cra. Dr. Jew. Pa. Pr. Sc.
**Price range** £100–£2,000
For artists see Commercial Gallery Artists.

PERTH

### ▶ Cross Keys Art Gallery & Coffee House C

Commercial Street, Bridgend, Perth, PH2 7DS.
**Tel** 01738 628622 **Fax** 01738 447976
**Opening times** Tue–Sat 10.30–4.30, Sun 1–4.30.
**Nearest Station** Perth.
**Personnel** Partners, Co-owners: Anthony Ramsay, Elizabeth Ramsay.
**Services and Facilities** Café. Commissioning Service. Disabled Access. Shop.
**Work Stocked and Sold** Cer. Dec. Dr. Gla. Pa. Sc. Tx. Wd.
**Price range** £50–£2,000
For artists see Commercial Gallery Artists.

### ▶ The Fergusson Gallery P

Marshall Place, Perth, PH2 8NU.
**Tel** 01738 441944 **Fax** 01738 443505
**Ws** www.pkc.gov.uk
**Opening times** Mon–Sat 10–5. Closed Christmas/New Year.
**Nearest Station** Perth bus & rail stations – Leonard St (5 minutes' walk from Gallery).
**Personnel** Fine & Applied Art Officer: Jenny Kinner.
**Services and Facilities** Disabled Access (Ground Floor)/WC. Parking. Shop.
*Opened in 1992. Gallery dedicated to the life and work of the Scottish Colourist John Duncan Fergusson (1874–1961), housing the largest collection of his work in existence. Temporary exhibition programme. Archive available for consultation by appointment. MGC registered.*

### ▶ Frames Contemporary Gallery C

10 Victoria Street, Perth, PH2 8LW.
**Tel** 01738 631085 **Fax** 01738 631085
**Email** hugh.goring@btinternet.com
**Ws** www.framesgallery.co.uk
**Opening times** Mon–Fri 9–5.30, Sat 9–5.
**Nearest Station** Perth.
**Personnel** Proprietor: Hugh Goring. Gallery Manager: Wanda Band.
**Services and Facilities** Art Consultancy. Art for Offices. Craftshop. Framing.
**Work Stocked and Sold** Cer. Cra. Dr. Jew. Pa. Sc. Wd.
**Price range** £100–£8,000
For artists see Commercial Gallery Artists.
*A new gallery specialising in high quality, individual, contemporary crafts.*
*The Gallery specialises in contemporary Scottish art. We hold four large mixed shows in spring, summer, autumn and winter. Each show has between 12 and 20 artists featuring painting, drawing, printmaking, sculpture and ceramics. As well as showing work by well-established artists we have a clear policy of encouraging younger, less well-known artists, particularly those recently out of art college.*

### ▶ Perth Museum and Art Gallery PS

George Street, Perth, PH1 5LB.
**Tel** 01738 632488
**Fax** 01738 443505
**Email** museum@pkc.gov.uk
**Opening times** Mon–Sat 10–5. Closed Christmas/New Year.
**Nearest Station** Perth (rail & bus).
**Personnel** Head of Arts & Heritage: Michael A. Taylor.
**Services and Facilities** Disabled Access. Lectures. Museum Shop. Parking. Workshop Facilities.

## RENFREWSHIRE

PAISLEY

### ▶ Paisley Arts Centre

New Street, Paisley, PA1 1EZ.
**Tel** 0141 887 1010

### ▶ Paisley Museum, Art Galleries and Coats Observatory PS

High Street, Paisley, PA1 2BA.
**Tel** 0141 889 3151
**Fax** 0141 889 9240
**Email** jennifer.evans@renfrewshire.gov.uk
**Ws** www.renfrewshire.gov.uk
**Opening times** Tue–Sat 10–5.
**Nearest Station** Paisley Gilmar Street.
**Personnel** Acting Keeper of Art: Andrea Kusel.
**Services and Facilities** Disabled Access. Shop.
**Work Stocked and Sold** Pa.
**Price range** £50–£5,000

## SCOTTISH BORDERS

JEDBURGH

### ▶ Mainhill Gallery C

Ancrum, Jedburgh, TD8 6XA.
**Tel** 01835 830518
**Opening times** Mon–Sat 10–5.
**Personnel** Director: Diana Bruce.
**Work Stocked and Sold** Dr. Pa. Pr. Sc.
For artists see Commercial Gallery Artists.

PEEBLES

### ▶ Picture Gallery/ Tweeddale Museum P

High Street, Peebles, EH45 8AP.
**Tel** 01721 724820
**Personnel** Rachel Hunter.

### ▶ Tweeddale Museum & Art Gallery P

Chambers Institute, High Street, Peebles, EH45 8AP.
**Tel** 01721 724 820

SELKIRK

### ▶ Peebles Picture Gallery

c/o Municipal Buildings, High Street, Selkirk, TD7 4JX.
**Tel** 01750 20096

### ▶ Robson Gallery P

c/o Municipal Buildings, High Street, Selkirk, TD7 4JX.
**Tel** 01750 20096

### ▶ The Scott Gallery

Municipal Buildings, High Street, Selkirk, TD7 4JX.
**Tel** 01750 20096

## SOUTH AYRSHIRE

AYR

### ▶ Maclaurin Art Gallery C

Rozelle Park, Monument Road, Ayr, KA7 4NQ.
**Tel** 01292 443708/445447
**Opening times** Mon–Sat 10–5. Closed Sun.
**Personnel** Mike Bailey.
**Work Stocked and Sold** Pa.

### ▶ Rozelle House Gallery C

Rozelle Park, Monument Road, Ayr, KA7 4NQ.
**Tel** 01292 445447
**Opening times** Mon–Sat 10–5. Closed Sun.
**Personnel** Mike Bailey.
**Work Stocked and Sold** Pa.

## STIRLING

STIRLING

### ▶ MacRobert Arts Centre Gallery P

University of Stirling, Stirling FK9 4LA.
**Tel** 01786 467159

### ▶ Smith Art Gallery & Museum P

Dumbarton Road, Stirling FK8 2RQ.
**Tel** 01786 471917 **Fax** 01786 449523
**Opening times** Tues–Sat 10.30–5, Sun 2–5.
**Services and Facilities** Disabled Access. Museum Shop. Parking. Restaurant. Shop.

## WEST DUNBARTONSHIRE

DUMBARTON

### ▶ Dumbarton Public Library

Strathleven Place, Dumbarton, G82 1BD.
**Tel** 01389 763129

## WEST LOTHIAN

LIVINGSTON

### ▶ Balbardie Gallery P

West Lothian Council, Almondbank Campus, The Mall, Craigshill, Livingston, EH54 5BJ.
**Tel** 01592 756 016

## WESTERN ISLES

STORNOWAY

### ▶ An Lanntair PS

Town Hall, South Beach, Stornoway, HS1 2BX.
**Tel** 01851 703307
**Fax** 01851 703307
**Email** lanntair@sol.co.uk
**Ws** www.lanntair.com
**Personnel** Director: Roddy Murray.
**Services and Facilities** Bar. Bookshop. Café. Disabled Access. Friends Society. Gallery space for hire. Guided Tours. Museum Shop. Parking. Restaurant.
**Work Stocked and Sold** Dr.

# Welsh Galleries

*Where this information has been provided, entries are designated 'C' for commercial, 'P' for public gallery or museum or 'PS' for a public gallery or museum holding selling shows*

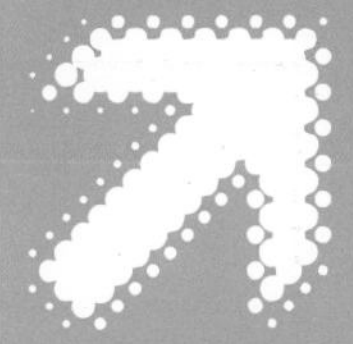

# Wales

Cardiff's Centre for Visual Arts closed in November 2000 after only a year. It took 30 years to bring the project from conception to birth; 8 months later, controversy is still rife about what is to happen to the building, the city's former central library, which cost hundreds of thousands to alter.

In the absence of a CVA, the National Eisteddfod is one of the best showcases for contemporary, cutting-edge art made by artists born or working in Wales. Next year it will be held in St David's, which is providential for the National Museums and Galleries of Wales, who can use it to tell us when it will return Sutherland's pictures to the county. NMGW is the guardian of some 780 paintings, drawings and prints by the artist (d. 1980) whose will stipulated that his pictures of Pembrokeshire should be displayed in the county. Ninety-two per cent of the NMGW's Sutherlands are works on paper. It's possible that the Sutherlands could be displayed in a new gallery which is being planned for St David's.

Mystery and intrigue still surrounds the gallery's exact location and size and all we can reveal is that it won't be in the Cathedral Close! An open day held in the Tourist Information Centre gave visitors the chance to see models and mock-ups of what the new gallery might contain, including interactive computer displays, photographs and 3-D models of the striking ancient landscapes of Pembrokeshire.

Prize-winning painter Phil Nichol plans to open a gallery in the Bute Street Studios, close to Cardiff's revitalised Bay area. The focus will be unashamedly on painting. Says Nichol, 'Wales tends to be 30 years behind London in terms of its art but that's something to celebrate, not worry about.'

Galleries and craft centres across rural Wales were hit hard by foot-and-mouth in 2001, even in places the disease did not reach. According to a report published by the Institute of Welsh Affairs, Wales's 'quality' crafts industry (which has as little as it can to do with kitsch dragons and Jemimas) accounts for a sizeable proportion of the country's income and deserves to be regarded as 'art', while many individual practitioners have to survive on a pittance.

In May 2001, the Arts Council of Wales funded a feasibility study for a new Welsh art magazine, encouraged by many of the country's most articulate artists, curators, art historians and writers.

Lynne Denman and Shelagh Hourahane in association with the Countryside Commission for Wales are working on a project entitled 'A Sense of Arrival'. Sculptors have been invited to pool their ideas before making their own individual pieces for five of the country's national parks. The aim is to use the sculptures to show why each place is special.

Caroline Juler

## ANGLESEY

ANGLESEY

### ▶ Central Gallery

Field Street, Llangefni,
Anglesey, LL77 7UR.
**Tel** 01248 723 527
**Opening times** Tues 9.30–12, Wed–Sat 9.30–5, or evenings by appointment. Closed Sun.
**Personnel** John Scotney.
**Services and Facilities** Framing.

### ▶ Michael Webb Fine Art C

Llangristiolus, Bodorgan,
Anglesey, LL62 5DN.
**Tel** 01407 840 336
**Fax** 01407 840 336
**Opening times** Available 7 days a week – by appointment.
**Nearest Station** Bangor, Gwynedd.
**Personnel** Proprietor: Michael Webb.
**Services and Facilities** Art Consultancy. Framing. Restoration. Valuation.
**Work Stocked and Sold** Dr. Pa. Pr.
**Price range** £100–£25,000
For artists see Commercial Gallery Artists.

*Alfred Fontville de Breanski,* Evening Lock Fad, *oil on canvas, 20" x 30", 1890, £8,000.*

*Michael Webb buys and sells Victorian oil paintings, watercolours and etchings. The list of artists given are those I have handled in recent months; I cannot guarantee to have any particular one in stock at any one time because we do have a continuous turnover of pictures. However, we are always pleased to help you find a particular artist. We also have a collection of watercolours by the living wild life artist Owen Williams.*
For artists see Commercial Gallery Artists.

### ▶ Oriel Fach

46a Castle Street, Beaumaris,
Anglesey, LL58 8BB.
**Tel** 01248 810 445
**Opening times** Daily 10–5 except in winter, when early closing Wed 10–1.
**Personnel** Mr Dooley.
**Services and Facilities** Framing. Shop.
**Work Stocked and Sold** Dr. Pa.

### ▶ Oriel Ynys Mon

Rhosmeirch, Llangefni,
Anglesey, LL77 7TQ.
**Tel** 01248 724 444
**Fax** 01248 750 282
**Opening times** Tue–Sun 10–5. Part free. Permanent exhibition – charge.
**Personnel** Principle Heritage Officer: Denise Morris. Exhibitions Officer: Alun Gruffydd. Education Officer & Technical Resources Officer: Mary Aris and John Smith.
**Services and Facilities** Workshop Facilities.

## BRIDGEND

BRIDGEND

### ▶ Nolton Gallery

66 Nolton Street, Bridgend, CF31 3BP.
**Tel** 01656 663 278
**Opening times** Mon–Sat 9.30–5.15, Wed 9.30–2.
**Personnel** Mr Parkes. Mrs Parkes.
**Services and Facilities** Framing.
**Work Stocked and Sold** Pa. Pr.

## CAERPHILLY

BLACKWOOD

### ▶ The Gallery

Blackwood Miners' Institute, High Street,
Blackwood, NP2 1BB.
**Tel** 01495 224 425 **Fax** 01495 226 457
**Opening times** 10–5 (excluding Sundays).
**Personnel** General Manager: Bryan Reynolds. Arts Development Officer/Visual Arts Programmer: Justine Ennion.
**Services and Facilities** Workshop Facilities.

## CARDIFF

CARDIFF

### ▶ Albany Gallery C

74B Albany Road, Cardiff CF2 3RS.
**Tel** 029 2048 7158
**Fax** 029 2048 9158
**Opening times** Mon–Sat 10–5.
**Personnel** Director: Mary Yapp.
**Work Stocked and Sold** Cer. Cra. Dr. Pa. Pr. Sc.
For artists see Commercial Gallery Artists.

### ▶ Cardiff Bay Arts Trust PS

123 Bute Street, Cardiff CF1 6AE.
**Tel** 029 2048 8772 **Fax** 029 2047 2439
**Email** Arts.Trust@ENABLIS.co.uk
**Opening times** Daily office hours.
**Personnel** Director: Carole-Anne Davies.
**Services and Facilities** Art Consultancy. Art for Offices. Commissioning Service. Gallery space for hire. Guided Tours. Lectures.

### ▶ Chapter Gallery

Market Road, Canton, Cardiff CF5 1QE.
**Tel** 029 2039 6061
**Personnel** Carol Jones.

### ▶ Howard Gardens Gallery PS

University of Wales Institute Cardiff, Howard Gardens, Cardiff CF24 OSP.
**Tel** 029 2041 6678
**Fax** 029 2041 6678
**Email** wwarrilow@uwic.ac.uk
**Opening times** Mon–Thu 9–8, Fri 9–6, Sat 9–6.
**Nearest Station** Cardiff Central.
**Personnel** Director: Walt Warrilow.
**Services and Facilities** Disabled Access. Lectures. Parking. Workshop Facilities.
*Purpose-built gallery of 264 sqm within the School of Art and Design. It has a continuous programme throughout the year which spans not only the visual and applied arts, but also other related disciplines including architecture, design, historical and cultural studies. There are complementary events, lectures, workshops etc. The gallery hosts the Faculty's final BA and MA Degree exhibitions.*

### ▶ Manor House Fine Arts C

73 Pontcanna Street, Pontcanna,
Cardiff CF1 9HS.
**Tel** 029 2022 7787
**Opening times** Tue, Thu, Fri, Sat 10.30–5.30 or by appointment.
**Personnel** Director: Steven Hill.
**Services and Facilities** Art Consultancy. Art for Offices. Commissioning Service. Framing. Restoration. Valuation.

### ▶ Martin Tinney Gallery C

6 Windsor Place, Cardiff CF1 3BX.
**Tel** 029 2064 1411
**Fax** 029 20641422
**Email** mtg@artwales.com
**Ws** www.artwales.dircon.co.uk
**Opening times** Mon–Fri 10–6, Sat 10–5.
**Personnel** Martin Tinney.
**Services and Facilities** Art Consultancy. Art for Offices. Commissioning Service.
**Work Stocked and Sold** Dr. Pa. Pr. Sc.
**Price range** £75–£10,000
For artists see Commercial Gallery Artists.

### ▶ National Museums & Galleries of Wales P

National Museum & Gallery, Cathays Park,
Cardiff CF10 3NP.
**Tel** 029 2039 7951
**Fax** 029 2037 3219
**Email** Post@nmgw.ac.uk
**Ws** www.nmgw.ac.uk
**Opening times** Tue–Sun 10–5; open bank holiday Mondays.
**Nearest Station** Cardiff Queen Street.
**Personnel** Oliver Fairclough. Keeper of Art: Oliver Fairclough. Exhibitions Coordinator: Deborah Spillards.
**Services and Facilities** Bookshop. Café. Disabled Access. Friends Society. Gallery space for hire. Guided Tours. Lectures. Museum Shop. Parking. Restaurant. Shop.
*One of eight sites under the umbrella of the National Museums & Galleries of Wales, the National Museum & Gallery Cardiff is home to one of the finest collections of art treasures in Europe. The Davies collection includes works by Monet, Manet, Renoir, Van Gogh and Sisley, also bronzes by Degas and Rodin, including Rodin's Kiss. A fine collection of 18th- and 19th-century landscapes and important works by Welsh artists Augustus and Gwen John are displayed and there is a regular programme of changing exhibitions. Works from the museum's collection are also displayed at Turner House Gallery, Penarth, in addition to exhibitions by local art societies.*

### ▶ St David's Hall PS

The Hayes, Cardiff CF10 1SH.
**Tel** 029 2087 8500
**Fax** 029 2087 8599
**Email** p.j.james@cardiff.gov.uk
**Opening times** Mon–Sat 10–4. Also open to concert-goers.
**Nearest Station** Cardiff – Central.
**Personnel** Exhibitions Officer: Gaynor Hill.
**Services and Facilities** Bar. Café. Craftshop. Disabled Access. Friends Society. Gallery space

for hire. Guided Tours. Lectures. Restaurant. Shop. Workshop Facilities, WC.
For artists see Commercial Gallery Artists.
*St David's Hall, the National Concert Hall of Wales, is situated in the city centre. The two main galleries currently show around 25 exhibitions each year.*
*Exhibitions include both group and single artist shows covering a wide range of work. There is also additional space for regular photography and craft exhibitions. St David's Hall's broad spectrum of concert hall events brings the visual arts to the attention of more than 10,000 people a week who pass through the foyers.*

## CARMARTHENSHIRE

### CARMARTHEN

**▶ Carmarthen Museum** P
Abergwili, Carmarthen, SA31 2JG.
**Tel** 01267 231 691
**Opening times** Mon–Sat 10–4.30.
**Personnel** County Museums Officer: Chris Delaney. Senior Museums Officer: Ann Dorsett.

**▶ Oriel Myrddin** C
Church Lane, Carmarthen, SA31 1LH.
**Tel** 01267 222 775
**Opening times** Mon–Sat 10.30–4.45 including bank holidays.
**Work Stocked and Sold** Cer. Cra. Gla. Jew. Tx. Wd.

### LAUGHARNE

**▶ The Powerhouse Gallery**
Behind the Clock, Laugharne, SA33 4SB.
**Tel** 01994 427 580
**Personnel** Fiona Scourfield. Steve Treacy.

### LLANDEILO

**▶ Fountain Fine Art**
Rhosmaen Street,
Llandeilo, SA19 6EN.
**Tel** 01558 823 328
**Opening times** Tue–Fri 10–1, 2.30–5.30, Sat 10–4.30.
**Personnel** Gillian Still.
**Work Stocked and Sold** Pa. Sc.

**▶ The Trapp Art and Craft Centre**
Llwyndewi, Trapp,
Llandeilo, SA19 6TT.
**Tel** 01269 850 362
**Opening times** Tues–Sun 10.30–6, Mar–Dec.
**Personnel** Owner: Nigel Card. Gallery Director: A Goolding.
**Services and Facilities** Café. Craftshop.

### LLANELLI

**▶ Parc Howard Mansion** P
Felinfoel Road, Llanelli, SA15 3AS.
**Tel** 01554 772 029.
Hire details 01554 741 100.
**Opening times** Apr–Sep 10–6, Oct–Mar 10–4. Admission free.
**Personnel** Carmarthenshire Cultural Services Manager: Mr D. F. Griffiths (01267 224824).
**Services and Facilities** Gallery space for hire.

### WHITLAND

**▶ Studio Gallery** C
Penclippen Farm, Blaenwaun,
Whitland, SA34 0JB.
**Tel** 01994 448 601 **Fax** 01994 448 601
**Opening times** Mon, Tue, Thu, Fri 11–1 & 2–5. Closed Wed, Sat and Nov to Easter except by appointment.

## CEREDIGION

### ABERYSTWYTH

**▶ Aberystwyth Arts Centre** C
Penglais, Aberystwyth, SY23 3DE.
**Tel** 01970 623 232/622 895
**Fax** 01970 622 883
**Opening times** Mon–Sat 10–5. Closed Sun. Open evenings on performance nights. Closed early June for University exams.
**Work Stocked and Sold** Cer. Cra. Gla. Jew. Pa. Sc. Tx. Wd.

**▶ Oriel Coliseum Gallery**
Ceredigion Museum, Terrace Road,
Aberystwyth, SY23 2AQ.
**Tel** 01970 633 086 **Fax** 01970 633 084
**Opening times** Mon–Sat, 10–5. Closed Good Friday and December 25–6.
**Personnel** Gwenllian Ashley.
**Services and Facilities** Gallery space for hire. Museum Shop. Shop.

**▶ School of Art Gallery & Museum** PS
University of Wales, Buarth Mawr,
Aberystwyth, SY23 1NG.
**Tel** 01970 622 460 **Fax** 01970 622 461
**Email** neh@aber.ac.uk
**Ws** www.aber.ac.uk/museum
**Opening times** Mon–Fri 10–5.30.
**Nearest Station** Aberystwyth.
**Personnel** Keeper of Art: Robert Meyrick. Assistant Curator: Neil Holland. Curator of Ceramics: Moira Vincentelli.
**Services and Facilities** Disabled Access. Guided Tours. Lectures. Parking.
**Price range** £25–£1,500
For artists see Commercial Gallery Artists.

***Derrick Greaves,*** **Woman in a Scarf and Floral Dress,** ***monoprint, 26" x 21", 1957.***

*Extensive teaching and research collection of fine and decorative art; European prints from 15th century to present, drawings, watercolours and photographs. George Powell of Nanteos collection of pictures, bronzes and* objet d'art *(including works on paper by Turner, Burne-Jones, Rossetti, Poynter, Rebecca and Simeon Solomon). 5,000 wood engravings for periodicals of the 1860s and a fine collection of prints representing the Etching Revival since Whistler, particularly etchings of the inter-war years. Art in Wales since 1945 and contemporary printmaking. Contemporary Welsh photography and an outstanding collection of post-war Italian photographs.*
*Changing exhibitions from the collection, touring shows and exhibitions by staff, students and invited artists. Graphic art study collection by appointment.*
*The School of Art Press publishes books, catalogues and research papers, and new Museum and Gallery Studies courses with the art collections at their core. All housed in a magnificent Edwardian building overlooking Cardigan Bay and a few minutes' walk to the town centre and railway station.*
*Also responsible for the Ceramics Gallery at Aberystwyth Arts Centre on the University campus with its important collection of early 20th-century British, European, American and Japanese studio pottery, 18th- and 19th-century Welsh and English slipware, Swansea and Nantgarw porcelain, Art Pottery and Oriental ceramics.*

### CARDIGAN

**▶ Frame by Frame**
11 Black Lion Mews, Cardigan, SQ43 1HJ.
**Tel** 01239 615 398
**Opening times** Closed Wed and Sun. Open 10–5 rest of the week.
**Personnel** Photographer: Graham Holdsworth.
**Services and Facilities** Framing.
**Work Stocked and Sold** Pa. Pr.

**▶ Glanhelyg Gallery**
Llechryd, Cardigan, SA43 2NJ.
**Tel** 01239 682 482
**Opening times** Daily 10–6. By appointment in Winter.
**Nearest Station** Carmarthen.
**Personnel** Robin Holtom. Rachel Holtom.
**Services and Facilities** Art Consultancy. Art for Offices. Commissioning Service. Parking. Workshop Facilities.
**Work Stocked and Sold** Dr. Pa. Pr. Sc.
**Price range** £50–£5,000

**▶ The Studio** C
3 Cambrian Quay, Cardigan, SA43 1EZ.
**Tel** 01239 613 711
**Email** david@david-wilson.net
**Ws** www.david-wilson.net
**Opening times** Open all year 11–5: Easter and Jul–Sep every day; Oct–Jun closed Thu and Sun.
**Nearest Station** Carmarthen.
**Personnel** David Wilson.
**Services and Facilities** Art for Offices. Commissioning Service. Parking. Shop.
**Work Stocked and Sold** Dr. Fur. Pa. Pr.
**Price range** £10–£3,000
For artists see Commercial Gallery Artists.

*David Wilson,* Kynance Cove, *watercolour, 11" x 15", 1998, £125.*

*This artist-run gallery overlooking the river Teifi near Cardigan bridge is also David Wilson's studio. His paintings and prints (figurative and abstract) draw their inspiration from many sources, but especially from the varied landscape and coast of West Wales. David Wilson's works are to be found in hundreds of private collections world-wide; several of his paintingshave been purchased by the National Library of Wales. Examples of fine furniture designed by Guy Wilson are also on display.*

LAMPETER

### ▶ Y Galeri

2 Bridge Street, Lampeter, SA48 7HG.
**Tel** 01570 423 317
**Opening times** Mon, Tue, Thu, Fri, Sat 9.30–5, Wed 9–1.
**Personnel** Jacky Pique.
**Services and Facilities** Framing.
**Work Stocked and Sold** Cra. Jew. Pr.

## CONWY

CONWY

### ▶ Ogilvy & Estill C

4 High Street, Conwy, LC32 8DZ.
**Tel** 01492 592 292 **Fax** 01492 592 292
**Email** art@ogilvyestill.demon.co.uk
**Ws** www.ogilvyestill.co.uk
**Opening times** Wed–Sat 1–5, Sun 12–4.
**Nearest Station** Conway.
**Personnel** Exhibition Coordinator: Shelley Hocknell. Exhibition Advisor: Tom Jones.
**Work Stocked and Sold** Cer. Pa. Ph. Sc.
**Price range** £100–£3,000
For artists see Commercial Gallery Artists.

LLANDUDNO

### ▶ Llandudno Museum and Art Gallery P

Chardon House, 17–19 Gloddaeth Street, Llandudno LL30 2DD.
**Tel** 01492 879 130
**Opening times** Mon–Sat 10.30–5, Sun 2.15–5.
**Personnel** Mrs. C.J. Cornwall.

### ▶ Oriel Mostyn PS

12 Vaughan Street, Llandudno LL30 1AB.
**Tel** 01492 879 201/870 875
**Fax** 01492 878 869
**Opening times** Mon–Sat 10–1, 1.30–5. Admission free.
**Nearest Station** Llandudno 3 minutes' walk.
**Personnel** Director: Martin Barlow. Administrator: Mary Heathcote. Education Officer: Alison Lebegue.
**Services and Facilities** Bookshop. Commissioning Service. Craftshop. Disabled Access. Friends Society. Guided Tours. Lectures. Workshop Facilities.
**Work Stocked and Sold** Ab. App. Cer. Cra. Dec. Dr. Fur. Gla. Jew. Pa. Ph. Pr. Sc. Tx. Wd.
**Price range** £6–£6,000

## DENBIGHSHIRE

DENBIGH

### ▶ Denbigh Library, Museum and Gallery P

Hall Square, Denbigh, LL16 3AU.
**Tel** 01745 816 313
**Opening times** Mon, Wed & Fri 9.30–7; Tues & Thurs 9.30–5.30; Sat 9.30–4.
**Personnel** Museum & Arts Officer: David Worthington. Gallery Assistant: Emma Parry.

LLANGOLLEN

### ▶ ECTARC

The European Centre for Traditional and Regional Cultures, Parade Street, Llangollen LL20 8RB.
**Tel** 01978 861 514 **Fax** 01978 861 804
**Opening times** Mon–Sat 10–5, Sun 11.30–4.30.
**Personnel** Arts & Exhibitions Officer: Sharon Thomas.
**Work Stocked and Sold** Pa.

### ▶ Royal International Pavilion PS

Abbey Road, Llangollen LL20 8SW.
**Tel** 01978 860 111 **Fax** 01978 860 046
**Email** enquiries@royal-pavilion.co.uk
**Ws** www.royal-pavilion.co.uk
**Opening times** Mon–Fri 9–5 and occasional weekends. Ring to confirm.
**Nearest Station** Chirk 5 miles, Ruabon 5 miles.
**Personnel** Duty Officer (Retail & Catering): Christine Griffith. Receptionist: Jim Allen.
**Services and Facilities** Craftshop. Disabled Access. Gallery space for hire. Parking.
**Work Stocked and Sold** Cer. Cra. Gla.
**Price range** £5–£100
For artists see Commercial Gallery Artists.
*Located in the unique Royal International Pavilion, the Gallery offers a diverse exhibition programme featuring six main exhibitions annually. The Gallery (18m x 12m) is available for hire, at very competitive rates, to both individuals and Art groups; the 'North Wales Federation of Art Societies' and 'Group 75' show here regularly. Sales are welcomed on a commission basis which helps to cover marketing support. Our Craft Showcase hosts displays by craftspeople and in the past has included textiles, ceramics and machine embroidery. In addition, displays of glass sculpture, stained glass and pottery animals provide a permanent feature. Partially funded by the European Regional Development Fund.*

RUTHIN

### ▶ The Gallery, Ruthin Craft Centre PS

Park Road, Ruthin, LL15 1BB.
**Tel** 01824 704 774 **Fax** 01824 702 060
**Opening times** summer: 10–5.30 daily, winter: Mon–Sat 10–5, Sun 12–5.
**Nearest Station** Chester, Rhyl.
**Personnel** Director: Philip Hughes. Administrator: Jane Gerrard.
**Services and Facilities** Craftshop. Disabled Access. Parking. Restaurant. Shop.
**Work Stocked and Sold** App. Cer. Cra. Gla. Jew. Tx. Wd.
**Price range** £5–£5,000
*A Craft Council Selected Gallery housed within a purpose-built Craft Centre in the picturesque Vale of Clwyd. The Gallery shows the best of fine crafts by contemporary designer-makers from all over the British Isles. We run an exciting programme of regularly changing exhibitions which aim, through a stimulating and diverse view of contemporary work, to show the breadth of excellence in the field of the applied arts. We receive financial support from the Arts Council of Wales.*

## FLINTSHIRE

HAWARDEN

### ▶ The Black Sheep Gallery C

The Old Stable Yard, Hawarden Castle, Hawarden, CH5 3NY.
**Tel** 01244 535 505
**Opening times** Tue–Fri 10–6, Sat & Sun 10–5. Closed Mon. Admission free.
**Nearest Station** Hawarden.
**Personnel** Director: Mr. F. P. Garbutt.
**Services and Facilities** Commissioning Service. Framing. Gallery space for hire. Parking. Workshop Facilities.
**Work Stocked and Sold** Cer. Dr. Pa. Ph. Pr. Sc. Tx. Wd.
**Price range** £75–£2,500
For artists see Commercial Gallery Artists.

MOLD

### ▶ Oriel Gallery PS

Clwyd Theatr Cymru, Mold, CH7 1YA.
**Tel** 01352 756 331 **Fax** 01352 758 323
**Email** drama@celtic.co.uk
**Opening times** Mon–Sat 10am–10pm.
**Nearest Station** Chester.
**Personnel** Curator: J. Le Vay.
**Services and Facilities** Art Consultancy. Bar. Bookshop. Café. Craftshop. Disabled Access. Gallery space for hire. Parking. Restaurant.

## GWYNEDD

ABERDOVEY

### ▶ The Gallery

11 New Street, Aberdovey, LL35 0EH.
**Tel** 01654 767 319, eves. 01654 710 523
**Opening times** Easter–mid Oct daily. Out of season please phone for details.
**Personnel** Owner: Mrs Claire Davies.
**Work Stocked and Sold** Cer. Dr. Pa. Pr.

BANGOR

### ▶ Bangor Museum & Art Gallery P

Ffordd Gwynedd, Bangor, LL57 1DT.
**Tel** 01248 353 368

**Opening times** Tue–Fri 12.30–4.30, Sat 10.30–4.30. Admission free.
**Personnel** Pat Benneyworth.

### ▶ David Windsor Gallery
201 High Street, Bangor, LL57 1NU.
**Tel** 01248 364 639
**Opening times** 10–5.30 daily. Closed Wed and Sun.
**Personnel** Mrs Creathorne.
**Services and Facilities** Framing. Restoration.
**Work Stocked and Sold** Pr.

BETWS-Y-COED

### ▶ The Gallery
Holyhead Road, Betws-y-Coed, LL24 0BW.
**Tel** 01690 710 432
**Opening times** Mon–Sat 9.30–5.30.
**Personnel** Irene Rudram. Kenneth Rudram.
**Services and Facilities** Craftshop.

CAERNARFON

### ▶ Arfon Gallery
Palace Street, Caernarfon, LL55 1RR.
**Tel** 01286 672 602 **Fax** 01286 76728
**Opening times** Mon–Sat 9–5, later in summer.
**Personnel** Glenys Gray-Thomas. Eric Gray-Thomas.
**Services and Facilities** Framing.
**Work Stocked and Sold** Pa. Pr.

CRICCIETH

### ▶ The Chapel of Art/ Capel Celfyddyd C
8 Marine Crescent, Criccieth, LL52 0EA.
**Tel** 01766 523 570
**Opening times** summer Tue–Sun 10–6. Winter hours check. Closed Christmas day and Mondays, except bank holidays.
**Nearest Station** Criccieth.
**Personnel** Artistic Director: Janet Kaiser.
**Services and Facilities** Art Consultancy. Art for Offices. Commissioning Service. Craftshop. Disabled Access. Friends Society. Lectures. Parking.
**Work Stocked and Sold** App. Cer. Cra. Dec. Dr. Fur. Gla. Pa. Ph. Sc. Tx. Wd.
**Price range** £9–£999
For artists see Commercial Gallery Artists.

DOLGELLAU

### ▶ The Library Gallery
Borthwog Hall, Bontddu, Dolgellau, LL40 2TT.
**Tel** 01341 430 271
**Fax** 01341 430 682
**Opening times** daily 10–5. Restaurant and hotel–phone for details.
**Personnel** Vicki Hawes.
**Services and Facilities** Café. Restaurant.
**Work Stocked and Sold** Cer. Pa. Pr.

HARLECH

### ▶ The White Room Gallery at Harlech Pottery
Pentre Fail, Harlech, LL46 2YG.
**Tel** 01766 247 397 (after 6pm in summer).
**Personnel** Lynette Gayden.

PWLLHELI

### ▶ Llanbedrog Pottery and Prints
The Pottery, Llanbedrog, Pwllheli, LL53 7UA.
**Tel** 01758 740 296
**Opening times** Easter–Oct 9–8, Winter 9–5.
**Personnel** Berwyn Jones. Janet Jones.
**Services and Facilities** Workshop Facilities.

### ▶ Oriel Plas Glyn-y-Weddw C
Llanbedrog, Pwllheli, LL53 7TT.
**Tel** 01758 740 763
**Fax** 01758 740 232
**Email** enquiry@oriel.org.uk
**Ws** www.oriel.org.uk
**Opening times** 11–5 except Tuesdays.
**Nearest Station** Pwllheli (Cambrian Railway) or Bangor (Main Line).
**Personnel** Director: David Jeffreys.
**Services and Facilities** Bookshop. Café. Craftshop. Disabled Access. Friends Society. Gallery space for hire. Lectures. Parking. Restaurant. Shop. Workshop Facilities.
**Work Stocked and Sold** Ab. Cer. Cra. Dr. Jew. Pa. Ph. Pr. Sc. Tx. Wd.
**Price range** £30–£6,000
For artists see Commercial Gallery Artists.
*Plas Glyn y Weddw Art Gallery, under new management, is one of the oldest public art galleries in Wales. Pictures, arts and crafts, are housed in a superb listed Victorian Gothic mansion, with fine views from the Llyn Peninsula over Cardigan Bay to Snowdonia. There are gardens, woodland and beach walks, and a tea room in the conservatory. Contemporary Welsh paintings form the core of the Gallery's collection, as well as changing exhibitions and a distinguished collection of porcelain.*
Programme of Residential Arts Courses available on request.

## MONMOUTHSHIRE

ABERGAVENNY

### ▶ Hill Court Gallery
Hill Court, Pen Y Pound, Abergavenny, NP7 7RW.
**Tel** 01873 854 180
**Opening times** Tue–Sun 2.30–7.
**Personnel** Joan Isaac. Bert Isaac.

CHEPSTOW

### ▶ The Workshop Gallery
13 Lower Church Street, Chepstow, NPH 5HJ.
**Tel** 01291 624 836
**Opening times** Mon–Sat 10–1, 2–6, Sun 2–6.
**Personnel** Ned Heywood.

MONMOUTH

### ▶ Beaver Framing Ltd
1 Monk Street, Monmouth, NP25 3LR.
**Tel** 01600 713 905
**Personnel** Brian Banfield.

### ▶ Beaver Art and Framing Centre
Monk Street, Monmouth, NP5 3NZ.
**Tel** 01600 713 905
**Opening times** Mon–Fri 9.30–5, Sat 9–1.
**Personnel** Landlord: Brian Banfield.
**Services and Facilities** Framing. Shop.

### ▶ Monmouth Museum P
Priory Street, Monmouth, NP5 3XA.
**Tel** 01600 713 519
**Opening times** Daily 10–1, 2–5, Sun 2–5.
**Personnel** Andrew Helme.

RAGLAN

### ▶ The Old Vicarage C
Penrhos, Raglan, NP5 2LE.
**Tel** 01600 780 239
**Personnel** H. J. Gerrish.
**Work Stocked and Sold** Pr.

USK

### ▶ The Arthouse
Pen Y Parc, Llangibby, Usk, NP5 1NY.
**Tel** 01633 450 320 **Fax** 01633 450 552
**Opening times** Temporary exhibitions – open as advertised or by appointment.
**Personnel** Susie Martin. Sarah Windrum.

## NEWPORT

NEWPORT

### ▶ Newport Museum & Art Gallery PS
John Frost Square, Newport NP20 1PA.
**Tel** 01633 840 064 **Fax** 01633 222 615
**Email** museum@newport.gov.uk
**Opening times** Mon–Thu 9.30–5, Fri 9.30–4.30, Sat 9.30–4.
**Nearest Station** Newport (Paddington/Swansea line).
**Personnel** Keeper of Art: Roger Cucksey. Exhibitions Officer: Sandra Jackaman.
**Services and Facilities** Café. Craftshop. Disabled Access. Lectures. Museum Shop. Shop. Valuation. WC.
**Work Stocked and Sold** App. Cer. Cra. Dec. Dr. Fur. Gla. Jew. Pa. Ph. Pr. Sc. Tx. Wd.
**Price range** Up to £1,000
*Founded 1888. Collection of early English watercolours, oil paintings, mainly British 20th century with emphasis on Welsh artists. Extensive changing exhibition programme with related events and activities. The John Wait Teapot collection 1780–1980 and the Iris and John Fox Collection.*

### ▶ Tower Gallery
Caldicot Castle Museum, Caldicot, Newport NP6 4HU.
**Tel** 01291 420 241
**Opening times** Mon–Fri 11–12.30, 1.30–5, Sat and bank holidays 10–1, 1.30–5, Sun 1.30–5.
**Personnel** Curator: Anne Rainsbury.

## PEMBROKESHIRE

FISHGUARD

### ▶ Oriel/Dragon Gallery
The Old Post Office, 9 West Street, Fishguard, SA65 9AE.
**Tel** 01348 875175

### ▶ West Wales Arts Centre, C
Castle Hill, 16 West Street, Fishguard, SA65 9AE.
**Tel** 01348 873 867 **Fax** 01348 873 867

**Opening times** Mon–Sat 9–5.30, Sundays by appointment.
**Nearest Station** Fishguard or Haverfordwest.
**Personnel** Myles Pepper. Vicki Craven.
**Services and Facilities** Art Consultancy. Art for Offices. Commissioning Service. Craftshop. Lectures.
**Work Stocked and Sold** App. Cer. Cra. Dr. Gla. Jew. Pa. Pr. Sc.
**Price range** £100–£5,000
For artists see Commercial Gallery Artists.

### ▶ Workshop Wales Gallery
Lower Town, Fishguard, SA65 9LY.
**Tel** 01348 872 261
**Opening times** 1 Mar–end Oct, daily 10–1, 2–5. Closed Wed, Sun in Sep and Oct.
**Personnel** John Cleal. Lel Cleal.
**Work Stocked and Sold** Cra. Pa. Sc.

## HAVERFORDWEST

### ▶ The Artists Studio C
'Red Rails' Marloes, Haverfordwest, SA62 3BB.
**Tel** 01646 636 380
**Opening times** Mon–Sun 9–6.
**Personnel** Keith M. Parsons.
**Services and Facilities** Commissioning Service. Parking.
**Work Stocked and Sold** Dr. Pa.
**Price range** £75–£600
For artists see Commercial Gallery Artists.

### ▶ The Gallery
Haroldston House, Clay Lanes, Haverfordwest, SA61 1UH.
**Tel** 01437 762 611
**Opening times** Telephone for details.
**Personnel** Anne Whalley NDD SWA.

### ▶ Gillian Richardson
Fine Art Photography, The Gallery, Fair Winds, Spittal, Haverfordwest, SA62 5QT.
**Tel** 01437 87311
**Opening times** Mon–Fri 10–5. Evenings and weekends by appointment.
**Personnel** Gillian Richardson.
**Work Stocked and Sold** Pa. Ph.

### ▶ Hamilton House Gallery
Caerfarchell, Solva, Haverfordwest, SA62 6XG.
**Tel** 01437 721 264
**Opening times** Daily 10–6, but telephone in winter.
**Personnel** Martin Griffiths.

### ▶ The Pink House
Contemporary Arts, Nine Wells, Solva, Haverfordwest, SA62 6UH.
**Tel** 01437 721 543
**Opening times** Daily 10–7. In winter please telephone to check times.
**Personnel** Peter Daniels. Elizabeth Daniels.
**Services and Facilities** Art for Offices. Commissioning Service.
**Work Stocked and Sold** Pa. Pr.

### ▶ Trevigan Gallery
Croesgoch, Haverfordwest, SA62 5JP.
**Tel** 01348 831 374
**Opening times** Mon–Sun 10–7. End Sep to Easter, closed intermittently. Phone for details.
**Personnel** John Knapp-Fisher.

## MILFORD HAVEN

### ▶ Torch Theatre
St Peters Road, Milford Haven, SA73 2BU.
**Tel** 01646 694 192
**Opening times** Mon–Sat 10–3.30, 5–8, some Sundays.
**Services and Facilities** Bar.

## NARBERTH

### ▶ The Golden Sheaf Gallery C
25 High Street, Narberth, SA67 7AR.
**Tel** 01834 860 407 **Fax** 01834 860 407
**Opening times** Mon–Sat 9.30–5.30 extended opening during the summer months and bank holiday weekends. Please phone for details.
**Personnel** Suzanne Morgan-Somers. Paul Morgan-Somers.
**Work Stocked and Sold** Cer. Cra. Gla. Jew. Pa. Pr. Tx. Wd.

## NEWPORT

### ▶ Carningli Centre C
East Street, Newport, SA42 0SY.
**Tel** 01239 820 724
**Email** info@carningli.co.uk
**Ws** www.carningli.co.uk
**Opening times** Mon–Sat 10–5.30.
**Nearest Station** Fishguard.
**Personnel** Mrs A. Gent.
**Services and Facilities** Commissioning Service.
**Work Stocked and Sold** Dr. Pa. Ph. Pr. Wd.
**Price range** £15–£500
For artists see Commercial Gallery Artists.
*We are on the A487 in the centre of Newport, specialising in paintings and prints of the area by various artists, plus occasional special exhibitions which can be quite different. As well as the gallery, Carningli Centre offers a second-hand bookshop, antiques rooms and furniture restoration service.*

### ▶ Fine Arts Gallery
Carningli Centre, East Street, Newport, SA42 0SY.
**Tel** 01239 820 724
**Opening times** Daily 9.30–5.30, Wed 9.30–1, shorter hours in winter.
**Personnel** Mr C. J. Field.
**Services and Facilities** Bookshop. Craftshop.

### ▶ Pauline Harries Gallery
Ty Clyd, Long Street, Newport, SA42 0TL.
**Tel** 01239 820 404
**Opening times** Mon–Ssat 10–5, Sun closed.
**Personnel** Pauline Harries.

### ▶ The Sessions House
East Street, Newport, SA42 0SY.
**Tel** 01239 820 853
**Opening times** Mon–Sat 9.30–5.30.
**Personnel** Richard Wilson.
**Services and Facilities** Framing.

## PEMBROKE

### ▶ The Golden Plover Studio Gallery C
Warren, Pembroke, SA17 5HR.
**Tel** 01646 661 201
**Opening times** Telephone for details. Normally 10–6.
**Nearest Station** Pembroke.
**Personnel** Artist: Arthur Giardelli. Artist: Bim Giardelli.
**Services and Facilities** Commissioning Service. Disabled Access. Parking.
**Work Stocked and Sold** Dr. Pa. Pr. Sc.
**Price range** £100–£4,000
For artists see Commercial Gallery Artists.
*Paintings and watercolours of Pembrokeshire and other places by Bim and Arthur Giardelli: France, Italy, near and Far East. Fabric pictures and relief sculptures exhibited in Wales, London and abroad. Works included in public collections: Tate Gallery, National Museum of Wales, Contemporary Art Society, Arts Council for Wales, Arts Council of Great Britain, Municipal Gallery of Modern Art, Dublin, Musée des Beaux Arts, Nantes, St Woolos Cathedral, Newport, National Gallery, Bratislava, National Gallery, Prague.*
*Book: Arthur Giardelli – Paintings, Constructions and Relief Sculpture, published by Seren.*
*Exhibition: England & Co., 16 June–7 July.*

## ST DAVID'S

### ▶ Albion Gallery
41 Nun Street, St David's, SA62 6NU.
**Tel** 01437 720 120
**Opening times** Daily 10–6 and by appointment. Telephone in winter to check details.
**Personnel** Anne Dixon. David Dixon.

### ▶ John Roberts Gallery
Ti Meini 16 Cross Street, St David's, SA62 6SE.
**Tel** 01437 720 220
**Opening times** Strictly by appointment.
**Personnel** John Roberts.

## TENBY

### ▶ The Harbour Gallery and Etching Studio
1 St Julian Street, Tenby, SA70 7AY.
**Tel** 01834 842 370
**Opening times** Daily 10–6.
**Personnel** John Cahill. Gillian Cahill.

### ▶ Tenby Museum & Art Gallery
Castle Hill, Tenby, SA70 7BP.
**Tel** 01834 842 809
**Fax** 01834 842 809
**Email** tenbymuseum@hotmail.com
**Ws** www.tenbymuseum.free-online.co.uk
**Opening times** Easter–end Oct, daily 10–5. Nov–Easter Mon–Fri 10–5.
**Nearest Station** Tenby.
**Personnel** Honorary Curator: Jon Beynon.
**Services and Facilities** Friends Society. Museum Shop.
*An independent, community museum since 1878, it is situated within the castle walls in a magnificent setting, overlooking Carmarthen Bay. The art gallery houses a permanent collection of works by local artists, Augustus John, Gwen John and Nina Hamnett, and paintings of the Tenby area by leading artists since the 18th century. The new art gallery displays a variety of temporary exhibitions, New Maritime, Natural History and Local History galleries. The museum has an outstanding display of geology, archaeology, natural history and maritime history of Pembrokeshire.*

## POWYS

### BRECON

**▶ Sable and Hogg Galleries** C
15 Lion Street, Brecon, LD3 7HY.
**Tel** 01874 625 901
**Opening times** Mon–Sat 10–5. Closed Wed.
**Nearest Station** Abergavenny (20 mins away).
**Personnel** Michael Egbers.
**Services and Facilities** Craftshop. Framing. Gallery space for hire. Restoration. Shop. Valuation.
**Work Stocked and Sold** Cra. Pa. Ph. Pr. Wd.
**Price range** £20–£5,000
For artists see Commercial Gallery Artists.
*Sales of original paintings, limited edition prints, etchings, photographs, cards. Bespoke picture framing, restoration, cleaning. Photographic work, events – social – industrial – commercial. Computer reconstruction of old photographs, copy work. Disabled access ground floor only.*

### HAY-ON-WYE

**▶ Brook Street Pottery** C
Brook Street, Hay-on-Wye, Hereford HR3 5BQ.
**Tel** 01497 821 026
**Opening times** Mon–Sat 10.30–5, Sun 12–4.30. Closed Tue.
**Work Stocked and Sold** Cra. Tx.

**▶ Kilvert Gallery** C
Ashbrook House, Clyro, Hay-on-Wye, Hereford HR3 5RZ.
**Tel** 01497 820 831
**Fax** 01497 820 831
**Opening times** Closed Christmas–Easter (except by appointment). From Easter: Open Tue–Sun 10–5 (closed Mon). Phone for details.
**Personnel** Elizabeth Organ. Eugene Fisk.
**Services and Facilities** Art Consultancy. Art for Offices. Commissioning Service. Craftshop. Lectures. Valuation.
**Work Stocked and Sold** Cer. Cra. Dec. Dr. Fur. Jew. Pa. Pr. Sc. Tx. Wd.
**Price range** £10–£6,000
For artists see Commercial Gallery Artists.

**▶ Meridian Contemporary Arts** C
13 High Town, Hay-on-Wye, Hereford HR3 5AE.
**Tel** 01497 821 633
**Opening times** Wed–Sat 10–5, Sun 2–5.
**Personnel** Proprietor: Anthea Britnell. Proprietor: Tony Britnell.
**Work Stocked and Sold** App. Cer. Jew.

### MACHYNLLETH

**▶ The Museum Of Modern Art, Wales** PS
Heol Penrallt, Machynlleth, SY20 8AJ.
**Tel** 01654 703 355
**Fax** 01654 702 160
**Email** momawales@tabernac.dircon.co.uk
**Ws** www.tabernac.dircon.co.uk
**Opening times** Mon–Sat 10–4. Admission free.
**Nearest Station** Machynlleth.
**Personnel** Chairman: Ruth Lambert .
**Services and Facilities** Bar. Disabled Access. Friends Society. Gallery space for hire. Parking.
**Work Stocked and Sold** Dr. Pa. Ph. Pr. Sc.
**Price range** £100–£15,000
For artists see Commercial Gallery Artists.
*The Museum Of Modern Art, Wales, forms part of a cultural centre which has grown around a former chapel, The Tabernacle, in the mid-Wales market town of Machynlleth. It has a permanent collection of 20th century British Art including works by Augustus John, Peter Prendergast and Shani Rhys James. Showcase Wales is a semi-permanent exhibition featuring Wales' top artists. MOMA, Wales is particularly vibrant in August when the Tabernacle Art Competition is held in conjunction with The Machynlleth Festival. Admission Free.*

### MONTGOMERY

**▶ Country Works Gallery** C
Broad Street, Montgomery, SY15 6PH.
**Tel** 01686 668 866
**Opening times** Tue–Sat 10–5.30, Sun and bank holidays 2–5.30. Jan–Easter, Wed–Sat 10–5.30.
**Nearest Station** Welshpool.
**Personnel** Directors: Richard Halstead, Clare Halstead.
**Services and Facilities** Craftshop.
**Work Stocked and Sold** Cer. Cra. Dr. Gla. Jew. Pa. Pr. Sc. Tx. Wd.

### NEWTOWN

**▶ Oriel 31, Davies Memorial Gallery** PS
The Park, Newtown, SY16 2NZ.
**Tel** 01686 625 041
**Fax** 01686 623 633
**Email** enquiries@oriel31.org
**Ws** www.oriel31.org
**Opening times** Mon–Sat 10–5.
**Nearest Station** Newtown British Rail.
**Personnel** Director: Amanda Farr. Exhibitions Officer: Sarah Blomfield. Administrator: Helen Lawson. Gallery Assistant: Sam Dignam.
**Services and Facilities** Bookshop. Disabled Access. Friends Society. Lectures. Shop. Workshop Facilities. Admission Free. Wheelchair access.
*The gallery presents a varied and continually changing programme of visual art and craft exhibitions throughout the year, with an emphasis on contemporary art from Wales, and other parts of the U.K. We also show international art. There are two top-lit gallery spaces with a total of 200 sq metres of gallery space.*
*Regular workshops and activities for young people and adults. The gallery shop stocks a wide range of art magazines, catalogues, postcards and greetings cards.*
*Oriel 31 is supported by the Arts Council of Wales.*

### PRESTEIGNE

**▶ The Eagle Gallery**
Broad Street, New Radnor, Presteigne, LD8 2SN.
**Tel** 01544 260 402
**Opening times** Winter opening Thur, Fri, Sat, Sun 10–5. Summer opening Wed, Thur, Fri, Sat, Sun 10–5.
**Personnel** Emily Player.
**Work Stocked and Sold** Cra.

## RHONDDA CYNON TAF

### ABERDARE

**▶ Dare Valley Country Park** PS
Visitor Centre, Aberdare, CF44 7RG.
**Tel** 01685 874 672 **Fax** 01685 882 919
**Opening times** Easter–end Sep daily 9–7. Winter 9–4. Closed Christmas week.
**Personnel** Manager: David Protheroe.
**Services and Facilities** Bar. Café. Disabled Access. Museum Shop. Parking.
**Work Stocked and Sold** Cra.

### PONTYPRIDD

**▶ Oriel y Bont**
University of Glamorgan, Pontypridd, CF37 1DL.
**Tel** 01443 480 480 ext 2568
**Email** asalisbu@glam.ac.uk
**Opening times** Term time only Mon–Fri 9–5.
**Nearest Station** Treforest.
**Personnel** Exhibition Organiser: Alan Salisbury (School of Humanities & Social Science).
**Services and Facilities** Lectures.
**Work Stocked and Sold** Cer. Dr. Pa. Ph. Pr.
**Price range** £250–£5,000
*Gallery in foyer of large building at front of the university campus. Space is roughly octagonal in shape with hanging surfaces 28' in length and 8' in height. Walls provide additional space of approx 20' x 8' also display cases. Sales not a priority. Intention is to provide arena for contemporary visual arts that will inform and extend students' visual and cultural awareness, acting as 'shop window' for institution establishing links with local community. Exhibitors usually give lectures/run workshops relating to exhibition.*

## SWANSEA

### SWANSEA

**▶ Attic Gallery** C
14 Cambrian Place, Swansea SA1 1PQ.
**Tel** 01792 653 387
**Email** roe@atticgallery.co.uk
**Ws** www.atticgallery.co.uk
**Opening times** Tue–Fri 10–5.30, Sat 10–4.30.
**Nearest Station** High Street Station.
**Personnel** Directors: Alexandra Roe, David Roe.
**Services and Facilities** Art Consultancy. Framing.
**Work Stocked and Sold** Cra. Dr. Pa. Pr. Sc.
**Price range** £50–£3,000.

**▶ Glynn Vivian Art Gallery** PS
Alexandra Road, Swansea SA1 5DZ.
**Tel** 01792 655 006 **Fax** 01792 651 713
**Opening times** Tue–Sun 10–5. Admission free.
**Personnel** Curator: Mrs Robin Paisey.
**Services and Facilities** Bookshop. Craftshop. Disabled Access. Friends Society. Lectures. Workshop Facilities.
**Work Stocked and Sold** Cer. Gla. Pa. Sc.

**▶ Oriel Ceri Richards Gallery** PS
Taliesin Arts Centre, University of Wales Swansea, Singleton Park, Swansea SA2 8PZ.
**Tel** 01792 295 526 **Fax** 01792 295 899
**Email** taliesin@swan.ac.uk

**Ws** www.whatsonwales.com
**Opening times** Mon 11–5, Tue 11–6, Sat 12–6.
**Personnel** Marketing Officer: Evaline Heinzl.
**Services and Facilities** Art Consultancy. Bar. Bookshop. Café. Disabled Access. Framing. Friends Society. Museum Shop. Parking. Shop.
**Work Stocked and Sold** Cer. Cra. Dr. Jew. Pa. Pr.

## VALE OF GLAMORGAN

PENARTH

### ▶ Turner House P
Plymouth Road, Penarth, CF64 3DM.
**Tel** 029 2070 8870
**Ws** www.nmgw.ac.uk
**Opening times** Tue–Sun 10–5. Closed Mondays. Opening times only apply during exhibition showings.
**Nearest Station** Penarth.

### ▶ The Washington Gallery PS
1–3 Washington Buildings, Stanwell Road, Penarth, CF64 2AD.
**Tel** 02920 712 100 **Fax** 02920 708 047
**Email** wash-gallery@ukgateway.net
**Ws** www.valeofglamorgan.gov.uk
**Opening times** Mon–Sat 10–6, Sun 1–5.
**Nearest Station** Penarth.
**Personnel** Director: Maggie Knight.
**Services and Facilities** Art Consultancy. Art for Offices. Bar. Bookshop. Café. Commissioning Service. Craftshop. Disabled Access. Friends Society. Gallery space for hire. Lectures. Restoration. Workshop Facilities.
**Work Stocked and Sold** Cer. Dr. Pa. Pr. Sc.
**Price range** £150–£1,500
For artists see Commercial Gallery Artists.

## WREXHAM

WREXHAM

### ▶ Wrexham Arts Centre PS
Rhosddu Road, Wrexham, LL11 1AU.
**Tel** 01978 292 093 **Fax** 01978 292 611
**Email** arts.centre@wrexham.gov.uk
**Opening times** Mon–Fri 9.30–6.45, Sat 9.30–5, Sun closed.
**Nearest Station** Wrexham.
**Personnel** Visual Arts Officer: Tracy Simpson. Cultural & Heritage Officer: Hazel Hawarden. Education Officer: Dawn Parry.
**Services and Facilities** Café. Craftshop. Disabled Access. Lectures. Parking. Workshop Facilities.
**Work Stocked and Sold** Ph.
*Gallery opened 1973 to show contemporary art from Wales, Britain and International. 109 sq. metre main gallery. Foyer craft cases showing contemporary crafts for sale. Gallery 2 shows mainly local artists and groups. Exhibitions for 2001/2002 include Wrexham Print International and the third Wales drawing Biennale.*

# Irish Galleries

*Where this information has been provided, entries are designated 'C' for commercial, 'P' for public gallery or museum or 'PS' for a public gallery or museum holding selling shows*

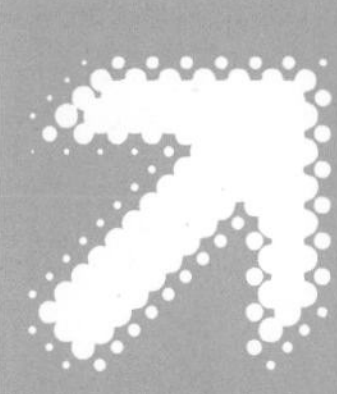

# Ireland

The period of confident expansion in Irish visual art that began with 1991's opening of the Irish Museum of Modern Art has come to a clamorous halt. 2001 saw curatorial and institutional changes that look likely to hold strong influence in the coming years, changes that have been accompanied by broiling rancour and public dissent between artists, curators and institutions.

New regimes at IMMA and at Dublin's Project may yet prove to be helpful in forcing artists to seek new outlets and new ways of connecting with their public. But however positive the future fallout, the arts in Ireland currently languish in what seems like the aftermath of a civil war. Just as the country's political system had begun, belatedly, to escape from what was called 'civil war politics', the question of whose side you were in the curatorial wars of 2001 seemed to be what counted in the visual arts. Were you for or against Declan? Did you sign the petition for Valerie?

Declan McGonagle resigned as Director of IMMA only after he had successfully fought off a campaign by his board to advertise his post. Differences of opinion concerning the role of the museum were blamed for the indecorous tussle that preceded the departure. Unfortunately for those left behind, the large-scale sponsors and donors who had backed McGonagle have now jumped ship. Consequently Ireland's two most important art awards, the Turner-like Glen-Dimplex and the lucrative Nissan Public Art Award, have both been ended.

Project's latest director, Kathy McArdle, arrived at her new job from the theatre. She had, her detractors were quick to point out, no particular knowledge or interest in the visual arts. Given that she was chosen to run perhaps the state's most influential gallery spaces, that always looked like being a problem. When McArdle decided not to renew the contract of Valerie Connor, the woman responsible for Project's visual arts programme, it was enough to mobilise dozens of Ireland's most prominent artists – including Dorothy Cross and Willie Doherty – against McArdle and her policies towards visual art.

Perhaps by this spring, the smell of cordite will have begun to clear. But for the present, the struggle for redefinition of the country's two prime visual art institutions seems easily capable of making focus on the real conversations of art temporarily impossible.

Luke Clancy

## CO. ANTRIM

### BELFAST

**▶ The Bell Gallery**
13 Adelaide Park, Malone Road, Belfast BT9 6FX.
**Tel** 028 9066 2998 **Fax** 028 9038 1524
**Opening times** Mon–Fri 9–5, Sat by appointment.
**Personnel** Director: James Nelson Bell.
**Services and Facilities** Framing. Gallery space for hire.
**Work Stocked and Sold** Dr. Pa. Pr. Sc.

**▶ Catalyst Arts**
5 Exchange Place, Belfast BT1 2NA.
**Tel** 028 9031 3303
**Opening times** Mon–Sat 10–6.
**Personnel** Directors: Síofra Campbell, Derval FitzGerald, Sandra Johnson, Dougal McKenzie, Eilís O' Baoill, Mark Orange, Robert Peters, Karen Vaughan.
**Services and Facilities** Gallery space for hire.
**Work Stocked and Sold** Pa. Ph. Sc.

**▶ Cresent Arts Centre**
2–4 University Road, Belfast BT7 1NT.
**Tel** 028 9024 2338
**Opening times** Mon–Fri 10–5, Sat 11–5.
**Personnel** Administrator: Rhoda MacManus.
**Services and Facilities** Café. Disabled Access.

**▶ The Fenderesky Gallery at Queen's**
5–6 Upper Crescent, Belfast BT7 1NT.
**Tel** 028 9023 5245
**Opening times** Tue–Fri 11.30–5.30, Sat 12–5.
**Personnel** Director: Dr Jamshid Mirfenderesky.
**Work Stocked and Sold** Cer. Dr. Pa. Ph. Pr. Sc.

**▶ The Gallery**
56–60 Dublin Road, Belfast BT2 7HP.
**Tel** 028 9032 1402
**Opening times** Tue–Sat 10–6.
**Services and Facilities** Bookshop. Café. Disabled Access.

**▶ John Magee Ltd**
455–457 Ormeau Road, Belfast BT7 3GQ.
**Tel** 028 9069 3830 **Fax** 028 9049 1009
**Opening times** Mon–Sat 9–5.
**Personnel** Managing Director: R. R. Miller.
**Work Stocked and Sold** Dr. Pa. Pr.

**▶ Old Museum Arts Centre** PS
7 College Square North, Belfast BT1 6AR.
**Tel** 028 9023 5053 **Fax** 028 9032 2912
**Email** info@oldmuseumartscentre.freeserve.co.uk
**Opening times** Mon–Sat 9.30–5.30, 9.30–7.30 on eves when live events occur in theatre.
**Personnel** Director: Anne McReynolds.
**Services and Facilities** Café. Commissioning Service. Guided Tours. Lectures. Workshop Facilities.
**Work Stocked and Sold** Ph. Pr.
**Price range** £250–£5,000

**▶ Ormeau Baths Gallery**
18 A Ormeau Avenue, Belfast BT2 8HS.
**Tel** 028 9032 1402 **Fax** 028 9031 2232
**Opening times** Tue–Sat, 10–5.
**Personnel** Acting Director: Alison Scott.
**Services and Facilities** Bookshop. Disabled Access.

**▶ Proposition Gallery**
Unit 22, North Street, Arcade, Belfast.
**Tel** 02890 234 072

**▶ Ulster Museum** PS
Botanic Gardens, Belfast BT9 5AB.
**Tel** 028 9038 1251/9038 3000
**Fax** 028 9066 5510/9038 3003/9038 3103
**Opening times** Mon–Fri 10–5, Sat 1–5, Sun 2–5.
**Nearest Station** Botanic.
**Personnel** Head of Fine and Applied Art: S. B. Kennedy. Exhibition Organiser: Anne Stewart.
**Services and Facilities** Bookshop. Café. Disabled Access. Friends Society. Guided Tours. Lectures. Museum Shop. Restaurant.

### LISBURN

**▶ Harmony Hill Arts Centre** PS
Clonmore House, 54 Harmony Hill, Lisburn, BT27 4ES.
**Tel** 028 9067 8219
**Fax** 028 9067 8219
**Email** manager.hhac@lisburn.gov.uk
**Ws** www.lisburn.gov.uk
**Opening times** Mon–Fri 9.30am–10pm, Sat 10–4.
**Nearest Station** Lambeg.
**Personnel** Arts Manager: Siobhan Stewart. Arts Centre Organiser: Christina Hurson.
**Services and Facilities** Commissioning Service. Disabled Access. Lectures. Parking. Workshop Facilities.
**Work Stocked and Sold** App. Cer. Cra. Dec. Dr. Fur. Gla. Jew. Pa. Ph. Pr. Sc. Tx. Wd.
**Price range** £30–£3,000

**▶ Seymour Galleries**
20 Seymour Street, Lisburn.
**Tel** 028 9066 2685
**Fax** 028 9066 2685
**Opening times** Mon–Fri 9–1, 2–5, Sat 10–12.
**Personnel** Director: Joan Kirk.
**Services and Facilities** Disabled Access. Parking.
**Work Stocked and Sold** Cer. Pa. Pr.

### PORTRUSH

**▶ Portrush Gallery**
93–95 Main Street, Portrush, BT56 8DA.
**Tel** 01265 823 739
**Personnel** Gabrielle Orok.

### RANDALSTOWN

**▶ Clotworthy Arts Centre**
Antrim Castle Gardens, Randalstown, BT41 4LH.
**Tel** 01849 428 000
**Fax** 01849 460 360
**Opening times** Mon–Fri 10–4.30.
**Personnel** Arts and Heritage Development Officer: Nick Livingston. Arts Assistant: Bertha Walker.
**Services and Facilities** Disabled Access.
**Work Stocked and Sold** Ph.

## CO. ARMAGH

### ARMAGH

**▶ Armagh County Museum** P
The Mall East, Armagh, BT61 9BE.
**Tel** 028 3752 3070 **Fax** 028 3752 2361
**Opening times** Mon–Fri 10–5, Sat 10–1, 2–5.
**Personnel** Curator: Catherine McCullogh.

**▶ Hayloft Gallery** P
Palace Stables Heritage Centre, The Palace Demesne, Armagh, BT60 4EL.
**Tel** 028 3752 9629 **Fax** 028 3752 9630
**Opening times** April–Sep: Mon–Sat 10–5.30, Sun 1–6. Oct–Mar: Mon–Sat 10–5, Sun 2–5.
**Personnel** Supervisor: Debbie Leacock.
**Services and Facilities** Bar. Café. Craftshop. Disabled Access. Gallery space for hire. Guided Tours. Parking. Restaurant.
**Work Stocked and Sold** Cer. Cra. Fur. Jew. Pr. Wd.
**Price range** £0.50–£100
For artists see Commercial Gallery Artists.

### CRAIGAVON

**▶ The Peacock Gallery**
Pinebank House Arts Centre, Tullygally Road, Craigavon, BT65 5BY.
**Tel** 028 3834 1618 **Fax** 028 3834 2402
**Opening times** Mon–Fri 10–1, 2–5; lunch-hour viewing by appointment.
**Personnel** Arts Development Officer: Rosaleen McMullan. Exhibition Organiser: Janni Knox. Exhibition Organiser: Pauline Humphries.
**Services and Facilities** Café. Disabled Access. Parking.

### PORTADOWN

**▶ Roy Edwards Fine Arts Ltd**
Mahon Road, Portadown, BT62 3EH.
**Tel** 028 3833 9116 **Fax** 028 3835 0179
**Opening times** Mon–Fri 9–5.30, evenings 7–9 during special exhibitions.
**Personnel** Directors: R.G. Woolsey, Edward Cassidy.
**Services and Facilities** Disabled Access. Parking.
**Work Stocked and Sold** Dr. Pa. Pr.

## CO. CARLOW

### CARLOW

**▶ Pembroke Studio Gallery**
1 Pembroke, Carlow.
**Tel** 00353 503 41562
**Fax** 00353 503 41562
**Opening times** Mon–Sat 10–6, Sun 2–6.
**Personnel** Proprietor: Bev Carbery.
**Services and Facilities** Disabled Access. Framing. Gallery space for hire. Workshop Facilities.

## CO. CAVAN

### CAVAN

**▶ Cavan County Arts Service**
Cavan County Library, 17 Farnham Street, Cavan.
**Tel** 00353 493 1799



**Ab** Artists' Books **App** Applied Art **Cer** Ceramics **Cra** Craft **Dec** Decorative **Dr** Drawing **Fur** Furniture

**Fax** 00353 496 1565/31384
**Opening times** Cavan: Mon–Fri 9.15–5.15. Bailieborough: Mon 10.30–2, 3–6; Tue, Thu, Fri 10.30–1, 2–5.15; Fri 6–8; Sat 2.30–5.15.
**Personnel** Arts Organiser: Catriona O'Reilly.
**Services and Facilities** Parking.
**Work Stocked and Sold** Pa. Ph.

## CO. CLARE

### BALLYVAUGHAN

#### ▶ Dallán Gallery
Ballyvaughan.
**Tel** 00353 657 7156
**Opening times** Daily 10–7, Mar–Dec; closed Jan–Feb.
**Personnel** Proprietor: Seamus McGuinness. Assistant: Orla McGuinness.
**Services and Facilities** Café. Disabled Access. Parking. Workshop Facilities.

### ENNIS

#### ▶ De Valera Library
Harmony Row, Ennis.
**Tel** 00353 656 821616
**Opening times** Mon, Thu 11–5.30, Tues, Wed, Fri 1–8.
**Personnel** County Arts Officer: Siobhan Mulcahy.
**Services and Facilities** Disabled Access.

### ENNISTYMON

#### ▶ Ennistymon Branch Library
The Square, Ennistymon.
**Tel** 00353 657 1245
**Opening times** Mon, Wed, Fri 11–1, 2.30–5.30, 7–8.30; Tues, Thurs 11–1, 2.30–5.30.
**Personnel** Senior Library Assistant: Brian G. Doyle.
**Services and Facilities** Disabled Access.

### KILSHANNY

#### ▶ The Atlantis Gallery
Caherkinalla, Kilshanny.
**Tel** 00353 657 4270
**Opening times** Wed–Sun 11–6, Mar–Oct, or by appointment.
**Personnel** Directors: Beverley O'Keeffe, William O'Keefe.
**Services and Facilities** Framing.
**Work Stocked and Sold** Pa. Ph. Pr.

## CO. CORK

### CORK

#### ▶ Blackcombe Art Gallery
44a MacCurtain Street, Cork.
**Tel** 00353 215 00040 **Fax** 00353 215 00040
**Opening times** Mon–Sat 10–6.
**Personnel** Director: Luis Poretta.
**Services and Facilities** Framing. Gallery space for hire.

#### ▶ Cork Arts Society Lavitt's Gallery
16 Lavitt's Quay, Cork.
**Tel** 00353 212 77749 **Fax** 00353 212 77749
**Opening times** Tues–Sat 10.30–2, 3–5.30.
**Personnel** Administrator: Charlo Quain.
**Services and Facilities** Gallery space for hire.

#### ▶ Cork Public Museum P
Fitzgerald Park, Mardyke, Cork.
**Tel** 00353 212 70679 **Fax** 00353 212 70931

#### ▶ Crawford Municipal Art Gallery
Emmet Place, Cork.
**Tel** 00353 214 273377
**Fax** 00353 214 805043
**Email** crawfordgallery@eircom.net
**Ws** www.synergy.ie/crawford
**Opening times** Mon–Fri 10–5, Sat 10–4.30.
**Personnel** Curator: Peter Murray. Exhibitions Officer: Anne Boddaert. Exhibition Officer: Dawn Williams. Gallery Secretary: Anne O'Connor. Administrator: Colleen O'Sullivan.
**Services and Facilities** Bookshop. Café. Disabled Access. Friends Society. Guided Tours. Restaurant.
*Located in the heart of the city, the Crawford Municipal Art Gallery is one of Cork's most important public buildings. Amongst the important Irish artists in the collection are James Barry, Nathaniel Grogan, Walter Osborne, Paul Henry, Jack B. Yeats, Harry Clarke and Sean Keating. The collection includes a considerable number of works by contemporary Irish artists, such as Tony O'Malley, Louis le Brocquy, Barrie Cooke and Robert Ballagh. Many of the contemporary artists working in Cork are also represented, including Vivienne Roche, Maud Cotter and James Scanlon. The Crawford Gallery runs a continuing programme of temporary exhibitions, both of Irish and international art.*

#### ▶ Triskel Arts Centre
14 Tobin Street, off South Main Street, Cork.
**Tel** 00353 212 72022/272023
**Fax** 00353 212 75945
**Opening times** Mon–Sat 10.30–5.30.
**Personnel** Director: Elizabeth McAvoy. Visual Arts Coordinator: Fiona Cunningham.
**Services and Facilities** Bookshop. Café. Disabled Access. Gallery space for hire. Restaurant. Workshop Facilities.

### KINSALE

#### ▶ Keane-on-Ceramics
Pier Road, Kinsale.
**Tel** 00353 1 217 74553
**Opening times** Daily 10–4, open late during summer.
**Personnel** Owner: Francis Keane.
**Services and Facilities** Gallery space for hire.

### MACROOM

#### ▶ Vangard Gallery
New Street, Macroom.
**Tel** 00353 264 1198
**Opening times** Mon–Sat 9–6, Sun 2.30–5.30.
**Personnel** Director: John P. Quinlan. Exhibition Organiser: John Philip Murray.
**Work Stocked and Sold** Cer. Pa.

### WEST CORK

#### ▶ O'Kane's Green Gallery
Glengarriff Road, Bantry, West Cork.
**Tel** 00353 275 0003
**Opening times** Mon–Sat 10–6, Jun–Sep; otherwise ask in craftshop next door (same ownership).
**Personnel** Owner: Christine Nicholas.
**Services and Facilities** Disabled Access. Framing.
**Work Stocked and Sold** Pa. Pr. Sc.

#### ▶ West Cork Arts Centre
Skibbereen, West Cork.
**Tel** 00353 282 2090
**Opening times** Mon–Sat 11–5, all year.
**Personnel** Administrator: Jackie Butler.
**Services and Facilities** Bookshop. Disabled Access.

## CO. DERRY

### COLERAINE

#### ▶ Town House Gallery
45 Milburn Road, Coleraine, BT52 1QT.
**Tel** 028 7044 4869
**Opening times** Mon–Sat 9.30–5.30.
**Personnel** Owner: Dale Cuthbert.

### DERRY

#### ▶ Context Gallery
The Playhouse, 5–7 Artillery Street, Derry.
**Tel** 028 7126 4481 **Fax** 028 7126 1884
**Opening times** Tues–Sat 9.30–4.30.
**Personnel** Exhibition Organiser: Hugh Mulholland.
**Services and Facilities** Disabled Access. Parking.

#### ▶ Gordon Galleries
7 London Street, Derry, BT48 6RQ.
**Tel** 028 7137 4044 **Fax** 028 7137 4044
**Opening times** Tues–Sat 11–5.30.
**Personnel** Directors: Richard Gordon, Nat Gordon.
**Services and Facilities** Framing. Shop.
**Work Stocked and Sold** Cra.

#### ▶ Orchard Gallery
Orchard Street, Derry, BT48 6EG.
**Tel** 028 7126 9675 **Fax** 028 7126 7273
**Opening times** Tue–Sat 10–6.
**Personnel** Director: Mr Liam Kelly. Exhibition Organiser: Noreen O'Hare. Administrative Assistant & Education Officer: Jacqueline McFarland & Brendon McMenamin.

### PORTSTEWART

#### ▶ Flowerfield Arts Centre
185 Coleraine Road, Portstewart, BT55 7HV.
**Tel** 028 7083 3959
**Opening times** Mon–Fri 10–1, 2–5, and by appointment.
**Personnel** Organiser: Malcolm Murchison. Secretary: Audrey Henderson.
**Services and Facilities** Café. Parking. Workshop Facilities.

## CO. DONEGAL

### GLEANN CHOLM CILLE

#### ▶ Foras Cultúir Uladh – Ulster Cultural Institute
Gleann Cholm Cille.
**Tel** 00353 733 0248 (Apr–Sep)
**Opening times** Daily 10–8, Apr–Sep.

**Personnel** Administrator: Siobhán Ní Churraighín.
**Services and Facilities** Bookshop. Disabled Access. Parking. Restaurant.

LETTERKENNY

### ▶ Donegal County Arts Service
c/o County Library, Letterkenny.
**Tel** 00353 1 742 1968
**Personnel** Arts Organiser: Traolach Ó Fionnáin.

### ▶ Donegal County Museum P
High Road, Letterkenny.
**Tel** 00353 742 4613
**Opening times** Tue–Fri 11–4.30, Sat 1–4.30.
**Services and Facilities** Disabled Access. Parking. Workshop Facilities.

### ▶ Glebe House and Gallery
Church Hill, Letterkenny.
**Tel** 00353 743 7071 **Fax** 00353 743 7072
**Opening times** Mon–Sun 11–6.30, end May–end Sep, Easter week.
**Personnel** Curator: Chris Wilson.
**Services and Facilities** Bookshop. Café. Parking.

### ▶ Port Gallery
Crossview House, Port Road, Letterkenny.
**Tel** 00353 742 5073
**Opening times** Mon–Sat 10–6.
**Personnel** Owner: John O'Connell.
**Services and Facilities** Framing.
**Work Stocked and Sold** Cra. Dr. Pa. Pr.

## CO. DOWN

BANGOR

### ▶ North Down Visitors and Heritage Centre PS
Town Hall, Castle Park Avenue, Bangor, BT20 4BT.
**Tel** 028 9127 0371 ext 275
**Fax** 028 9127 1370
**Opening times** Tue–Sat 10.30–4.30, Sun 2–4 (open until 5.30 Jul–Aug), bank holiday Mons.
**Nearest Station** Bangor.
**Personnel** Manager: Ian Wilson.
**Services and Facilities** Bookshop. Café. Commissioning Service. Disabled Access. Gallery space for hire. Restaurant.
**Work Stocked and Sold** Cra. Jew. Pr.
**Price range** £5–£30
For artists see Commercial Gallery Artists.

COMBER

### ▶ Salem Gallery
29 Mill Street, Comber.
**Tel** 028 9187 4455
**Opening times** Mon–Sat 11–5; after hours by appointment.
**Personnel** Owner: W.L. Morrison.
**Services and Facilities** Café. Framing. Restaurant.
**Work Stocked and Sold** Dr. Fur. Pa. Pr.

DONAGHADEE

### ▶ The Cleft Art Gallery
3 Market House, New Street, Donaghadee,
**Tel** 028 9188 8502
**Opening times** Mon–Sat 11–5.
**Personnel** Owner: W. L. Morgan.
**Services and Facilities** Café. Disabled Access. Framing. Restaurant.
**Work Stocked and Sold** Dr. Pa. Pr.

DOWNPATRICK

### ▶ Down Arts Centre
2–6 Irish Street, Downpatrick, BT30 6BN.
**Tel** 028 4461 5283 **Fax** 028 4461 6621
**Opening times** Mon, Fri, Sat 10–5, Tue, Thu 10am–10pm, (Jun–Aug Mon–Sat 9–5).
**Personnel** Arts Centre Administrator: Michael McMahon. Arts and Cultural Development Officer: Belinda Loftus. Arts Officer: Rita Byrne.
**Services and Facilities** Café. Disabled Access. Gallery space for hire. Parking.

HILLSBOROUGH

### ▶ Shambles Art Gallery
Dromore Road/Park Lane, Hillsborough.
**Tel** 028 9066 7528 **Fax** 028 9068 1469
**Opening times** By appointment between exhibitions; for opening times, visitors should telephone gallery or check press or Artslink.
**Personnel** Owner: Sheelagh Flanagan.
**Services and Facilities** Framing.
**Work Stocked and Sold** Cer. Pa. Sc.

HOLYWOOD

### ▶ Priory Art Gallery
10 Shore Road, Holywood BT18 9HX.
**Tel** 028 9042 8173/9042 4570
**Opening times** Daily 10–4, except Wed and Sun.
**Personnel** Director: Elizabeth Ballard.
**Services and Facilities** Disabled Access. Framing.
**Work Stocked and Sold** Cra. Pa.

NEWCASTLE

### ▶ Grant Fine Art C
87c Bryansford Road, Newcastle.
**Tel** 028 4372 2349 **Fax** 028 4372 2349
**Opening times** Mon–Sat 2–5 during exhibitions, or by appointment (phone ahead to confirm).
**Personnel** Owner: Margaret Grant.
**Work Stocked and Sold** Dr. Gla. Pa. Pr. Sc.
For artists see Commercial Gallery Artists.

### ▶ Newcastle Art Gallery
18–22 Main Street, Newcastle.
**Tel** 028 4372 3555
**Opening times** Mon–Fri 12–5.30, Sat 12–6, Sun 3–6.
**Personnel** Proprietor: Denis Murphy.
**Services and Facilities** Framing.
**Work Stocked and Sold** Gla. Pa. Sc.

NEWTOWNARDS

### ▶ Ards Arts Centre
Townhall, Conway Square, Newtownards, BT23 4DD.
**Tel** 028 9181 0803 **Fax** 028 9182 3131
**Opening times** Mon–Sat 10–5.
**Nearest Station** Bangor, Co. Down.
**Personnel** Contact: Angela Haley.
**Services and Facilities** Disabled Access. Workshop Facilities.

## CO. DUBLIN

DALKEY

### ▶ The James Gallery
7 Railway Road, Dalkey.
**Tel** 00353 1 285 8703
**Opening times** Tue–Fri 3–10, Sat 3–6, Sun 2–6.
**Personnel** Owner: Pat Hopper.
**Work Stocked and Sold** Pa. Sc.

DUN LAOIGHRE

### ▶ The Arts Office Dun Laoighre
Rathdown Co Council, Marine Rd, Dun Laoighre.
**Tel** 00353 1 205 4719

DUBLIN

### ▶ The Architecture Centre PS
The Royal Institute of the Architects of Ireland, 8 Merrion Square, Dublin 2.
**Tel** 00353 1 676 1703
**Fax** 00353 1 661 0948
**Email** info@riai.ie
**Ws** www.riai.ie
**Opening times** Mon–Fri 9–5; some evenings and weekend openings for special events.
**Nearest Station** Pearse Street.
**Personnel** Events Officer: Jill Gibney.
**Services and Facilities** Bookshop. Gallery space for hire. Lectures.
**Work Stocked and Sold** Ab.
*The Architecture Centre in the RIAI headquarters building, is a permanent public exhibition facility, which showcases the work of international and national architects and artists. Its aim is to make people aware of our architectural heritage, to enrich Ireland's cultural life and to increase public awareness of architecture as social, economic and artistic process.*

### ▶ City Arts Centre PS
23–25 Moss Street, Dublin 2.
**Tel** 00353 1 677 0643
**Fax** 00353 1 677 0131
**Email** cityartscentre@eircom.net
**Ws** http://homepage.eircom.net/-cityarts
**Opening times** 9.15–5.30.
**Nearest Station** Tara Street Dart Station Busaras – main bus depot
**Personnel** Executive Director: Mr Sandy Fitzgerald.
**Services and Facilities** Bar. Café. Disabled Access. Gallery space for hire. Restaurant. Workshop Facilities.
*City Arts Centre 'putting the arts to work for the community in a way that is relevant, practical and exciting'. Founded in 1974, City Arts Centre is located on the River Liffey. Rooted in Dublin's South inner city community, the centre has a wide and varied policy-driven programme which includes performances, exhibitions, publications, debates and an extensive education and training provision. This programme takes place in the Centre's three-storey building housing a venue, gallery, music rehearsal rooms and training workshops, and in the wider community. An important*

*element of these activities are national and international in nature.*

### ▶ Combridge Fine Arts Ltd
Gainboro House, 24 Suffolk Street, Dublin 2.
**Tel** 00353 1 677 4652
**Opening times** Mon–Fri 9.30–5.45, Sat 9.30–5.30.
**Personnel** Managing Director: Brian Sibley.
**Services and Facilities** Framing.
**Work Stocked and Sold** Pa.

### ▶ Crafts Council Gallery
Powerscourt Town House, South William Street, Dublin 2.
**Tel** 00353 1 679 7368
**Fax** 00353 1 679 9197
**Opening times** Mon 10–5, Tue–Sat 10–6.
**Personnel** Gallery Administrator: Mairead MacAnallen. Gallery Assistant: Greg McAteer.

### ▶ Davis Gallery C
11 Capel Street, Dublin 1.
**Tel** 00353 1 872 6969
**Fax** 00353 1 872 5580
**Opening times** Mon–Fri 10–5, Sat 11–5.
**Personnel** Owner: Gerald Davis.
**Services and Facilities** Art Consultancy. Art for Offices. Gallery space for hire.
**Work Stocked and Sold** Cra. Pa. Sc.
**Price range** £50–£3,000
For artists see Commercial Gallery Artists.

### ▶ Designyard
12 East Essex Street, Dublin 2.
**Tel** 00353 1 677 8453/677 8467
**Fax** 00353 1 677 8482
**Opening times** Mon–Sat 10.30–5.30.
**Personnel** Chief Executive: Danae Kindness. Administrator: Cornelia McCarthy. Jewellery Gallery Director: Jackie Blackman.
**Services and Facilities** Gallery space for hire.

### ▶ Douglas Hyde Gallery
Trinity College, Nassau Street, Dublin 2.
**Tel** 00353 1 702 1116
**Fax** 00353 1 677 2694 (attn: DHG)
**Opening times** Mon–Fri 11–6, Thu 11–7, Sat 11–4.45.
**Personnel** Director: John Hutchinson. Education Officer: Janet Pierce-Egan. Administration & Gallery Assistant: Sheila Gorman & Charlotte O'Connor.
**Services and Facilities** Bookshop. Gallery space for hire.

### ▶ Dublin Photographic Centre
10 Lower Camden Street, Dublin 2.
**Tel** 00353 1 660 8513
**Opening times** Sat 11.30–6, otherwise phone to check.
**Personnel** Hon Treasurer, Dublin Camara Club: Eddie Chandler.
**Services and Facilities** Café. Disabled Access. Workshop Facilities.

### ▶ The Gallery of Photography
Meeting House Square, Temple Bar, Dublin 2.
**Tel** 00353 1 671 4654
**Fax** 00353 1 671 4654
**Opening times** Mon–Sat 11–6.
**Personnel** Director: Christine Redmond. Administrator: Patricia Lambe.
**Services and Facilities** Bookshop. Workshop Facilities.

### ▶ Gorry Gallery
20 Molesworth Street, Dublin 2.
**Tel** 00353 1 679 5319
**Fax** 00353 1 679 5319
**Opening times** Mon–Fri 10.30–5.30, Sat 10.30–1.
**Personnel** Exhibition Organiser: James Gorry.
**Services and Facilities** Framing. Gallery space for hire.
**Work Stocked and Sold** Pa.

### ▶ Graphic Studio Dublin Gallery C
Through the Arch, Off Cope Street, Temple Bar, Dublin 2.
**Tel** 00353 1 679 8021
**Fax** 00353 1 679 4575
**Opening times** Mon–Fri 10.30–6, Sat 11–5.
**Personnel** Administrator: Karen O'Connor.
**Services and Facilities** Framing. Gallery space for hire.
**Work Stocked and Sold** Pr.
**Price range** £40–£1,500
For artists see Commercial Gallery Artists.

### ▶ Green on Red Gallery
26–28 Lombard Street East, Dublin 2.
**Tel** 00353 1 671 3414 **Fax** 00353 1 661 3881
**Opening times** Mon–Fri 11–6, Sat 11–3.
**Personnel** Director: Jerome O Drisceoil. Administrator: Alison Scott.
**Services and Facilities** Gallery space for hire.
**Work Stocked and Sold** Pa. Ph. Pr. Sc.

### ▶ Guinness Gallery
Foxrock Village, Dublin 18.
**Tel** 00353 1 289 7955
**Opening times** Mon–Sat 11.30–5.30, Sun 2.30–5.30.
**Personnel** Director: Elizabeth Guinness.
**Services and Facilities** Disabled Access.

### ▶ Hallward Gallery C
64 Merrion Square, Dublin 2.
**Tel** 00353 1 662 1482
**Fax** 00353 1 662 1700
**Email** hallward@indigo.i.e.
**Opening times** Mon–Fri 10.30–5.30, Sat 1–3, or by appointment.
**Nearest Station** Pearse Station.
**Personnel** Directors: Mary Tuohy, Phyllis O'Kane.
**Services and Facilities** Art Consultancy. Art for Offices. Commissioning Service. Gallery space for hire. Parking. Valuation.
**Work Stocked and Sold** Dr. Pa. Pr. Sc. Tx.
**Price range** £100–£1,000
For artists see Commercial Gallery Artists.

### ▶ Hugh Lane Municipal Gallery of Modern Art P
Charlemont House, Parnell Square North, Dublin 1.
**Tel** 00353 1 874 1903 **Fax** 00353 1 872 2182
**Email** info@hughlane.ie
**Ws** www.hughlane.ie
**Opening times** Tue–Thu 9.30–6. Apr–Aug late night opening Thu until 8. Fri–Sat 9.30–5, Sun 11–5. Closed Mon.
**Nearest Station** Connolly.
**Personnel** Director: Barbara Dawson.
**Services and Facilities** Bookshop. Café. Disabled Access. Friends Society. Guided Tours. Lectures.
*The Gallery's collection ranges from the mid-19th century to contemporary art practice and includes artists such as Degas, Morisot, Monet and Jack B. Yeats. The nucleus of the collection was assembled by the late Sir Hugh Lane and it was he who bought Renoir's Les Parapluies and Manet's Concert aux Tuileries for a Gallery of Modern Art in Dublin. The most spectacular recent acquisition is Francis Bacon's 7 Reece Mews studio, donated to the Gallery by John Edwards, together with its entire contents numbering over 7000 items. Drawings, slashed canvases, books and correspondence were among the fascinating items found in the studio. Accompanying the studio is an audio visual room, a micro gallery with touch screen terminals and an exhibition gallery with paintings by Francis Bacon.*

### ▶ Irish Museum Of Modern Art
Royal Hospital, Military Road, Kilmainham, Dublin 8.
**Tel** 00353 1 612 9900
**Fax** 00353 1 612 9999
**Email** info@modernart.ie
**Ws** www.modernart.ie
**Opening times** Tue–Sat 10–5.30, Sun and bank holidays 12.00–5.30. Closed Mon. Admission free.
**Nearest Station** Heuston.
**Personnel** Director and Chief Executive: Declan McGonagle. Senior Curators: Exhibitions: Brenda McParland, Collection: Catherine Marshall, Education & Community: Helen O'Donoghue.
**Services and Facilities** Bookshop. Café. Disabled Access. Friends Society. Gardens, Guided Tours, Heritage Video. Lectures. Parking. Workshop Facilities.
*The Irish Museum of Modern Art is Ireland's leading national institution for the collection and presentation of modern contemporary art. The museum is housed in the magnificent 17th-century Royal Hospital Kilmainham, which includes a formal garden, meadows and medieval burial grounds. The museum presents a wide variety of art in a dynamic programme of exhibitions, which regularly includes bodies of works from the museum's own Collection and its award-winning Education and Community Department. It also creates more widespread access to art and artists through its Studio and National Programmes.*

### ▶ Kerlin Gallery C
Anne's Lane, South Anne Street, Dublin 2.
**Tel** 00353 1 670 9093
**Fax** 00353 1 670 9096
**Email** gallery@kerlin.ie
**Ws** www.kerlin.ie
**Opening times** Mon–Fri 10–5.45, Sat 11–4.30.
**Personnel** Directors: John Kennedy, David Fitzgerald. Kirsten Dunne. Marion Keogh.
**Services and Facilities** Art Consultancy.
**Work Stocked and Sold** Pa. Ph. Pr. Sc.
For artists see Commercial Gallery Artists.

### ▶ Milmo-Penny Fine Art Ltd C
55 Ailesbury Road, Ballsbridge, Dublin 4.
**Tel** 00353 1 269 3486
**Fax** 00353 1 283 0414

**Email** finearts@indigo.ie
**Opening times** By appointment.
**Nearest Station** Sydney Parade.
**Personnel** Director: Dominic Milmo-Penny.
**Services and Facilities** Art Consultancy. Art for Offices. Framing. Restoration.
**Work Stocked and Sold** Dr. Pa. Sc.
**Price range** £500–£5,000
For artists see Commercial Gallery Artists.

### ▶ National Gallery of Ireland
Merrion Square West, Dublin 2.
**Tel** 00353 1 661 5133
**Fax** 00353 1 661 5372
**Email** artgall@eircom.net
**Ws** www.nationalgallery.ie
**Opening times** Mon–Sat 9.30–5.30, Thu 9.30–8.30, Sun 2–5. Closed Dec 24–6 and Good Friday. Admission free.
**Nearest Station** Pearse station, Westland Row.
**Personnel** Director: Raymond Keaveney. Keeper & Head of Education: Marie Bourke. Keeper of the Collection: Sergio Benedetti. Keeper of Conservation: Andrew O'Connor.
**Services and Facilities** Bookshop. Café. Disabled Access. Friends Society. Gallery space for hire. Guided Tours. Lectures. Museum Shop. Restaurant.
*The National Gallery of Ireland was established by an Act of Parliament in 1854 and opened to the public in 1864 (architect, Francis Fowke). A new 40,000 sq ft wing (architects, Benson & Forsyth) opened in Autumn 2001. There are over 13,000 items in the Gallery's collection; 3,000 oil paintings, 5,000 watercolours and drawings, the remainder, prints and sculpture.*
*It houses a prestigious collection of European masterpieces dating from the 14th to the 20th century; Fra Angelico, Mantegna, Caravaggio, Vermeer, Rembrandt, Ruysdael; Zurbarán, Goya, Picasso; Rubens, Jordaens, van Dyck; Poussin, Cézanne, Degas; Hogarth, Gainsborough, Reynolds. It also houses an important historic collection of Irish paintings (17th to 20th Century) with works by Thomas Roberts, Nathaniel Hone the Elder and Younger, Hugh Douglas Hamilton, James Barry, Daniel Maclise, Sarah Purser, Roderic O'Conor, William Leech, Paul Henry, William Orpen, John Lavery and Jack B. Yeats. Exhibition and Education Programme, Friends of the National Gallery.*

### ▶ New Apollo Gallery C
18 Duke Street, Dublin 2.
**Tel** 00353 1 671 2609
**Fax** 00353 1 679 7558
**Opening times** Mon–Fri 11–6, Sat 10–6, Sun 12–6.
**Personnel** Owner: Hugh Charlton.
**Services and Facilities** Disabled Access. Framing.
**Work Stocked and Sold** Dr. Pa. Pr. Sc.

### ▶ Oisín Art Gallery
44 Westland Row, Dublin 2.
**Tel** 00353 1 661 1315
**Fax** 00353 1 661 0464
**Email** donal@oisingallery.com
**Ws** www.oisingallery.com
**Opening times** Mon–Fri 9–5.30, Sat 10–5.30.
**Personnel** Director: Donal McNeela.
**Services and Facilities** Disabled Access. Framing.
**Work Stocked and Sold** Dr. Pa. Sc.

### ▶ Oriel Gallery
17 Clare Street, Dublin 2.
**Tel** 00353 1 676 3410
**Opening times** Mon–Fri 10–5.30, Sat 10.30–1.
**Personnel** Director: Oliver Nulty.
**Services and Facilities** Framing.
**Work Stocked and Sold** Dr. Pa. Sc.

### ▶ The Project Arts Centre
39 East Essex Street, Temple Bar, Dublin 2.
**Tel** 00353 1 671 2321
**Fax** 00353 1 671 3327
**Opening times** Mon–Sat 11–6.
**Services and Facilities** Café. Disabled Access.

### ▶ Royal Hibernian Academy PS
Gallagher Gallery 15 Ely Place, Dublin 2.
**Tel** 00353 1 661 2558
**Fax** 00353 1 661 0762
**Email** rhagallery@eircom.net
**Ws** www.royalhibernianacademy.com
**Opening times** 10–5 Tue–Sat 2–5 Sun. Thurs late opening until 8. Admission to the gallery is free as are regular tours of current exhibitions.
**Personnel** Director: Patrick T. Murphy. Exhibitions Officer: Ruth Carroll. Academy Officer: Ella Wilkinson.
**Services and Facilities** Disabled Access. Friends Society. Gallery space for hire. Guided Tours. Lectures.
*The Royal Hibernian Acadamy, established in 1823, occupies a unique place in Irish Art. An artist-led organisation it is run by artists for artists. The Academy seeks to foster both traditional strengths along with innovatory practice. The exhibition programme reflects this commitment, ranging from the tradition of its Annual Exhibition to internationally based contemporary forms including new media and installation. The Academy shows work from leading Irish and international artists including Cho Duck Hyun, Leonardo Drew, Charles Tyrell, Siobhan Hapaska and Richard Gorman.*

### ▶ Rubicon Gallery C
1st Floor, 10 St Stephens Green, Dublin 2.
**Tel** 00353 1 670 8055
**Fax** 00353 1 670 8057
**Email** rubi@iol.ie
**Opening times** Mon–Sat 11–5.30.
**Nearest Station** Grafton Street
**Personnel** Director: Josephine Kelliher.
**Services and Facilities** Art Consultancy. Art for Offices. Commissioning Service. Framing. Gallery space for hire. Valuation.
**Work Stocked and Sold** Dr. Pa. Pr. Sc.
**Price range** £400–£20,000
For artists see Commercial Gallery Artists.

### ▶ The Solomon Gallery C
Powerscourt Town House, South William Street, Dublin 2.
**Tel** 00353 1 679 4237
**Fax** 00353 1 671 5262
**Email** solomon@indigo.ie
**Ws** www.solomongallery.com
**Opening times** Mon–Sat 10–5.30.
**Personnel** Owner: Suzanne MacDougald. Director: Tara Murphy.
**Services and Facilities** Art Consultancy. Art for Offices. Commissioning Service. Disabled Access. Export valuation.
**Work Stocked and Sold** Dr. Gla. Pa. Sc.
**Price range** £50–£10,000
For artists see Commercial Gallery Artists.
*The Solomon Gallery was established in 1981 and is situated in the original drawing-room of an 18th-century Georgian townhouse formerly owned by Lord Powerscourt. Now considered one of Ireland's leading contemporary art galleries, the Solomon has built its reputation on representing Irish and international painters and sculptors working primarily in a figurative style. The Solomon Gallery also deals in fine Irish period paintings and sculpture. Exhibitions are mounted every three to four weeks. Artists include: Martin Mooney, Rowan Gillespie, Brian Ballard, Hector McDonnell, John Bellany, Sarah Spackman, Elizabeth Cope and Peter Collis RHA.*

### ▶ Taylor Galleries
34 Kildare Street, Dublin 2.
**Tel** 00353 1 676 6055
**Fax** 00353 1 676 8305
**Opening times** Mon–Fri 10–5.30, Sat 11–1.
**Personnel** Directors: John Taylor, Patrick Taylor.
**Work Stocked and Sold** Dr. Pa. Pr. Sc.

### ▶ Temple Bar Gallery & Studios PS
5–9 Temple Bar, Dublin 2.
**Tel** 00353 1 671 0073
**Fax** 00353 1 677 7527
**Email** tbgs@indigo.ie
**Opening times** Tue–Sat 11–6 (Thu until 7), Sun 2–6.
**Personnel** Curator: Vaari Claffey. Press and Personnel: Declan Long.
**Services and Facilities** Art Consultancy. Art for Offices. Commissioning Service. Disabled Access. Friends Society. Guided Tours. Lectures.
**Work Stocked and Sold** Dr. Pa. Ph. Sc.
**Price range** £10–£10,000
*Temple Bar Gallery and Studios is located in the centre of Dublin's cultural quarter. The building contains a gallery, an atrium exhibition space on three floors and 29 artist's studios. The work selected and exhibited is by emerging and established contemporary artists. Artist-curated shows are regularly facilitated. Ancillary programming supports artist-led initiatives inside and outside the TBG&S space and provides a forum for artists and curators through debates and discussions on contemporary arts issues.*
*Three studios are reserved for artists working on specific short-term projects and international residencies. Studio members are open to international studio exchanges.*
*TBG&S is also host to 'Multiples', an ongoing exhibition which commissions artworks from established and emerging artists. The work is also sold through mail order and the Internet. The work commissioned is updated every six months, providing a varied and affordable way to build a collection of contemporary art. Featured artists include Bank, Billy Childish, Martin Creed, Jeremy Deller, Peter Doig, Jim Lambie, Elizabeth Peyton, Bob and Roberta Smith.*

### ▶ Wyvern Gallery
2 Temple Lane, Temple Bar, Dublin 2.
**Tel** 00353 1 679 9589
**Opening times** Mon–Fri 10–6, Sat 11–5.
**Personnel** Owner: Terry Carroll.
**Work Stocked and Sold** Dr. Pa. Ph. Pr. Sc.

HOWTH

### ▶ Howth Harbour Gallery
6 Abbey Street, Howth.
**Tel** 00353 1 839 3366
**Opening times** Wed–Sun 2–7.
**Personnel** Director: Phyllis Geraci.
**Work Stocked and Sold** Dr. Pa. Pr.

SKERRIES

### ▶ Village Art Gallery
Thomas Hand Street, Skerries.
**Tel** 00353 1 849 2236
**Opening times** Tue–Sat 10–5.30, Sun 2.30–5.30.
**Personnel** Director: Emer Mullins.
**Services and Facilities** Commissioning Service.
**Work Stocked and Sold** Dr. Pa. Pr. Tx.

## CO. GALWAY

CONNEMARA

### ▶ An Dánlann
Casla, Connemara.
**Tel** 00353 917 2141
**Opening times** Mon–Fri 10.30–6, Sat, Sun 1–6.
**Personnel** Owner: Marion, Nic, Con Lomaire.
**Services and Facilities** Café. Disabled Access.
**Work Stocked and Sold** Pa. Sc.

GALWAY

### ▶ Galway Arts Centre
47 Dominick Street, (also 23 Nun's Island, Galway), Galway.
**Tel** 00353 915 65886
**Opening times** Mon–Sat 10–5.30.
**Personnel** Director: Michael Diskin.
**Services and Facilities** Disabled Access. Workshop Facilities.

### ▶ The Kenny Gallery
High Street, Galway.
**Tel** 00353 916 1014/61021
**Fax** 00353 916 8544
**Opening times** Mon–Sat 9–6.
**Personnel** Directors: Tom Kenny, Conor Kenny.
**Services and Facilities** Bar. Bookshop.
**Work Stocked and Sold** Ab. Cer. Dr. Gla. Pa. Ph. Pr. Sc. Wd.

OUGHTERARD

### ▶ West Shore Gallery
Camp Street, Oughterard.
**Tel** 00353 918 2562
**Opening times** Mon–Sat 10–6, Sun 1–5 May–Sep.
**Personnel** Exhibition Organiser: Peter Connelly. Exhibition Organiser: Kathleen Furey.
**Services and Facilities** Disabled Access. Framing.

## CO. KERRY

KILLARNEY

### ▶ The Frank Lewis Gallery
6 Bridewell Lane, Killarney.
**Tel** 00353 643 1108/34843 – after hours 00353 643 1734 **Fax** 00353 643 1570
**Opening times** Mon–Sat 9–6, Sun by appointment.
**Personnel** Director: Frank Lewis. Administrator: Mary O'Shea.
**Services and Facilities** Café. Disabled Access. Framing. Guided Tours. Lectures.
**Work Stocked and Sold** Cer. Pa. Ph. Pr. Sc. Tx. Wd.

### ▶ The Killarney Art Gallery
4 Plunkett Street, Killarney.
**Tel** 00353 643 4628
**Opening times** Mon–Sat 11–1, 2–6; also 8.30pm–10pm Apr–Sep.
**Personnel** Proprietor: Declan Mulvany.
**Services and Facilities** Framing.
**Work Stocked and Sold** Pa.

TRALEE

### ▶ Bín Bán Gallery
124 Lower Rock Street, Tralee.
**Tel** 00353 662 2520
**Opening times** Mon–Sat 9–6, Sun by appointment.
**Personnel** Owner: Helen Shanahan.
**Services and Facilities** Framing.
**Work Stocked and Sold** Cer. Pa. Pr. Sc. Tx.

### ▶ The Wellspring Gallery
16 Denny Street, Tralee.
**Tel** 00353 662 1218 **Fax** 00353 662 3870
**Opening times** Mon–Sat 10–6, or by appointment.
**Personnel** Owner: Louise O'Donnell.
**Services and Facilities** Framing. Gallery space for hire.
**Work Stocked and Sold** App. Cer. Pa. Pr. Sc. Tx.

## CO. KILDARE

KILCOCK

### ▶ Kilcock Art Gallery
School Street, Kilcock.
**Tel** 00353 628 7619/628 8586/ 00353 885 78283
**Opening times** Mon–Fri 10–4, Sat 2–5, and by appointment.
**Personnel** Proprietor: Breda Smyth.
**Services and Facilities** Commissioning Service. Disabled Access.
**Work Stocked and Sold** App.

## CO. KILKENNY

KILKENNY

### ▶ Butler Gallery PS
The Castle, Kilkenny.
**Tel** 00353 566 1106 **Fax** 00353 567 0031
**Email** butlrgal@indigo.ie
**Ws** www.Butlergallery.com
**Opening times** Oct–Mar Tue–Sun 10.30–5. Apr–May Tue–Sun 10–5. Jun–Sep daily 10–7.
**Nearest Station** Kilkenny.
**Services and Facilities** Bookshop. Café. Friends Society. Guided Tours. Lectures.

## CO. LEITRIM

CARRICK-ON-SHANNON

### ▶ Old Barrel Store Arts Centre
The Quays, Carrick-on-Shannon.
**Tel** 00353 782 0911/after hours 00353 784 2093
**Opening times** Daily 10.30–6.
**Personnel** Exhibition Organiser: David Knight. Exhibition Organiser: Sandra Vernon.
**Services and Facilities** Workshop Facilities.

## CO. LIMERICK

LIMERICK

### ▶ Belltable Arts Centre
69 O'Connell Street, Limerick.
**Tel** 00353 1 613 19866
**Opening times** Mon–Sat 10–6; theatre until 11pm.
**Personnel** Director: Mary Coll. Gallery Assistant: Niall Kingston.
**Services and Facilities** Framing. Restaurant.

### ▶ Chris Doswell's Gallery
The Basement, 28 Mallow Street, Limerick.
**Tel** 00353 613 18292
**Opening times** Mon–Fri 9–5.30, Sat 10.30–2.30.
**Personnel** Exhibition Organiser: Chris Doswell.
**Work Stocked and Sold** Pr.

### ▶ Dolmen Gallery
Honan's Quay, Limerick.
**Tel** 00353 614 17929
**Opening times** Mon–Sat 10–6.
**Personnel** Administrator: Helen O'Donnell. Administrator: Rachel Murphy.
**Services and Facilities** Café. Craftshop. Shop.

### ▶ Limerick City Gallery of Art
Pery Square, Limerick.
**Tel** 00353 613 10633 **Fax** 00353 614 15266
**Opening times** Mon–Fri 10–1, 2–5 (Thurs 2–7); Sat 10–1.
**Personnel** Director: Paul M. O'Reilly.
**Services and Facilities** Bookshop. Café. Workshop Facilities.

### ▶ Muse Gallery
75 O'Connell Street, Limerick.
**Tel** 00353 613 14699
**Opening times** Mon–Sat 10–5.30, Sun 2.30–5.
**Personnel** Proprietor: Gerard Ryan.
**Services and Facilities** Gallery space for hire.

### ▶ University of Limerick – AV Gallery P
Plassey Technology Park, University of Limerick, Limerick.
**Tel** 00353 61 202040 **Fax** 00353 61 202938
**Email** David.Lilburn@ul.ie.
**Opening times** Daily 8am–10pm.
**Personnel** Exhibition Organiser: David Lilburn.
**Services and Facilities** Disabled Access. Parking.

**Work Stocked and Sold** Ab. Dr. Pa. Pr.
**Price range** £100–£1,000
For artists see Commercial Gallery Artists.

## CO. LONGFORD

LONFORD

### ▶ Carroll Gallery

6 Keon's Terrace, Lonford.
**Tel** 00353 434 1148
**Opening times** Mon–Fri 9.30–5.30, Sat, Sun by appointment.
**Personnel** Director: Kevin Carroll. Assistant: Rose Dennigan.
**Services and Facilities** Disabled Access.
**Work Stocked and Sold** Cer. Dr. Pa. Pr. Sc.

## CO. LOUTH

CARLINGFORD

### ▶ Artistic License

The Old Coach House, Dundalk Street, Carlingford.
**Tel** 00353 417 3745
**Fax** 00353 427 3745
**Opening times** Tue–Sun 12–7; spring, summer.
**Personnel** Exhibition Organiser: P. Mussen.
**Services and Facilities** Framing.

DUNDALK

### ▶ The Basement Gallery

The Town Hall, Dundalk.
**Tel** 00353 423 2276
**Fax** 00353 423 6171
**Opening times** Mon–Fri 10–12.45, 1.45–5; Sat 10–1.
**Personnel** Art Organiser: Brian Harten.

### ▶ County Museum Dundalk P

Jocelyn Street, Dundalk.
**Tel** 00353 1 422 7056/27057
**Fax** 00353 1 422 7058
**Opening times** Tue–Sat 10.30–5.30, Sun 2–6.
**Personnel** Curator: Carol Gleeson.
**Services and Facilities** Disabled Access. Gallery space for hire. Parking.

## CO. MAYO

ACHILL ISLAND

### ▶ Western Light Art Gallery

The Sandybanks, Keel, Achill Island.
**Tel** 00353 984 3325 **Fax** 00353 984 3325
**Opening times** Daily 10–6.
**Personnel** Exhibitions Organiser: Seán Cannon.
**Services and Facilities** Disabled Access. Parking.
**Work Stocked and Sold** Cra. Pa. Ph. Pr. Sc.

CLAREMORRIS

### ▶ Claremorris Gallery

James Street, Claremorris.
**Tel** 00353 947 1348
**Opening times** Tues, Wed, Fri, Sat 12–5, during summer; and during exhibitions at other times of year.
**Personnel** Director: Patricia Noone.
**Services and Facilities** Framing.
**Work Stocked and Sold** Dr. Pa. Pr. Sc.

## CO. MONAGHAN

MONAGHAN

### ▶ Market House Gallery

Tourist Office, Market House, Monaghan.
**Tel** 00353 478 1122
**Opening times** Mon–Fri 9–1, 2–5, Sep–May; Mon–Fri 9–5, Sat 9–1, 2–5, Jun–Aug.
**Personnel** Somhairle MacConghail, Monaghan County Council 00 353 478 2211.

### ▶ Monaghan County Museum P

1–2 Hill Street, Monaghan.
**Tel** 00353 1 478 2928
**Opening times** Tue–Sat 11–1, 2–5.
**Personnel** Curator: Patrick Long.
**Services and Facilities** Disabled Access. Workshop Facilities.

## CO. SLIGO

RIVERSTOWN

### ▶ Taylor's Art Gallery

Taunagh, Riverstown.
**Tel** 00353 716 5138
**Fax** 00353 716 5138
**Opening times** Mon–Fri 9–6, or by appointment.
**Personnel** Owner: Alec Taylor.
**Services and Facilities** Disabled Access. Framing. Gallery space for hire. Parking.
**Work Stocked and Sold** Pa. Pr. Sc.

SLIGO

### ▶ Sligo Art Gallery

Yeats Memorial Building, Hyde Bridge, Sligo.
**Tel** 00353 714 5847 **Fax** 00353 716 2301
**Opening times** Mon–Sat 10–5.30.
**Personnel** Director: Ronan MacEvilly.
**Services and Facilities** Gallery space for hire.

## CO. TIPPERARY

BIRDHILL

### ▶ The Lucy Erridge Gallery

Birdhill.
**Tel** 00353 613 79366
**Fax** 00353 613 02459
**Opening times** Mon–Sat 10.30–5.30, Sun 1.30–5.30, closed Tue.
**Personnel** Exhibition Organiser: Lucy Erridge. Exhibition Organiser: Pauline Quigley.
**Work Stocked and Sold** Cer. Cra. Jew. Tx. Wd.

## CO. WESTMEATH

ATHLONE

### ▶ Dolan Moore Gallery

33 Church Street, Athlone.
**Tel** 00353 902 78507
**Opening times** Mon–Fri 9.30–6, Sat 10.30–5.30.
**Personnel** Director: Amy Moore.
**Work Stocked and Sold** Dr. Pa. Pr. Sc.

## CO. WEXFORD

BUNCLODY

### ▶ The Chantry Gallery

Bunclody.
**Tel** 00353 547 7482
**Opening times** By appointment only.
**Personnel** Owner: Betty Craig.
**Work Stocked and Sold** Cer. Dr. Pa. Pr. Sc.

GOREY

### ▶ Woodland Arts & Crafts Gallery

Tinnock, Gorey.
**Tel** 00353 402 37474
**Opening times** Mon–Sat 12–6, Sun 2–6.
**Personnel** Artistic Director: Michael G. Murphy.
**Services and Facilities** Café. Disabled Access. Framing. Gallery space for hire. Workshop Facilities.
**Work Stocked and Sold** Cer. Cra. Pa. Pr. Sc. Wd.

WEXFORD

### ▶ Wexford Arts Centre

Cornmarket, Wexford.
**Tel** 00353 1 532 3764/24544
**Opening times** Mon–Sat 10–6.
**Personnel** Artistic Director: Denis Collins.
**Services and Facilities** Restaurant.

## CO. WICKLOW

BRAY

### ▶ Craft Art Gallery

74 Main Street, Bray.
**Tel** 00353 286 6728
**Opening times** Tues–Sat 10–1, 2–6.
**Personnel** Owner: Jean Colohan.
**Services and Facilities** Framing. Gallery space for hire. Workshop Facilities.

### ▶ The Hangman Gallery

2 Westbourne Terrace, Quinnsborough Road, Bray.
**Tel** 00353 286 6208 **Fax** 00353 286 6207
**Opening times** Mon–Sat 11–5.30.
**Personnel** Owner: Val Byrne.
**Services and Facilities** Framing.
**Work Stocked and Sold** Cer. Pa. Pr. Sc. Wd.

WICKLOW

### ▶ Renaissance III Gallery

County Buildings, Wicklow.
**Tel** 00353 1 404 67324
**Fax** 00353 1 404 67792
**Opening times** Mon–Fri 9–5.
**Personnel** Coordinator: Brendan O'Connor.
**Services and Facilities** Café. Disabled Access. Parking.

# Crafts

# Crafts

The crafts make up a diverse and vibrant sector of the creative industries. In the recent Creative Industries Mapping Document produced by the Department of Culture, Media and Sport in 2001, it was estimated that there were around 23,700 people working in the crafts in 2000. Since the early 1970s The Crafts Council has been the organisation supporting and promoting the crafts, giving it a clearer identity in the public's mind. This has been achieved through a variety of services and activities including exhibitions, retail, *Crafts Magazine*, educational activities and research, Chelsea Crafts Fair and the development of Photostore, an image database of craft work.

What is now evident is that craft is no longer an enclave of artistic activity that relates only to itself, but now forms a central part of the visual arts. Not only is the artistic credibility of craft work well established, but the dated arguments surrounding the divide between the arts and the crafts no longer hold water when much of the innovative work now being produced belies easy categorisation in either camp.

The idea of 'art' as being something identified by invisible social relation and institutional presentation, has left the idea of the 'art object' free to merge with ideas of the 'craft object'. The material culture of aesthetic objects has passed over to craft activity while its lessening importance in recent art activity has given room for extensions of context and meaning in craft work. The conceptual problems created by this are probably in direct relation to the creative freedom it has afforded. Theory follows practice and fortunately craft practice is not limited by problems of categorisation. Indeed, the current scene is openly transgressive of them. The increased aesthetic range of craft work is reflected in the fact that many galleries and museums are exhibiting craft as an integral part of their visual art programmes and several are collecting significant works for their permanent collections.

The level of interest by those enrolled in courses in crafts is indicative of the attractiveness of the sector as a creative profession. In 1998/99 a total of 448 students were enrolled in higher education crafts courses alone. The international reputation of British Crafts is almost certain to continue to develop as it is already established as a rich source of innovative practice and ideas.

This is certainly an exciting and dynamic time for the crafts.

Janet Barnes
Director
Crafts Council

**▶ Alan Vallis@OXO**
209 OXO Tower Wharf, Bargehouse Street, London SE1 9PH.

**▶ The Appledore Crafts Company**
5 Bude Street, Appledore, Bideford, EX32 1PS
**Tel** 01237 423 547

**▶ Art and Design Movement**
4 New Station Street, Leeds LS1 5DL.

**▶ Art in Action**
Waterperry, near Wheatley, Oxon OX33 1JZ.
**Tel** 01844 338 085

**▶ Artemidorus**
27b Half Moon Lane, London SE24 9JU.
**Tel** 020 737 7747

**▶ Artful Expression**
23/24 Warstone Lane, Hockley, Birmingham B75 6NA.
**Tel** 0121 212 0430

**▶ Artifex Gallery** C
Unit 7, The Hungry House Craft Centre, Weeford Road, Sutton Coldfield, B7S 6NA.
**Tel** 0121 323 3776 **Fax** 0121 323 3776

**▶ The Arts Shed Craft Workshop**
2 Collswell Lane, Blakesley, Towcester, NN12 8RB.

**▶ Bay Tree Gallery**
26 West Street, Alresford, near Winchester, SO24 9AT.
**Tel** 01962 735 8888

**▶ The Beacons Pottery and Gallery**
The Old School House, Defynnog, Brecon, LD3 8SU.
**Tel** 01874 638 919, Home 015504619
**Opening times** Easter to Christmas, Tue, Wed, Thu & Sun 10–5.
**Personnel** Colin Horsman. Carole Longhurst.
**Services and Facilities** Workshop Facilities.
**Work Stocked and Sold** Cer. Pa. Ph. Pr.

**▶ The Beetroot Tree**
South Street, Draycott, DE72 3PP.

**▶ The Bell Street Gallery**
17 Bell Street, Shaftesbury, Dorset, SP7 8AR.

**▶ Bircham Contemporary Arts**
14 Market Place, Holt, NR25 66BW.
**Tel** 01263 713 312

**▶ Booth House Gallery and Pottery**
3 Booth House, Holmfirth, Huddersfield.
**Tel** 01484 685 270

**▶ Bottle Kiln Gallery**
High Lane East, West Hallam, Ilkeston, DE7 6HP.
**Tel** 0115 932 9442
**Personnel** Charles Stone.

**▶ Bowie & Hulbert**
5 Market Street, Hay on Wye, HR3 5AF.

**▶ Bridget Wheatley Contemporary Jewellery** C
38 Cowley Road, Oxford OX4 1HZ.
**Tel** 01865 722 184 **Fax** 01865 790 858
**Ws** www.bridgetwheatley.com
**Opening times** Tue–Sat 10–5.30.
**Personnel** Assistant Buyer: Helen Musselwhite.
**Work Stocked and Sold** Jew.
**Price range** £10–£1200
*The shop is twenty minutes' walk from oxford City centre on the increasingly popular and vibrant Cowley Road. It is a light and airy showroom for the work of many designer/makers, alongside Bridget's own ranges of unique jewellery. Bridget opened her shop in October 2000. There is a welcoming atmosphere within a working environment. The shop is a haven of creativity and innovation, even the displays, made on the premises, are original. The jewellery is from an eclectic group of artists. It is diverse in design and materials. The individuality of each designer is immediately striking. The collections continue to evolve.*

**▶ Burford Woodcraft** C
144 High Street, Burford, OX18 4QU.
**Tel** 01993 823 479
**Email** enquiries@burford-woodcraft.co.uk
**Ws** www.burford-woodcraft.co.uk
**Opening times** Mon–Sat 9.30–5.00 Sun 11–4.45. Sun mid-Feb–Christmas.
**Personnel** Partner: Mrs Jayne Lewin. Partner: Mr Robert Lewin.
**Services and Facilities** Commissioning Service. Craftshop.
**Work Stocked and Sold** Cra. Fur. Jew. Sc. Wd.
**Price range** £5–£10,000
For artists see Commercial Gallery Artists.
*Burford Woodcraft is one of only a handful of galleries specializing in wood. Here contemporary British craftsmanship has been successfully promoted for over twenty years. The skill and talent displayed encompasses the unusual, the creative, and the practical. The natural beauty and diversity of the wood, the smell and the unique touch bind the extensive collection together through carving, furniture making, sculpting and turning. The one-off pieces, furniture, mirrors, sculptures, jewellery, bowls and platters coexist with boxes, desk and kitchen ware, jewellery boxes, small accessories, games, toys and more. Commissions are welcomed and regularly sought. An exhibition is held each Autumn.*

**▶ Bury St Edmund's Art Gallery** PS
The Market Cross, Bury St Edmund's, IP33 1BT.
**Tel** 01284 762 081
**Fax** 01284 750 74
**Email** enquiries@burysted-artgall.org
**Ws** www.burysted-artgall.org
**Opening times** Tue–Sat 10.30–5.
**Personnel** Director: Barbara Taylor. Gallery Manager: Barbara Murray.
**Services and Facilities** Craftshop. Friends Society. Lectures. Shop. Workshop Facilities.
*Housed on the first floor of a magnificent grade one listed Adam building and playing a key role for visual arts in the region, the gallery presents a changing programme of contemporary fine art and craft exhibitions. The gallery has built an international reputation for its work in art textiles and a strong position in promoting craft practice. It curates exhibitions that tour nationally. The Crafts Council listed shop sells work by both leading British makers and emerging talent. Run as an educational charitable trust, the gallery's mission is to increase public awareness and enjoyment of art.*

**▶ Cedar House Craft Shop & Gallery**
Main Street, Peatling Pava, Lutterworth, LE17 5QA.
**Personnel** Jet Shackleton.

**▶ The Chapel Gallery, The National Trust** C
Saltram House, Plympton, Plymouth PL7 1UH.
**Tel** 01752 347 852 **Fax** 01752 347 852
**Email** dsargx@smtp.ntrust.org.uk
**Ws** www.chapelgallery@hotmail.com
**Opening times** Apr–Nov: 10.30–5 daily (except Fri & Sat). Nov–Dec: 11.30–4.30 (closed Fri). Jan: please call. Feb–Mar: 11.30–4 weekends only.
**Nearest Station** Plymouth.
**Personnel** Gallery Manager: Rebecca Green.
**Services and Facilities** Commissioning Service. Craftshop. Disabled Access. Parking. Workshop Facilities.
**Work Stocked and Sold** Ab. Cer. Cra. Dec. Dr. Fur. Gla. Jew. Pa. Pr. Sc. Tx. Wd.
**Price range** £1–£30,000
For artists see Commercial Gallery Artists.

***Blandine Anderson,* Moon Gazing Hares, *stoneware, 35.5 x 30.5 cm, January 2001, £295.***
*The Chapel Gallery is based in a converted Chapel and is set within the idyllic Historic Gardens of The National Trust property Saltram House. The Chapel Gallery has gained a national reputation for quality and some of the best contemporary works displayed which include representations in sculptural ceramics, pottery, jewellery, textiles, furniture, automata, glass paintings & prints, all by local recognised artists and makers from predominantly the South West region. The gallery shows a wide selection of Contemporary and Applied Arts in the Lower Gallery where seasonal exhibitions run throughout the year. To complement this the Upper Gallery includes a varied programme of solo and themed exhibitions which will include Blandine Anderson's beautiful sculptural ceramics for 2002. The gallery also presents a programme of arts events such as three craft fairs a year in spring, summer and at Christmas. The Chapel Gallery is an ArtCred selected Gallery.*

**▶ Collections of Harpenden** C
The Leys, 38 High Street, Harpenden, AL5 2SY.

**Tel** 01582 620 015
**Fax** 01582 620 015
**Email** prcollections@aol.com
**Opening times** 10–5 Tue–Sat.
**Personnel** Owner/Director: Mrs Pat Ring.
**Works Stocked and Sold** App. Cer. Cra. Dec. Fur. Jew. Ph. Sc. Tx. Wd.
**Price range** £10–£400
For artists see Commercial Gallery Artists.
*Collections sells individual arts and crafts by both recognised and up-and-coming British artists. Ceramics, jewellery and glass make up the hub of the business but many other media are also stocked, including wood, metal and textiles. The gallery shows a wide variety of styles of work to suit all tastes, price ranges and every occasion. Gift wrapping is provided free of charge. The regularly changing display of work is all chosen personally by the owner and themed exhibitions are held twice a year. Collections is a Craft Council listed gallery.*

### ▶ The Contemporary Craftsman
19 Church Street, Monmouth, NP5 3BX.
**Tel** 01600 714 527

### ▶ Counter Culture
21 East Gate Row, Chester CH1 1LQ.
**Tel** 01244 312 288

### ▶ Cowdy Gallery C
31 Culver Street, Newent, GL18 1DB.
**Tel** 01531 821 173 **Fax** 01531 821 173
**Opening times** Tue–Fri 10–12.30, 1.30–5, Sat 10–12.30.
**Nearest Station** Gloucester
**Personnel** Director: Harry Cowdy.
**Services and Facilities** Art for Offices. Commissioning Service. Craftshop. Parking.
**Work Stocked and Sold** Ab. App. Cra. Gla.
**Price range** £20–£5000
*Cowdy Gallery specializes in studio glass – unique works by notable artists, both established and emerging, as well as functional pieces by designer/makers. The gallery is in a recently refurbished listed building, with 125 square metres of display space on two floors. It is located in Newent, an historic market town between Gloucester and Ross-on-Wye, 100 metres from the centre (B4216) with private parking. It was established in 1989 by Harry Cowdy and his wife, glass artist Pauline Solven.*

### ▶ Craftco
40A High Street, Southwold, IP18 6AE.
**Tel** 01502 723 211

### ▶ Crafts Council
44a Pentonville Road, Islington, London N1 9BY.
**Tel** 020 7278 7700 **Fax** 020 7837 6891
**Ws** www.craftscouncil.org.uk
**Opening times** Free entry. Tue–Sat 11–6, Sun 2–6, closed Mon.
**Nearest Station** Angel.
**Personnel** Director: Janet Barnes. Director of Exhibitions, Collection and Education: Louise Taylor.
*The national centre for the crafts showing five exhibitions a year, including ceramics, textiles, glass, wood, furniture, metalwork and jewellery. Reference library. Photostore, the digital picture library for crafts. Gallery shop stocking a wide variety of objects and books.*

### ▶ Craftwork
18 Sadlers Walk, East Street, Chicester, PO19 1HQ.
**Tel** 01243 532 588

### ▶ Crich pottery
Market Place, Crich, DE4 5DD.
**Tel** 01773 853 171
**Ws** www.crichpottery.com

### ▶ Dansel Gallery C
Rodden Row, Abbotsbury, Weymouth, DT3 4JL.
**Tel** 01305 871 515 **Fax** 01305 871 518
**Email** dansel@wdi.co.uk
**Ws** www.wdi.co.uk/dansel
**Opening times** Daily 10–5 including weekends.
**Nearest Station** Dorchester South.
**Services and Facilities** Bookshop. Commissioning Service. Craftshop. Parking. Workshop Facilities.
**Work Stocked and Sold** Fur. Wd.
**Price range** £1–£3,000
For artists see Commercial Gallery Artists.

### ▶ Derek Topp
Derek Topp Gallery, Chatsworth Road, Rowsley, Matlock, DE4 2EH.

### ▶ The Design Shop House
Dean Clough, Halifax, West Yorkshire, HX3 5AX.

### ▶ Desmoulin at the Granary
The Wharf, Newbury, RG14 5AS.
**Tel** 01635 35001

### ▶ Devon Guild of Craftsmen C
Riverside Mill, Bovey Tracey, TQ13 9AF.
**Tel** 01626 832 223 **Fax** 01626 834 220
**Email** devonguild@crafts.org.uk
**Ws** www.crafts.org.uk
**Opening times** Daily 10–5.30 (except winter bank holidays). Café 10–5.
**Nearest Station** Newton Abbot
**Price range** £5–£5,000
For artists see Commercial Gallery Artists.

### ▶ Dundee Contemporary Arts
One Five Two Gallery, 152 Nethergate, Dundee DD1 4DY.
**Tel** 01382 606 252

### ▶ From the Wood
No 6, The Craft Centre, Oxford Road, Hay-On-Wye, HR3 5DG.
**Tel** 01497 821 355

### ▶ The Gallery, Ruthin Craft Centre
Park Road, Ruthin, LL15 1BB.
**Tel** 01824 704 774 **Fax** 01824 702 060
**Opening times** Summer: 10–5.30 daily. Winter: Mon–Sat 10–5, Sun 12–5.
**Personnel** Director: Phillip Hughes. Administrator: Jane Gerrard.
**Services and Facilities** Craftshop. Disabled Access. Parking. Restaurant. Shop.
**Work Stocked and Sold** App. Cer. Cra. Gla. Jew. Tx. Wd.

**Yr Oriel** Canolfan Grefft Rhuthun
**The Gallery** Ruthin Craft Centre

*A Craft Council Selected Gallery housed within a purpose-built craft centre in the picturesque Vale of Clwyd. The Gallery shows the best of fine crafts by contemporary designer–makers from all over the British Isles. We run an exciting programme of regularly changing exhibitions which aim, through a stimulating and diverse view of contemporary work, to show the breadth of excellence in the field of the applied arts. We receive financial support from the Arts Council of Wales.*

### ▶ Haddenham Studios
28 Denmark Road, Cottenham, CB4 8QS.

### ▶ The Harley Gallery
Welbeck, Worksop, Nottinghamshire, S80 3LW.

### ▶ The Hay Makers
St Johns Place, Hay-on-Wye, Hereford HR3 5BN.
**Tel** 01974 820 556
**Opening times** Daily 10.30–5.
**Personnel** Sue Hiley-Harris.
**Services and Facilities** Commissioning Service. Craftshop. Workshop Facilities.
**Work Stocked and Sold** App. Cer. Cra. Fur. Gla. Tx. Wd.
For artists see Commercial Gallery Artists.
*Gallery has traded successfully since it opened as a coop in 1989. Broad range of work from pottery to furniture.*

### ▶ John Dibben Jewellery Shop & Workshop
40a Smithbrook Kilns, Cranleigh, near Guildford, GU6 8JJ.
**Tel** 01483 278 170

### ▶ Julia Mills Gallery
Fore Street, Portleven, TR13 9HH.
**Tel** 01326 569 340

### ▶ Kent Potters Gallery
22 Union Street, Maidstone ME14 1ED.
**Tel** 01622 681 962

### ▶ Manchester Craft Centre
17 Oak Street, Smithfield, Manchester M4 5JD.
**Tel** 0161 832 4274
**Fax** 0161 832 3416
**Personnel** Manager: Sarah Rowland.

### ▶ Mosaic Contemporary Art & Craft Gallery
10 Hall Bank, Buxton, SK17 6EW.
**Tel** 0129 877 557

### ▶ National Glass Centre
Liberty Way, Sunderland SR6 0GL.

### ▶ New Craftsman C
24 Fore Street, St Ives, TR26 1HE.
**Tel** 01736 795 652
**Opening times** Summer: Mon–Fri 10–6, Sat 10–5. Winter: Mon–Sat 10–5.
**Work Stocked and Sold** Cer. Cra. Gla. Jew. Pa. Pr. Sc. Wd.

### ▶ The Oak Blakehouse
Main Road, Fishbourne, Chichester, PO18 8BD.

**▶ Old Court House Gallery**
Market Place, Ambleside, LA22 9BU.
**Tel** 01539 432 022 **Fax** 01539 433 022
**Email** andrew@oldcourtgallery.demon.co.uk

**▶ Old House Gallery**
13 Market Place, Oakham, LE15 6DT.

**▶ Opus Gallery**
34 St Johns Street, Ashbourne, DE6 1GH.

**▶ Oxfordshire Craft Guild**
7 Goddards Lane, Chipping Norton, OX7 5NP.
**Tel** 01993 811 449

**▶ Oxo Tower Wharf**
Barge St, off Upper Ground, South Bank, London SE1 9PH.
**Tel** 020 7401 2255
**Opening times** Tue–Sun 11–6.
**Services and Facilities** Café. Commissioning Service. Gallery space for hire. Restaurant. Shop.
**Work Stocked and Sold** App. Cer. Cra. Fur. Gla. Jew. Sc. Tx.
For artists see Commercial Gallery Artists.
*Since opening in 1996, leading in contemporary applied art. Venue for festivals exhibitions and temporary museums. Hosts Peugeot Design awards.*

**▶ Paddon & Paddon**
113 South Street, Eastbourne, BN21 4LU.

**▶ Peter Wills Ceramics**
Pottery and Gallery, 44 Newcastle Hill, Bridgend, CF31 4EY.
**Tel** 01656 662 902
**Opening times** Tue–Sat 10–5 (but telephone to check). Other times by arrangement.
**Personnel** Owner: Peter Wills.

**▶ Platform Gallery**
Station Road, Clitheroe, BB7 2JT.
**Tel** 01200 443 701
**Email** platform-gallery@ribblevalley.gov.uk

**▶ Portcullis Craft Gallery**
7 The Arcade, Metro Centre, Gateshead, London NE11 9YL.
**Tel** 0191 460 6345 **Fax** 0191 460 4285
**Opening times** Mon–Fri 10–8, Thu 10–9, Sat 9–7. Open bank holidays.
**Personnel** Manager: Wendy Turnbull.

**▶ Porticus** C
1 Middleton Street, Llandrindod Wells, LD1 5ET.
**Tel** 01597 823 989
**Opening times** Mon–Sat 10–5. Early closing Wed.
**Personnel** Rosemary Studman.
**Work Stocked and Sold** Cer. Cra. Gla. Jew. Tx. Wd.

**▶ Primavera** C
10 King's Parade, Cambridge CB2 1SJ.
**Tel** 01223 357 708 **Fax** 01223 576 920
**Opening times** Mon–Sat 9.30–5.30.
**Services and Facilities** Commissioning Service. Craftshop. Shop.
**Work Stocked and Sold** App. Cer. Cra. Fur. Gla. Jew. Pa. Sc. Tx. Wd.
**Price range** £10–£5,000
For artists see Commercial Gallery Artists.

**▶ Printmakers Gallery**
8 Tregenna Hill, St Ives, TR26 1SE.
**Tel** 01736 796 654 **Fax** 01736 796 324

**▶ Pruden & Smith**
2 South Street, Ditchling.

**▶ Quintessence**
21 Paul Street, Catherine Hill, Frome, BA11 1DT.

**▶ The Red Gallery** C
17a Spittal Street, Marlow, Bucks, SL7 3HJ.
**Tel** 01628 483 169
**Fax** 01628 483 169
**Email** contact@redgallery.co.uk
**Ws** www.redgallery.co.uk
**Opening times** Mon & Sat 10–6, Tue–Fri 10–5.30, closed lunch 2–3, open late and Sun on request.
**Nearest Station** Maidenhead to Marlow every 45 minutes.
**Personnel** Proprietor: Miss Micky Middleton.
**Services and Facilities** Art Consultancy. Art for Offices. Commissioning Service. Craftshop. Framing. Restoration.
**Work Stocked and Sold** Cer. Cra. Dec. Gla. Jew. Pa. Pr. Sc. Tx. Wd.
**Price range** £3,000–£25,000
For artists see Commercial Gallery Artists.
*We are committed to an ongoing, ever-changing exhibition programme, which endeavours to charm, excite, humour and stimulate every visitor! There is a continual display of new work by our popular gallery artists, as well as inspiring newcomers and respected makers who are chosen for their dexterity, innovation and our passion for unexpected and whimsical characteristics. With a wide range of media including bronze, ceramics, prints, glass, wood, textiles, papier-mâché and mirrors, the gallery also houses a broad array of refreshing contemporary jewellery from jewellers all over the UK. A visit to The Red Gallery in Marlow is a rare treat indeed!*

**▶ The Red Gallery**
98 Marmion Road, Southsea, Hants, PO5 2BB.

**▶ The Reserve Gallery**
22 Fore Street, Topsham, EX3 0PH.
**Tel** 01392 875 499

**▶ The Room**
158 Walton St, London SW3.

**▶ The Ropewalk Gallery**
Maltkiln Road, Barton-on-Humber, North Lincolnshire.

**▶ The Round House**
The Firs, Foston, Derby DE65 5DL.

**▶ Rufford Craft Centre**
near Ollerton, Newark, NG22 9DF.
**Tel** 01623 822 944 x 208
**Fax** 01623 824 702
**Email** ruffordceramiccentre@nottscc.gov.uk
**Ws** www.ruffordceramiccentre.org.uk
**Opening times** 10.30–5.
**Nearest Station** Newark, Nottingham.
**Personnel** Craft Officer: Bryony Robins.
**Services and Facilities** Bookshop. Café. Commissioning Service. Craftshop. Disabled Access. Guided Tours. Lectures. Parking. Restaurant. Shop. Workshop Facilities.
**Work Stocked and Sold** Ab. App. Cer. Cra. Fur. Gla. Jew. Pa. Ph. Pr. Sc. Tx. Wd.
**Price range** £50–£1000
*Set within the grounds of Rufford Country Park, the Craft Centre comprises a gallery, Ceramic Centre and sculpture garden. The gallery at Rufford shows a changing programme of exhibitions that includes all forms of contemporary craft, sculpture, prints and photography. The Ceramic Centre shows an exhibition of historical studio pottery and has a study area, which includes computers and a library. The Ceramic Centre also houses a retail area for contemporary studio pottery. Rufford provides an ongoing programme of education activities, from the artist in residence scheme to workshops, talks, conferences, community events and family activities.*

**▶ S. M. Jewellery**
10a The High Street, Horbury, WF4 5AA.

**▶ Shepherd's Bothy**
Ledmore by Lairg, Sutherland, IV27 4HH.

**▶ Silver Street Gallery**
12 Silver Street, Bradford-on-Avon, BA15 1JY.
**Tel** 01225 863 532

**▶ Somerset Guild of Craftsmen**
Hurst Works, Yandles, Martock.

**▶ Spectrum**
Maengmyn Street, Machynlleth, Powys, SY20 8EB.

**▶ Splinter Group**
High Street, Hindon, near Salisbury, SP3 5AQ.

**▶ St Ives Ceramics**
1 Fish Street, St Ives, TR26 1LT.
**Tel** 0173 679 4930

**▶ Steam Pottery**
Pendeen, TR19 7DN.

**▶ Strand Gallery**
164 High Street, Aldeburgh, Suffolk, 1P15 5AQ.

**▶ Studio Fusion**
Unit 1: 06 Oxo Tower Wharf, Bargehouse Street, London SE1 9PH.

**▶ Surrey Guild of Craftsman**
1 Mouse Hill Lane, Milford, GU8 5BH.

**▶ Temptations**
4–7 Old Kings Head, Dorking, RH4 1AR.
**Tel** 01306 889 355

**▶ Throstle Nest Gallery**
Old Lindley, Holywell Green, Halifax HX4 9DF.
**Tel** 01422 374 388

**▶ Trelowarren Gallery**
Cornwall Crafts Association, Park View, Point Road, Carnon Downs.
**Tel** 01872 864 084

**▶ Trelyon Gallery**
Fore Street, St Ives, TR26 1HE.
**Tel** 01736 797 955

### ▶ Tremayne Applied Arts
Street-on-Pol, St Ives, TR26 2DS.
**Tel** 01736 797 779

### ▶ Turning Heads
52 Meeting House Lane,
Brighton BN1 1HB.

### ▶ Twenty Twenty Applied Arts
3 High Street, Much Wenlock, TF13 6AA.

### ▶ Vena Bunker Gallery
166 Park Road, Stapleton, Bristol BS16 1DW.

### ▶ Verandah
13 North Parade, Oxford OX2 6LX.

### ▶ Walford Mill Craft Centre C
Stone Lane, Wimborne Minster, BH21 1NL.
**Tel** 01202 841 400
**Opening times** Daily 10–5. Jan–Mar: closed Mon.
**Personnel** Margaret Woodhead.
**Work Stocked and Sold** Cer. Cra. Fur. Gla. Jew. Tx.

### ▶ Warwick Gallery C
14 Smith Street, Warwick, CV34 4HH.
**Tel** 01926 495 880
**Ws** members.aol.com/ukgallery
**Opening times** Mon–Sat 9.30–5.30.
**Nearest Station** Warwick or Leamington Spa.
**Services and Facilities** Art Consultancy. Art for Offices. Commissioning Service. Craftshop. Framing. Shop.
**Work Stocked and Sold** Cer. Cra. Dec. Dr. Gla. Jew. Pa. Pr. Sc. Tx. Wd.
**Price range** £1–£2,000
For artists see Commercial Gallery Artists.

### ▶ We Three Kings
19 Bridge Street, Witney, Oxfordshire OX8 6DA.

### ▶ Wensley Gallery
6–8 Market Place, Ramsbottom,
Bury, BL0 9HT.
**Tel** 01706 824 772

### ▶ The West End Gallery
4 West End, Winksworth, Derbyshire DE4 4EG.

### ▶ White Gallery C
86/87 Western Rd, Hove,
Brighton BN3 1JB.
**Tel** 01273 774 870
**Fax** 01273 748 475
**Email** artists@whitegallery.co.uk
**Ws** www.whitegallery.co.uk
**Opening times** Tue–Sat 10–6, Sun 11–4, Mon closed.
**Nearest Station** Brighton.
**Personnel** Director: Simon Owers. Director: Tim Owers. Ceramics Curator: Tina Davies. Jewellery Curator: Heidi Smith.
*The White Gallery is an independent commercial gallery committed to promoting and presenting the best of contemporary art and craft in the South East. It is one of the few galleries outside London to consistently show non-figurative painters, and one of the few places to see ceramics, glass and jewellery by known makers in a gallery setting. The White Gallery shows affordable works of art for the home and office.*

### ▶ William Sissons Gallery
23 Market Place, Helmsley, York YO6 5BJ.

### ▶ Williamson Brown
290a Clayton Road, Jesmond, Tyne & Wear, SA65 9AE.

### ▶ Wobage Farm Showroom
Upton Bishop, Ross-On-Wye, HR9 7QP.
**Tel** 01989 780 233

# Prints and Printmaking

# Prints

Print collecting, by private individuals or large corporations and institutions, forms a significant part of the UK's art market. Apart from generally being an affordable way to buy an artist's work, there is also a fascinating quality to a print that stems from the mystery created by the maker. The technique can very often be as seductive as the actual image.

But 'print' is a term used to cover a wide field and as a result the business of making, identifying and collecting prints is a minefield of confusion. Diversification within existing techniques and exciting new developments in digital printmaking make prints even more complex. The language used to define an original print, as opposed to a poster for example, is as deceptive as is the terminology used to describe the various techniques themselves.

Printmakers (either artists who make their own work or studio-based master-printers collaborating with artists) are adept at spinning magic and part of the delight of printmaking is to baffle the viewer. It is not uncommon to find combinations of techniques within an image, often causing perplexity for collectors and curators trying to identify the method. What you see is not always obvious; there are classic signs to look for, such as plate marks, but sometimes these are unreliable. Professional artists and studios use sophisticated versions of the methods listed below, but basic skills are taught in schools and art colleges: screenprinting; intaglio printing for example, hard and soft ground etching, dry point, aquatint, sugar lift, calligraphy and mezzotint; relief printing (woodcuts or linocuts are the most common); lithography; digital printing.

Any of these methods, singly or combined, may be used to produce an original print in either a multiple of the same image, a 'limited edition', or a single one-off, a 'monoprint' or 'monotype'. Sometimes collectors are concerned about the edition number; the common misunderstanding is that low numbers are more valuable. They may not know what is an artist's proof (A/P). Once a run has been completed the plates or stencils are destroyed. Artist's proofs are the exception. These are produced as an extension of the edition, amounting to approximately 10 per cent in quantity, for example an edition of 50 may have 5 A/Ps, which are usually retained by the artist.

Other considerations for the collector include how well the work has been framed, particularly whether specialist conservation methods have been used or not. In addition, prints are traditionally produced on handmade paper and attention should be given to the condition of the sheet, particularly if buying older work on the secondary market. However, auction houses readily give condition reports.

Louise Peck
Partner
Advanced Graphics London

## FINE PRESS PRINTERS/PUBLISHER

### ▶ Basement Press
Basement Flat, 29 Burrell Road, Ipswich IP2 8AH.
**Tel** 01473 601 596
**Personnel** Peter Gauld.

### ▶ Circle Press C
26 St Luke's Mews, London W11 1DF.
**Tel** 020 7792 9298
**Personnel** Ron King.
**Work Stocked and Sold** Ab.

### ▶ Delos Press
11 School Road, Moseley,
Birmingham B13 9ET.
**Tel** 0121 449 1406
**Personnel** Peter Baldwin.

### ▶ First Folio Cards
Hollow Cottage, Charingworth,
Chipping Campden, GL55 6NY.
**Tel** 01386 593477
**Personnel** Louise Hare.

### ▶ Golden Apple Press
Pebble Court Cottage, Swinbrook,
Burford, OX18 4DY.
**Tel** 01993 824 097
**Personnel** Jean Rhodes Zivkovic.

### ▶ Hayloft Press
99 Oakfield Road, Birmingham B29 7HW.
**Tel** 0121 472 1768
**Personnel** David Wishart. Eva Wishart.

### ▶ Incline Press
11A Printer Street, Oldham OL1 1PN.
**Tel** 0161 627 1966
**Personnel** Graham Moss.

### ▶ Jones and Palmer Ltd
95 Carver Street, Birmingham B1 3AR.
**Tel** 0121 236 9007; isdn 0121 200 8380
**Fax** 0121 236 5513
**Email** info@jonesandpalmer.co.uk
**Ws** www.@jonesandpalmer.co.uk
**Personnel** Sales: David Binch.

### ▶ Ken Ferguson
20 Lanercost Park, Cramlington, NE23 6RU.
**Tel** 01670 733927

### ▶ Nine Elms Press
21 Gwendolen Avenue, London SW15 6ET.
**Tel** 020 8788 4029
**Personnel** Harold Smith.

### ▶ Old School Press
The Old School, The Green, Hinton
Charterhouse, Bath BA3 6BJ.
**Email** mao@praxis.co.uk
**Ws** www.praxis.co.uk/ppuk/osp.htm
**Personnel** Martyn Ould.

### ▶ Oleander Press
17 Stansgate Avenue, Cambridge CB2 2QZ.
**Tel** 01223 244 688
**Personnel** Philip Ward. Audrey Ward.

### ▶ Prospect Hill Press
35 Bank Street, Herne Bay, CT6 5AW.
**Personnel** Nikky Baker.

### ▶ Redlake Press
Brook House, Clun, SY7 8LY.
**Tel** 01588 640 524
**Personnel** Ursula Freeman.

### ▶ Ruth Bader Gilbert
8 Portland Road, Oxford OX2 7EY.
**Tel** 01865 559 176

### ▶ Tern Press
Saint Mary's Cottage, Great Hales Street,
Market Drayton, TF9 1JN.
**Tel** 01630 652 153
**Personnel** Nicholas Parry. Mary Parry.

### ▶ Woodcraft Press
152 Hadlow Road, Tonbridge TN9 1PB.
**Tel** 01732 359 206
**Personnel** Owen Legg.

### ▶ The Yew Tree Press
Park Place, Aldsworth, Cheltenham, GL54 3QZ.
**Tel** 01451 844 487
**Opening times** By appointment.
**Nearest Station** Cheltenham.
**Personnel** Colin Honnor.
**Services and Facilities** Guided Tours.

## PRINT PUBLISHER/DEALER/GALLERY

### ▶ Advanced Graphics London C
B206 The Gallery and C103 The Studio
Faircharm, 8–12 Creekside,
London SE8 3DX.
**Tel** 020 8691 1330 **Fax** 020 8694 9930
**Email** gallery@advancedgraphics.co.uk
**Ws** www.advancedgraphics.co.uk
**Opening times** Mon–Fri 10–6, evenings and weekends by appointment.
**Nearest Station** Rail: Deptford and DLR: Deptford Bridge.
**Personnel** Fay Davey. Louise Peck. Charlotte Dixon.
**Services and Facilities** Art Consultancy. Art for Offices. Disabled Access. Framing. Parking.
**Work Stocked and Sold** Ab. Pr.
**Price range** £300–£2,000
For artists see Commercial Gallery Artists.
*Printers and publishers of limited edition original prints, specialising in silkscreen and woodblock. Own publications include prints made directly with the following artists: Craigie Aitchison, Basil Beattie, Paul Benjamins, Neil Canning, Anthony Frost, Terry Frost, Donald Hamilton Fraser, Tom Hammick, Clyde Hopkins, John Hoyland, James Hugonin, Albert Irvin, Trevor Jones, Anita Klein, John McLean, Matthew Radford, Ray Richardson and Kate Whiteford.*

### ▶ Anderson O'Day Graphics C
5 St Quintin Avenue, London W10 6NX.
**Tel** 020 8969 8085 **Fax** 020 8960 3641
**Opening times** Mon–Fri 9.30–6, by appointment.
**Nearest Station** Ladbroke Grove.
**Personnel** Don Anderson.
**Work Stocked and Sold** Pr.
**Price range** £75–£1,500
For artists see Commercial Gallery Artists.

### ▶ Art from Scotland C
65 The Shore, Port of Leigh, Edinburgh EH6 6RA.
**Tel** 0131 555 5580 **Fax** 0131 553 5655
**Work Stocked and Sold** Pa.

### ▶ The Art Group Ltd C
146 Royal College Street, London NW1 0TA.
**Tel** 020 7482 3206 **Fax** 020 7284 0435
**Personnel** Director: Sian Rees. John Murtagh.

### ▶ Brandler Galleries C
1 Coptfold Road, Brentwood, CM14 4BN.
**Tel** 01277 222 269 **Fax** 01277 222 786
**Email** John@Brandler-Galleries.com
**Ws** www.brandler-galleries.com and www.thesaurus.co.uk/brandler
**Opening times** Tue–Sat 10–5.30.
**Nearest Station** Brentwood (400 yards), Shenfield (1 mile).
**Personnel** Director: John Brandler. Linda Rodrigues.
**Services and Facilities** Art Consultancy. Art for Offices. Commissioning Service. Framing. Parking. Restoration. Valuation.
**Work Stocked and Sold** Cer. Dr. Pa. Pr. Sc.
**Price range** £50–£65,000

### ▶ CCA Galleries C
517–523 Fulham Road, London SW6 1HD.
**Tel** 020 7386 4900 **Fax** 020 7386 4919
**Email** gallery@ccagalleries.com
**Ws** www.ccagalleries.com
**Opening times** Mon–Sat 9.30–5.30.
**Personnel** Retail Director: Marion Orchard-Webb. Gallery Manager: Lisa McLaren. Publishing Dept.: Teffany Tooke.
*Leading publishers of limited edition silkscreens, etchings and lithographs. Catalogue of new publications produced three times a year. Exciting programme of exhibitions. Artists include Donald Hamilton-Fraser, Annora Spence, Sir Terry Frost, Richard Spare. An excellent bespoke framing service is also available.*

### ▶ Connaught Galleries
44 Connaught Street, London W2.
**Tel** 020 7723 1660 **Fax** 020 7723 1660
**Opening times** Mon–Fri 10–6.30, Sat 10–1.
**Nearest Station** Paddington, Lancaster Gate, Marble Arch.
**Personnel** Partner: Michael Hollamby.
**Services and Facilities** Art for Offices. Framing. Gallery space for hire. Parking. Restoration. Shop. Workshop Facilities.

### ▶ Contemporary Art Holdings C
The Old Chapel, 14 London Road,
Cirencester, GL7 1AL.
**Tel** 01285 644 990 **Fax** 01285 644 992
**Email** CAH@contemporary-art-holdings.co.uk
**Ws** www.contemporary-art-holdings.co.uk
**Opening times** Mon–Fri 9.30–5.30, by appointment.
**Personnel** Celia Wickham. Janet Sheridan. Suzanne Hern.
**Services and Facilities** Art Consultancy. Art for Offices. Commissioning Service.
**Work Stocked and Sold** Cer. Gla. Pa. Pr. Sc. Tx.
**Price range** £200–£50,000
For artists see Commercial Gallery Artists.
*Contemporary Art Holdings publish a range of limited edition original and reproduction prints for the corporate and domestic market. Lithographs, screenprints, etchings and giclee prints are avail-*

*able by artists including Vanda Harvey, Mark Godwin, Lee Crew, Katy Lynton and Paul Hogarth OBE RA. Contemporary prints are distributed to galleries and agents worldwide and a mail order service is available for private clients. A selection of the work available can be seen on our website. CAH also provide a full corporate art consultancy service.*

### ▶ contemporary print gallery C
6a Goodge Place, London W1P 1FL.
**Tel** 020 7436 4007 **Fax** 020 7436 2755
**Email** cpg@artnet.co.uk
**Ws** www.artnet.co.uk
**Opening times** Wed–Sat 12–6.
**Nearest Station** Goodge Street, Tottenham Court Road.
**Personnel** Director: Clive Jennings.
**Services and Facilities** Art Consultancy. Art for Offices. Commissioning Service. Framing.
**Work Stocked and Sold** Ab. Pr.
**Price range** £50–£5,000
For artists see Commercial Gallery Artists.

### ▶ Curwen Gallery
4 Windmill Street, (off Charlotte Street), London W1P 1HF.
**Tel** 020 7636 1459 **Fax** 020 7436 3059
**Email** gallery@curwen.demon.co.uk
**Ws** www.curwen.demon.co.uk
**Opening times** Mon–Fri 10–6, Sat 11–5. Closed bank holiday weekends.
**Nearest Station** Goodge Street, Tottenham Court Road.
**Personnel** Directors: John Hutchings, Jill Hutchings. Contact: Caroline Brown.
**Work Stocked and Sold** Pr.

### ▶ Editions Alecto C
Head Office: The Court House, Lower Woodford, Salisbury, SP4 6NQ.
**Tel** 01722 782 544 **Fax** 01722 782 669
**Email** Alectouk@aol.com
**Opening times** By appointment.
**Nearest Station** Salisbury.
**Personnel** Director: Joe Studholme.
**Services and Facilities** Art Consultancy. Art for Offices. Commissioning Service.
**Work Stocked and Sold** Ab. Pr.
**Price range** £50–£100,000

### ▶ Elizabeth Harvey Lee – Original Prints c.1490–c.1940 C
1 West Cottages, Middle Aston Road, North Aston, OX25 5QB.
**Tel** 01869 347 164 **Fax** 01869 347 956
**Email** North.Aston@btinternet.com
**Opening times** By appointment.
**Personnel** Proprietor: Elizabeth Harvey-Lee.
**Services and Facilities** Lectures.
**Work Stocked and Sold** Pr.
**Price range** £100–£6,000
For artists see Commercial Gallery Artists.
*Private printdealer, offering a large range of fine etchings and engravings. Interesting and unusual old masters and 19th- and 20th-century British and European artists; both major and minor masters of printmaking from five centuries. Two fully illustrated new stock catalogues each year (annual subscription £20 or US$45). Previous reference catalogues still available:* Lasting Impressions – A Survey of the Techniques & History of Printmaking c.1490–c.1940 *(£15 + p&p).* Mistresses of the Graphic Arts – Famous & Forgotten Women Printmakers c.1550–c.1950 *(£13.50 + p&p).* The Seductive Art: The British Passion for Etching 1850–1950 *(£25 + p&p). Regular exhibitor at the London Original Print Fair at the Royal Academy, Art on Paper at the Royal College of Art, and at the June and November Olympia Fine Art & Antiques Fairs.*

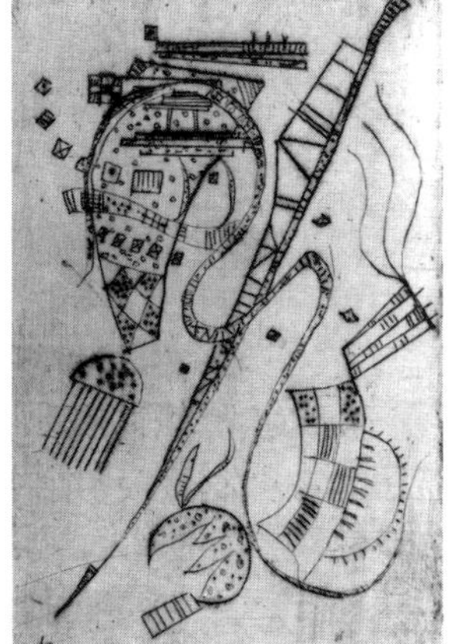

*Wassily Kandinsky,* Radierung für 'Fraternity', *original drypoint, 129 x 83 mm, 1939.*

### ▶ The Goldmark Gallery C
14 Orange Street, Uppingham, LE15 9SQ.
**Tel** 01572 821 424 **Fax** 01572 821 503
**Email** Mike@mgoldmark.freeserve.co.uk
**Opening times** Daily 9.30–5.30, Sun afternoons.
**Nearest Station** Kettering, Oakham.
**Personnel** Director: Mike Goldmark. Emma Goldmark. Roger Porter. Jay Goldmark. Kate Owens. Chris Davies.
**Services and Facilities** Art for Offices. Bookshop. Disabled Access. Framing.
**Work Stocked and Sold** Ab. Pa. Pr. Sc.
**Price range** £250–£3,000
For artists see Commercial Gallery Artists

*Rigby Graham,* 'Tomas O'Crohan', *woodcut, 44" x 21", 1997.*

*2500 sq. ft of the best in contemporary figurative British art. With neither Cork Street landlords nor an Armani habit to support, we offer competitive prices and no art cojones. The gallery carries a large selection of original prints with a particular penchant for artists who thought it of marginal importance to have learnt to draw!*

### ▶ Greenwich Printmakers Association C
1a Greenwich Market, London SE10 9HZ.
**Tel** 020 8858 1569
**Ws** www.longitude0.co.uk/printmakers/
**Opening times** Tue–Sun 10.30–5.30.
**Nearest Station** Greenwich, Island Gardens (Docklands).
**Services and Facilities** Art for Offices. Commissioning Service.
**Work Stocked and Sold** Dr. Pr.
**Price range** £25–£500
For artists see Commercial Gallery Artists.

*Anthony Salter,* The Sower, *etching.*
*Founded 1979. The Greenwich Printmakers is a cooperative of 45 artists including some of the country's leading printmakers as well as recent graduates. Mixed exhibitions of etchings, lithographs, silkscreen, relief prints, watercolours and drawings. Each fortnight one artist's work is specially featured in a mini-exhibition. Work not on display is in plan chests for browsing.*

### ▶ Gresham Studio
4 Chapel Street, Duxford, CB2 4RY.
**Tel** 01223 576 558 **Fax** 01223 576 559
**Email** studio@gresham.demon.co.uk
**Opening times** Not open to the public.
**Nearest Station** Cambridge, Whittlesford.
**Personnel** Studio Director: Kip Gresham. Ian Wilkinson. Chris Wood. Jimi Kazak.
**Work Stocked and Sold** Pr.
**Price range** £150–£3,500
For artists see Commercial Gallery Artists.

### ▶ Hilary Chapman, 20th Century Gallery C
821 Fulham Road, London SW6 5HG.
**Tel** 020 7731 5888 **Fax** 020 7731 5888
**Email** chapmanprints@cs.com
**Ws** www.hilarychapmanfineprints.co.uk
**Opening times** Mon–Fri 10–6, Sat 10–1.
**Personnel** Ms Hilary Chapman.
**Services and Facilities** Art for Offices. Framing. Lectures. Shop. Valuation.
**Work Stocked and Sold** Pr.
*Specialist print dealer in late-nineteenth- and early-twentieth-century British prints. Stock includes etchings, engravings, lithographs, wood-*

*engravings and colour prints by major and minor artists of the period up to the 1950s. At least two exhibitions are held each year and illustrated lists issued periodically. Please send details to the gallery to be included on the mailing list. Exhibitions for 2001 include 'John Hassall RE 1906–1988' (October).*

### ▶ Kensington Church Street Antique Centre C

58–60 Kensington Church Street, London W8 4DB.
**Tel** 020 7937 0425
**Fax** 020 8686 5610
**Personnel** Celia Bailey.

### ▶ Marlborough Graphics C

6 Albemarle Street, London W1X 4BY.
**Tel** 020 7629 5161 **Fax** 020 7495 0641
**Email** graphics@marlboroughfineart.com
**Ws** www.marlboroughfineart.com
**Opening times** Mon–Fri 10–5.30, Sat 10–12.30.
**Nearest Station** Green Park.
**Personnel** Director: David Case. Assistant: Nicola Togneri. Assistant: Ole Koch.
**Services and Facilities** Art Consultancy. Art for Offices. Framing. Valuation.
**Work Stocked and Sold** Ab. Cer. Dr. Ph. Pr. Sc.
**Price range** £300–£60,000
*The leading dealers in Freud etchings. Contemporary publications and prints available by the following gallery artists: Arikha, Auerbach, Conroy, Davies, Hambling, Jacklin, Kliff, Kitaj, Le Brun, Oulton, Pasmore, Paul, Piper and Rego. Modern Master prints available by: Bacon, Hepworth, Kokoschka, Matisse, Miró, Moore, Nicholson, Picasso, Riley and Sutherland.*

### ▶ The Medici Society Ltd

Grafton House, Hyde Estate Road, London NW9 6JZ.
**Tel** 020 8205 2500
**Fax** 020 7495 2997
**Ws** www.medicigalleries.co.uk
**Opening times** 9–5.
**Nearest Station** Brent Cross, Colindale. Rail: West Hendon.
**Services and Facilities** Shop.
**Work Stocked and Sold** Pr.
For artists see Commercial Gallery Artists.

### ▶ Pratt Contemporary Art/ Pratt Editions C

The Gallery, Ightham, Sevenoaks, TN15 9HH.
**Tel** 01732 882 326/884 417
**Fax** 01732 885 502
**Email** pc.art@cwcom.net
**Ws** www.prattcontemporaryart.cwc.net
**Opening times** Seven days a week, by appointment.
**Nearest Station** Charing Cross to Sevenoaks, or Victoria to Borough Green.
**Personnel** Directors: Bernard Pratt, Susan Pratt. P/A: Sarah Chambers. Studio: Peter Notton. Studio: Martin Saull.
**Services and Facilities** Art Consultancy. Commissioning Service. Framing.
**Work Stocked and Sold** Ab. Dr. Pa. Pr. Sc.
**Price range** £100–£200,000
For artists see Commercial Gallery Artists.

*Ana Maria Pacheco,* **Study for Land of No Return,** ***monoprint, plate size 68 x 59.8 cm, 2000, price on application.***

*Established in 1976. Printers and publishers of original limited edition prints working directly with artists: screenprints, etchings, drypoints, woodcuts, monoprints, artists' books. Proofing and editioning service. Artists include: Ana Maria Pacheco, Seyed Edalatpour, Akram Rahmanzadeh, Kristian Krokfors, Michael Kenny RA, Marcus Rees Roberts, Leonam Nogueira Fleury, Pitágoras Lopes Gonçalves. Also handles and exhibits sculpture, paintings and drawings by artists represented*

### ▶ School of Art Gallery & Museum PS

University of Wales, Buarth Mawr, Aberystwyth, SY23 1NG.
**Tel** 01970 622 460 **Fax** 01970 622 461
**Email** neh@aber.ac.uk
**Ws** www.aber.ac.uk/museum
**Opening times** Mon–Fri 10–5.30.
**Personnel** Keeper of Art: Robert Meyrick. Assistant Curator: Neil Holland. Curator of Ceramics: Moira Vincentelli.
**Services and Facilities** Disabled Access. Guided Tours. Lectures. Parking.
*Extensive teaching and research collection of fine and decorative art; European prints from 15th century to present, drawings, watercolours and photographs. George Powell of Nanteos collection of pictures, bronzes and objets d'art (including works on paper by Turner, Burne-Jones, Rossetti, Poynter, Rebecca and Simeon Solomon). 5,000 wood engravings for periodicals of the 1860s and a fine collection of prints representing the Etching Revival since Whistler, particularly etchings of the inter-war years. Art in Wales since 1945 and contemporary printmaking. Contemporary Welsh photography and an outstanding collection of post-war Italian photographs. Changing exhibitions from the collection, touring shows and exhibitions by staff, students and invited artists. Graphic art study collection by appointment. The School of Art Press publishes books, catalogues and research papers, and new Museum and Gallery Studies courses with the art collections at their core. All housed in a magnificent Edwardian building overlooking Cardigan Bay and a few minutes' walk to the town centre and railway station. Also responsible for the Ceramics Gallery at Aberystwyth Arts Centre on the University campus with its important collection of early-20th-century British, European, American and Japanese studio pottery, 18th- and 19th-century Welsh and English slipware, Swansea and Nantgarw porcelain, Art Pottery and Oriental ceramics.*

### ▶ Scolar Fine Art/ Gordon Samuel C

35 Bruton Place, London W1J 6WS.
**Tel** 020 7629 4944 **Fax** 020 7629 4494
**Email** gsamuel@cwcom.net
**Ws** www.scolarfineart.com
**Opening times** Mon–Fri 10–5.30.
**Nearest Station** Green Park, Bond Street.
**Personnel** Director: Gordon Samuel.
**Work Stocked and Sold** Dr. Pa. Pr. Sc.
**Price range** £200–£100,000
For artists see Commercial Gallery Artists.
*Modern British, international and contemporary paintings, drawings, sculpture, and fine prints. The gallery also specialises in the British colour linocuts of the 1920s and 30s by artists of the Grosvenor School of Modern Art including Andrews, Flight, Power and Tschudi. Scolar also details in Modern Master prints, broadly from Picasso to Hockney. Contemporary artists including Richmond Burton, Jane Dickson, Felicity Powell and Graciela Sacco are represented. Scolar Fine Art will also stock art book publications by Scolar Press, Ashgate and Lund Humphries and Special Editions of Scolar Press publications or artist's monographs including original prints.*

### ▶ Tina Holley

Cae Dasydd, Llanfrothen LL48 6SN.
**Tel** 01766 890 474
**Work Stocked and Sold** Pa.

### ▶ The Wild Hawthorn Press

Saint Paulinus, Brough Park, Richmond, DL10 7PJ.
**Tel** 01748 812 127 **Fax** 01748 812 127
**Email** tote@grev.demon.co.uk
**Nearest Station** Darlington.
**Services and Facilities** Bookshop. Framing. Parking.
**Work Stocked and Sold** Ab. Pr. Sc.
**Price range** £0.50–£400
For artists see Commercial Gallery Artists.

## PRINT WORKSHOPS

### ▶ Art House Editions

25 Bruton Street, London W1X 7AB.
**Tel** 020 7491 3337
**Personnel** Judith Aniney.

### ▶ Artichoke Print Workshop

Unit 51, Shakespeare Business Centre, 245 Coldharbour Lane, London SW9 8RR.
**Tel** 020 7924 0600
**Personnel** Colin Gall.

### ▶ Artizan Editions

Unit 6, Hove Business Centre, Font Hill Road, Hove, BN3 6HA.
**Tel** 01273 773 959
**Personnel** Anne Hamlett.

### ▶ Bath Artist Printmakers

7 Lower Borough Walls, Bath BA1 1QS.
**Tel** 01225 446 136

### ▶ Belfast Print Workshop

185 Stranmillis Road, Belfast BT9 5EE.
**Tel** 028 9068 7223 **Fax** 028 9066 3593
**Email** info@belfastprintworkshop.co.uk
**Opening times** Mon–Fri 10–5.30.

**Personnel** Manager: James Allen. Workshop Assistant: Struan Hamilton.
**Services and Facilities** Workshop Facilities.
*The workshop is an independent non-profit-making company with charitable status. It is a professional printmaking workshop providing member artists with comprehensive specialist facilities and equipment for etching, screenprinting, lithography and relief printing at very reasonable rates.*

### ▶ Blue Dragon Press
2 Holly House, Roce Hill, Barking, RH4 2EQ.
**Tel** 01306 877 246
**Personnel** Diana Mills.
**Work Stocked and Sold** Ab.

### ▶ Bookworks
19 Holywell Row, London EC2A 4JB.
**Tel** 020 7247 2536
**Personnel** Anna Pank. Jane Rolo.
**Work Stocked and Sold** Ab.

### ▶ Coriander
56 Kings Bridge Crescent, Southall, UB1 2DL.
**Tel** 020 8893 6888
**Personnel** Brad Faire.

### ▶ Counterprint Studio
Unit 3B1, 133 Rye Lane, Peckham, London SE15 4ST.
**Tel** 020 7642 1295 **Fax** 020 7642 1295
**Email** Osip534600@aol.com
**Ws** www.counter-print.co.uk
**Opening times** Mon–Fri 9.30–5.30, weekends by appointment.
**Nearest Station** Peckham Rye.
**Personnel** Director: Charlie Fox. Members: David Jarvis, Emma Thompson, Matthew Dennis, Tricia Finnegan, Chris Turnbull, Sarah Hardy, Marcus James, Claire Zakiewicz, Brede Korsmo, Anne-Catherine Le Deunff, Tony Lee, Jessica Potter, Andrew Smith.
**Services and Facilities** Art Consultancy. Art for Offices. Commissioning Service. Framing. Lectures. Workshop Facilities.
**Work Stocked and Sold** Ab. Dr. Pr.
**Price range** £5–£1500
*Counterprint offers open-access membership facilities for the printing and editioning of work in a wide variety of media, including screenprinting, lithography, digital and intaglio. A cross-spectrum of artists and imagemakers wishing to exploit print media to disseminate their ideas and images are encouraged to explore and experiment using the studio's equipment and expertise. The studio seeks to maintain the production of a high standard of contemporary and innovative prints and editions. For further information or a prospectus write, ring or email.*

### ▶ The Curwen Studio
Chilford Hall, Linton, Cambridge CB1 6LE.
**Tel** 01223 893 544 **Fax** 01223 893 638
**Email** info@thecurwenstudio.co.uk
**Ws** www.thecurwenstudio.co.uk
**Opening times** Mon–Fri 9–5.30.
**Nearest Station** Cambridge.
**Personnel** Directors: Stanley Jones, Jenny Roland.
**Services and Facilities** Art for Offices. Café. Commissioning Service. Disabled Access. Guided Tours. Parking. Shop.
**Work Stocked and Sold** Pr. Sc.
**Price range** £65–£2,000
For artists see Commercial Gallery Artists.
*Creative original print making with artists on a limited edition basis. With facilities for lithography and screenprinting, both methods allow the ability to hand-draw colour separations, although we can work from photographically produced film.*
*We have been working with artists to produce their prints since 1958 and have technicians with tremendous skills and knowledge in both lithography and screenprinting to ensure you get the best results. Working with artists we are challenging the boundaries of our processes.*

### ▶ Edinburgh Printmakers
23 Union Street, Edinburgh EH1 3LR.
**Tel** 0131 557 2479 **Fax** 0131 558 8418
**Email** printmakers@ednet.co.uk
**Opening times** Tue–Sat 10–6.
**Personnel** Director: Robert Adam.
**Services and Facilities** Art Consultancy. Art for Offices. Framing. Workshop Facilities.
**Work Stocked and Sold** Pr.

### ▶ Enitharmon Press
38 St Georges Avenue, London N7 0HD.
**Tel** 020 7607 7144

### ▶ Four Impressions
Cherry Tree Cottage, 12 Bassetsbury Lane, High Wycombe, HP11 1QU.
**Tel** 01494 443 607

### ▶ Glasgow Print Studio Workshop C
22 King Street (1st floor), Glasgow G1 5QP.
**Tel** 0141 552 0704 **Fax** 0141 552 2919
**Email** gallery@gpsart.co.uk
**Ws** www.gpsart.co.uk
**Opening times** Tue–Thu 10–9, Fri/Sat 10–6.
**Nearest Station** Glasgow Queen Street or Glasgow Central.
**Personnel** Workshop Manager: Stuart Duffin. Development Officer: Leona Stewart. Director: John Mackechnie.
**Services and Facilities** Art Consultancy. Art for Offices. Bookshop. Commissioning Service. Craftshop. Framing. Friends Society. Gallery space for hire. Guided Tours. Lectures. Shop. Workshop Facilities.
**Work Stocked and Sold** Ab. App. Cer. Cra. Dec. Gla. Jew. Pa. Ph. Pr.
**Price range** £50–£5,000
For artists see Commercial Gallery Artists.

***Adrian Wiszniewski,* One Man, Two Trees, Four Branches, *etching, 20" x 22", 2001, £200 + VAT.***
*Glasgow Print Studio, Workshop, Galleries I & II and Retail Outlet, Gallery III and Print Shop.*
*In the workshop, the high standard of printmaking is encouraged by the range and versatility of the facilities. The studio attracts artists from the UK and worldwide, creating a lively atmosphere and friendly environment. Access is open to all members of the public with printmaking experience. Regular classes for those who wish to learn new skills. There are facilities for all printmaking media, with expert advice on hand from the staff. Editioning facilities include studio co-publications by Blackadder, Howson, Wiszniewski and John Byrne among others. Disabled access on request.*

### ▶ Half Moon Studio
F1 Shakespeare Business Centre, 245A Coldharbour Lane, London SW9 8RR.
**Tel** 020 7733 9166

### ▶ Harwood King Fine Art
Unit 8, E-Plan Estate, New Road, Newhaven, BN9 0EX.
**Tel** 01273 512 554 **Fax** 01273 512 809
**Personnel** Quentin King.

### ▶ Heatherley School of Fine Art
HEATHERLEY'S
Chelsea - Est. 1845

80 Upcerne Road, Chelsea, London SW10 0SH.
**Tel** 020 7351 4190 **Fax** 020 7361 6945
**Email** info@heatherleys.org
**Ws** www.heatherleys.org
**Opening times** 9.30–5.
**Nearest Station** Fulham Broadway, Sloane Square. Rail: Victoria.
**Personnel** School Office: The Registrar. Marketing Assistant: Sarah Cloonan.
**Services and Facilities** Friends Society. Parking. Shop. Workshop Facilities.
*Heatherley's is a small independent art school based in Chelsea. It offers a wide range of full-time and part-time fine art courses for both beginners and experienced artists. Professional artists specialised in their academic field tutor the courses. The classes are small and have a high tutor to student ratio. Courses include painting, drawing, life drawing, portraiture, sculpture, watercolour/pastel, printmaking, art history, the Heatherley's Print Workshop, the Heatherley Diploma in Portraiture, the Heatherley Diploma in Figurative Sculpture, and a structured one-year Foundation course. An open studio for life and portrait drawing and painting.*

### ▶ London Print Studio PS
425 Harrow Road, London W10 4RE.
**Tel** 020 8969 3247 **Fax** 020 8964 0008
**Email** info@londonprintstudio.org.uk
**Ws** www.londonprintstudio.org.uk
**Opening times** Tue–Sat 10.30–6.
**Nearest Station** Westbourne Park.
**Personnel** Director: John Phillips. Administrator: Louise Thirlwall. Print studio coordinator: Gill Day. Print studio coordinator: Paul Dewis.
**Services and Facilities** Disabled Access. Lectures. Workshop Facilities.
**Work Stocked and Sold** Pr.

**Price range** £50–£5,000
*Specialist centre for printmaking and the graphic arts: comprises printmaking studio, computer graphics facility and gallery. LPS runs a programme of exhibitions, short courses and events. It provides open access resource for artists using screenprint, intaglio, relief printing, and computer graphics facilities. Professional staff are on hand to provide support.*
*Charges from £5.50 (cons.) for a 3-hour session. A wide selection of artists' prints are available for sale in the gallery.*

### ▶ Paupers Press
Standpoint Studios, 45 Coronet Street,
London N1 6HD.
**Tel** 020 7729 5272
**Personnel** Michael Taylor.

### ▶ St Barnabas Press C
Belfast Yard, Cambridge CB1 3EW.
**Tel** 01223 413 792 or 077 0344 2646
**Fax** 01223 212 440
**Email** jameshill@stbarnabaspress.FSBusiness.co.uk and jameshill64@hotmail.com
**Ws** stbarnabaspress.co.uk
**Opening times** Mon–Sat 10–10, additional hours for members.
**Nearest Station** Cambridge.
**Personnel** Director/Master Printer: James Hill. Technician: Fiona Thomas.
**Services and Facilities** Art for Offices. Commissioning Service. Framing. Gallery space for hire. Lectures. Parking. Restoration. Shop. Workshop Facilities.
**Work Stocked and Sold** Pa. Pr. Sc.
**Price range** £65–£1,000
For artists see Commercial Gallery Artists.

***James Hill proofing screenprint with artist.***
*St Barnabas Press offers open access facilities, studio spaces and has an on-site gallery. Editioning and proofing by contract or co-publication utilising James Hill's many years' collaborative experience in producing high quality original prints. Artists may take an experimental approach, using the infinite possibilities of mark-making that printmaking processes can offer.*
*The Press gives experienced printmakers access to fully equipped areas of etching, screenprinting, relief printing, lithography and allied photo-reprographic facilities. Also available are evening classes, short courses and individual supervised sessions.*

### ▶ Signs by Design
Unit 12, Eastmead Trading Estate,
Lavant, Chichester, PO18 0DB.
**Tel** 01243 787 230 **Fax** 01243 787 258
**Email** k.phare@signsbydesign.fsbusiness.co.uk
**Personnel** John Bradford. Avril Bradford.

### ▶ Zink Editions
33 Charlotte Road, London EC2A 3PB.
**Tel** 020 7739 7207 **Fax** 020 7739 7207
**Opening times** Mon–Fri 10–6.
**Nearest Station** Old Street.
**Personnel** Alan Cox.
**Services and Facilities** Workshop Facilities.
**Work Stocked and Sold** Pr.
**Price range** £100–£1,000
For artists see Commercial Gallery Artists.
*Fine art limited edition lithographic printing and publishing. Offset – max. sheet size 29" x 40" for art work from hand-drawn plates plus 4 col; half-tone work, typographic sheets and limited edition books. Direct lithography – from hand-drawn plates. Also capable of printing monoprints, lino and up to 0.25" thick woodcuts from materials such as plywood and hardboard. Max. sheet size 47" x 33".*

## PRINTS & PRINTMAKING

### ▶ The Printmakers Council
Clerkenwell Workshop, 31 Clerkenwell Close,
London EC1R 0AT.
**Tel** 020 7250 1927
**Ws** www.printmaker.co.uk/pmc/index.html
**Opening times** Wed & Thu 2–6.
**Nearest Station** Farringdon.
**Personnel** President: Mr Stanley Jones. Administrator: Helen Ward.
*The Printmakers Council is a non-profitmaking artist-run group. Their objectives are to promote the use of both traditional and innovative printmaking techniques by: holding exhibitions of prints, providing information on prints and printmaking to both its membership and the public, encouraging cooperation and exchanges between members, other associations and interested individuals. Exhibitions in major London venues and throughout the UK. Exchange shows recently in Paris, Landau, Germany and Fremantle, Australia. A slide index of members' work is held in the London office for consultation. Membership is open to all printmakers.*

# The Internet

# Internet Art Galleries

The last eighteen months have seen the birth of a revolution in art for even though still in their infancy, electronic art galleries or e-galleries are changing the way art is being bought.

Generally, e-galleries are not taking market share from traditional art galleries and auction houses, but are enabling a whole new generation of art lovers to navigate the often intimidating art world with confidence. Specifically marketed e-commerce sites give this new generation confidence to buy art. Dedicated e-galleries differ from the many websites that offer an e-brochure as an extension to their existing traditional gallery business and whose purpose is often only to direct customers back to the physical gallery space for purchase.

The success of the e-gallery players can be attributed to a number of factors. First, e-galleries are open 24 hours a day, 365 days a year and offer no geographical obstacle to their customers. They can be accessed as and when it is convenient for potential buyers and will also deliver anywhere in the world. This contrasts starkly with traditional galleries whose limited trading hours and location can limit buyers' ability to view the artwork, let alone to buy it or take it home.

Second, the unlimited 'space' inside an e-gallery allows many more artists' work to be on view at any one time. Thus e-galleries are able to offer a much wider selection than most traditional galleries. Their innovative online search facilities also provide time-pressed customers with the ability to easily find works that suit, usually far more quickly than trailing around a large number of traditional galleries.

Thirdly, e-galleries provide talented artists with access to a huge number of potential customers who would not see their work through more traditional channels, even if such an artist was lucky enough to be picked to be represented by one of the big established galleries.

But most important, e-galleries have to be able to create a totally unintimidating environment for existing and potential collectors to browse and learn about art before they buy. This is widely perceived to be the biggest weakness of traditional galleries.

Clearly there are sceptics who question whether art will be bought without it being seen. Britart.com addresses this head-on by offering the option of a 14-day home trial, enabling would-be buyers not only to see the work in the flesh but, even more importantly, in situ in their home or at their office.

E-galleries are here to stay. Over time, they will serve an increasing market, often giving a new breed of customer the confidence to buy his or her first piece of art. It is this new breed of customer who will eventually become a committed art collector addicted to buying art, and will have the confidence and skills to further this passion. This can only be good for all who make art.

Giles Howard
Managing director
Britart.com

## INTERNET ART CONSULTANCY

### ▶ Art for Offices C
The Galleries, 15 Dock Street, London E1 8JL.
**Tel** 020 7481 1337 **Fax** 020 7481 3425
**Email** enquiries@afo.co.uk
**Ws** www.afo.co.uk
**Opening times** Mon–Fri 9.30–5.30.
**Personnel** Director: Andrew Hutchinson. Director: Peter Harris. Amanda Basker.
*We have 20 years' experience advising architects, designers and corporate clients on the planning and implementation of art programmes. Our 10,000-square-foot galleries provide a central source of art, enabling clients and specifiers to view a comprehensive range of art on a single visit to one location. We deal directly with over 800 artists and have a large visual reference library covering art in all media which is cross-referenced by style and price. This makes it possible to research works of art or artists for commission quickly and effectively. Art can be purchased, commissioned or acquired on a flexible rental basis.*

## INTERNET GALLERY

### ▶ Advanced Graphics London
B206 The Gallery and C103 The Studio, Faircharm, 8–12 Creekside, London SE8 3DX.
**Tel** 020 8691 1330 **Fax** 020 8694 9930
**Email** gallery@advancedgraphics.co.uk
**Ws** www.advancedgraphics.co.uk
**Opening times** Mon–Fri 10–6, evenings & weekends by appointment.
**Personnel** Louise Peck. Fay Davey. Charlotte Dixon.
**Services and Facilities** Art Consultancy. Art for Offices. Disabled Access. Framing. Parking.
**Work Stocked and Sold** Ab. Pr.
**Price range** £300–£2,000
*Printers and publishers of limited edition original prints, specialising in silkscreen and woodblock. Own publications include prints made directly with the following artists: Craigie Aitchison, Basil Beattie, Paul Benjamins, Neil Canning, Anthony Frost, Terry Frost, Donald Hamilton Fraser, Tom Hammick, Clyde Hopkins, John Hoyland, James Hugonin, Albert Irvin, Trevor Jones, Anita Klein, John McLean, Matthew Radford, Ray Richardson and Kate Whiteford.*

### ▶ Art Arena Gallery C
4 Bennett Hill Close, Wootton Bassett, Wilts, SN4 8LR.
**Tel** 01793 848 742 **Fax** 01793 848 742
**Email** katy@art-arena.com
**Ws** www.art-arena.com
**Opening times** Website 24 hours a day.
**Personnel** Artist & Owner: Katy Kianush-Wallace.
**Services and Facilities** Art for Offices. Bookshop. Friends Society.
**Work Stocked and Sold** Dr. Pa. Pr.
**Price range** £90–£3,500
For artists see Commercial Gallery Artists.
*Art Arena is a virtual gallery providing a comprehensive and varied collection of original landscapes, portraits, miniatures, and greeting card designs by an award-winning artist. The artist's varied use of media and painting techniques, and the multiplicity of subjects treated, encourage appreciation of her art on many levels.*
*Art Arena brings together two of Iran's well known and established literary figures, to give an insight into modern Persian poetry and prose. In addition to this, it opens a window onto Persian history, art, and culture.*
*Art Arena is host to the National Acrylic Painters' Association (UK) website.*

### ▶ Art Connection
47 Maddox Street, London W1R 9LA.
**Tel** 020 7355 1303 **Fax** 020 7495 0600
**Email** curator@art-connection.com
**Ws** www.art-connection.com
**Opening times** 24 hours a day.
**Personnel** Sales Manager: Nick Chapman.
**Work Stocked and Sold** Ab. Cer. Dec. Dr. Fur. Gla. Jew. Pa. Ph. Pr. Sc.
**Price range** £55–£120,000
*The only comprehensive pictorial search facility on the internet. We aim to support the gallery trade via the web and the art fairs they attend. Over 4,000 works of art and antiques pictured. As a complete site we have around 1,000 artists on the site, from 11th century through to the present day. We offer assistance where works of art or artists are not listed, so email the curator for help.*

### ▶ Art London.Com
Suite 958, 28 Old Brompton Road, London SW7 3SS.
**Tel** 020 7402 2897 **Fax** 020 7402 1028
**Email** art@artlondon.com
**Ws** www.artlondon.com

### ▶ avenues-of-sight.com C
74 Kimbolton Road, Bedford, MK40 2NZ.
**Tel** 01234 328 397 **Fax** 01234 328 397
**Email** sarah@avenues-of-sight.com
**Ws** www.avenues-of-sight.com
**Personnel** Sarah Longlands.
**Services and Facilities** Art for Offices. Commissioning Service.
**Work Stocked and Sold** Dr. Pa.
**Price range** £100–£3,000
For artists see Commercial Gallery Artists.

### ▶ Axis
Leeds Metropolitan University, 8 Queen Square, Leeds LS2 8AJ.
**Tel** 0113 245 7946 **Fax** 0113 245 7950
**Email** axis@lmu.ac.uk
**Ws** www.axisartists.org.uk
**Opening times** Mon–Fri 9–5.
**Nearest Station** Leeds.
**Personnel** Principal Information Officer: Robin Bourne.

### ▶ Britart.com
Britart Online Ltd, 60–62 Commercial St, London E1 6LT.
**Tel** 020 7392 7200 **Fax** 020 7392 7272
**Email** b4b@britart.com

### ▶ Fine Art Commissions Ltd
107 Walton Street, Knightsbridge, London SW3 2HT.
**Tel** 020 7589 4111 **Fax** 020 7589 3888
**Email** facl@btinternet.com
**Ws** www.facl.com
**Opening times** By appointment 10–6.
**Nearest Station** South Kensington or Knightsbridge.
**Personnel** Director: Sara Stewart.
**Services and Facilities** Art Consultancy. Art for Offices. Commissioning Service. Framing. Restoration.
**Work Stocked and Sold** Dec. Pa. Sc.
**Price range** £300–£70,000

### ▶ Jonathan Poole C
Compton Cassey Gallery, near Withington, Cheltenham, GL54 4DE.
**Tel** 01242 890 224 **Fax** 01242 890 479
**Email** jonathanpoole@comptoncassey.demon.co.uk
**Ws** www.jonathanpoole.co.uk
**Opening times** By appointment.
**Nearest Station** Cheltenham
**Personnel** Jonathan Poole. Selina Rutherson. Amy Cameron.
**Services and Facilities** Art Consultancy. Art for Offices. Gallery space for hire. Parking. Valuation.
**Work Stocked and Sold** Dr. Pa. Pr. Sc.
**Price range** £50–£15,000
For artists see Commercial Gallery Artists.
*European representatives for John Lennon and Miles Davis Estates. Exhibition organisers with venues in Europe and the Middle East. Contemporary sculpture, paintings and sculpture by Jonathan Poole and Bobby Plisnier and many other artists.*

### ▶ Mutch Art
157 Bradenham Close, Walworth, London SE17 2BD.
**Tel** 020 7703 5477
**Email** gil@mutchart.ndo.co.uk
**Ws** www.mutchart.com
**Personnel** Artist: Gil Mutch.
**Services and Facilities** Art for Offices. Commissioning Service.
**Work Stocked and Sold** Pa. Pr.
**Price range** £50–£5,000
For artists see Commercial Gallery Artists.

### ▶ newartportfolio.com C
PO Box 144, Stroud, GL5 4YG.
**Tel** 01453 750 486 **Fax** 01453 750 486
**Email** info@newartportfolio.com
**Ws** www.newartportfolio.com
**Opening times** 24/7
**Personnel** Managing Director: Mark Barrow. Art Director: Jonathan Gooders.
**Services and Facilities** Art Consultancy. Art for Offices. Bookshop. Commissioning Service. Framing.
**Work Stocked and Sold** Shop. Ab. App. Cer. Cra. Dec. Dr. Gla. Jew. Pa. Ph. Pr. Sc. Wd.
**Price range** £50–£50 000

*Marina Kim,* The Russian, *oil on canvas, 60 x 80 cm, 2000, £750.*

*Displaying and promoting affordable, contemporary original works by painters, sculptors, photographers, ceramicists, jewellers and glassware makers from around the globe. New Art Portfolio offers a complete online resource for artists, collectors, and art enthusiasts, including a monthly online magazine, directory of services, free virtual postcards, discussion forum, featured artist interviews, free desktop wallpapers, commisssioning service, limited edition art prints and much much more! New Art Portfolio – the only site on the web dedicated to empowering independent artists.*

### ▶ Peter's Barn Gallery C

South Ambersham, near Midhurst,
West Sussex GU29 0BX.
**Tel** 01798 861 388 **Fax** 01798 861 388
**Email** peters.barn@ic24.net
**Ws** www.petersbarngallery.co.uk
**Opening times** Website: 24 hours. Gallery: Apr–Sep: Tue–Fri 2–6, Sat, Sun and holidays 11–6. Jan, Feb, Mar: by appointment.
**Personnel** Gabrielle & Annabel.
**Services and Facilities** Commissioning Service. Disabled Access. Parking.
**Work Stocked and Sold** Ab. App. Cer. Cra. Dr. Gla. Jew. Pa. Pr. Sc. Wd.
**Price range** £10–£9000

***Nicholas Homoky, white porcelain inlaid with black porcelain, 17 x 14 cm, October 2000.***

*Widely acknowledged as one of the most enchanting garden galleries in the south. Peter's Barn shows work by known, established and up and coming artists. Set in a wild wooded water garden, this little gallery makes full use of the beautiful garden space, giving artists the opportunity to exhibit their work in an outside environment. The varied exhibitions change monthly. From the A272 – 3 miles east of Midhurst and 3 miles west of Petworth, take road opposite the Half Way Bridge Inn and follow the brown gallery signs.*

### ▶ Plazzotta Ltd C

18 Shoa Road, London W3 7LN.
**Tel** 020 8743 0937
**Email** oconor@plazzotta.co.uk
**Ws** www.plazzotta.co.uk
**Opening times** The office and storeroom are open by appointment.
**Nearest Station** Sloane Square, Earls Court.
**Personnel** Director: Richard S. O'Conor.
**Services and Facilities** Valuation.
**Work Stocked and Sold** Ab. Sc.
**Price range** £400–£50,000
For artists see Commercial Gallery Artists.

### ▶ Watershed Exhibitions

Watershed Media Centre, 1 Canons Road, Bristol BS1 5TX.
**Tel** 0117 927 6444, 925 3845
**Fax** 0117 921 3958
**Email** info@watershed.co.uk
**Ws** www.watershed.co.uk
**Opening times** 7 days a week.
**Nearest Station** Bristol Temple Meads.
**Personnel** Head of Exhibitions: Mark Cosgrove. Marketing: Louise Gardner.
**Services and Facilities** Bar. Café. Disabled Access. Gallery space for hire. Guided Tours. Lectures. Restaurant. Shop. Workshop Facilities.
*www.watershed.co.uk – visit us wherever you are. Situated on the harbourside of Bristol, Watershed is the South West's leading media centre for the digital age, providing opportunities for all to experience, enjoy and learn about contemporary moving image media. The programme of feature film, videos, multimedia, the Internet, still photography, courses and events is presented in two cinemas, a digital café, darkrooms, a digital suite and on the world wide web. We also have one of the most relaxed and welcoming café/bars in the city and we are an ideal venue to host conferences and events.*

### ▶ www.aarti.co.uk C

'Bygones', The Street, Rickinghall,
Diss, IP22 1EG.
**Tel** 01379 890 608 **Fax** 0870 055 7896
**Email** margaret@aarti.demon.co.uk
**Ws** www.aarti.co.uk
**Opening times** 24 hours a day, 7 days a week.
**Personnel** Owner: Margaret Horrocks.
**Services and Facilities** Art for Offices. Bookshop. Commissioning Service. Craftshop. Gallery space for hire. Shop.
**Work Stocked and Sold** Ab. Cra. Dec. Dr. Pa. Pr. Sc.
**Price range** £25–£3,000
For artists see Commercial Gallery Artists.

### ▶ www.britishart.co.uk

Orchard Cottage, Brookmans Valley,
Iwerne Minster, Blandford, DT11 8NG.
**Tel** 0870 2412 128 **Fax** 0870 131 2999
**Email** info@britishart.co.uk
**Ws** www.britishart.co.uk
**Personnel** Guy Little.
**Services and Facilities** Commissioning Service. Gallery space for hire.
**Work Stocked and Sold** Cer. Dr. Fur. Pa. Ph. Pr. Sc. Tx.

**OTHER WEB SITES**

## Art Book Publishers

**Art Sales Index Ltd**
www.art-sales-index.com
**Ashgate Publishing Group incorporating Lund Humphries**
www.ashgate.com
**Craft Galleries Guide**
www.707.co.uk/craftgalleries
**Macmillan online Publishers Ltd The Dictionary of Art**
www.groveartmusic.com
**Oxford University Press**
www.oup.co.uk
**Second Steps**
www.707.co.uk/craftgalleries
**Thames & Hudson**
www.thameshudson.co.uk/
www.world-of-art.com
**V&A Publications**
www.vandashop.co.uk/books

## Art Consultants

**Art Contact Ltd**
www.artcontact.co.uk
**Art For Offices**
www.afo.co.uk
**Artists in Residence**
www.artistsinresidence.co.uk
**Brandler Galleries**
www.brandler-galleries.com and
www.thesaurus.co.uk/brandler
**Business Art Galleries**
www.curwengallery.com
**Christopher Wood**
www.christopherwoodgallery.com
**Contemporary Art Holdings**
www.contemporary-art-holdings.co.uk
**de Putron Art Consultants Ltd**
www.art@dpac.demon.co.uk
**Egee Art Consultancy**
www.egeeart.com
**Federation of British Artists**
www.mallgalleries.org.uk
**Moreton Contemporary Art**
www.moretonart.com
**Sheeran Lock - Specialist Independent Art Consultants**
www.sheeranlock.com
**Thomas Corman Arts**
www.thomascormanarts.com

## Art Education

**The Arts Institute at Bournemouth**
www.arts-inst-bournemouth.ac.uk
**Bath Spa University College**
www.bathspa.ac.uk
**Birkbeck College**
www.bbk.ac.uk/fce
**Bridgwater College**
www.bridgwater.ac.uk
**Byam Shaw School of Art**
www.byam-shaw.ac.uk
**Carmarthenshire College**
www.wwsota.ac.uk
**Central Saint Martins College of Art & Design**
www.csm.linst.ac.uk
**The Cheshire School of Art & Design, Mid-Cheshire College**
www.midchesh.u-net.com
**Christie's Education**
www.christies.com
**City & Guilds of London Art School**
www.cityandguildsartschool.ac.uk
**Coventry University**
www.csad.coventry.ac.uk
**Cumbria College of Art and Design**
www.cumbriacad.ac.uk
**Edinburgh College of Art**
www.eca.ac.uk
**Falmouth College of Arts**
www.falmouth.ac.uk
**Glasgow University**
www.arts.gla.ac.uk/ArtHist/decarts.htm
**Goldsmiths College**
www.gold.ac.uk/
**Heatherley School of Fine Art**
www.heatherleys.org
**The Institute**
www.hgsi.ac.uk
**Lancaster University, School of Creative Arts, The Art Department**
www.lancs.ac.uk/users/art/
**Leeds College of Art and Design**
www.leeds-art.ac.uk
**Nottingham Trent University**
www.ntu.ac.uk/vpa
**Plymouth College of Art and Design**
www.pcad.plym.ac.uk
**The Prince's Foundation**
www.princes-foundation.org
**Ravensbourne College of Design and Communication**
www.rave.ac.uk
**Reigate School of Art and Design**
www.esc.org.uk
**Ruskin School of Drawing and Fine Art**
www.ruskin-sch.ox.ac.uk/
**Rycotewood College**
www.rycote.ac.uk
**S.P.A.C.E. Studios**
www.spacestudios.org.uk
**Slade School of Fine Art**
www.ucl.ac.uk/slade/
**Sotheby's Institute**
www.sothebys.com/education
**Swansea Institute of Higher Education**
www.sihe.ac.uk
**University of Central England in Birmingham**
www.biad.uce.ac.uk
**University of Plymouth**
www.plymouth.ac.uk
**Westminster College**
www.westminster-cfe.ac.uk
**York College**
www.yorkcollege.ac.uk

## Art in Country Houses

**Drumlanrig Castle**
www.drumlanrigcastle.org.uk
**Upton House**
www.nationaltrust.org.uk

## Art Management

**Art For Offices**
www.afo.co.uk

## Art Societies

**AOP (Association of Photographers)**
www.aophoto.co.uk
**Association of Art Historians**
www.aah.org.uk
**The British Society of Master Glass Painters**
www.proteusweb.com/bsmgp
**Contemporary Art Society**
www.contempart.org.uk
**The Design and Artists Copyright Society Ltd**
www.dacs.co.uk
**Hesketh Hubbard Art Society**
www.mallgalleries.org.uk
**National Acrylic Painters' Association**
www.art-arena.com/napa
**National Association of Memorial Masons**
www.namm.org.uk
**New English Art Club**
www.mallgalleries.org.uk
**Pastel Society**
www.mallgalleries.org.uk
**The Printmakers Council**
www.printmaker.co.uk/pmc
**Royal Academy of Arts**
www.RoyalAcademy.org.uk
**Royal Cambrian Academy of Art**
www.oriel-cambria.co.uk/gallery/rca
**Royal Institute of Oil Painters**
www.mallgalleries.org.uk
**Royal Institute of Painters in Water Colours**
www.mallgalleries.org.uk
**The Royal Photographic Society**
www.rps.org
**Royal Society of British Artists**
www.mallgalleries.org.uk
**Royal Society of Marine Artists**
www.mallgalleries.org.uk
**Royal Society of Portrait Painters**
www.mallgalleries.org.uk
**SAA**
www.saa.co.uk
**Scottish Sculpture Trust**
www.scottishsculpturetrust.org
**Society of Equestrian Artists**
www.equestrianartists.co.uk
**Society of Wildlife Artists**
www.mallgalleries.org.uk/
**Society of Women Artists**
www.soc-women-artists.co.uk
**Visual Arts and Galleries Association**
www.vaga.co.uk

## Artists' Materials

**Alec Tiranti Ltd**
www.tiranti.co.uk
**Cowling & Wilcox Ltd**
www.cowlingandwilcox.com
**John Jones Artsauce**
www.johnjones.co.uk

## Arts Councils

**Arts Council of England**
www.artscouncil.org.uk
**Arts Council of Northern Ireland**
www.artscouncil-ni.org/
**Arts Council of Wales**
www.ccc-acw.org.uk
**The Arts Council/ An Chomhairle Ealaíon**
www.artscouncil.ie

## Auction Houses

**Phillips de Pury & Luxemburg**
www.phillips-auctions.com
**Sotheby's**
www.sothebys.com
**Woolley & Wallis**
www.auctions-on-line.com/woolleywallis

## Competitions
**Alastair Salvesen Art Scholarship**
www.royalscottishacademy.org
**Artist & Young Artist of the Year**
www.saa.co.uk
**Eastern Arts Board (Visual and Media Arts Department)**
www.arts.org.uk
**Fulbright Postgraduate Awards**
www.fulbright.co.uk
**John Kinross Memorial Fund**
www.royalscottishacademy.org
**Kettle's Yard Fellowship**
www.kettlesyard.co.uk
**Kraszna-Krausz Book Awards**
www.editor.net/k-k
**National Eisteddfod of Wales**
www.eisteddfod.org.uk
**Queen Elizabeth Scholarship Trust**
www.quest.org.uk
**ROSL ART, Royal Over-Seas League**
www.rosl.org.uk
**Royal Scottish Academy Annual Exhibition**
www.royalscottishacademy.org.uk
**Royal Scottish Academy (RSA) Art for Architecture**
www.rsa.org.uk/afa
**Royal Scottish Academy (RSA) Student Design Awards**
www.rsa.org.uk/projects/details
**The National Art Library Illustration Awards**
www.nal.vam.ac.uk
**The RPS International Print Competition**
www.rps.org

## Conservation Materials
**Conservation By Design**
www.conservation-by-design.co.uk

## Conservators and Restorers
**John Jones Artsauce**
www.johnjones.co.uk
**Rankins (Glass) Company Ltd**
www.rankinsglass.co.uk
**Simon R. Gillespie**
www.art-connection.com

## Crafts
**Bridget Wheatley Contemporary Jewellery**
www.bridgetwheatley.com
**Burford Woodcraft**
www.burford-woodcraft.co.uk
**Bury St Edmund's Art Gallery**
www.burysted-artgall.org
**The Chapel Gallery, The National Trust**
www.chapelgallery@hotmail.com
**Crich Pottery**
www.crichpottery.com
**Dansel Gallery**
www.wdi.co.uk/dansel
**Rufford Craft Centre**
www.ruffordceramiccentre.org.uk
**The Red Gallery**
www.redgallery.co.uk
**White Gallery**
www.whitegallery.co.uk
**Warwick Gallery**
www.members.aol.com/ukgallery

## Dry Mounters
**A. Bliss**
www.abliss.co.uk

## Fairs & Festivals
**Asian Art in London**
www.asianartinlondon.com
**Aldeburgh Festival of Music and the Arts**
www.aldeburgh.co.uk
**Art Cologne**
www.artcologne.de
**Art Frankfurt**
www.artfrankfurt.de
**Art in Action**
www.artinaction.org.uk
**Art Innsbruck**
www.art-innsbruck.at
**The Art on Paper Fair**
www.artonpaper.co.uk
**The Bath Art Fair**
www.penman-fairs.co.uk
**BDC Events**
www.freshartfair.co.uk
**Bracknell Festival 2002**
www.southhillpark.org.uk
**Brighton Festival**
www.brighton-festival.org.uk
**The Chelsea Art Fair**
www.penman-fairs.co.uk
**Chester Antiques and Fine Art Fair**
www.penman-fairs.co.uk
**City of London Festival**
www.colf.org
**The Contemporary Print Show & The Contemporary Print Fair**
www.artnet.co.uk
**The Craft Show**
www.easternevents.com
**The Craft Show for Calke**
www.easternevents.com
**Cultura: the World Art and Antiques Fair**
www.cultura-fair.ch
**Edinburgh International Festival**
www.eif.co.uk
**Felbrigg Coast and Country Show**
www.easternevents.com
**Grassington Festival**
www.grassington-festival.org.uk
**Greenwich and Docklands International Festivals**
www.festival.org
**The Grosvenor House of Art and Antiques Fair**
www.grosvenor-antiquesfair.co.uk
**Harrogate International Festival**
www.harrogate-festival.org.uk
**The Highland Festival: Scotland**
www.highland-festival.co.uk
**The International Art and Design Fair**
www.haughton.com
**International Asian Art Fair**
www.haughton.com
**The International Ceramics Fair and Seminar**
www.haughton.com
**The International Fine Art and Antique Dealers Show.**
www.haughton.com
**The International Fine Art Fair**
www.haughton.com
**Living Crafts**
www.livingcrafts.co.uk
**National Eisteddfod of Wales**
www.eisteddfod.org.uk
**Outsider Art Fair**
www.sandfordsmith
**Patchings Art & Craft Festival**
www.patchingsartcentre.co.uk
**Rye Festival**
www.ryefestival.co.uk
**Ryedale Festival**
www.ryedalefestival.co.uk
**Spitalfields Festival (London)**
www.spitalfieldsfestival.org.uk
**The 20/21 Century British Art Fair**
www.britishartfair.co.uk
**The WaterColours and Drawings Fair**
www.watercoloursfair.com
**The Winter Fine Art and Antiques Fair**
www.olympia-antiques.com
**Winter Olympia Fine Art and Antiques Fair**
www.olympia-antiques.co.uk
**West London Antiques and Fine Art Fair**
www.penman-fairs.co.uk
**Westminster Gallery**
www.wch.co.uk
**Working Craft Show**
www.easternevents.com

## Fine Art Founders
**Black Isle Bronze**
www.blackislebronze.co.uk
**Bronze Age Sculpture Foundry**
www.netcomuk.co.uk/-duncanh
**Burleighfield Arts Limited**
www.polestarltd/sculpture/
**Leander Architectural**
www.leanderarch.demon.co.uk
**Lunts Castings Ltd**
www.luntscastings.co.uk
**Nautilus Fine Art Foundry Ltd**
www.nautilus-foundry.co.uk

## Fine Art Magazines
**Art Monthly**
www.artmonthly.co.uk
**Art Review**
www.art-review.co.uk
**Circa Art Magazine**
www.recirca.com
**Crafts Magazine**
www.craftscouncil.org.uk
**Image Magazine**
www.aophoto.co.uk

## Fine Art Printers
**Loudmouth Postcards**
www.loudworld.co.uk
**The Postcard Company Limited**
www.thepostcardcompany.com

## Fine Art Printers – Art Cards

**Thought Factory**
www.kpegroup@aol.com

## Fine Press Printers/Publishers
**Jones and Palmer Ltd**
www.@jonesandpalmer.co.uk
**Old School Press**
www.praxis.co.uk/ppuk/osp.htm

## Framers
**Academy Framing**
**Royal Academy of Arts**
www.royalacademy.org.uk
**Alec Drew Picture Frames Ltd**
www.hugill.demon.co.uk/adrew.htm
**John Jones Artsauce**
www.johnjones.co.uk
**Simon Beaugie Picture Framers**
www.simonbeaugiepictureframes.com

## Framing Supplies
**Arqadia Ltd**
www.arqadia.co.uk

## Gallery Hanging Supplies
**Frank B. Scragg & Co**
www.frankscragg.co.uk

## Gallery Space for Hire
**Abbott & Holder**
www.artefact.co.uk/AaH.html
**The Air Gallery**
www.airgallery.co.uk
**AOP (Association of Photographers)**
www.aophoto.co.uk
**Artbank Gallery**
www.artbank.com
**Charlotte Street Gallery**
www.28charlottestreet.com
**Collins & Hastie**
www.chelseaart.co.uk
**Fine Art Commissions Ltd**
www.fineartcommissions.com
**The Gallery in Cork Street and Gallery 27**
www.gallery27.com
**Mall Galleries**
www.mallgalleries.org.uk
**Merriscourt Gallery**
www.merriscourt.com
**Royal Hibernian Academy**
www.royalhibernianacademy.com
**S.P.A.C.E. Studios**
www.spacestudios.org.uk
**South London Gallery**
www.southlondonart.co.uk
**Westminster Gallery**
www.wch.co.uk

## Information Services
**AOP (Association of Photographers)**
www.aophoto.co.uk
**The Art Loss Register**
www.artloss.com
**Axis**
www.axisartists.org.uk
**International Arts Bureau**
www.international-arts.org
**National Irish Visual Arts Library**
www.ncad.ie

## Insurance Companies
**Hiscox plc**
www.hiscox.co.uk

## Internet other
**artcyclopedia.com**
www.artcyclopedia.com
**artsjournal.com**
www.artsjournal.com
**artnet.com**
www.artnet.com
**artvitae.com**
www.artvitae.com
**fineartindex.co.uk**
www.fineartindex.co.uk
**fine-art.com**
www.fine-art.com
**museumnetwork.com**
www.museumnetwork.com

## Irish Galleries
**The Architecture Centre**
www.riai.ie
**Butler Gallery**
www.Butlergallery.com
**Crawford Municipal Art Gallery**
www.synergy.ie/crawford
**Harmony Hill Arts Centre**
www.lisburn.gov.uk
**Hugh Lane Municipal Gallery of Modern Art**
www.hughlane.ie
**Irish Museum Of Modern Art**
www.modernart.ie
**Kerlin Gallery**
www.kerlin.ie
**National Gallery of Ireland**
www.nationalgallery.ie
**Oisín Art Gallery**
www.oisingallery.com
**Royal Hibernian Academy**
www.royalhibernianacademy.com
**The Solomon Gallery**
www.solomongallery.com

## London Commercial Galleries
**Aaron Gallery**
www.aarongallery.com
**Abbott & Holder**
www.abbottandholder.co.uk
**Adam Gallery**
www.adamgallery.com
**Advanced Graphics London**
www.advancedgraphics.co.uk
**Agnew's**
www.agnewsgallery.com
**The Air Gallery**
www.airgallery.co.uk
**Alan Cristea Gallery**
www.alancristea.com
**Albemarle Gallery**
www.albemarlegallery.co.uk
**Alex Wengraf**
www.wengraf.com
**Alexandra Gallery**
www.alexandragallery.demon.co.uk
**Anne Faggionato**
www.anne-faggionato.com
**Annely Juda Fine Art**
www.annelyjudafineart.co.uk
**Art First**
www.artfirst.co.uk
**Art For Offices**
www.afo.co.uk
**AOP Gallery (Association of Photographers)**
www.aophoto.co.uk
**Barry Davies Oriental Art**
www.antiques-on-line.com/barrydavies
**BCA – Boukamel Contemporary Art**
www.BCA-gallery.com
**Beaux Arts London**
www.beauxartslondon.co.uk
**Bengstrom**
www.bengstromart.co.uk
**The Bow House Gallery**
www.johnbrown-sculptor.co.uk
**Burlington Paintings**
www.burlington.co.uk
**Cadogan Contemporary Art**
www.artcad.co.uk
**Catto Gallery**
www.catto.co.uk
**CCA Galleries Ltd**
www.ccagalleries.com
**Collins & Hastie Ltd**
www.chelseaart.co.uk
**Colville Place Gallery**
www.romanesque.co.uk/gallery.html
**The Coningsby Gallery**
www.debutart.com
**Curwen Gallery**
www.curwengallery.com
**Daniel Katz Ltd**
www.katz.co.uk
**Davies & Tooth**
www.art-net.co.uk/banca/toodav
**Florence Trust Studios**
www.florencetrust.org
**Flowers East**
www.flowerseast.com
**Francis Graham-Dixon**
www.francisgrahamdixon.com
**Gagosian Gallery**
www.gagosian.com
**Galleria Enterprise**
www.galleria-art.co.uk
**Gallery Different**
www.davidbegbie.com
**Gallery K**
www.gallery-k.co.uk
**Goedhuis Contemporary**
www.goedhuiscontemporary.com
**Hales Gallery**
www.halesgallery.com
**Hilary Chapman, 20th Century Gallery**
www.hilarychapmanfineprints.co.uk
**Hirschl Contemporary Art**
www.hirschlcontemporary.com
**Houldsworth**
www.houldsworth.co.uk
**IAP Fine Art**
www.iapfineart.com
**Jill George Gallery**
www.jillgeorgegallery.co.uk
**Julian Hartnoll**
www.art-on-line.com\hartnoll
**Kings Road Gallery**
www.kingsroadgallery.com
**Lamont Gallery**
www.lamontart.com
**Lefevre Gallery**
www.lefevre-gallery.com
**Linda Blackstone Gallery**
www.blackstoneart.com

**Lisson Gallery**
www.lisson.co.uk
**Long & Ryle Art International**
www.long-and-ryle.demon.co.uk
**Lumley Cazalet**
www.slad.org/lumley-cazalet-ltd
**Marlborough Graphics**
www.marlboroughfineart.com
**Matthiesen Fine Art Limited**
www.Europeanpaintings.com
**The McHardy Sculpture Company**
www.mchardy-sculpture.com
**The Medici Galleries**
www.medicigalleries.co.uk
**Mercury Gallery**
www.mercury-gallery.co.uk
**Moreton Contemporary Art**
www.moretonart.com
**New Academy Gallery and Business Art Galleries**
www.newacademygallery.com
**The October Gallery**
www.theoctobergallery.com
**The Osborne Studio Gallery**
www.osg.uk.com
**Piccadilly Gallery Ltd**
www.piccadillygall.demon.co.uk
**Plazzotta Ltd**
www.plazzotta.co.uk
**Portal Gallery**
www.portal-gallery.com
**Purdy Hicks Gallery**
www.purdyhicks.com
**Rebecca Hossack Gallery**
www.r-h-g.co.uk
**ROSL ART, Royal Over-Seas League**
www.rosl.org.uk
**Scolar Fine Art/Gordon Samuel**
www.scolarfineart.com
**Simmons Gallery**
www.simmonsgallery.co.uk
**The Special Photographer's Company**
www.specialphoto.co.uk
**Spink-Leger**
www.spinkandson.co.uk
**Stern Art Dealers**
www.stern-art.com
**Waddington Galleries**
www.waddington-galleries.com
**Westminster Gallery**
www.wch.co.uk
**Whitford Fine Art**
www.artnet.com/whitford.html
**Will's Art Warehouse**
www.willsart.demon.co.uk
**William Thuillier**
www.thuillart.com
**Wiseman Originals**
www.wisemanoriginals.com

## London Public Galleries

**198 Gallery**
www.198gallery.co.uk
**Barbican Centre**
www.barbican.org.uk
**The Ben Uri Gallery**
www.benuri.com
**Bethnal Green Museum of Childhood**
www.vam.ac.uk/bgm/welcome.html
**Chalk Farm Gallery**
www.chalk-farm-gallery.co.uk
**Contemporary Applied Arts**
www.caa.org.uk
**Crafts Council**
www.craftscouncil.org.uk
**Design Museum**
www.designmuseum.org
**Estorick Collection of Modern Italian Art**
www.estorickcollection.com
**Federation of British Artists,**
www.mallgalleries.org.uk
**Geffrye Museum**
www.lattimore.co.uk/geffrye
**Goethe-Institut London**
www.goethe.de/gr/lon/enindex.htm
**Guildhall Art Gallery**
www.guildhall-art-gallery.org.uk
**Hayward Gallery**
www.haywardgallery.org.uk
**The Horniman Museum and Gardens**
www.horniman.demon.co.uk
**Imperial War Museum**
www.iwm.org.uk
**Institute of Contemporary Arts**
www.illumin.co.uk/ica/
**Kingsgate Gallery**
www.kingsgategallery.org.uk
**Lauderdale House, Arts & Education**
www.lauderdale.org.uk
**Museum of Installation**
www.moi.dircon.co.uk
**The Museum of London**
www.museumoflondon.org.uk
**National Army Museum**
www.failte.com/nam/
**National Gallery**
www.nationalgallery.org.uk
**National Portrait Gallery**
www.npg.org.uk
**Orleans House Gallery**
www.guidetorichmond.co.uk/orleans.html
**Pitshanger Manor Gallery**
www.ealing.gov.uk/pitshanger
**Pump House Gallery**
www.wandsworth.gov.uk/gallery
**Royal Academy of Arts**
www.royalacademy.org.uk
**South London Gallery**
www.southlondonart.co.uk
**Tate Britain/Tate Modern Bankside**
www.tate.org.uk
**TWO10 Gallery**
www.wellcome.ac.uk
**Victoria and Albert Museum The National Museum of Art and Design**
www.vam.ac.uk
**Wallace Collection**
www.demon.co.uk/heritage/wallace
**Westminster Gallery**
www.wch.co.uk
**William Morris Gallery and Brangwyn Gift**
www.lbwf.gov.uk

## Marketing Services and PR

**Parker Harris Partnership**
www.parkerharris.co.uk

## Packers & Shippers

**Art Move Ltd**
www.artmove.co.uk
**C'ART**
www.cart.uk.com
**Cadogan Tate Fine Art Services**
www.cadogantate.com
**Constantine**
www.artservices@ukbusiness.com.
**Hedley's Humpers Ltd**
www.hedleyshumpers.com
**MTEC International Ltd**
www.arttransport.com

## Photographers

**The Photography of Art**
www.books.mcmail.com/photo.htm

## Print Publishers/ Dealers/Galleries

**Advanced Graphics London**
www.advancedgraphics.co.uk
**Brandler Galleries**
www.brandler-galleries.com and
www.thesaurus.co.uk/brandler
**CCA Galleries**
www.ccagalleries.com
**Contemporary Art Holdings**
www.contemporary-art-holdings.co.uk
**contemporary print gallery**
www.artnet.co.uk
**Curwen Gallery**
www.curwen.demon.co.uk
**Greenwich Printmakers Association**
www.longitude0.co.uk/printmakers/
**Hilary Chapman, 20th Century Gallery**
www.hilarychapmanfineprints.co.uk
**Marlborough Graphics**
www.marlboroughfineart.com
**Pratt Contemporary Art/Pratt Editions**
www.prattcontemporaryart.cwc.net
**School of Art Gallery & Museum**
www.aber.ac.uk/museum
**Scolar Fine Art/Gordon Samuel**
www.scolarfineart.com

## Print Workshops

**Counterprint Studio**
www.counter-print.co.uk
**The Curwen Studio**
www.thecurwenstudio.co.uk
**Glasgow Print Studio Workshop**
www.gpsart.co.uk
**Heatherley School of Fine Art**
www.heatherleys.org
**London Print Studio**
www.londonprintstudio.org.uk
**St Barnabas Press**
www.stbarnabaspress.co.uk

## Prints & Printmaking

**The Printmakers Council**
www.printmaker.co.uk/pmc/index.html

## Public Art Agencies

**Art For Offices**
www.afo.co.uk
**Artangel**
www.innercity.demon.co.uk
**Cywaith Cymru . Artworks Wales**
www.cywaithcymru.org

## Regional Art Boards

**South West Arts**
www.swa.co.uk
**West Midlands Arts**
www.arts.org.uk/
**Yorkshire Arts**
www.arts.org.uk

## Regional Galleries

**Abbot Hall Art Gallery**
www.abbothall.org.uk
**Adam Gallery**
www.adamgallery.com
**AdHoc Gallery**
www.northtynesidearts.org.uk
**Alpha Gallery**
www.art-alpha.co.uk
**Arnolfini Gallery**
www.arnolfini.demon.co.uk
**Ashmolean Museum of Art and Archaeology**
www.ashmol.ox.ac.uk/
**The Barber Institute of Fine Arts**
www.barber.org.uk
**Beatrice Royal Contemporary Art and Craft**
www.beatriceroyal.com
**Birmingham Museum and Art Gallery, including the Gas Hall Exhibition Gallery**
www.bmag.co.uk
**Blackthorn Galleries**
www.galleries.u-net.com
**Blackwell – The Arts & Crafts House**
www.blackwell.org.uk
**Bourne Gallery**
www.bournegallery.com
**Brandler Galleries**
www.brandler-galleries.com and
www.thesaurus.co.uk/brandler
**Bromham Mill Art Gallery**
www.borneo.co.uk/bromham-mill/
**Broughton House Gallery**
www.picassomio.com/broughtonhousegallery
**Bury Art Gallery & Museum**
www.bury.gov.uk/culture.htm
**Bury St Edmund's Art Gallery**
www.burysted-artgall.org
**CCA Galleries**
www.ccagalleries.com
**Cheltenham Art Gallery & Museum**
www.cheltenham.org.uk
**Christ Church Picture Gallery**
www.chch.ox.ac.uk
**City Art Gallery**
www.leeds.gov.uk
**Contemporary Fine Art Gallery & Sculpture Park**
www.CFAG.co.uk
**Corrymella Scott Gallery**
www.corrymella.co.uk
**Cupola Gallery**
www.cupolagallery.co.uk
**De La Warr Pavilion**
www.dlwp.com
**The Dean Clough Galleries**
www.DeanClough.com
**Djanogly Art Gallery**
www.nottingham.ac.uk/artscentre/
**Durham Art Gallery**
www.durham.gov.uk
**Durham University Oriental Museum**
www.dur.ac.uk/
**Ferens Art Gallery**
www.hullcc.gov.uk/museums
**Firstsite**
www.firstsite-online.org.uk
**Fitzwilliam Museum**
www.fitzmuseum.cam.ac.uk
**Fox Talbot Museum of Photography**
www.fox-talbot.org.uk/foxtalbot
**Foyer Gallery/James Hockey Gallery**
www.surrart.ac.uk
**Future Factory at the Bonington Gallery**
www.future-factory.org
**Gainsborough's House**
www.gainsborough.org
**The Gallery, Gateshead Central Library**
www.wamses.unn.ac.uk
**The Gallery Manchester's Art House**
www.manchestersarthouse.com
**The Gallery**
www1.btwebworld.com/carpathian/
**Gordon Reece Gallery**
www.gordonreecegalleries.com
**Graham Clarke**
www.grahamclarke.co.uk
**Harris Museum & Art Gallery**
www.preston.gov.uk/museum
**The Henry Moore Foundation**
www.henry-moore-fdn.co.uk/hnt
**The Henry Moore Institute**
www.henry-moore-fdn.co.uk
**Herbert Art Gallery and Museum**
www.coventry.org/coventrymuseums
**The Holburne Museum of Art**
www.bath.ac.uk/holburne
**Ikon Gallery**
www.ikon-gallery.co.uk
**The John Davies Gallery**
www.The-John-Davies-Gallery.co.uk
**Jonathan Poole**
www.jonathanpoole.co.uk
**Lady Lever Art Gallery**
www.nmgm.org.uk
**Leeds Metropolitan University Gallery**
www.lmu.ac.uk/arts
**Lion Gallery**
www.cogent-comms.co.uk/lion.htm
**Lupton Square Gallery**
www.luptonsquaregallery.co.uk
**mac (Midlands Arts Centre)**
www.birminghamarts.org.uk
**Maltby Contemporary Art**
www.maltbyart.fsnet.co.uk
**Manchester City Art Gallery**
www.u-net.com/set/mcag/cag.html
**Merriscourt Gallery**
www.merriscourt.com
**Milton Keynes Gallery**
www.mkweb.co.uk/mkg
**Montage Studio Gallery**
www.montage-gallery.co.uk
**Museum of Modern Art**
www.moma.org.uk
**Museum of Reading**
www.readingmuseum.org
**The Museum of Science & Industry in Manchester**
www.edes.co.uk/mussci
**Nevill Gallery**
www.nevillgallery.com
**New Ashgate Gallery**
www.newashgate.com
**Norfolk Museums Service**
www.norfolk.gov.uk/tourism/museums/museums/htm
**Northern Gallery for Contemporary Art (NGCA)**
www.ngca.co.uk
**Number Nine The Gallery**
www.No9thegallery.com
**Object 57**
www.object57.co.uk
**Parkview Fine Paintings**
www.ourworld.compuserve.com/homepages/parkviewpaintings
**Peter Scott Gallery**
www.lancs.ac.uk/users/PETERSCOTT/Scott.htm
**Peter's Barn Gallery**
www.petersbarn.co.uk
**Piece Hall Art Gallery**
www.calderdale.gov.uk
**Portsmouth City Museum and Records Office**
www.xpcclsde@hants.gov.uk
**Royal Albert Memorial Museum and Art Gallery**
www.exeter.gov.uk
**Rugby Art Gallery & Museum**
www.rugbygalleryandmuseum.org.uk
**Snape Maltings Gallery**
www.snapemaltings.co.uk
**The Stanley Picker Gallery for the Arts**
www.JPEGDESIGN.CO.UK
**Stanley Spencer Gallery**
www.stanleyspencer.org
**Sudley House**
www.nmgm.org.uk
**Tate Gallery St Ives**
www.tate.org.uk
**Tate Liverpool**
www.tate.org.uk
**Terrace Gallery**
www.harewood.org
**Tunbridge Wells Museum and Art Gallery**
www.tunbridgewells.gov.uk/museum
**Turnpike Gallery**
www.wiganmbc.gov.uk
**University Gallery Leeds**
www.leeds.ac.uk/library/gall/exhibs.html
**University of Essex Gallery**
www.essex.ac.uk
**University of Hertfordshire Galleries**
www.herts.ac.uk/artdes/
**University of Hull Art Collection**
www.hull.ac.uk/history/art/arthome.htm
**Walker Art Gallery**
www.nmgm.org.uk
**White Gallery**
www.whitegallery.co.uk
**Wolverhampton Art Gallery**
www.wolverhamptonart.org.uk
**Woodbine Cottage Gallery**
www.woodbinecottagegallery.co.uk
**Wysing Arts**
www.wysing.demon.co.uk
**York City Art Gallery**
www.york.gov.uk/heritage/museums/art

## Scottish Galleries

**An Lanntair**
www.lanntair.com
**Art on the Links Gallery**
www.oldcoursehotel.co.uk
**Danish Cultural Institute**
www.dancult.demon.co.uk
**Dean Gallery**
www.natgalscot.ac.uk
**University of Dundee Exhibitions**
www.exhibitions.dundee.ac.uk
**The Fergusson Gallery**
www.pkc.gov.uk
**Frames Contemporary Gallery**
www.framesgallery.co.uk
**Glasgow Print Studio Gallery**

www.gpsart.co.uk
**Hunterian Art Gallery**
www.hunterian.gla.ac.uk
**Ingleby Gallery**
www.inglebygallery.com
**Museum of Scotland**
www.nms.ac.uk
**National Gallery of Scotland**
www.natgalscot.ac.uk
**Open Eye Gallery**
www.openeye.co.uk
**Paisley Museum, Art Galleries and Coats Observatory**
www.renfrewshire.gov.uk
**Portfolio Gallery**
www.ednet.co.uk/-portfolio
**Project Ability Centre for Developmental Arts/ Trongate Studios**
www.project-ability.co.uk
**Royal Museum**
www.nms.ac.uk
**Royal Scottish Academy**
www.royalscottishacademy.org
**Scottish Gallery (Aitken Dott Ltd)**
www.scottish-gallery.co.uk
**Scottish National Gallery of Modern Art**
www.natgalscot.ac.uk
**Scottish National Portrait Gallery**
www.natgalscot.ac.uk
**Strathearn Gallery and Pottery**
www.strathearn-gallery.com
**The Vennel Gallery**
www.northayrshiremuseums.org.uk

## Sculpture Parks

**The Henry Moore Foundation**
www.henry-moore-fdn.co.uk/hmf
**New Art Centre Sculpture Park and Gallery**
www.sculpture.uk.com
**Peter's Barn Gallery**
www.petersbarngallery.co.uk
**Scottish Sculpture Workshop**
www.ssw.org.uk
**Sculpture at Goodwood**
www.sculpture.org.uk
**Yorkshire Sculpture Park**
www.ysp.co.uk

## Studio Space for Hire

**S.P.A.C.E. Studios**
www.spacestudios.org.uk

## Welsh Galleries

**Attic Gallery**
www.atticgallery.co.uk
**Carningli Centre**
www.carningli.co.uk
**Martin Tinney Gallery**
www.artwales.dircon.co.uk
**The Museum Of Modern Art, Wales**
www.tabernac.dircon.co.uk
**National Museums & Galleries of Wales**
www.nmgw.ac.uk
**Ogilvy & Estill**
www.ogilvyestill.co.uk
**Oriel 31, Davies Memorial Gallery**
www.oriel31.org
**Oriel Ceri Richards Gallery**
www.whatsonwales.com
**Oriel Plas Glyn-y-Weddw**
www.oriel.org.uk
**Royal International Pavilion**
www.royal-pavilion.co.uk
**School of Art Gallery & Museum**
www.aber.ac.uk/museum
**The Studio**
www.david-wilson.net
**Tenby Museum & Art Gallery**
www.tenbymuseum.free-online.co.uk
**Turner House**
www.nmgw.ac.uk
**The Washington Gallery**
www.valeofglamorgan.gov.uk

NOTES

# Auction Houses

# Auction Houses

The year 2001 has been an exciting year for the international art market and contemporary art has been leading the way. Dozens of new world records have been achieved at many major auctions in both London and New York and the widespread fears of an impending slump in the market's momentum have receded. Despite (or perhaps as a result of) the ups and downs of the stock market and the controversial introduction of the euro as hard currency in twelve European countries on 1 January 2002, an increasing number of collectors around the globe are buying young contemporary art as a more solid investment than shares.

But what should the collector look for when buying young contemporary art at auction? If it's consultation or advice, many auction house specialists can certainly help. It would also be advisable to have long conversations with the gallery owners and dealers who represent these artists on the primary market. Ideally, the collector should make a visit to the artist's studio – something many gallery owners are happy to organise. The truth is, contemporary art is difficult to understand without at least a little previous knowledge of the artist and his surrounding environment.

It's hard to say what comprises a great work of art. It's generally something you feel in your bones – at least, that's what most well-known collectors have told me over the years. It should be daring and provocative – after all, that's what the avant-garde is all about. At the same time, it should fit easily into art history. And it should somehow reflect or respond to the 'zeitgeist' of the time in which it was created or conceived. So, a great work of art should be radical and traditional, of the moment and timeless, all at the same time – not an easy task, but one that some young artists have come to master.

What is contemporary art anyway? That's one of the most difficult questions to answer, and there's probably no 100 per cent correct answer. If an artist calls it art, then so be it! And if the artist is courageous enough to call it art, then why not just trust him or her and muster up the courage to acquire it? More than anything else, art is a catalyst for communication. Join in the dialogue and participate in the making of art history.

In the end, it doesn't matter if you're buying art at auctions, galleries, art fairs or even directly from the artists' studios – the point is, just do it and enjoy it! Go out on a ledge. It's impossible to lose, because, even if the market does crash one day, you'll at least have made an extraordinary journey and, unlike stocks and bonds, there's still the satisfaction of owning something you like to hang on the wall and live with.

Gérard A Goodrow
Director
Christie's Contemporary Art

### ▶ Bonhams & Brooks C
Montpelier Street, Knightsbridge, London SW7 1HH.
**Tel** 020 7584 9161, 020 7393 3962/3900
**Fax** 020 7589 4072, 020 7393 3905
**Personnel** Prints Department: Pippa Toolan.

### ▶ Cheffins Grain & Comins C
2 Clifton Road, Cambridge CB1 4BW.
**Tel** 01223 213 343 **Fax** 01223 413 396

### ▶ Christie's
8 King Street, St James's, London SW1Y 6QT.
**Tel** 020 7839 9060
**Opening times** Weekdays 9–4.30.
**Personnel** Chairman: Christopher Balfour.

### ▶ Christie's C
85 Old Brompton Road, London SW7 3LD.
**Tel** 020 7321 3120, 020 7581 7611
**Fax** 020 7581 3679
**Personnel** Jill Potterton. Rachel Cook. Emma Sully.

### ▶ Christie's Scotland
164–166 Bath Street, Glasgow G2 4TB.
**Personnel** Neil McRae.

### ▶ Grays Auction Rooms C
5–7 Buck Street, London NW1.
**Tel** 020 7284 2026

### ▶ Harman Healy C
340 Grays Inn Road, London WC1X.
**Tel** 020 7833 5885

### ▶ Henry Spencer & Son
20 The Square, Retford DN22 6BX.

### ▶ Lloyds International Auction Galleries C
118 Putney Road, London SW15 2NQ.
**Tel** 020 8788 7777

### ▶ Mallams C
St Michael's Street, Oxford OX1 2EB.

### ▶ Outhwaite & Litherland C
Kingsway Galleries, Fontenoy Street, Liverpool L3 2BE.

### ▶ Phillips de Pury & Luxemburg C
101 New Bond Street, London W1Y 0AS.
**Tel** 020 7629 6602 **Fax** 020 7629 8876
**Ws** www.phillips-auctions.com
**Opening times** Mon–Fri 8.30–5 and most Sundays for viewing 2–5.
**Nearest Underground** Bond Street.
**Personnel** Chairman: Christopher Weston. Managing Director: Roger Hollest.
**Services and Facilities** Art for Offices. Valuation.
**Work Stocked and Sold** Dr. Pa. Sc.

### ▶ Phillips West C
2 Salem Road, London W2.
**Tel** 020 7221 5303

### ▶ Russel Balwin & Bright C
Rylelands Road, Leominster HR6 8NZ.

### ▶ Sotheby's
34–35 New Bond Street, London W1A 2AA.
**Tel** 020 7293 5000 **Fax** 020 7293 5959
**Ws** www.sothebys.com
**Opening times** 9–4.30.
**Nearest Underground** Bond Street.
**Personnel** Chairman: Henry Wyndham. Chief Executive Europe and Asia: Robin Woodhead. Managing Director: George Bailey.
**Services and Facilities** Art Consultancy. Bookshop. Café. Disabled Access. Gallery space for hire. Guided Tours. Lectures. Valuation.
**Work Stocked and Sold** Ab. App. Dr. Fur. Jew. Pa. Ph. Pr. Sc.
**Price range** All ranges
*Founded more than 250 years ago in 1744, Sotheby's is the oldest and largest internationally recognised firm of fine art auctioneers in the world. It has an international network of 98 offices in 38 countries in Europe, Asia and the Americas, with 17 worldwide auction centres. We also hold regular online auctions at www.sothebys.com. We are happy to advise on buying, selling and valuations for insurance and probate. Central to our ability to achieve great successes are our reputation for knowledge and expertise and our long-standing client relationships around the world, of which we are extremely proud.*

### ▶ Sotheby's C
Summers Place, Billingshurst, West Sussex RH14 9AD.
**Tel** 01403 833 500 **Fax** 01403 833 699
**Ws** www.sothebys.com
**Opening times** Mon–Fri 9.30–4.30, Sat 9.30–12.30.
**Nearest Station** Billingshurst.
**Personnel** Chairman: Tim Wonnacott. Managing Director: Alistair Morris.
**Services and Facilities** Art Consultancy. Café. Disabled Access. Parking. Restaurant. Valuation.
**Work Stocked and Sold** Cer. Fur. Gla. Jew. Pa. Pr. Sc.
*This is the largest regional auction saleroom in Great Britain. Specialising in garden statuary and sporting guns, the expert staff at our Sussex sale room are always happy to advise on buying, selling and valuations for insurance and probate.*

### ▶ Sotheby's
Hammersmith Road, Kensington, London W14 8UX.
**Tel** 020 7293 5000 **Fax** 020 7293 5859
**Email** olympia@sothebys.com
**Ws** www.sothebys.com
**Opening times** Mon–Sat 10–5, Sun 12–5.
**Personnel** Chairman: Tim Wonnacott. Managing Director: Paul Sumner.
**Services and Facilities** Art Consultancy. Bookshop. Café. Disabled Access. Gallery space for hire. Guided Tours. Lectures. Parking. Valuation.
**Work Stocked and Sold** Ab. App. Cer. Dec. Fur. Gla. Pa. Tx.
**Price range** £400–£59,999 approx
*Opening in September 2001, Sotheby's new sale room at Olympia almost doubles Sotheby's central London exhibition space and will offer a full calendar of sales across a range of categories. These are Arms, Armour and Militaria, Ceramics and Glass, Clocks, Watches and Scientific Instruments, Japanese Works of Art, Rugs and Carpets, Rock and Roll and Entertainment Memorabilia, Silver and Vertu, Sporting Memorabilia, and Textiles and Fashion. We also have specialists in Furniture and Works of Art and in Paintings, offering regular sales. The expert staff at Olympia are always happy to advise on buying, selling and valuations for insurance and probate.*

### ▶ Southgate Auction Rooms C
55 High Street, Southgate, London N14 6LD.
**Tel** 020 8886 7888 **Fax** 020 8982 5065

### ▶ Stanley Gibbons C
399 Strand, London WC2R 0LX.
**Tel** 020 7836 8444

### ▶ Thompson Anthony C
7 Kensington Park Gardens, London W11.
**Tel** 020 7221 5072

### ▶ TWK C
8 Seymour Place, London W1H.
**Tel** 020 7724 7144

### ▶ Woolley & Wallis C
Salisbury Salerooms, 51–61 Castle Street, Salisbury SP1 3SU.
**Tel** 01722 424 500 **Fax** 01722 424 508
**Email** woolley@interalpha.co.uk
**Ws** www.auctions-on-line.com/woolleywallis
**Opening times** Mon–Fri 9–5.30, Sat 9–12.
**Nearest Station** Salisbury.
**Personnel** Managing Director: Paul Viney.
**Services and Facilities** Parking. Valuation.

# Art in Country Houses

NOTES

# Art in Country Houses

Many, if not all, museums' worthy socioeconomic and political functions have been pursued since the 19th century. The more stimulating projects are increasingly the preserve of new and smaller museums, where response to traditional and authoritarian curatorial expectations is less rigid.

Compton Verney, for instance, a Grade 1 listed Adam House within a Capability Brown park, was purchased by the Peter Moores Foundation in 1993 to provide an environment in which art could be encountered in fresh and non-didactic ways. From the artist's point of view, a faded mansion in middle England must by definition offer a more independent context in which to exhibit work than an institutional gallery.

For artists, Compton Verney is inspirational, both physically and historically. Its position, dimension, form, colour and mood are conceptually a set piece against which new art can position itself.

Key to the Compton Verney experience is the intervisibility of the site; it interacts as both a gallery and a park. Adam's mansion draws in the visitor from vistas, each composed by Capability Brown to invite exploration and experience of a picturesque landscape which is always visible from the house. Simon Patterson's work *Landskip* (1998), for instance, animated and engaged a historical sequence of vistas from the mansion, using a palette of coloured smoke at set intervals, both changing the colour and mood in the park and recalling experimental warfare which took place on the site in the 1940s.

Artists will want to work within an institutional museum context, partly because of the important historic collections with which they can interact or intervene. Peter Moores's project in Liverpool's Walker Art Gallery in the early 1970s provides a good example, selecting international contemporary art and juxtaposing it, not as part of a book of history, but as itself.

But if artists and curators are quizzed about their favourite museum, chances are their choices will not be huge, suffocating civic buildings. Add to this the threat from architecture, where the spectacle of a concrete or a reclaimed monument can emasculate the art inside, and a pretty clear reason emerges as to why the popularity of ad hoc venues such as Compton Verney is accelerating.

Mass audiences cannot move effortlessly from the appeal of blockbuster galleries and museums to places such as Compton Verney. Less than 200,000 can be accommodated on the site annually, posing the question of what impact this new gallery can have.

Compton Verney houses its collections and exhibitions in both historic and contemporary galleries, strikingly simple and neither domestic nor institutional. It is a place where landscape, weather, light and an exemplary sense of calm can enhance an artist's response or dialogue with the world, and with the visitor.

Richard Gray
Director
Compton Verney

### ▶ Ascott House
Ascott Estate Office Wing,
Leighton Buzzard LU7 0PS.
**Tel** 01296 688 242 **Fax** 01296 681 904

### ▶ Blenheim Palace P
Woodstock OX20 1PX.
**Tel** 01993 811 091
**Fax** 01993 813 527
**Opening times** Mid-Mar–end Oct 10.30–5.30 (last admission 4.45).
**Nearest Station** Oxford.
**Personnel** Education Officer: Mr J. D. Forster.
**Services and Facilities** Bookshop. Café. Guided Tours. Museum Shop. Parking. Restaurant. Shop.

### ▶ Blickling Hall
Blickling, Aylsham NR11 6NF.
**Tel** 01263 733 471 **Fax** 01263 734 924
**Opening times** Opening times for both hall and gardens vary. Please phone for details.

### ▶ Bodelwyddan Castle
Bodelwyddan, Rhyl LL18 5YA.
**Tel** 01745 583 539/584 060
**Fax** 01745 584 563
**Opening times** Open throughout the year. Please ring for details.
**Personnel** Director: Bryn Hughes.

### ▶ Bowhill
Selkirk.
**Tel** 01750 22204
**Fax** 01750 22204
**Email** bht@buccleuch.com
**Opening times** House: public opening in Jul. Country Park: May–Aug. Times and dates vary annually. Educational groups by appointment throughout the year.
**Nearest Station** Edinburgh Waverly 40 miles, Berwick 40 miles.
**Personnel** The Duke of Buccleuch.
**Services and Facilities** Café. Disabled Access. Gallery space for hire. Guided Tours. Lectures. Parking. Restaurant. Shop.
*This part of the renowned Buccleuch Collection includes Canaletto's* Whitehall, *a key Ruiysdael, and several Guardis, works by Gainsborough, Reynolds, Claude, Vernet, Raeburn and Wilkie. French furniture 1680–1780. Porcelain includes a Sèvres set made for Madame du Barry. Lecture theatre, arts courses, visitor centre, conference centre, audiovisual. Bowhill Little Theatre (drama, music, dance). Gardens/Grounds. Adventure Playground. Education Service.*

### ▶ Brodie Castle
Brodie, Forres IV36 0TE.
**Tel** 01309 641 371 **Fax** 01309 641 600

### ▶ Bryn Bras Castle
Llanrug, near Llanberis, Caernarfon LL55 4RE.
**Tel** 01286 870 210
**Opening times** Telephone for times. Admission charge.
**Personnel** Marita Gray-Parry.
**Services and Facilities** Café.

### ▶ Chirk Castle
Chirk, Wrexham LL14 5AF.
**Tel** 01691 777 701 **Fax** 01691 774 706

### ▶ Compton Verney House
Warwickshire CV35 9HJ.
**Tel** 01926 641 777
**Fax** 01926 642 224

### ▶ Dalmeny House
South Queensferry EH30 9TQ.
**Tel** 0131 331 1888
**Fax** 0131 331 1788
**Opening times** Jul and Aug: Mon–Tue 12–5.30, Sun 1–5.30 (last admission 4.45). Closed other days except by appointment.
**Nearest Station** Dalmeny.
**Personnel** Administrator: Mrs Linda Edgar.
**Services and Facilities** Café. Disabled Access. Guided Tours. Parking.

### ▶ Drumlanrig Castle
Thornhill DG3 4AQ.
**Tel** 01848 330 248
**Fax** 01848 331 682
**Email** bre@drumlanrigcastle.org.uk
**Ws** www.drumlanrigcastle.org.uk
**Opening times** Please phone for details of opening times.
**Nearest Station** Sanquhar 10 miles.
**Personnel** House Manager: Claire Fisher.
**Services and Facilities** Craftshop. Disabled Access. Guided Tours. Lectures. Parking. Restaurant. Shop.
*Renowned Buccleuch collection includes Rembrandt's* Old Woman Reading, *Holbein's* Sir Nicholas Carew, *Leonardo da Vinci's* Madonna with the Yarnwinder, *Merton's* Countess of Dalkeith. *Cabinets made for Versailles, much French and English furniture 1680–1750 and 1670 silver chandelier. Gardens/Grounds.*

### ▶ Dunrobin Castle and Museum
Dunrobin Castle, Golspie KW10 6RR.
**Tel** 01408 633 177
**Fax** 01408 633 800
**Personnel** Custodians: Mr Keith Jones, Mrs Sheila Broad.

### ▶ Eastnor Castle
Portcullis Office, Eastnor, Ledbury HR8 1RN.
**Tel** 01531 633 160 **Fax** 01531 631 776
**Opening times** Opening hours: Sundays, Easter–end of Sep, bank holiday Mondays and Sun–Fri Jul and Aug 12–5.

### ▶ Euston Hall
Estate Office, Euston, Thetford IP24 2QP.
**Tel** 01842 766 366
**Opening times** Thu only 2.30–5 in Jun, Jul, Aug, Sep plus 25 Jun and 3 Sep 2.30–5.
**Personnel** Duke of Grafton.

### ▶ Floors Castle
Roxburghe Estates Office, Kelso TD5 7SF.
**Tel** 01573 223 333
**Fax** 01573 226 056
**Opening times** Easter–Sep: daily 10.30–5.30. Oct: Sun and Wed 10.30–4.30.

### ▶ Glamis Castle
Glamis DD8 1RL.
**Tel** 01307 840 202
**Fax** 01307 840 257
**Opening times** Opening times vary. Please phone for details.
**Personnel** Earl of Strathmore and Kinghorne.

### ▶ Hatfield House, Park and Gardens
Hatfield AL9 5NQ.
**Tel** 01707 287 010 **Fax** 01707 287 033
**Opening times** 26 Mar–29 Sep 2002 Tue–Fri 12–4, Sun 1–4.30.
**Nearest Station** Hatfield (opposite main gates).
**Personnel** The Marquess of Salisbury.
**Services and Facilities** Café. Disabled Access. Guided Tours. Parking. Restaurant. Shop.
*Where Elizabethan history began. Home of Marquess of Salisbury. Jacobean house with famous portraits, tapestries and embroidery. Portraits of each generation of Cecil family since Wm. Cecil, Lord Burghley. Artists include Reynolds, Lawrence, Romney and Richmond. Rainbow and Ermine portraits of Queen Elizabeth I and* A Fête at Bermondsey, *c.1570, by Joris Hoefnagel. Spectacular organic gardens. National collection of model soldiers, childrens play area, marked Park trails, restaurant and shops.*

### ▶ Hopetoun House
South Queensferry EH30 9SL.
**Tel** 0131 331 2451
**Opening times** 14 Apr–2 Oct 10–5.30 (last entry 4.45).
**Personnel** The Marquess of Linlithgow.
**Services and Facilities** Disabled Access. Lectures. Parking. Restaurant. Shop.

### ▶ House of the Binns
Linlithgow EH49 7NA.
**Tel** 01506 834 255

### ▶ Knebworth House
Knebworth SG3 6PY.
**Tel** 01438 813 303/812 661
**Fax** 01438 811 908

### ▶ Losely House
Guildford GU3 1HS.
**Tel** 01483 304 440
**Fax** 0148 302 036
**Opening times** 3 May 1995–30 Sep 1995, Wed–Sat 2–5.
**Personnel** Director: Major J. R. More-Molyneux.

### ▶ Manderston
Duns TD11 3PP.
**Tel** 01361 883 450 **Fax** 01361 882 010
**Opening times** 14 May–27 Sep: Thu and Sun 2–5.30, also bank holidays 25 May and 31 Aug. Group visits any time of year by appointment.
**Personnel** Lord Palmer. Secretary: Julie Bareham.
**Services and Facilities** Café. Shop.

### ▶ Melbourne Hall P
Melbourne DE73 1EN.
**Tel** 01332 862 502
**Fax** 01332 862 263

### ▶ Penshurst Place and Gardens
Penhurst, Tonbridge TN11 8DG.
**Tel** 01892 870 307 **Fax** 01892 810 866
**Opening times** 1 Apr–29 Sep, 11–6 grounds (last entry to house 5). Also open weekends in Mar and Oct.
**Services and Facilities** Guided Tours. Parking. Restaurant. Shop.

### ▶ Ragley Hall
Alcester B49 5NJ.
**Tel** 01789 762 090 **Fax** 01789 764 791
**Opening times** Easter–end of Sep 1–5 every day except Mon and Fri.
**Personnel** Director: Earl of Yarmouth.

### ▶ Sudeley Castle
Winchcombe.
**Tel** 01242 602 308 **Fax** 01242 602 959
**Opening times** Apr-Oct 12–5.

### ▶ Tatton Park
Knutsford WA16 6QN.
**Tel** 01565 654 822 **Fax** 01565 650 179

### ▶ Temple Newsam House
Leeds City Council, Leeds LS15 0AE.
**Tel** 01532 647 321 or
0113 264 7321/264 1358
**Fax** 01532 602 285 or 0113 260 2285
**Opening times** Tue–Sun 10.30–5.30 (dusk in winter), closed Mon except bank holidays.

### ▶ Towneley Hall
Burnley BB11 3RQ.
**Tel** 01282 424 213 **Fax** 01282 361 138
**Opening times** Mon–Fri 10–5, closed Sat. Sun 12–5. Admission free.

### ▶ Traquair House
Innerleithen EH44 6PW.
**Tel** 01896 830 323 **Fax** 01896 830 639
**Email** traquair.house@scotborders.co.uk
**Services and Facilities** Lectures.

### ▶ Tredegar House and Park P
Coedkernew, Newport NP1 9YW.
**Tel** 01633 815 880 **Fax** 01633 815 895
**Opening times** Easter–Oct, Wed–Sun. Aug open all week, Oct open weekends only. Open bank holidays and special Halloween and Christmas openings.
**Nearest Station** Newport.
**Personnel** Marketing and Events Officer: Sarah Freeman.
**Services and Facilities** Bookshop. Café. Craftshop. Guided Tours. Lectures. Parking. Restaurant. Shop.

### ▶ Turton Tower P
Chapeltown Road, Turton BL7 0HG.
**Tel** 01204 852 203 **Fax** 01204 853 759
**Opening times** May–Sep Mon–Thu 10–12 and 1–5, weekends 1–5; Mar, Oct Sat–Wed 1–4; April Sat–Wed 2–5; Nov, Feb 1–4.
**Nearest Station** Bromley.
**Personnel** Keeper: M. J. Robinson Dowland.
**Services and Facilities** Bookshop. Café. Craftshop. Disabled Access. Friends Society. Guided Tours. Lectures. Museum Shop. Parking. Shop. Workshop Facilities.

### ▶ Upton House
Banbury OX15 6HT.
**Tel** 01295 670 266 (National Trust)
**Fax** 01295 670 266
**Email** vuplan@smtp.ntrust.org.uk
**Ws** www.nationaltrust.org.uk
**Opening times** House, restaurant, shop and garden open 1 Apr–31 Oct 2002 Sat–Wed 1–5 (last admission 4.30). Closed Thu and Fri.
**Nearest Station** Banbury 7 miles.
**Personnel** Property Manager: Oliver Lane.
**Services and Facilities** Disabled Access. Guided Tours. Lectures. Parking. Restaurant. Shop.
*Upton House is a rare and outstanding example of a 20th-century oil magnate's country mansion, the wealth and taste of its owner being reflected in the contents of the house and its garden.*
*The house itself, built of a mellow local stone, dates from 1695, but the internationally important collections it contains are the chief attraction. Assembled this century by the 2nd Lord Bearsted, they include paintings by English and Continental Old Masters including Hogarth, Stubbs, Brueghel, El Greco, Guardi and Caneletto; also Brussels tapestries, Sèvres porcelain, Chelsea figures and 18th-century furniture.*

### ▶ Wilton House
Wilton, Salisbury SP2 0BJ.
**Tel** 01722 746 720 **Fax** 01722 744 447
**Opening times** Opening times vary. Please phone for details.
**Nearest Station** Salisbury.
**Personnel** Tourism Assistant: Sally Watkins.
**Services and Facilities** Bar. Bookshop. Café. Disabled Access. Gallery space for hire. Parking. Restaurant. Shop.

### ▶ Woburn Abbey
Woburn MK43 0TP.
**Tel** 01525 290 666 **Fax** 01525 290 271
**Opening times** 11–4 (5 Sun and bank holidays). Open daily Mar–Oct, and weekends only from Oct.
**Nearest Station** Flitwick or Milton Keynes.
**Personnel** Controller: Mr W. Lash.
**Services and Facilities** Café. Guided Tours. Parking. Shop.
*Woburn Abbey is the home of the Marquess and Marchioness of Tavistock and their family. One of the most important private art collections in the world can be seen here, including paintings by Van Dyck, Gainsborough, Reynolds, Velazquez and Canaletto. The collection also includes French and English 18th-century furniture, silver and gold. The tour of the Abbey covers three floors, including the vaults, filled with exquisite French, Japanese, German and English porcelain. There is an Antiques Centre, coffee shop and gift shops. Call for opening details.*

# NOTES

# Sculpture Parks

# NOTES

# Sculpture Parks

There are many sculpture parks in the world; some large, some small, some good and some indifferent. The UK has an interesting array of contrasting sites concerned with the creation and display of sculpture in the landscape. These include: the Yorkshire Sculpture Park, set in 500 acres of historical parkland; the Grisedale Sculpture Trail, integrated into the magnificent Grisedale Forest; the 20-acre Sculpture at Goodwood, overlooking Chichester; Roche Court, which houses the New Art Centre near Salisbury; and several others.

Although the post-war Battersea Park and Holland Park exhibitions influenced the establishment of such sculpture parks in Europe as the Middleheim Park in Belgium and the Kroller-Muller Rijksmuseum in Holland, no permanent open-air sites for sculpture were established in this country until 1977.

In Britain, initiatives to site sculpture in a landscape emerged away from the influence of major galleries and public collections and evolved into either open-air art galleries or sculpture trails.

The logistics of siting sculpture in the landscape are quite formidable. Sometimes temporary roads have to be built, landscape reorganised, electricity lines laid and cranes employed to find the best location for works. Other important factors to take into consideration include the security of the works, not only against possible damage from the public but also against wildlife and the elements.

The assumption that the outdoors is better for sculpture is deeply misplaced. Certainly, the notion that if a sculpture is too big for a gallery space it should be placed out of doors is not a criterion for selection.

Context should always be the most important consideration. Many works do not have the scale or form to cope with the space or changing background of nature. Landscape can generate a more conceptual response from some artists who develop ideas stimulated by the site. This may result in a publication, action, video or computer-generated work, or some other form of practice.

Projects concerned with the open air need not be considered separately from gallery and museum exhibitions, as all have to justify their relevance and curatorial rationale. The landscape, however, does pose a distinctive challenge for artists and, indeed, curators.

Peter Murray
Director
Yorkshire Sculpture Park

### ▶ Barbara Hepworth Museum and Sculpture Park

Barnoon Hill, St Ives. **Tel** 01736 792 226

### ▶ The Chilford Hall Sculpture Centre C

**Tel** 01223 892 641 **Fax** 01223 894 056
**Personnel** MD: Simon Alper.
**Services and Facilities** Art Consultancy. Café. Commissioning Service. Disabled Access. Gallery space for hire. Parking. Shop.
**Work Stocked and Sold** Sc.
For artists see Commercial Gallery Artists.

### ▶ The Garden Gallery C

Rookery Lane, Broughton, Stockbridge SO20 8AZ.
**Tel** 01794 301 144 **Fax** 01794 301 761
**Email** gardengallery@compuserve.com
**Opening times** Early May–end Jul Tue/Thu/Sat 10–5.
**Nearest Station** Winchester or Salisbury.
**Personnel** Director: Rachel Bebb.
**Services and Facilities** Art Consultancy. Art for Offices. Commissioning Service. Disabled Access. Lectures. Parking.
**Work Stocked and Sold** Cer. Fur. Sc.
**Price range** £20–£40,000
For artists see Commercial Gallery Artists.

### ▶ The Henry Moore Foundation

Dane Tree House, Perry Green,
Much Hadham SG10 6EE.
**Tel** 01279 843 333 **Fax** 01279 843 647
**Email** info@henry-moore-fdn.co.uk
**Ws** www.henry-moore-fdn.co.uk/hmf
**Personnel** C. M. Joint.
**Services and Facilities** Guided Tours. Lectures. Parking. Restaurant. Shop.
**Work Stocked and Sold** Pr.
**Price range** £500–£5,000
For artists see Commercial Gallery Artists.

### ▶ New Art Centre Sculpture Park and Gallery C

Roche Court, East Winterslow, Salisbury, SP5 1BG
**Tel** 01980 862 224 **Fax** 01980 862 447
**Email** nac@globalnet..co.uk
**Ws** www.sculpture.uk.com
**Opening times** Every day 11- 4,
**Nearest Station** Salisbury or Andover.
**Personnel** Curator: Helen Simpson, Gallery Manager: Suzanne Caclard, Registrar: Tim Courage, Director: Madeline Bessborough
**Services and Facilities** Art Consultancy. Art for Offices. Commissioning Service. Guided Tours. Lectures, Parking.
**Work Stocked and Sold** Sc, Cer, Fur, Pa, Ph, Wd
**Price range** £5,000 upwards
For artists see Commercial Gallery Artists.

*Gallery at Roche Court*

*20th Century sculpture from Europe and the USA, shown throughout the gardens and parkland. Works by Antony Gormley, Nigel Hall, Tania Kovats, Christopher Le Brun, Richard Long, David Nash, Louise Nevelson, Mimmo Paladino, Rachel Whiteread, Bill Woodrow, Daphne Wright and many others. The New Art Centre represents the Estate of Barbara Hepworth, with many works on display.Lettering in the Walled Garden. Changing exhibitions in the award winning new gallery by Muckenback + Marshall. New artist's house designed by Stephen Marshall opening June 2001. All works for sale.*

### ▶ Peter's Barn Gallery C

South Ambersham, Midhurst GU29 0BX.
**Tel** 01798 861 388
**Fax** 01798 861 581
**Email** peters.barn@ic24.net
**Ws** www.petersbarngallery.co.uk
**Opening times** Apr–Sep Tue–Fri 2–6, Sat, Sun and holidays 11–6 and by appointment Jan, Feb and Mar.
**Nearest Station** Chichester, Petersfield, Pulborough, Haslemere, then taxi or bus.
**Personnel** Directors: Gabrielle and Annabel.
**Services and Facilities** Commissioning Service. Disabled Access. Parking.
**Work Stocked and Sold** Ab. App. Cer. Cra. Dr. Gla. Jew. Pa. Pr. Sc. Wd.
**Price range** £10–£9,000
For artists see Commercial Gallery Artists.

*Walter Keeler,* **Table with 'House Leeks',** ***ceramic, 73 x 72 cm, 1999.***
*Widely acknowledged as one of the most enchanting garden galleries in the South. Peter's Barn shows work by known, established and up-and-coming artists. Set in a wild wooded water garden, this little gallery makes full use of the beautiful garden space, giving artists the opportunity to exhibit their work in an outside environment. The varied exhibitions change monthly. From the A272: 3 miles east of Midhurst and 3 miles west of Petworth, take road opposite the Half Way Bridge Inn and follow the brown gallery signs.*

### ▶ Sculpture at Goodwood PS

Hat Hill Copse, Goodwood, Chichester PO18 0QP.
**Tel** 01243 538 449
**Fax** 01243 531 853
**Email** w@sculpture.org.uk
**Ws** www.sculpture.org.uk
**Opening times** Thu–Sat 10.30–4.30 Apr–Nov. Directions: 01243 771 114.
**Nearest Station** Barnham.
**Personnel** Founder: Wilfred Cass.
**Services and Facilities** Art Consultancy. Bookshop. Commissioning Service. Disabled Access. Guided Tours. Parking.
**Work Stocked and Sold** Sc.
**Price range** £6,000–£500,000
For artists see Commercial Gallery Artists.

***Steve Dilworth,*** **Dream Container,** ***bronze, nickel, silver, height 170 cm, 2000, £55,000.***
*Founded and privately endowed by Wilfred and Jeannette Cass in 1994, Sculpture at Goodwood is a charitable foundation dedicated to fostering contemporary British sculpture. Some 25 monumental sculptures are commissioned each year and are displayed temporarily in our grounds. Together with the new concepts for sculpture programme, Goodwood provides an unequalled resource for people wishing to commission sculpture. This resource is freely available to registered art professionals and collectors. The foundation's showcase is situated 50 miles south of London, in an area of outstanding natural beauty. Twenty acres of woodland walks and glades provide an idyllic venue for the changing display of sculpture.*

### ▶ Sculpture Park

Queen Mary's College, Cliddesden Road,
Basingstoke RG1 3HF
**Tel** 01256 479 221

### ▶ The Turill Sculpture Garden

South Parade, Summertown,Oxford.
**Tel** 01865 515 584
**Personnel** Gallery Director: Sarah-Jane Wiseman

### ▶ Yorkshire Sculpture Park PS

Bretton Hall, West Bretton, Wakefield WF4 4LG.
**Tel** 01924 830 302 **Fax** 01924 830 044
**Email** office@ysp.co.uk
**Ws** www.ysp.co.uk
**Opening times** Summer: Grounds 10–6 daily, Galleries/Café 11–5, Information Centre 10–5. Winter: Grounds 10–4, Galleries/Café 11–4, Information Centre 10–4.
**Nearest Station** Wakefield Westgate.
**Personnel** Executive Director: Peter Murray.
**Services and Facilities** Bookshop. Café. Craftshop. Disabled Access. Friends Society. Lectures. Parking. Shop. Workshop Facilities.
*Yorkshire Sculpture Park, one of Europe's leading open-air art galleries, is set within 500 acres of beautiful 18th-century landscaped grounds.*
*It presents a programme of international open-air exhibitions alongside smaller projects, providing opportunities for the practice, understanding and enjoyment of sculpture for everyone. Monumental sculptures by Henry Moore in the adjacent 96-acre Bretton Country Park constitute a significant collection of the artist's work. Changing displays from the collection include sculpture by Hepworth, Frink, Bourdelle, Nash, LeWitt and Paladino.*
*A sensory trail has been developed for people with disabilities; audio guides and electric scooters available. A new Visitor's Centre will open late 2001.*

# Art Societies and Organisations

# NOTES

# Contemporary Art Society

The Contemporary Art Society (CAS) was founded in 1910, at a time when the Tate Gallery had insufficient funds to purchase works by young British artists. It has since given the museum its first works by Pablo Picasso, Henry Moore and Damien Hirst.

A group of private collectors, curators and critics established the CAS as an independent private charity to support and encourage contemporary art collecting. Its main aim is to purchase works of art and present them to CAS member museums throughout Britain.

Sixty-nine museums, national and regional, belong to the CAS through an annual subscription and receive a major work of art, as an outright gift, about once every four years.

To purchase these gifts and to maintain itself as a national charity that acts as an advocate and champion of contemporary art, CAS raises and earns funds in a range of ways. CAS is primarily a membership organisation of individuals whose subscription enables them to take part in visits, events and trips within Britain and abroad. Contemporary Art Society Projects is a corporate and commissioning advisory service that helps companies and individuals to develop their contemporary art collections. ARTfutures, the CAS's annual art fair held every November/December, offers over 1,000 works of art at very low prices to encourage new collectors.

What distinguishes CAS from other art charities is that it is very proactive. For over 90 years, it has encouraged museums to take risks and to accept gifts of work that are often avant-garde or by an 'unknown' artist whose career is beginning its ascendancy. The current fundraising appeal is called 'Catching Comets' for that reason. All purchases are selected by individuals – curators and private collectors – and never by committee.

Throughout its history, the CAS has always worked closely with museum colleagues to help them to make the most of their collections and to develop international networks. As a result, in partnership with 15 member museums, CAS runs a £3.5 million purchase and travel scheme for curators, funded by ACE Lottery.

Indeed, all CAS activities are for the benefit of museums and audiences throughout Britain with a commitment to contemporary art. Most important of all, artists benefit directly from all CAS activities.

Gill Hedley
Director
Contemporary Art Society

### ▶ 56 Group Wales
18 Tydfil Place, Roath Park, Cardiff CF2 5HP.
**Tel** 029 2048 7369
**Personnel** Bob Weir.

### ▶ 57 Art Group
9 Clwyd Avenue, Prestatyn LL19 9NG.
**Tel** 01745 856 565

### ▶ Aberdeen Artists Society
556 Holburn Street Aberdeen AB10 7LL.
**Tel** 01224 263 625 **Fax** 01224 263 636

### ▶ An Taisce The National Trust for Ireland
The Tailor's Hall, Back Lane, Dublin 8.
**Tel** 00353 1 454 1786
**Fax** 00353 1 453 3255

### ▶ The Antiquities Dealers Association
c/o Faustus Ancient Art and Jewellery, 41 Dover Street, London W1S 4NS.
**Tel** 020 7930 1864 **Fax** 020 7495 2882
**Personnel** Chairman: Miss Joanna Van Der Land.

### ▶ AOP (Association of Photographers)
81 Leonard Street, London EC2A 4QS.
**Tel** 020 7739 6669 **Fax** 020 7739 8707
**Email** general@aophoto.co.uk
**Ws** www.aophoto.co.uk
**Opening times** Mon–Fri 9.30–6.
**Personnel** CEO: Gwen Thomas.
*You've found it! Whether you're a professional photographer, an assistant, an agent or a graduate, the Association of Photographers is here to work for you. What is the Association of Photographers? It began in 1968, as the Association of Fashion, Advertising and Editorial Photographers. Then, it was a small group of photographers united by a common interest – to promote the highest standards of work and practice throughout the industry, and to protect and improve the rights of all professional photographers based in the UK. Today, it's the Association of Photographers (AOP), with over 1,700 photographers and photographic assistants as members. It's supported by agents, printers, manufacturers and suppliers of photographic equipment, and affiliated colleges. Though our principal aim has not changed in over 30 years, our areas of influence have expanded dramatically!*

### ▶ The Architectural Association
36 Bedford Square London WC1.
**Tel** 020 7887 4000

### ▶ Art Workers Guild
6 Queen Square, Bloomsbury, London WC1N 3AR.
**Tel** 020 7837 3474

### ▶ Artangel
31 Eyre Street Hill, London EC1R 5EW.
**Tel** 020 7713 1400
**Fax** 0207 713 1401
**Personnel** Gerry Wall.

### ▶ Artists Association of Ireland
Arthouse, Curved Street, Temple Bar, Dublin 2.
**Tel** 00353 1 874 0529
**Fax** 00353 1 677 1585
**Email** artists-ireland@connect.ie
**Personnel** Chairperson: Una Walker. Director: Stella Coffey.

### ▶ Artists' General Benevolent Institution
Burlington House, Piccadilly, London W1V 0DJ.
**Tel** 020 7734 1193 **Fax** 020 7734 9926
**Personnel** Secretary: Miss April Connett-Dance.
*A charity managed by artists to provide financial assistance for members of the profession who are in need, as result of illness, accident or old age. Widows of artists are also eligible to apply. The AGBI depends on voluntary contributions to carry out this work. There is also an Artists' Orphan Fund.*

### ▶ Artists' Orphan Fund
Burlington House, Piccadilly, London W1V 0DJ.
**Tel** 020 7734 1193
**Fax** 020 7734 9926

### ▶ Arts World Wide
309a Aberdeen House, 22 Highbury Grove, London N5 2DQ.
**Tel** 020 7354 3030
**Personnel** Adam Jeanes.

### ▶ Aspex Visual Arts Trust
27 Brougham Road, Southsea, Portsmouth PO5 4PA.
**Tel** 023 9281 2121

### ▶ Association for Advancement Through Visual Art
23–29 Faroe Road, London W14 0EL.
**Tel** 020 7603 3039
**Fax** 020 7603 3278
**Personnel** Duncan Smith.
**Services and Facilities** Commissioning Service.

### ▶ Association of Art Galleries in Wales
Ffotogallery Wales, 31 Charles Street, Cardiff CF1 4EA.
**Tel** 029 2034 1667 **Fax** 029 2034 1672

### ▶ Association of Art Historians
70 Cowcross Street, London EC1M 6EJ.
**Tel** 020 7490 3211 **Fax** 020 7490 3277
**Email** admin@aah.org.uk
**Ws** www.aah.org.uk
**Personnel** Administrator: Claire Davies.
*The Association of Art Historians represents the interests of art and design historians in all aspects of the discipline including art, design, architecture, film, media and photography, cultural studies and conservation. Members are active in museums and galleries, publishing, teaching, research and environmental work. Among the benefits offered to members are an annual conference, a journal,* Art History, *a quarterly magazine,* The Art Book, *a newsletter,* Bulletin, *three times a year, symposia on a great variety of subjects and periods, and professional interest groups with their own programme of activities – universities and colleges, art galleries and museums, freelances, schools and students. Membership is open to art and design historians and to those interested in the advancement of the study of history of art. Special subscription rates to students and the unwaged.*

### ▶ The Association of British Picture Restorers
Station Avenue, Kew TW9 3QA.
**Tel** 020 8948 5644
**Fax** 020 8948 5644
**Personnel** Jan Robinson.

### ▶ Association of Illustrators
1st Floor, 32–38 Saffron Hill, London EC1N 8FH.
**Tel** 020 7831 7377 **Fax** 020 7831 6277
**Personnel** Stephanie Smith.

### ▶ Beca Group
99 Windsor Road, Penarth CF6 41JF.
**Tel** 029 2070 3492
**Personnel** Ivor Davies.
*The artists work separately and collectively on paintings, assemblages and performance, observing destruction of Welsh communities and language, censorship of history and public demonstrations. The group exhibits internationally and has experienced censorship here. The destruction of races and cultures by dominating centralised powers is our concern as a universal group, rather than the internationalism which is merely Anglo-American.*

### ▶ The Blake Trust
43 Gordon Square, London WC1H 0PD.
**Tel** 020 7388 0708 **Fax** 020 7388 0854
**Personnel** Director: John Commander.

### ▶ British American Arts Association
116–118 Commercial Street, London E1 6NF.
**Tel** 020 7247 5385 **Fax** 020 7247 5256
**Personnel** Executive Director: Ms Jennifer Williams.

### ▶ British Artists in Glass
The Glass Gallery, St Erth, Hayle TR27 6HT.
**Tel** 01736 756 577

### ▶ British Association of Art Therapists
11a Richmond Road, Brighton BN2 3RL.
**Tel** 0118 926 5407 **Fax** 01273 685 852
**Personnel** Liz Waller.

### ▶ British Computer Arts Association
College Manor, Farquhar Road, London SE19 1SS.
**Tel** 020 8761 9807

### ▶ British Institute of Professional Photography
Fox Talbot House, Amwell End, Ware SG12 9HN.
**Tel** 01920 464 011 **Fax** 01920 487 056
**Personnel** Mark Berry. James MacDonald.
*The BIPP exists to: achieve and maintain standards in professional practice and conduct for the benefit of photographers and buyers of photography; inquire into and deal with matters which affect professional photography, thus safeguarding the future of the industry; and improve the technical knowledge and professional status of people in the photographic industry.*

### ▶ The British Society of Master Glass Painters
6 Queen Square, London WC1.
**Tel** 01943 602 521 **Fax** 01943 602 521

**Email** bsmgp@dircon.co.uk
**Ws** www.proteusweb.com/bsmgp
**Personnel** Secretary: Ruth Cooke.

### ▶ The British Sporting Art Trust
BSAT Gallery, 99 High Street,
Newmarket CB8 8JL.
**Tel** 01264 710 344 **Fax** 01264 710 114
**Email** barnart@compuserve.com
**Personnel** Organising Secretary:
Mrs M. Lawton.
*The Trust's objectives are the formation and display of a representative collection of British sporting art at the Trust's Vestey Galleries of Sporting Art at the National Horseracing Museum, Newmarket, and other galleries and houses open to the public. Also to support and publish research on the subject of sporting art.*

### ▶ CADW: Welsh Historic Monuments
Crown Building, Cathays Park, Cardiff CF1 3NQ.
**Tel** 029 2050 0200 **Fax** 029 2082 6375
**Personnel** Chief Executive: Tom Cassidy.
David Pitman.

### ▶ Charles Rennie Mackintosh Society
Queen's Cross, 870 Garscube Road,
Glasgow G20 7EL.
**Tel** 0141 946 6600
**Fax** 0141 945 2321
**Personnel** Director: Patricia Douglas.

### ▶ The Charleston Trust
Charleston Farmhouse, near Firle,
Lewes BN8 6LL.
**Tel** 01323 811 626
**Fax** 01323 811 628
**Personnel** Shaun Romain.

### ▶ Contemporary Art Society
17 Bloomsbury Square, London WC1A 2NG.
**Tel** 020 7831 7311 **Fax** 020 7831 7345
**Email** cas@contempart.org.uk
**Ws** www.contempart.org.uk
**Opening times** By appointment only.
**Nearest Underground** Holborn.
**Personnel** Director: Gill Hedley. Projects Director: Cat Newton-Groves. Collections Curator: Mary Doyle. Events/Membership Manager: Kate Steel. Projects Manager: Lara Sampson. Assistant Collections Curator: Jessica Wallwork. Office Manager: Paula Hollings.
**Services and Facilities** Art Consultancy. Art for Offices. Commissioning Service. Friends Society. Guided Tours. Lectures.
*The Contemporary Art Society is a charity. We acquire paintings, sculpture, photographs, video, installation work and applied art and crafts by contemporary artists to give to member museums. We have given over 5,000 works since 1910. Date established: 1910. Number of full members: 1,400. Membership options: individual, joint, institutional and corporate. Membership fees (in same order): £30, £35, £75 and £500. Membership benefits: national and international trips to art fairs; private views, artists' studios and private collections; discounts at participating institutions and at events. Publications: Contemporary Art Society Newsletter, quarterly. For more information on our Corporate Advisory service, contact Cat Newton-Groves.*

### ▶ The Contemporary Art Society for Wales
1 Court Cottages, Michaelston Road,
St Fagans, Cardiff CF5 6EN.
**Tel** 029 2059 5206
**Personnel** Gareth Davies.

### ▶ Council of Museums in Wales
The Courtyard, Letty Street, Cathays,
Cardiff CF2 4EL.
**Tel** 029 2022 5432 **Fax** 029 2066 8516
**Personnel** Jane Pierson Jones.

### ▶ Council of Regional Arts Associations
Litton Lodge, 13a Clifton Road,
Winchester SO22 5BP.
**Tel** 01962 51063

### ▶ Craft Potters Association (CPA)
21 Carnaby Street, London W1V 1PH.
**Tel** 020 7439 3377 **Fax** 020 7287 9954
**Personnel** Chairman: Jack Doherty.
Administrator: Tony Ainsworth.
**Services and Facilities** Bookshop.
Craftshop. Lectures.

### ▶ The Crafts Council
44a Pentonville Road, Islington, London N1 9BY.
**Tel** 020 7278 7700 **Fax** 020 7837 6891
**Ws** www.craftscouncil.org.uk
**Opening times** Free entry Tue–Sat 11–6, Sun 2–6, closed Mon.
**Nearest Underground** Angel.
**Personnel** Director: Janet Barnes.
Director of Exhibitions, Collection and Education: Louise Taylor.
**Services and Facilities** Café. Disabled Access. Lectures. Shop.
*The Crafts Council is the national centre for the crafts showing five exhibitions a year, including ceramics, textiles, glass, wood, furniture, metal work and jewellery. Reference library. Photostore, the digital picture library for crafts. Gallery shop stocking a wide variety of objects and books.*

### ▶ Crafts Council of Ireland
Powerscourt Townhouse Centre,
South William Street, Dublin 2.
**Tel** 00353 1 679 7368
**Fax** 00353 1 679 9197
**Personnel** Chief Executive: Leslie Reed.
Exhibitions Co-ordinator: Rhoda McManus.

### ▶ The Decorative Arts Society
47 Combe Crescent, Bury,
Pulborough RH20 1PE.
**Tel** 01798 831 734
**Personnel** Hon. Secretary: Helen Grogan.
Governor: Conny Michael.

### ▶ The Design and Artists Copyright Society Ltd
Parchment House, 13 Northburgh Street,
London EC1V 0JP.
**Tel** 020 7336 8811
**Fax** 020 7336 8822
**Email** info@dacs.co.uk
**Ws** www.dacs.co.uk
**Opening times** Office hours 10–6.
**Nearest Underground** Barbican.
**Personnel** Chief Executive: Joanna Cave.
Director of Finance: David Remington.
*DACS is the copyright and collecting society for the visual arts in the UK. DACS is a non-profit organisation which exists to secure and enhance the copyright interests of visual artists and to provide the user community with an efficient service by obtaining mandates, issuing licenses, collecting revenues and distributing income. We represent over 40,000 artists of all disciplines from all over the world in matters of copyright in the UK.*

### ▶ The Design Council
34 Bow Street, Covent Garden,
London WC2E 7DL.
**Tel** 020 7420 5200 **Fax** 020 7420 5300

### ▶ Fine Art Trade Guild
16–18 Empress Place, London SW6 1TT.
**Tel** 020 7381 6616 **Fax** 020 7381 2596

### ▶ The Georgian Group
6 Fitzroy Square, London W1P 6DX.
**Tel** 020 7387 1720 **Fax** 020 7387 1721
**Personnel** Neil Burton. Caroline Lightburn.

### ▶ Government Art Collection
c/o Dept for Culture, Media and Sport,
2–4 Cockspur Street, London SW1Y 5DH.
**Tel** 020 7211 6200

### ▶ Guild of Aviation Artists
DFC, Bondway Business Centre, 71 Bondway,
Vauxhall Cross, London SW8 1SQ.
**Tel** 020 7735 0634 **Fax** 020 7735 0634
**Personnel** Hugo Trotter.

### ▶ The Guild of Glass Engravers
35 Ossulton Way, Hampstead Garden Suburb,
London N2 0JY.
**Tel** 020 8731 9352 **Fax** 020 8731 9352
**Personnel** Christine Weatherhead.

### ▶ The Guild of Railway Artists
45 Dickins Road, Warwick CV34 5NS.
**Tel** 01926 499 246
**Personnel** Chief Executive: Frank Hodges.

### ▶ GWELED
Pen Roc, Rhodfa'r Môr, Aberystwyth SY23 3DE.
**Tel** 01970 623 690 **Fax** 01970 612 245
**Personnel** Development Officer: Jaci Taylor.
**Services and Facilities** Lectures.
Workshop Facilities.

### ▶ The Henry Moore Foundation
Dane Tree House, Perry Green,
Much Hadham SG10 6EE.
**Tel** 01279 843 333 **Fax** 01279 843 647
**Personnel** C. M. Joint.

### ▶ Hesketh Hubbard Art Society
Mall Galleries, 17 Carlton House Terrace,
London SW1Y 5BD.
**Tel** 020 7930 6844 **Fax** 020 7839 7830
**Ws** www.mallgalleries.org.uk
**Personnel** President: Simon Whittle.
**Services and Facilities** Art Consultancy. Commissioning Service. Friends Society. Gallery space for hire. Workshop Facilities.

### ▶ The Institute of International Visual Arts
6-8 Standard Place Rivington Street,
London EC2A 3BE.

**Tel** 020 7636 1930 **Fax** 020 7636 1931
**Personnel** Victoria Clarke. Nick Hallum.

### ▶ The International Association of Art, British National Committee
49 Stainton Road, Sheffield S11 7AX.
**Tel** 0114 266 9889 **Fax** 0114 266 9298
**Personnel** Roland Miller.

### ▶ International Association of Art Critics
91 Eton Hall, Eton College Road, London NW3 2DH.
**Personnel** President: Keith Patrick. Secretary: David Cohen.

### ▶ Irish Association of Art Historians
c/o National Gallery of Ireland, Merrion Square, Dublin 2.
**Tel** 00353 1 661 5133 **Fax** 00353 1 661 5372
**Personnel** Chairman: Dr. Brian Kennedy.

### ▶ Irish Georgian Society
74 Merrion Square, Dublin 2.
**Tel** 00353 1 676 7053
**Fax** 00353 1 662 0290
**Personnel** Mary Bryan.

### ▶ Irish Museums Association
c/o 59 Lambard Street West, Dublin 8.
**Tel** 00353 1 454 1947

### ▶ Irish Watercolour Society
68 Crannagh Road, Rathfarnham, Dublin 14.
**Tel** 00353 1 490 4248
**Personnel** George McCaw.

### ▶ Live Art Press
49 Stainton Road, Sheffield S11 7AX.
**Tel** 0114 266 9889 **Fax** 0114 266 9298
**Personnel** Roland Miller.
**Services and Facilities** Commissioning Service.

### ▶ Manchester Academy of Fine Arts
4 Delph Greaves, Delph, Oldham OL3 5TY.
**Tel** 01457 875 718
**Fax** 01422 370 256
**Personnel** President: Ian Thompson NDD DA ATC ARBS FRSA. Vice President: Glenys Latham Dip AD CIE. Hon. Secretary: Cliff Moorhouse TD. Hon. Treasurer: Philip Livesey FCA.
**Services and Facilities** Friends Society. Guided Tours. Lectures.
*The Academy is a society of artists which seeks to promote the fine arts in general and the work of its members in particular; initiating exhibition and commission opportunities whilst maintaining its long historical association with the City Art Gallery. It actively encourages membership applications from committed artists, especially from the North West, and aims to attract work of the highest quality from non-members into its Annual Open Exhibition.*

### ▶ The Masters Photographers Association
Hallmark House, 2 Beaumont Street, Darlington DL1 5SZ.
**Tel** 01325 356 555
**Fax** 01325 357 813
**Personnel** Honorary RMPA: Colin R. Buck. Mark Buck.
*Association for full-time professional photographers.*

### ▶ The Museums and Galleries Commission
16 Queen Anne's Gate, London SW1H 9AA.
**Tel** 020 7233 4200 **Fax** 020 7233 3686
**Personnel** Emma Wright.

### ▶ Museums Association
42 Clerkenwell Close, London EC1R 0PA.
**Tel** 020 7250 1834 **Fax** 020 7250 1929
**Personnel** Head of Marketing: Michael Wright.

### ▶ National Acrylic Painters' Association
134 Rake Lane, Wallasey CH45 1JW.
**Tel** 0151 639 2980 **Fax** 0151 639 2980
**Email** katy@art-arena.com
**Ws** www.art-arena.com/napa
**Opening times** 24 hours a day, as it is on the internet.
**Personnel** President: Alwyn Crawshaw. Director General and Founder: Kenneth J. Hodgson.
**Services and Facilities** Friends Society.

### ▶ National Art Collections Fund
Millais House, 7 Cromwell Place, London SW7 2JN.
**Tel** 020 7225 4800 **Fax** 020 7225 4848
**Opening times** Mon–Fri 9.30–5.30.
**Personnel** Director: David Barrie. Chairman: Sir Nicholas Goodison. Stephanie Banchero.

### ▶ National Artists Association
Space Place, 43–45 Dace Road, London E3 2NG.
**Tel** 08000 857 217 **Fax** 020 7790 6630
**Email** naa@gn.apc.org
**Nearest Underground** Limehouse.
**Personnel** Director: Alan Humberstone.

### ▶ National Association for Fine Art Education
University of the West of England, Faculty of Art, Media and Design, Clanage Road, Bower Ashton, Bristol BS3 2JU.
**Tel** 01179 660 222 **Fax** 01179 763 946

### ▶ The National Association of Decorative and Fine Arts Societies
All enquiries to the Chief Executive, NADFAS, 8 Guilford Street, London WC1N 1DT.
**Tel** 020 7430 0730 **Fax** 020 7242 0686
**Email** admin@nadfas.org.uk
**Opening times** Mon–Fri 9.30–5.30.
**Nearest Underground** Russell Square.
**Personnel** Patron: HRH The Duchess of Gloucester, GCVO. President: Mr Timothy Clifford. Chief Executive: Jeremy Warren.
**Services and Facilities** Lectures. Restoration. Shop.

### ▶ National Association of Memorial Masons
27a Albert Street, Rugby CV21 2SG.
**Tel** 01788 542 264 **Fax** 01788 542 276
**Email** enquiries@namm.org.uk
**Ws** www.namm.org.uk
**Personnel** Chief Executive: Theresa Quinn.

### ▶ National Campaign for the Arts
Pegasus House, 37–43 Sackville Street, London W1S 3EH.
**Tel** 020 7333 0375 **Fax** 020 7333 0660
**Email** nca@artscampaign.org.uk

### ▶ National Portraiture Association
59/60 Fitzjames Avenue, London W14 0RR.
**Tel** 020 7602 0892 **Fax** 020 7602 6705
**Personnel** Director: William Deeves.

### ▶ The National Society for Education in Art and Design
The Gatehouse, Corsham Court, Corsham SN13 0BZ.
**Tel** 01249 714 825 **Fax** 01249 716 138
**Personnel** Dr John Steers.

### ▶ National Society of Painters, Sculptors and Printmakers
122 Copse Hill, Wimbledon, London SW20 0NL.
**Tel** 020 8946 7878
**Personnel** President: Denis C. Baxter UA FRSA. Vice President: Jenifer Ford FRSA. Honorary Treasurer: Chris Spencer FCA. Honorary Secretary: Gwen Spencer.

### ▶ The National Trust for Places of Historic Interest or Natural Beauty P
36 Queen Anne's Gate, London SW1H 9AS.
**Tel** 020 7222 9251 **Fax** 020 7222 5097
**Personnel** President: H.M The Queen Mother. Director General: Mr M. Drury. Historic Buildings Secretary: Mr S. Jervis. Director of Public Affairs: Mr M. Taylor.

### ▶ National Trust for Scotland
5 Charlotte Square, Edinburgh EH2 4DU.
**Tel** 0131 226 5922 **Fax** 0131 243 9501
**Personnel** Trevor Croft.

### ▶ New English Art Club
FBA, Mall Galleries, 17 Carlton House Terrace, London SW1Y 5BD.
**Tel** 020 7930 6844 **Fax** 020 7839 7830
**Ws** www.mallgalleries.org.uk
**Personnel** President: Ken Howard RA RWS NEAC. Keeper: Charlotte Halliday NEAC.
**Services and Facilities** Art Consultancy. Commissioning Service. Friends Society. Gallery space for hire. Guided Tours. Lectures. Workshop Facilities.

### ▶ Northern Ireland Museums Council
185 Stranmillis Road, Belfast BT9 5DU.
**Tel** 028 9066 1023 **Fax** 028 9068 3513
**Personnel** Director: Aidan Walsh.

### ▶ Oriental Ceramic Society
30b Torrington Square, London WC1E 7JL.
**Tel** 020 7636 7985 **Fax** 020 7580 6749
**Services and Facilities** Lectures.

### ▶ Paintings in Hospitals Sheridan Russell Gallery PS
16 Crawford Street, London W1H 1PF.
**Tel** 020 7935 0250 **Fax** 020 7935 1701
**Opening times** Mon–Fri 10–5.
**Nearest Underground** Baker Street.
**Personnel** Director: Marjorie Power. Curator: Mary-Alice Stack.

**Services and Facilities** Gallery space for hire. Shop.
**Work Stocked and Sold** Pa. Ph. Pr.
**Price range** £50–£3,000

## ▶ Paisley Museum and Art Gallery

High Street, Paisley PA1 2BA.
**Tel** 0141 889 3151 **Fax** 0141 889 9240
**Email** RKelsey@compuserve.com
**Opening times** Tue–Sat 10–5.
**Nearest Station** Paisley Gilmour Street.
**Personnel** President: Joe Hargan PAI. Vice President: Dr. George Addis. Secretary and Hon. Treasurer: Margaret Duff. Hon. Collector: Ruth Donald.
**Services and Facilities** Lectures. Museum Shop. Parking. Workshop Facilities.

## ▶ Pastel Society

Mall Galleries, 17 Carlton House Terrace, London SW1Y 5BD.
**Tel** 020 7930 6844
**Fax** 020 7839 7830
**Ws** www.mallgalleries.org.uk
**Personnel** President: Tom Coates PPRBA RP RWS NEAC. Vice President: Moira Huntly RI RWA RSMA.
**Services and Facilities** Art Consultancy. Commissioning Service. Friends Society. Gallery space for hire. Guided Tours. Lectures. Workshop Facilities.

## ▶ Patrons of British Art

Development Office, Tate Gallery, Millbank, London SW1P 4RG.
**Tel** 020 7887 8743 **Fax** 020 7887 8755

## ▶ Patrons of New Art

Development Office, Tate Gallery, Millbank, London SW1P 4RG.
**Tel** 020 7887 8743
**Fax** 020 7887 8755

## ▶ The Printmakers Council

Clerkenwell Workshop, 31 Clerkenwell Close, London EC1R 0AT.
**Tel** 020 7250 1927
**Fax** 020 7250 1927
**Ws** www.printmaker.co.uk/pmc
**Opening times** Wed and Thu 2–6.
**Nearest Underground** Farringdon.
**Personnel** President: Mr Stanley Jones. Administrator: Helen Ward.
*The Printmakers Council is a non-profit-making artist-run group. Their objectives are to promote the use of both traditional and innovative printmaking techniques by: holding exhibitions of prints; providing information on prints and printmaking to both its membership and the public; and encouraging co-operation and exchanges between members, other associations and interested individuals. Exhibitions in major London venues and throughout the UK. Exchange shows recently in Paris, Landau Germany and Fremantle Australia. A slide index of members' work is held in the London office for consultation. Membership is open to all printmakers.*

## ▶ Public Art Forum

Halfpenny Wharf, Torrington Street, East-the-Water, Bideford EX39 4DP.
**Tel** 01237 470 440 **Fax** 01237 470 440
**Personnel** Lisa Harty.

## ▶ Royal Academy of Arts PS

Burlington House, Piccadilly, London W1V 0DS.
**Tel** 020 7300 8000 **Fax** 020 7300 8001
**Ws** www.RoyalAcademy.org.uk
**Opening times** Mon–Sun 10–6.
**Nearest Underground** Piccadilly Circus, Green Park.
**Personnel** Press and Promotions Officer: Katharine Jones.
**Services and Facilities** Bookshop. Café. Disabled Access. Framing. Friends Society. Guided Tours. Lectures. Museum Shop. Restaurant. Shop.

## ▶ Royal Birmingham Society of Artists

69a New Street, Birmingham B2 4DU.
**Tel** 0121 643 3768 **Fax** 0121 644 5298
**Opening times** 10.30–5.
**Nearest Station** New Street, Snow Hill.
**Personnel** PRBSA: Marylane Barfield. Curator: Roger Forbes. Secretary: Paul Bartlett. Treasurer: Andrew Matheson.
**Services and Facilities** Commissioning Service. Disabled Access. Friends Society. Gallery space for hire. Lectures. Workshop Facilities.

## ▶ Royal Cambrian Academy of Art

Crown Lane, Conwy LL32 8BH.
**Tel** 01492 593 413 **Fax** 01492 593 413
**Email** rca@nol.co.uk
**Ws** www.oriel-cambria.co.uk/gallery/rca
**Opening times** 11–5 Tue–Sat, 1–4.30 Sun. Closed Mon.
**Nearest Station** Llandudno Junction, Conway.
**Personnel** President: Sir Kyffin Williams OBE RA. Curator: Gwyneth Jones. Assistant Curator: Gill Burtwell. Technician: David Huntington.
**Services and Facilities** Friends Society.

## ▶ Royal Commission on the Ancient and Historical Monuments of Scotland

John Sinclair House, 16 Bernard Terrace, Edinburgh EH8 9NX.
**Tel** 0131 662 1456 **Fax** 0131 662 1477
**Personnel** R. J. Merler.

## ▶ Royal Commission on the Ancient and Historical Monuments of Wales

Crown Building, Plas Crug, Aberystwyth SY23 1NJ.
**Tel** 01970 621 227 **Fax** 01970 627 701
**Personnel** Mervyn Hughes.

## ▶ Royal Commission on the Historical Monuments of England/ National Monuments Record

Kemble Drive, Swindon SN2 2GZ.
**Tel** 01793 414 600 **Fax** 01793 414 606

## ▶ Royal Dublin Society

Ballsbridge, Dublin 4.
**Tel** 00353 1 668 0866 **Fax** 00353 1 660 4014
**Opening times** Daily 8.15–11.
**Personnel** Chair of the Visual Arts Committee: John Turpin. Arts Development Executive: Sinéad Ó Duinnín.
**Services and Facilities** Disabled Access. Parking.

## ▶ Royal Glasgow Institute of the Fine Arts

5 Oswald Street, Glasgow G1 4QR.
**Tel** 0141 248 7411 **Fax** 0141 221 0417
**Personnel** Secretary: Gordon C. McAllister CA. Mrs Lesley Nicholl.
**Services and Facilities** Disabled Access. Gallery space for hire. Lectures.

## ▶ Royal Institute of British Architects

66 Portland Place, London W1N 4AD.
**Tel** 020 7636 4389 **Fax** 020 7637 5775
**Personnel** Tony Chapman.

## ▶ Royal Institute of Oil Painters

Mall Galleries, 17 Carlton House Terrace, London SW1Y 5BD.
**Tel** 020 7930 6844 **Fax** 020 7839 7830
**Ws** www.mallgalleries.org.uk
**Personnel** President: Dr Richard Baines.
**Services and Facilities** Art Consultancy. Commissioning Service. Friends Society. Gallery space for hire. Guided Tours. Lectures. Workshop Facilities.

## ▶ Royal Institute of Painters in Water Colours

Mall Galleries, 17 Carlton House Terrace, London SW1Y 5BD.
**Tel** 020 7930 6844 **Fax** 020 7839 7830
**Ws** www.mallgalleries.org.uk
**Personnel** President: Ronald Maddox PRI Hon. RWS.
**Services and Facilities** Art Consultancy. Commissioning Service. Friends Society. Gallery space for hire. Guided Tours. Lectures. Workshop Facilities.

## ▶ The Royal Photographic Society

Octagon Galleries, Milsom Street, Bath BA1 1DN.
**Tel** 01225 462 841 **Fax** 01225 448 688
**Email** rps@rps.org
**Ws** www.rps.org
**Opening times** Daily 9.30–5.30. Admission: adults £2.50, concessions £1.75.
**Nearest Station** Bath Spa 10 minutes walk.
**Personnel** Secretary General: Barry Lane. Curator: Pam Roberts. Exhibitions Officer: Carole Sartain. Membership Secretary: Sara Beaugeard.
**Services and Facilities** Bookshop. Café. Disabled Access. Friends Society. Gallery space for hire. Lectures. Museum Shop. Restaurant. Shop. Workshop Facilities.

## ▶ The Royal Scottish Academy

The Mound, Edinburgh EH2 2EL.
**Tel** 0131 225 6671 **Fax** 0131 225 2349
**Opening times** During exhibitions 10–5, Sun 2–5, office 9–4.30.
**Nearest Station** Waverley.
**Personnel** President: Dr Ian McKenzie-Smith RSA. Secretary: William Scott RSA. Admin Secretary: Bruce Laidlaw. Treasurer: Izi Metzstein.

## ▶ Royal Scottish Society of Painters in Water Colours

29 Waterloo Street, Glasgow G2 6BZ.
**Tel** 0141 226 3838 **Fax** 0141 221 1397
**Personnel** Roger C. C. Frame.
**Services and Facilities** Lectures.

### ▶ Royal Society of British Artists
Mall Galleries, 17 Carlton House Terrace, London SW1Y 5BD.
**Tel** 020 7930 6844 **Fax** 020 7839 7830
**Ws** www.mallgalleries.org.uk
**Personnel** President: Romeo Di Girolamo PRBA.
**Services and Facilities** Art Consultancy. Commissioning Service. Friends Society. Gallery space for hire. Guided Tours. Lectures. Workshop Facilities.

### ▶ The Royal Society of British Sculptors
108 Old Brompton Road, South Kensington, London SW7 3RA.
**Tel** 020 7373 5554
**Fax** 020 7373 9202
**Opening times** 9.30–5.30.
**Nearest Underground** South Kensington
**Personnel** President: Philomena Davidson-Davis. Administrator: Sarah Herman.

### ▶ Royal Society of Marine Artists
Mall Galleries, 17 Carlton House Terrace, London SW1Y 5BD.
**Tel** 020 7930 6844
**Fax** 020 7839 7830
**Ws** www.mallgalleries.org.uk
**Personnel** President: Bert Wright.
**Services and Facilities** Art Consultancy. Commissioning Service. Friends Society. Gallery space for hire. Guided Tours. Lectures. Workshop Facilities.

### ▶ Royal Society of Painter-Printmakers
Bankside Gallery, 48 Hopton Street, London SE1 9JH.
**Tel** 020 7928 7521
**Fax** 020 7928 2820
**Email** bankside@freeuk.com
**Opening times** Tue 10–8, Wed–Fri 10–5, Sat and Sun 1–5. Closed Mon.
**Nearest Underground** Blackfriars, Southwark.
**Personnel** Director: Judy Dixey.
**Services and Facilities** Art for Offices. Commissioning Service. Friends Society. Lectures.

### ▶ Royal Society of Portrait Painters
Mall Galleries, 17 Carlton House Terrace, London SW1Y 5BD.
**Tel** 020 7930 6844 **Fax** 020 7839 7830
**Email** kletmanmallgalleries@pipex.com.uk
**Ws** www.mallgalleries.org.uk
**Personnel** President: Daphne Todd. Commissions Consultant: Katy Letman.
**Services and Facilities** Art Consultancy. Commissioning Service. Friends Society. Gallery space for hire. Guided Tours. Lectures.

### ▶ Royal Watercolour Society
Bankside Gallery, 48 Hopton Street, London SE1 9JH.
**Tel** 020 7928 7521
**Fax** 020 7928 2820
**Email** bankside@freeuk.com
**Opening times** Tue 10–8, Wed–Fri 10–5, Sat and Sun 1–5. Closed Mon.
**Nearest Underground** Blackfriars, Southwark.
**Personnel** Director: Judy Dixey.
**Services and Facilities** Art for Offices. Commissioning Service. Friends Society. Lectures.

### ▶ Ruskin Society of London
351 Woodstock Road, Oxford OX2 7NX.
**Tel** 01865 310 987/515 962

### ▶ SAA
PO Box 50, Newark, Notts NG23 5GY.
**Tel** 01949 844 050 **Fax** 01949 844 051
**Email** inspiration@saa.co.uk
**Ws** www.saa.co.uk
**Personnel** Managing Director: John Hope-Hawkins. Membership Secretary: Nicky Applewhite.
**Services and Facilities** Workshop Facilities.
*The SAA was founded in 1992 to inform, encourage and inspire all who want to paint, whatever their ability. With over 18,000 members in 62 countries, the society holds meetings and events, publishes a newsletter,* Paint *(quarterly), and organises painting holidays, workshops, local and international exhibitions, and competitions. It provides individual paintings insurance and third-party public liability cover for members and groups. Anyone can join and any art club or society may affiliate to benefit from very generous insurance terms.*
*Competition: Artist and Young Artist of the Year. Entries by 1 March.*
*Organised by the SAA, this competition has categories for all artists, from beginner to professional, in all mediums, with awards totalling over £5,000 in prizes.*

### ▶ Scottish Artists' Benevolent Association
Second Floor, 5 Oswald Street, Glasgow G1 4QR.
**Tel** 0141 248 7411
**Fax** 0141 221 0417
**Personnel** R. C. Liddle.

### ▶ Scottish Glass Society
32 Farington Street, Dundee DD2 1PF.
**Tel** 01382 669 864
**Personnel** Jack Searle.

### ▶ Scottish Potters Association
77 Spottiswood Gardens, St Andrews KY16 8SB.
**Tel** 01334 472 303 **Fax** 01334 472 303
**Email** ap12@st-andrews.ac.uk
**Personnel** Chairman: Anne Perrett.

### ▶ Scottish Sculpture Trust
6 Darnaway Street, Edinburgh EH3 6BG.
**Tel** 0131 220 4788 **Fax** 0131 220 4787
**Email** info@scottishsculpturetrust.org
**Ws** www.scottishsculpturetrust.org
**Nearest Station** Edinburgh.
**Personnel** Director: Andrew Guest. Information Officer: Fiona Pilgrim.
**Services and Facilities** Art Consultancy. Commissioning Service. Lectures.
*The Scottish Sculpture Trust was created in 1978 to 'promote the advancement of public education in contemporary sculpture'. It aims to create more opportunities for artists working in sculpture, a greater audience for, and a greater understanding of, their work, and a culture in which that work can thrive. It provides information and advice to artists and those wanting to work with artists, runs projects to develop new opportunities and promote education, and arranges seminars and events to broaden understanding of the role of sculpture in contemporary society. The Trust also publishes* Sculpture Matters, *a subscription magazine about contemporary art and culture published three times a year.*

### ▶ The Sculptors' Society of Ireland
119 Capel Street, Dublin 2.
**Tel** 00353 1 872 2296/2364
**Fax** 00353 1 872 2364
**Personnel** Director: Aisling Prior.

### ▶ The Sculpture Company
108 Old Brompton Road, South Kensington, London SW7 3RA.
**Tel** 020 7373 8615/7244 8431
**Fax** 020 7370 3721
**Opening times** 9.30–5.30.
**Nearest Underground** South Kensington.
**Personnel** Managing Director: Philomena Davidson-Davis. Non-Executive Directors: Sir Peter Michael CBE, Michael Lyons VPRBS FRSA, Hamish Bryce.

### ▶ Society of Botanical Artists
1 Knapp Cottages, Wyke, Gillingham SP8 4NQ.
**Tel** 01747 825 718 **Fax** 01747 825 718
**Email** hendersons@dial.pipex.com
**Personnel** Pam Henderson.

### ▶ Society of Catholic Artists
c/o 19 Cranford Close, West Wimbledon, London SW20 0DP.
**Tel** 020 8947 6476
**Personnel** Chairperson: Margaret Farley. Secretary: Patrick Pike.

### ▶ Society of Equestrian Artists
Golf Cottages, Godden Green, Sevenoaks, Kent TN1S OJJ.
**Tel** 01732 762 908 **Fax** 01732 764 029
**Email** enquiries@equestrianartists.co.uk
**Ws** www.equestrianartists.co.uk
**Personnel** Secretary: Corinne Bickford. Chairman: Caro Skyrme.
**Services and Facilities** Friends Society. Workshop Facilities.
*Founded in 1978/9, the Society of Equestrian Artists promotes the practice of equestrian painting and sculpture and appreciation of equine art. By mutual assistance between members, it encourages the highest levels of artistic competence. The society runs master classes, lectures and workshops. An annual exhibition is normally held in August/September at Christie's, St James's, London. Membership comprises Associate and Full members, who have attained a consistently high standard in their work, and Friends, who may be artist or non-artist.*

### ▶ Society of Graphic Fine Art
15 Willow Way, Hatfield AL10 9QD.
**Tel** 01205 820 178
**Personnel** President/Chairman: David Brooke. Vice President: Jo Hall. Vice President/Publicity: Geraldine Jones. Hon. Treasurer: Rodger Lewis. Secretary: Mrs Sharon Curtis.
*The Society of Graphic Fine Art, which was founded in 1919, is a professional society that exists to promote good drawing skills. Members are selected solely on their quality of work, and membership is open to any artist working in any drawing medium or any form of original print-making. Oil painting or 'pure' watercolours are*

*inadmissible. The society holds an annual open exhibition in central London and has been increasing its out-of-town exhibitions. Members receive a newsletter and occasional visits and painting weekends are arranged.*

## ▶ The Society of London Art Dealers

91 Jermyn Street, London SW1Y 6JB.
**Tel** 020 7930 6137 **Fax** 020 7321 0685
**Opening times** 10–5.
**Nearest Underground** Green Park.
**Personnel** Secretary General: Neil Smith CMG.

## ▶ Society of Scottish Artists

11a Leslie Place, Edinburgh EH4 1NF.
**Tel** 0131 332 2041
**Personnel** Secretary: Susan Cornish.

## ▶ Society of Scottish Artists and Artists' Craftsmen

10 Wellington Street, Edinburgh EH7 5ED.
**Tel** 0131 556 0244 **Fax** 0131 556 0244
**Personnel** Deirdre Brittain.

## ▶ Society of Wildlife Artists

Mall Galleries, 17 Carlton House Terrace, London SW1Y 5BD.
**Tel** 020 7930 6844 **Fax** 020 7839 7830
**Ws** www.mallgalleries.org.uk/
**Personnel** President: Mr Bruce Pearson.
**Services and Facilities** Art Consultancy. Commissioning Service. Friends Society. Gallery space for hire. Guided Tours. Lectures. Workshop Facilities.

## ▶ Society of Women Artists

1 Knapp Cottages, Wyke, Gillingham SP8 4NQ.
**Tel** 01747 825 718 **Fax** 01747 826 835
**Email** hendersons@dial.pipex.com
**Ws** www.soc-women-artists.co.uk
**Opening times** 10–7.
**Nearest Station** St James's Park or Victoria.
**Personnel** President: Elizabeth Meek. Vice Presidents: Joyce Wyatt, Muriel Owen, Susan Millis, Joyce Rogerson. Admin, Sec: Pamela Henderson.
**Services and Facilities** Café. Commissioning Service. Disabled Access. Friends Society. Guided Tours. Lectures. Restaurant. Workshop Facilities.
**Work Stocked and Sold** Pa. Sc.
*Founded in 1885, the SWA Annual Open Exhibition is held in March each year at the Westminster Central Hall, Storey's Gate, London SW1 (admission free). Its aim is to exhibit the best of women artists' work and it features approximately 700 new works by many leading artists in a range of media, including oils, pastels, etchings, miniatures, sculptures and showcase pieces. Membership is by election only but non-members may enter work. To apply for submission forms write to above address. Archives are held by V&A Museum's Archive of Art and Design, Blythe House, 23 Blythe Road, London W14 0QF. Website: http://www.nal.vam.ac.uk/*

## ▶ Society of Wood Engravers

North Lodge, Hamstead Marshall, Newbury RG20 0JD.
**Tel** 01635 524 255
**Fax** 01635 524 255
**Personnel** General Secretary: Mrs Sue Brown.
**Services and Facilities** Art Consultancy. Commissioning Service. Friends Society.

## ▶ The Textile Society

Macclesfield Museum, Roe Street, Macclesfield SK11 6UT.
**Tel** 01625 613 210 **Fax** 01625 617 880
**Personnel** Louanne Collins.

## ▶ The Turner Society

BCM Box Turner, London WC1N 3XX.
**Personnel** Editor, *Turner Society News*: C. Powell. Chairman: Evelyn Joll.

## ▶ United Society of Artists

207 Sunny Bank Road, Potters Bar EN6 2NJ.
**Tel** 01707 851 439 **Fax** 01707 646 613
**Personnel** President: Leo Gibbons-Smith.

## ▶ Visiting Arts

11 Portland Place, London W1N 4EJ.
**Tel** 020 7389 3019 **Fax** 020 7389 3016
**Email** 101363.1471@compuserve.com
**Personnel** Director: Terry Sandell OBE. Camilla Edwards.
*Cultural relations through the arts.*

## ▶ Visual Arts and Galleries Association

The Old Village School, The High Street, Witcham, Ely CB6 2LQ.
**Tel** 01353 776 356
**Fax** 01353 775 411
**Email** admin@vaga.co.uk
**Ws** www.vaga.co.uk
**Personnel** Director: Hilary Gresty. Chair: Peter Jenkinson.
**Services and Facilities** Art Consultancy.
*The national association working for the public exhibition, presentation and development of the visual arts. The Association (membership 350 organisations and individuals) works primarily as an advocacy body on behalf of visual arts organisations throughout the UK. Activities include regular briefings (free entry to museums and galleries, lobbying MPs, etc), seminars and specialist networks such as academic galleries, curatorship etc. Bi-monthly newsletter.*

## ▶ Voluntary Arts Network

PO Box 200, Cardiff CF5 1YH.
**Tel** 029 2039 5395
**Fax** 029 2039 7397
**Email** info@vanmail.demon.co.uk
**Personnel** Director: Roger Fox. Information Officer: Jenny Saunders. Administration: Liz Hitch. Information and Training Officer: Lydia Bassett.

## ▶ Watercolour Society of Wales (Cymdeithas Dyfrlliw Cymru)

4 Castle Road, Raglan NP15 1JZ.
**Tel** 01291 690 260
**Personnel** Secretary: Margaret Butler.
*The Watercolour Society of Wales was established in 1959. Contemporary developments in art and in paint technology have extended interpretation of the medium to include a wider range of essentially water-based media and techniques. Recent exhibitions have clearly expressed this affinity with the contemporary scene, through an increasing diversity in scale and character of the works on show. The Society exhibits in prestigious galleries throughout the year. The 2002 programme includes Turner House, Penarth (National Museum and Gallery of Wales), 2 Feb–31 Mar 2002.*

## ▶ The Welsh Group

28 Rowan Way, Lisvane, Cardiff CF4 5TB.
**Tel** 029 2075 6653 **Fax** 029 2075 6653
**Personnel** Secretary: Jean Walcott.

# NOTES

# Arts Boards and Councils

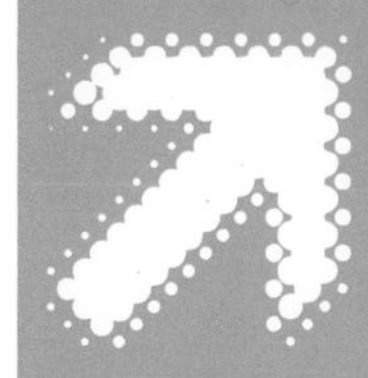

NOTES

# The British Council

The purpose of Art, Architecture and Design at the British Council is to develop and enlarge knowledge and appreciation overseas of British achievements in the fields of fine art, photography, design, the crafts and architecture. Working closely with the Council's international offices and with professional colleagues in Britain and abroad, the department mounts a programme of exhibitions and related projects around the world.

Partnerships with overseas museums and galleries are a key to the success of the department's loan exhibitions, which range from solo to group and thematic exhibitions. While priority is given to the promotion of contemporary art and design, the department does occasionally mount historical exhibitions.

In 2002, a major Constable exhibition is planned for the Grand Palais, the first solo exhibition of his work to be shown in Paris since 1814.

The British Council also owns one of the most comprehensive collections of British art, which contains more than 8,000 original and editioned works. Works from the collection form the basis of a programme of smaller touring exhibitions that are designed for extensive travel to areas of the world where it would be very difficult to negotiate for borrowed works to be shown. In February 2001, the ARCO International prize (Spain) was awarded to the British Council collection in recognition of its mission to 'promote, educate and inform about contemporary art' on an international stage.

Catalogues accompany all exhibitions, serving as both academic and documentary records. The department administers a reference library comprising over 23,000 publications and additional material on British artists.

Art, Architecture and Design is also responsible for the organisation of Britain's contribution at regular international events such as the São Paulo Biennale, the Istanbul Biennale, the Indian Triennale, and the Venice Biennale, where the Council maintains the British Pavilion.

In addition to its programme of exhibitions, the department also supports independent initiatives by overseas galleries wishing to show work by British artists. Artists who have been invited to exhibition abroad can apply for financial assistance under the Grants to Artists scheme run by the department.

Brett Rogers
Deputy Director, Visual Arts
The British Council

### ▶ The Arts Council/ An Chomhairle Ealaíon
70 Merrion Square, Dublin 2.
**Tel** 00353 1 618 0200
**Fax** 00353 1 676 1302
**Email** info@artscouncil.ie
**Ws** www.artscouncil.ie
**Opening times** 9.15–5.30.
**Personnel** Visual Arts Officer: Oliver Dowling. Exhibition Organiser: Helena Gorey.

### ▶ Arts Council of England
14 Great Peter Street, London SW1P 3NQ.
**Tel** 020 7333 0100 **Fax** 020 7973 6590
**Email** enquiries@artscouncil.org.uk
**Ws** www.artscouncil.org.uk
**Nearest Underground** St James's Park, Westminster.

### ▶ Arts Council of Northern Ireland
MacNeice House, 77 Malone Road, Belfast BT9 6AQ.
**Tel** 028 9038 5200, Lottery tel: 028 9066 7000
**Fax** 028 9066 1715, Lottery fax: 028 9066 4766
**Email** publicaffairs@artscouncil-ni.org
**Ws** www.artscouncil-ni.org/
**Opening times** Mon–Thu 9–5.30, Fri 9–5.
**Personnel** Chairman (028 9038 5220, chair@artscouncil-ni.org): Prof Brian Walker. Chief Executive (028 9038 5217, chief@artscouncil-ni.org): Roisin McDonough. Public Affairs Officer (028 9032 5204, dsmyth@artscouncil-ni.org): Damian Smyth. Director of Creative Arts (028 9038 5216, nmckinney@artscouncil-ni.org): Nóirin McKinney. Lottery Director (028 9038 5206, tgreenfield@artscouncil-ni.org): Tanya Greenfield.
*'The Mission of the Arts Council of Northern Ireland is to develop the arts in Northern Ireland so that as many people as possible can enjoy as many forms of art as possible to as high a standard as possible.'*
*The Arts Council of Northern Ireland is the prime distributor of public support for the arts and, since 1995, it has distributed National Lottery funds for the arts in Northern Ireland. It was established in 1962 as a successor to the Committee for the Encouragement of Music and the Arts (CEMA) which had operated since 1942. The Arts Council (Northern Ireland) Order 1995 set up the Arts Council as a statutory body. In addition to providing funding for the arts, its principal functions are: to develop and improve the knowledge, appreciation and practice of the arts; to increase public access to and participation in the arts; to advise the Department of Culture, Arts and Leisure and other government departments, district councils and other bodies, on matters relating to the arts; to develop and improve the knowledge, appreciation and practice of the arts; and to increase the knowledge of the Department of Culture, Arts and Leisure and other government departments, district councils and other bodies, on matters relating to the arts.*
*Key publication:* To The Millennium: A Strategy for the Arts in Northern Ireland *(1995).*

### ▶ Arts Council of Wales
Museum Place, Cardiff CF10 3NX.
**Tel** 029 2037 6500 **Fax** 029 2022 1447
**Email** information@ccc-acw.org.uk
**Ws** www.ccc-acw.org.uk
**Opening times** Mon–Fri 9–5.15.
**Nearest Station** Cardiff Central.
**Personnel** Senior Visual Arts and Craft Officer, Artform Development Division: John Hambley. Tessa Hartog.
*The Arts Council of Wales (ACW) is the national organisation with specific responsibility for the funding and development of the arts in Wales, including the visual arts and the crafts. It receives grants from central and local government of which the largest is from the Welsh Assembly (ACW has become an Assembly-Sponsored Public Body). It is also the distributor of funds for the arts in Wales generated by the National Lottery. From these resources, ACW makes grants to support art activities and facilities. Some of this funding is allocated in the form of annual revenue grants to full-time arts organisations. ACW also operates schemes which provide financial and other forms of support for individual activities and projects. ACW is a Registered Charity and is set up by Royal Charter. ACW works through the medium of both the Welsh and English languages. ACW also has offices in Carmarthen and Colwyn Bay. ACW is currently restructuring its organisation to a decentralised regional model. This will be completed and fully operational from 1 April 2002.*

### ▶ The British Council
Visual Arts, 11 Portland Place, London W1B 1EJ.
**Tel** 020 7389 3009 **Fax** 020 7389 3101
**Email** Hymie.Dunn@britcoun.org
**Nearest Underground** Oxford Circus
**Personnel** Director: Andrea Rose. Grants Officer: Katie Boot. Head of Exhibitions: Brett Rogers. Collection Manager: Diana Eccles. Grants Officer: Katie Boot (Tel: 020 7389 3045, Fax: 020 7389 3101, Email: Katie.Boot@britcoun.org).
*Working with museums and galleries abroad as well as colleagues in British Council offices around the world, the department organises major exhibitions of British art for overseas audiences, involving loans from national, regional and private collections, as well as mounting touring exhibitions drawn from its collection of over 7,000 works by British artists. The Grants to Artists scheme offers assistance to artists who have been invited to exhibit abroad and to overseas galleries wishing to exhibit the work of UK artists. Programmes and study tours are organised by invitation for curators from abroad wishing to update their knowledge of British art.*

### ▶ East England Arts
Cherry Hinton Hall, Cherry Hinton Road, Cambridge CB1 8DW.
**Tel** 01223 215 355 **Fax** 01223 248 075
**Email** info@eearts.co.uk
**Opening times** Mon–Fri 9–5.
**Nearest Station** Cambridge.
**Personnel** Arts Development Officer (Visual Arts): Niki Braithwaite.
*East England Arts is the regional development agency for the east of England. It is one of 10 Regional Arts Boards and covers the counties of Bedfordshire, Cambridgeshire, Essex, Hertfordshire, Norfolk and Suffolk, and the unitary authorities of Luton, Peterborough, Southend-on-Sea and Thurroch. Its open access funding scheme is the Regional Arts Lottery programme. Funds for individual artists are available from Commissions East (01223 356 882), which manages the scheme in partnership with East England Arts. Ifree art, the region's interest-free loan scheme for purchases of contemporary art, is currently available in 14 galleries in the region.*

### ▶ London Arts Board
Elme House, 133 Long Acre, London WC2E 9AF.
**Tel** 020 7240 1313

### ▶ North West Arts Board
Manchester House, 22 Bridge Street, Manchester M3 3AB.
**Tel** 0161 834 6644 **Fax** 0161 834 6969
**Personnel** Aileen McEvoy.

### ▶ Northern Arts
Central Square, Forth Street, Newcastle-upon-Tyne NE1 3PJ.
**Tel** 0191 281 6334 **Fax** 0191 281 3276

### ▶ Scottish Arts Council
12 Manor Place, Edinburgh EH3 7DD.
**Tel** 0131 226 6051 **Fax** 0131 225 9833
**Personnel** Information Officer: Giulio Romano. Christine Galey.

### ▶ South East Arts Board
10 Mount Ephraim, Tunbridge Wells TN4 8AS.
**Tel** 01892 515 210 ext 213
**Fax** 01892 549 383
**Personnel** Jim Shea.

### ▶ South West Arts
Bradninch Place, Gandy Street, Exeter EX4 3LS.
**Tel** 01392 218 188 **Fax** 01392 413 554
**Email** info@swa.co.uk
**Ws** www.swa.co.uk
**Personnel** Chairman: John Prescott Thomas. Acting Chief Executive: Nick Capaldi.

### ▶ Southern Arts Board
13 St Clement Street, Winchester SO23 9DQ.
**Tel** 01962 855 099 **Fax** 01962 861 186
**Personnel** Philip Smith. David Kay.

### ▶ West Midlands Arts
82 Granville Street, Birmingham B1 2LH.
**Tel** 0121 631 3121, Lottery Line: 0121 693 6878
**Fax** 0121 643 7239
**Email** west.midarts@midnet.com
**Ws** www.arts.org.uk/
**Opening times** 9–5.
**Personnel** Chief Executive: Sally Luton.
**Services and Facilities** Disabled Access.

### ▶ Yorkshire Arts
21 Bond Street, Dewsbury WF13 1AX.
**Tel** 01924 455 555 **Fax** 01924 466 522
**Email** info@yarts.co.uk
**Ws** www.arts.org.uk
**Opening times** Mon–Thu 9–5.30, Fri 9–5.
**Personnel** Chief Executive: Roger Lancaster.
**Services and Facilities** Art Consultancy. Disabled Access.
*Yorkshire Arts is the Regional Arts Board for Yorkshire and The Humber. Its mission is to promote creativity in the region through sustaining and developing the arts and creative industries.*

# Education

Institutions by course
Awards and Qualifications
Main address listings

# Education

Art in Higher Education is enjoying an interesting if somewhat schizophrenic time at the moment. Britain still enjoys a great reputation and media profile for its very successful marketing of young, exciting art, backed up by a strong group of well-established artists. It is a good moment to be a young artist beginning a career within the challenging and supportive context of an art school. People are interested in what is going on, work is being sold, and more importantly, many different approaches to making art are seen as equally viable and worthy of investigation and development.

This openness, together with a pluralistic approach to making art, subverts dominant styles and avoids subservience to fashion or passing trends. This is, I feel, one of the most positive features of current art school experience.

However, the increasing dominance within art schools of bureaucratic, managerial and academic processes is having a negative effect. Any attempts to define, control, quantify and justify the rather slippery subject of fine art, and fit it in the generalised patterns now being applied to Higher Education, ultimately undermines studio practice and open investigation.

Thus, while openness is apparent within the work being produced by students, a certain cynicism is becoming apparent within institutions. This can and should be resisted. In this respect, the Slade is entering an exciting new period in its development with the appointment of a group of new staff across all the subject areas and a new structure to the administration of the courses which fosters initiative and opportunity for positive development.

All students at the Slade are treated as emerging artists and are respected for their individual progression. They are taught, encouraged and made critically aware by staff who see value in working within higher education while maintaining and developing active careers as artists.

John Aiken
Slade Professor
Director of the Slade School

## FINE ART

**The Arts Institute at Bournemouth**
**Core Subjects:**
Drawing. Painting. Photography. Printmaking. Textiles.

**Bath Spa University College**
**Core Subjects:**
Drawing. Installation. Painting. Photography. Printmaking. Sculpture. Video.

**Bridgwater College**
**Core Subjects:**
Art Theory. Art History. Ceramics. Drawing. Installation. Media. Painting. Phonic Arts. Photography. Printmaking. Sculpture. Textiles. Time-based Media. Video.

**Byam Shaw School of Art**
**Core Subjects:**
Film. Painting. Performance. Photography. Printmaking. Sculpture. Video.

**Carmarthenshire College**
**Core Subjects:**
Art Theory. Art History. Ceramics. Drawing. Media. Painting. Photography. Printmaking. Sculpture. Textiles. Time-based Media. Video.

**Central Saint Martins College of Art & Design**
**Core Subjects:**
Ceramics. Painting. Photography. Printmaking. Sculpture. Textiles.

**The Cheshire School of Art & Design, Mid-Cheshire College**

**Christie's Education**
**Core Subjects:**
Art History.

**The City Literary Institute for Adult Studies, Department of Visual Arts**
**Core Subjects:**
Art Theory. Art History. Ceramics. Drawing. Installation. Painting. Photography. Printmaking. Sculpture. Textiles. Video.

**Coventry University**
**Core Subjects:**
Art History. Ceramics. Drawing. Installation. Media. Painting. Photography. Printmaking. Sculpture. Textiles. Time-based Media. Video.

**Cumbria College of Art and Design**
**Core Subjects:**
Art History. Ceramics. Painting. Photography. Printmaking. Sculpture.

**Edinburgh College of Art**
**Core Subjects:**
Ceramics. Drawing. Painting. Photography. Printmaking. Sculpture. Textiles.

**Falmouth College of Arts**
**Core Subjects:**
Art History. Ceramics. Painting. Photography. Printmaking. Sculpture.

**Goldsmiths College**
**Core Subjects:**
Art Theory. Art History. Drawing. Media. Painting. Photography. Printmaking. Sculpture. Textiles. Video.

**Heatherley School of Fine Art**
**Core Subjects:**
Art History. Drawing. Painting. Printmaking. Sculpture.

**The Institute**
**Core Subjects:**
Art History. Ceramics. Drawing. Painting. Photography. Sculpture.

**Kingston University, Faculty of Design**
**Core Subjects:**
Artists' Books. Art Theory. Art History. Drawing. Installation. Painting. Photography. Printmaking. Sculpture. Video.

**Lancaster University, School of Creative Arts, The Art Department**
**Core Subjects:**
Art History. Drawing. Painting. Printmaking. Sculpture.

**Leeds College of Art and Design**
**Core Subjects:**
Art History. Ceramics. Drawing. Painting. Photography. Sculpture. Textiles. Time-based Media.

**Nottingham Trent University**
**Core Subjects:**
Drawing. Installation. Media. Painting. Photography. Printmaking. Sculpture. Textiles. Time-based Media. Video.

**Plymouth College of Art and Design**

**The Prince's Foundation**

**Reigate School of Art and Design**
**Core Subjects:**
Art Theory. Art History. Drawing. Installation. Media. Painting. Photography. Printmaking. Sculpture. Time-based Media. Video.

**Ruskin School of Drawing and Fine Art**
**Core Subjects:**
Art Theory. Art History. Drawing. Installation. Painting. Photography. Printmaking. Sculpture. Video.

**Slade School of Fine Art**
**Core Subjects:**
Media. Painting. Photography. Printmaking. Sculpture. Time-based Media. Video.

**Swansea Institute of Higher Education**
**Core Subjects:**
Art Theory. Art History. Ceramics. Drawing. Installation. Media. Painting. Photography. Printmaking. Textiles. Time-based Media. Video.

**University of Central England in Birmingham**
**Core Subjects:**
Art Theory. Art History. Ceramics. Drawing. Installation. Media. Painting. Photography. Printmaking. Sculpture. Textiles. Time-based Media. Video.

**University of Plymouth**
**Core Subjects:**
Art History. Media. Painting. Photography. Printmaking. Sculpture. Textiles. Time-based Media. Video.

**Westminster College**
**Core Subjects:**
Media. Photography. Textiles.

**York College**
**Core Subjects:**
Art History. Ceramics. Drawing. Media. Photography. Printmaking. Sculpture. Textiles.

## INDIVIDUAL COURSES

### ANIMATION

**The Arts Institute at Bournemouth**
**Bridgwater College**
**Carmarthenshire College**
**Central Saint Martins College of Art & Design**
**The City Literary Institute for Adult Studies, Department of Visual Arts**
**Cumbria College of Art and Design**
**Edinburgh College of Art**
**Nottingham Trent University**
**Swansea Institute of Higher Education**
**University of Central England in Birmingham**
**York College**

### ARCHITECTURE

**Birkbeck College**
**Edinburgh College of Art**
**Nottingham Trent University**

### ARCHEOLOGICAL ILLUSTRATION

**Swansea Institute of Higher Education**

### ART HISTORY

**Bath Spa University College**
**Birkbeck College**
**Christie's Education**
**The City Literary Institute for Adult Studies, Department of Visual Arts**
**Cumbria College of Art and Design**
**Falmouth College of Arts**
**Glasgow University**
**The Institute**

Lancaster University,
School of Creative Arts,
The Art Department
Leeds College of Art and Design
Slade School of Fine Art
Sotheby's Institute
Swansea Institute
of Higher Education
University of Central
England in Birmingham
University of Plymouth
York College

## CERAMICS

The Arts Institute at Bournemouth
Bath Spa University College
Bridgwater College
Carmarthenshire College
Central Saint Martins
College of Art & Design
Central Saint Martins College of
Art & Design (London Institute)
The Cheshire School of Art &
Design, Mid-Cheshire College
Christie's Education
The City Literary Institute for
Adult Studies, Department
of Visual Arts
Coventry University
Cumbria College of Art and Design
Falmouth College of Arts
The Institute
Kingston University,
Faculty of Design
Nottingham Trent University
Plymouth College
of Art and Design
Sotheby's Institute
Swansea Institute
of Higher Education
University of Central
England in Birmingham
York College

## CONTEMPORARY ARTS

Christie's Education
City & Guilds of
London Art School
The City Literary Institute for
Adult Studies, Department
of Visual Arts
Falmouth College of Arts
The Institute
Nottingham Trent University
Sotheby's Institute
Swansea Institute
of Higher Education

## DECORATIVE ART

Christie's Education
City & Guilds of
London Art School
The City Literary Institute for
Adult Studies, Department
of Visual Arts
The Institute
Nottingham Trent University
Sotheby's Institute
Swansea Institute
of Higher Education

## FURNITURE

Bridgwater College
Christie's Education
The Institute
Kingston University,
Faculty of Design
Leeds College of Art and Design
Nottingham Trent University
Ravensbourne College of
Design and Communication
Rycotewood College
Sotheby's Institute
University of Central
England in Birmingham
University of Plymouth
York College

## ILLUSTRATION

The Arts Institute at Bournemouth
Bath Spa University College
Bridgwater College
Carmarthenshire College
The Cheshire School of Art &
Design, Mid-Cheshire College
The City Literary Institute for
Adult Studies, Department
of Visual Arts
Edinburgh College of Art
Falmouth College of Arts
Nottingham Trent University
Reigate School of Art and Design
Swansea Institute
of Higher Education
University of Central
England in Birmingham
University of Plymouth
Westminster College
York College

## JEWELLERY/SILVER

Bridgwater College
Central Saint Martins
College of Art & Design
Central Saint Martins College of
Art & Design (London Institute)
Christie's Education
The City Literary Institute for
Adult Studies, Department
of Visual Arts
Coventry University
Cumbria College of Art and Design
Edinburgh College of Art
The Institute
Leeds College of Art and Design
Plymouth College
of Art and Design
Reigate School of Art and Design
Sotheby's Institute
University of Central
England in Birmingham
York College

## MEDIA

The Arts Institute
at Bournemouth
Birkbeck College
Bridgwater College
Carmarthenshire College
The Cheshire School of Art &
Design, Mid-Cheshire College
Coventry University
Cumbria College of Art and Design
Falmouth College of Arts
Nottingham Trent University
Plymouth College
of Art and Design
Ravensbourne College of
Design and Communication
Swansea Institute
of Higher Education
University of Central
England in Birmingham
University of Plymouth
Westminster College
York College

## MULTIMEDIA

The Arts Institute at Bournemouth
Bath Spa University College
Birkbeck College
Bridgwater College
Carmarthenshire College
The Cheshire School of Art &
Design, Mid-Cheshire College
The City Literary Institute for
Adult Studies, Department
of Visual Arts
Coventry University
Cumbria College of Art and Design
Falmouth College of Arts
The Institute
Leeds College of Art and Design
Nottingham Trent University
Plymouth College
of Art and Design
Ravensbourne College of
Design and Communication
Swansea Institute
of Higher Education
University of Central
England in Birmingham
University of Plymouth
Westminster College
York College

## PAINTING

The Arts Institute at Bournemouth
Bath Spa University College
Bridgwater College
Byam Shaw School of Art
Carmarthenshire College
Central Saint Martins
College of Art & Design
The Cheshire School of Art &
Design, Mid-Cheshire College
Christie's Education
City & Guilds of London Art School
The City Literary Institute for
Adult Studies, Department
of Visual Arts
Coventry University
Cumbria College of Art and Design
Heatherley School of Fine Art
The Institute
Kingston University,
Faculty of Design
Lancaster University,
School of Creative Arts,
The Art Department

Nottingham Trent University
Swansea Institute of Higher Education
University of Central England in Birmingham
University of Plymouth
York College

### PHOTOGRAPHY

The Arts Institute at Bournemouth
Bath Spa University College
Bridgwater College
Carmarthenshire College
Central Saint Martins College of Art & Design
The Cheshire School of Art & Design, Mid-Cheshire College
Christie's Education
The City Literary Institute for Adult Studies, Department of Visual Arts
Edinburgh College of Art
The Institute
Leeds College of Art and Design
Nottingham Trent University
Plymouth College of Art and Design
Reigate School of Art and Design
Swansea Institute of Higher Education
University of Central England in Birmingham
University of Plymouth
Westminster College
York College

### STAINED GLASS

Central Saint Martins College of Art & Design
City & Guilds of London Art School
The City Literary Institute for Adult Studies, Department of Visual Arts
Edinburgh College of Art
The Institute
Leeds College of Art and Design
Swansea Institute of Higher Education
York College

### TEXTILES

Bath Spa University College
Bridgwater College
Carmarthenshire College
Central Saint Martins College of Art & Design
The Cheshire School of Art & Design, Mid-Cheshire College
The City Literary Institute for Adult Studies, Department of Visual Arts
Cumbria College of Art and Design
Goldsmiths College
Leeds College of Art and Design
Nottingham Trent University
Reigate School of Art and Design
Sotheby's Institute
Swansea Institute of Higher Education
University of Central England in Birmingham
Westminster College
York College

## DESIGN COURSES

### AUTOMOTIVE

Coventry University

### CRAFT

Bridgwater College
Carmarthenshire College
The Cheshire School of Art & Design, Mid-Cheshire College
City & Guilds of London Art School
Coventry University
Cumbria College of Art and Design
Nottingham Trent University
Reigate School of Art and Design

### 3D

The Arts Institute at Bournemouth
Bath Spa University College
Bridgwater College
Carmarthenshire College
Central Saint Martins College of Art & Design
The Cheshire School of Art & Design, Mid-Cheshire College
The City Literary Institute for Adult Studies, Department of Visual Arts
Coventry University
Falmouth College of Arts
Nottingham Trent University
Plymouth College of Art and Design
Ravensbourne College of Design and Communication
Reigate School of Art and Design
University of Central England in Birmingham
University of Plymouth
York College

### DISPLAY

The Cheshire School of Art & Design, Mid-Cheshire College
Swansea Institute of Higher Education

### FASHION

The Arts Institute at Bournemouth
Bridgwater College
Carmarthenshire College
Central Saint Martins College of Art & Design
The Cheshire School of Art & Design, Mid-Cheshire College
Edinburgh College of Art
Leeds College of Art and Design
Nottingham Trent University
Plymouth College of Art and Design
Ravensbourne College of Design and Communication
Reigate School of Art and Design
University of Central England in Birmingham
Westminster College

### FURNITURE

Bridgwater College
The Cheshire School of Art & Design, Mid-Cheshire College
Edinburgh College of Art
The Institute
Leeds College of Art and Design
Nottingham Trent University
Ravensbourne College of Design and Communication
Rycotewood College
University of Central England in Birmingham
University of Plymouth

### GRAPHIC

The Arts Institute at Bournemouth
Bath Spa University College
Bridgwater College
Carmarthenshire College
Central Saint Martins College of Art & Design
The Cheshire School of Art & Design, Mid-Cheshire College
The City Literary Institute for Adult Studies, Department of Visual Arts
Coventry University
Cumbria College of Art and Design
Edinburgh College of Art
Falmouth College of Arts
Leeds College of Art and Design
Nottingham Trent University
Plymouth College of Art and Design
Ravensbourne College of Design and Communication
Reigate School of Art and Design
Swansea Institute of Higher Education
University of Central England in Birmingham
University of Plymouth
Westminster College
York College

### INTERACTIVE

Bath Spa University College
The Cheshire School of Art & Design, Mid-Cheshire College
Coventry University
Ravensbourne College of Design and Communication
Swansea Institute of Higher Education

### INTERIOR

The Arts Institute at Bournemouth
Bridgwater College
Carmarthenshire College
The Cheshire School of Art & Design, Mid-Cheshire College
The City Literary Institute for Adult Studies, Department of Visual Arts

Edinburgh College of Art
Falmouth College of Arts
The Institute
Leeds College of Art and Design
Nottingham Trent University
Plymouth College of Art and Design
Ravensbourne College of Design and Communication
Reigate School of Art and Design
University of Central England in Birmingham
University of Plymouth
Westminster College
York College

## MUSEUM & EXHIBITION

The Cheshire School of Art & Design, Mid-Cheshire College
The City Literary Institute for Adult Studies, Department of Visual Arts
The Institute
University of Lincolnshire & Humberside
The Hull School of Art & Design

## PHOTOGRAPHY

The Arts Institute at Bournemouth
Bath Spa University College
Bridgwater College
Carmarthenshire College
Central Saint Martins College of Art & Design
The Cheshire School of Art & Design, Mid-Cheshire College
The City Literary Institute for Adult Studies, Department of Visual Arts
Falmouth College of Arts
The Institute
Leeds College of Art and Design
Nottingham Trent University
Reigate School of Art and Design
Swansea Institute of Higher Education
University of Central England in Birmingham
University of Plymouth
Westminster College
York College

## PRODUCT

Bridgwater College
Central Saint Martins College of Art & Design
The Cheshire School of Art & Design, Mid-Cheshire College
Coventry University
Nottingham Trent University
Ravensbourne College of Design and Communication
Reigate School of Art and Design
University of Central England in Birmingham
University of Plymouth

## PUBLIC ART

The Cheshire School of Art & Design, Mid-Cheshire College
Coventry University
Nottingham Trent University
Swansea Institute of Higher Education

## SURFACE

Bridgwater College
Carmarthenshire College
The Cheshire School of Art & Design, Mid-Cheshire College
The City Literary Institute for Adult Studies, Department of Visual Arts
Cumbria College of Art and Design
Leeds College of Art and Design
Reigate School of Art and Design
Swansea Institute of Higher Education
University of Central England in Birmingham

## TEXTILE

The Arts Institute at Bournemouth
Bridgwater College
Carmarthenshire College
Central Saint Martins College of Art & Design
The Cheshire School of Art & Design, Mid-Cheshire College
The City Literary Institute for Adult Studies, Department of Visual Arts
Cumbria College of Art and Design
Falmouth College of Arts
Leeds College of Art and Design
Nottingham Trent University
Ravensbourne College of Design and Communication
Reigate School of Art and Design
Swansea Institute of Higher Education
University of Central England in Birmingham
Westminster College

## THEORY

Bridgwater College
Falmouth College of Arts
Reigate School of Art and Design
Swansea Institute of Higher Education

## TYPOGRAPHY

Bridgwater College
The Cheshire School of Art & Design, Mid-Cheshire College
The City Literary Institute for Adult Studies, Department of Visual Arts
Plymouth College of Art and Design
Reigate School of Art and Design
Swansea Institute of Higher Education
University of Plymouth
York College

## THEATRE

The Arts Institute at Bournemouth
Carmarthenshire College
Central Saint Martins College of Art & Design
Coventry University
Nottingham Trent University
University of Central England in Birmingham

## TV AND FILM

The Arts Institute at Bournemouth
Bridgwater College
Carmarthenshire College
The Cheshire School of Art & Design, Mid-Cheshire College
Edinburgh College of Art
Nottingham Trent University
Ravensbourne College of Design and Communication
University of Central England in Birmingham

# AWARDS AND COURSE TYPES

## ADULT EDUCATION

The Arts Institute at Bournemouth
Birkbeck College
Bridgwater College
Carmarthenshire College
The Cheshire School of Art & Design, Mid-Cheshire College
Christie's Education
The City Literary Institute for Adult Studies, Department of Visual Arts
Cumbria College of Art and Design
Edinburgh College of Art
Heatherley School of Fine Art
The Institute
Leeds College of Art and Design
Plymouth College of Art and Design
Reigate School of Art and Design
Rycotewood College
Swansea Institute of Higher Education
University of Central England in Birmingham
Westminster College
York College

## DEGREE

The Arts Institute at Bournemouth
Bath Spa University College
Byam Shaw School of Art
Carmarthenshire College
Central Saint Martins College of Art & Design
The Cheshire School of Art & Design, Mid-Cheshire College
Christie's Education
Coventry University
Cumbria College of Art and Design
Edinburgh College of Art
Falmouth College of Arts

Goldsmiths College
Kingston University, Faculty of Design
Lancaster University, School of Creative Arts, The Art Department
Leeds College of Art and Design
Nottingham Trent University
Plymouth College of Art and Design
Ravensbourne College of Design and Communication
Ruskin School of Drawing and Fine Art
Slade School of Fine Art
Swansea Institute of Higher Education
University of Central England in Birmingham
University of Plymouth

## DIPLOMA, CERAMICS

The City Literary Institute for Adult Studies, Department of Visual Arts

## DIPLOMA, PORTRAITURE

Heatherley School of Fine Art

## DIPLOMA, SCULPTURE

Heatherley School of Fine Art

## FOUNDATION

The Arts Institute at Bournemouth
Bridgwater College
Byam Shaw School of Art
Carmarthenshire College
Central Saint Martins College of Art & Design
The Cheshire School of Art & Design, Mid-Cheshire College
The City Literary Institute for Adult Studies, Department of Visual Arts
Coventry University
Cumbria College of Art and Design
Falmouth College of Arts
Heatherley School of Fine Art
Leeds College of Art and Design
Nottingham Trent University
Plymouth College of Art and Design
Ravensbourne College of Design and Communication
Reigate School of Art and Design
Rycotewood College
Swansea Institute of Higher Education
University of Central England in Birmingham
Westminster College
York College

## HNC

The Arts Institute at Bournemouth
The Cheshire School of Art & Design, Mid-Cheshire College
Cumbria College of Art and Design
Leeds College of Art and Design
Plymouth College of Art and Design
Ravensbourne College of Design and Communication
Reigate School of Art and Design

## HND

The Arts Institute at Bournemouth
Bridgwater College
Carmarthenshire College
The Cheshire School of Art & Design, Mid-Cheshire College
Cumbria College of Art and Design
Leeds College of Art and Design
Nottingham Trent University
Plymouth College of Art and Design
Ravensbourne College of Design and Communication
Reigate School of Art and Design
Rycotewood College
Swansea Institute of Higher Education
University of Central England in Birmingham
Westminster College
York College

## POSTGRADUATE

Bath Spa University College
Byam Shaw School of Art
Central Saint Martins College of Art & Design
Christie's Education
Coventry University
Cumbria College of Art and Design
Edinburgh College of Art
Falmouth College of Arts
Glasgow University
Goldsmiths College
Lancaster University, School of Creative Arts, The Art Department
Nottingham Trent University
The Prince's Foundation
Ravensbourne College of Design and Communication
Ruskin School of Drawing and Fine Art
Slade School of Fine Art
Swansea Institute of Higher Education
University of Central England in Birmingham
University of Plymouth

## PRACTICAL

Bridgwater College
Carmarthenshire College
The Cheshire School of Art & Design, Mid-Cheshire College
The City Literary Institute for Adult Studies, Department of Visual Arts
Coventry University
Heatherley School of Fine Art
The Institute
Ravensbourne College of Design and Communication

## PRE-FOUNDATION

The Arts Institute at Bournemouth
Bridgwater College
Carmarthenshire College
The Cheshire School of Art & Design, Mid-Cheshire College
The City Literary Institute for Adult Studies, Department of Visual Arts
Heatherley School of Fine Art
The Institute
Leeds College of Art and Design
Nottingham Trent University
University of Central England in Birmingham
York College

## TEACHER TRAINING

Bath Spa University College
University of Central England in Birmingham
University of Plymouth

## MAIN ADDRESS LISTINGS

### ▶ The Arts Institute at Bournemouth

Wallisdown, Poole BH12 5HH.
**Tel** 01202 533 011 **Fax** 01202 537 729
**Email** general@arts-inst-bournemouth.ac.uk
**Ws** www.arts-inst-bournemouth.ac.uk
**Opening times** 8–5 Mon–Fri.
**Nearest Station** Bournemouth.
**Personnel** Lifelong Learning Manager: Jo Long. Promotions Officer: Ms Violet McClean.
*The Arts Institute at Bournemouth, formerly Bournemouth and Poole College of Art and Design, is one of the UK's leading specialist colleges offering courses in art, design and media. Established in 1883, the Arts Institute has built up a national and international reputation for the creativity and innovation of its courses and was awarded Higher Education status in August 2001. The strengths of the Institute at Further and Higher Education level are reflected in the specialist nature of the courses on offer and the professional ethos of the working environment. All courses are designed to give students a clear progression leading to nationally validated awards with flexible points of entry.*
**Courses:**
**Animation. Ceramics. Design (3-D, Fashion, Graphic, Interior, Photography, TV & Film, Textile, Theatre). Fine Art (Drawing, Painting, Photography, Printmaking, Textiles). Illustration. Media. Multi-Media. Painting. Photography.**
**Qualifications:**
**Adult Education. Degree. Foundation. Pre-foundation. HND.**

### ▶ Bath Spa University College

Faculty of Art and Music, Sion Hill Place, Lansdown, Bath BA1 5SF.
**Tel** 01225 875 875 **Fax** 01225 875 666
**Email** staffinitial.surname@bathspa.ac.uk
**Ws** www.bathspa.ac.uk
**Nearest Station** Bath Spa.
**Personnel** Dean of Faculty of Art and Music: Mr Alan Carter.

*The Faculty of Art and Music, which offers undergraduate and postgraduate courses, is characterised by its wide use of practising artists, designers and musicians as part-time and associate lecturers. This policy ensures that students are in regular tutorial contact with staff who actively engage in research. Many of our staff operate internationally, resulting in a highly creative and professional environment at Bath Spa University College. Our courses have an excellent reputation for the quality of educational experience available to students. Work takes place in either refurbished or purpose-built specialist accommodation. The cities of Bath and Bristol, as well as ease of access to London, ensure excellent resources for creative study. A QAA Subject Review for Art and Design in October 1999 scored 22 out of a maximum 24 points.*

**Courses:**
**Art History. Ceramics. Design (3-D, Graphic, Interactive, Photography). Fine Art (Drawing, Installation, Painting, Photography, Printmaking, Video). Illustration. Multi-Media. Painting. Photography. Textiles.**
**Qualifications:**
**Degree. Postgraduate. Teacher Training.**

### ▶ Birkbeck College

Faculty of Continuing Education, 26 Russell Square, London WC1B 5DQ.
**Tel** 020 7631 6660 **Fax** 020 7631 6686
**Email** c.sherman@.bbk.ac.uk
**Ws** www.bbk.ac.uk/fce
**Nearest Underground** Russell Square.
**Personnel** Executive Officer, Art History: Michelle Pickford.
*The Faculty offers about 90 part-time day/evening courses on the history of art and architecture in various centres in the Greater London area. The courses are for adults, and all are open to anyone, without prior qualification. The programme covers a Certificate/Diploma (equivalent to the first year of a BA); accredited courses of one or two terms; non-accredited courses; weekend study days; and a residential summer school. Classroom meetings are supplemented by gallery visits. Emphasis is on developing ways of seeing art, thinking about it and understanding critical approaches to it.*
**Courses:**
**Architecture. Art History. Media. Multi-Media.**
**Qualifications:**
**Adult Education.**

### ▶ Bridgwater College

Bath Road, Bridgwater TA6 4PZ.
**Tel** 01278 441 234 **Fax** 01278 444 363
**Email** guidance@bridgwater.ac.uk
**Ws** www.bridgwater.ac.uk
**Nearest Station** Bridgwater.
**Personnel** Adult and Community Education Co-ordinator: Ms Jill Frazer.
**Courses:**
**Animation. Ceramics. Design (Craft, 3-D, Fashion, Furniture, Graphic, Interior, Photography, Product, Surface Decoration, TV & Film, Textile, Theory, Typographic). Fine Art. Furniture. Illustration. Jewellery/Silversmithing. Media. Multi-Media. Painting. Photography. Textiles.**
**Qualifications:**
**Adult Education. Foundation. Pre-foundation. HND. Practical.**

### ▶ Byam Shaw School of Art

2 Elthorne Road, Archway, London N19 4AG.
**Tel** 020 7281 4111 **Fax** 020 7281 1632
**Email** info@byam-shaw.ac.uk
**Ws** www.byam-shaw.ac.uk
**Nearest Underground** Archway.
**Personnel** Principal: Alister Warman. Director of Studies: Douglas Allsop.
*Independent Fine Art School committed to the education of intending artists. Three-year BA (Hons) in Fine Art, Fine Art Foundation, MA Fine Art, Postgraduate Studies.*
**Courses:**
**Fine Art (Painting, Photography, Printmaking, Sculpture, Video). Painting.**
**Qualifications:**
**Degree. Foundation. Postgraduate.**

### ▶ Carmarthenshire College

West Wales School of the Arts, Jobswell Road, Carmarthen SA31 3HY.
**Tel** 01267 221 774 **Fax** 01267 221 515
**Email** gillian.cole@ccta.ac.uk
**Ws** www.wwsota.ac.uk
**Nearest Station** Carmarthen.
**Personnel** Acting Head of Faculty: Mr Paul Evans.
*The West Wales School of the Arts has a reputation for providing high quality education, with one of the broadest ranges of Art and Design courses available within one establishment. A unique creative ambience exists within the school, produced by excellent teaching and first-rate workshop and studio facilities. Creative practice ranges from the traditional and craft-based work through to cutting edge design with sophisticated technical support. Students on every course develop a specific range of skills which equips them with the knowledge and expertise relevant to their intended career routes. The school is proud of its friendly and supportive atmosphere and its open access ethos encourages cross-pollination between diverse areas of study.*
**Courses:**
**Animation. Ceramics. Design (Craft, 3-D, Fashion, Graphic, Interior, Photography, Surface Decoration, TV & Film, Textile, Theatre). Fine Art (Art Theory, Art History, Ceramics, Drawing, Media, Painting, Photography, Printmaking, Sculpture, Textiles, Time-based Media, Video). Illustration. Media. Multi-Media. Painting. Photography. Textiles.**
**Qualifications:**
**Adult Education. Degree. Foundation. Pre-foundation. HND. Practical.**

### ▶ Central Saint Martins College of Art & Design

Southampton Row, London WC1B 4AP.
**Tel** 020 7514 7022/3 **Fax** 020 7514 7254
**Email** applications@csm.linst.ac.uk
**Ws** www.csm.linst.ac.uk
**Nearest Underground** Holborn.
**Personnel** Information Office Administrator: Emma Cameron.
*Central Saint Martins has a distinguished international reputation and offers the most diverse and comprehensive range of undergraduate and postgraduate courses in art and design in the country – it is, in essence, the complete art college. Central Saint Martins believes that its graduates, both artists and designers, have a strategic role to play in setting the agendas by which we shape our lives, not only now but in the future, whether we are in a learning or working environment, enjoying our leisure time or old age, or with disability.*
**Courses:**
**Animation. Ceramics. Design (3-D, Fashion, Graphic, Photography, Product, Textile, Theatre). Fine Art (Ceramics, Painting, Photography, Printmaking, Sculpture, Textiles). Jewellery/Silversmithing. Painting. Photography. Architectural Stained Glass. Textiles.**
**Qualifications:**
**Degree. Foundation. Postgraduate.**

### ▶ Central Saint Martins College of Art & Design (London Institute)

107–109 Charing Cross Road, London WC2H 0DU.
**Tel** 020 7514 7000 **Fax** 020 7514 7208
**Courses:**
**Ceramics. Fine Art. Jewellery/Silversmithing.**

### ▶ The Cheshire School of Art & Design, Mid-Cheshire College

Hartford Campus, Hartford, Northwich CW8 1LJ.
**Tel** 01606 74444 **Fax** 01606 75101
**Email** admin@midchesh.ac.uk
**Ws** www.midchesh.u-net.com
**Nearest Station** Greenbank and Hartford.
**Personnel** Head of Faculty: Ms Susan Ainsworth. Programme Leader HE Art & Design: Mr Alex Ellis. Administrator HE Art & Design: Ms Debbie Cooke. Faculty Secretary: Ms Michelle Holt.
**Courses:**
**Ceramics. Design (Craft, 3-D, Display, Fashion, Furniture, Graphic, Interactive, Interior, Museums & Exhibitions, Photography, Product, Public Art, Surface Decoration, TV & Film, Textile, Typographic). Fine Art. Illustration. Media. Multi-Media. Painting. Photography. Textiles.**
**Qualifications:**
**Adult Education. Degree. Foundation. Pre-foundation. HND. Practical.**

### ▶ Christie's Education

5 King Street, St James's, London SW1Y 6QS.
**Tel** 020 7747 6800 **Fax** 020 7747 6801
**Email** education@christies.com
**Ws** www.christies.com
**Nearest Underground** Green Park
**Personnel** Managing Director: Irmgard Pickering. Academic Director: Dr Michael Michael.
*Christie's Education runs a wide variety of challenging, specialist and general interest courses in the Fine and Decorative Arts. They cover all periods from classical antiquity to contemporary art, and range from fully validated diploma and Masters courses to certificate courses, short courses and evening classes. Courses are run in London, Paris, New York and Australia. All of them place great importance on training the eye and the first-hand examination of works of art, with vocational as well as academic instruction. Students are of all*

*ages, nationalities and backgrounds, and postgraduate and mature students are well catered for. The courses are ideal for those seeking a career in the art world, for those making a career change or for those who wish to develop their knowledge and interests.*
**Courses:**
**Art History. Ceramics. Contemporary Art. Decorative Art. Fine Art (Art History). Furniture. Jewellery/Silversmithing. Painting. Photography.**
**Qualifications:**
**Adult Education. Degree. Postgraduate.**

## ▶ City & Guilds of London Art School

124 Kennington Park Road, London SE11 4DJ.
**Tel** 020 7735 2306
**Fax** 020 7582 5361
**Email** info@cityandguildsartschool.ac.uk
**Ws** www.cityandguildsartschool.ac.uk
**Opening times** 9–5 Mon–Fri.
**Nearest Underground** Kennington.
**Personnel** Principal: Tony Carter MFA. Senior Administrator: Judith Maroon. Academic Registrar: suzanne Barker.
*In many ways, the City & Guilds of London Art School is unique in the UK. In addition to Fine Art (painting, sculpture and printmaking), the School offers courses in Stonecarving, Woodcarving and Contemporary and Historic Conservation and Restoration, continuing the skills and craft base which in many other institutions has been in decline in recent years. Situated in a pleasant and historically interesting part of South London, it has independent fee-paying status and a strong craft base. Its scale is intimate and its atmosphere one of relaxed concentration.*
**Courses:**
**Contemporary Art. Decorative Art. Design (Craft). Fine Art (Art Theory, Art History, Drawing, Painting, Printmaking, Sculpture). Painting. Architectural Stained Glass.**
**Qualifications:**
**Adult Education. Degree. Foundation. Postgraduate. Practical.**

## ▶ The City Literary Institute for Adult Studies, Department of Visual Arts

6 Bolt Court, off Fleet Street, London EC4A 3DQ.
**Tel** 020 7353 0402
**Fax** 020 7538 7500
**Email** visualarts@citylit.ac.uk
**Opening times** 10–9 teaching, 10–6 office.
**Nearest Underground** Blackfriars, Chancery Lane.
**Personnel** Head of Visual Arts: Cass Breen. Administrator: Sarah Jones.
**Courses:**
**Animation. Art History. Ceramics. Contemporary Art. Decorative Art. Design (3-D, Graphic, Interior, Museums & Exhibitions, Photography, Surface Decoration, Textile, Typographic). Fine Art. Illustration. Jewellery/Silversmithing. Multi-Media. Painting. Photography. Architectural Stained Glass. Textiles.**
**Qualifications:**
**Adult Education. Diploma in Ceramics. Foundation. Pre-foundation. Practical.**

## ▶ Coventry University

School of Art and Design, Priory Street, Coventry CV1 5FB.
**Tel** 024 7688 7688
**Fax** 024 7683 8667
**Email** afuture.ad@coventry.ac.uk
**Ws** www.csad.coventry.ac.uk
**Nearest Station** Coventry.
**Personnel** Dean: Mr M. Tovey. Head of Fine Art: Ms Jill Journeaux. Head of Information Design: Ms Sandra Harrison. Head of Industrial Design: Ms Jenny Hann. Head of Performing Arts: Ms Sarah Whatley. Head of Communication, Culture and Media: Mr John Downey.
**Courses:**
**Ceramics. Design (3-D, Automotive, Craft, Graphic, Interactive, Product, Public Art, Theatre). Fine Art. Jewellery/Silversmithing. Media. Multi-Media. Painting.**
**Qualifications:**
**Degree. Foundation. Postgraduate. Practical.**

## ▶ Cumbria College of Art and Design

Brampton Road, Carlisle CA3 9AY.
**Tel** 01228 400 300
**Fax** 01228 514 491
**Email** q@cumbriacad.ac.uk
**Ws** www.cumbriacad.ac.uk
**Nearest Station** Carlisle1.5 miles.
**Personnel** Marketing: Allison J. Roberts.
**Courses:**
**Animation. Art History. Ceramics. Design (Craft, Graphic, Surface Decoration, Textile). Fine Art. Jewellery/Silversmithing. Media. Multi-Media. Painting. Textiles.**
**Qualifications:**
**Adult Education. Degree. Foundation. HND. Postgraduate.**

## ▶ Edinburgh College of Art

Lauriston Place, Edinburgh EH3 9DF.
**Tel** 0131 221 6000
**Fax** 0131 221 6001
**Ws** www.eca.ac.uk
*Edinburgh College of Art is one of the oldest and largest art schools in Europe, with an outstanding reputation for originality, creativity and research. Our staff regularly participate in high-profile exhibitions and contribute to major publications and symposia. As a result of their creative engagement in their chosen fields, the college offers teaching of the highest calibre. This is reflected, in turn, by the success of our graduates, many of whom have achieved international recognition, while most enjoy excellent career prospects. Students of the College enjoy a stimulating studio-based environment which encourages experimentation and originality. They also benefit from close contact with teachers and mentors. Beyond the College, the City of Edinburgh, one of Europe's finest capitals, provides a further source of inspiration and is an ideal place in which to study. It is home to many important cultural institutions – for example, the National Museum and Galleries, which are all within easy walking distance of the College.*
**Courses:**
**Animation. Architecture. Design (Fashion, Furniture, Graphic, Interior, TV & Film). Fine Art (Ceramics, Drawing, Painting, Photography, Printmaking, Sculpture, Textiles). Illustration. Jewellery/Silversmithing. Architectural Stained Glass.**
**Qualifications:**
**Adult Education. Degree. Postgraduate.**

## ▶ Falmouth College of Arts

Woodlane, Falmouth TR11 4RH.
**Tel** 01326 211 077
**Fax** 01326 212 261
**Email** admissions@falmouth.ac.uk
**Ws** www.falmouth.ac.uk
**Nearest Station** Falmouth Town (The Dell).
**Personnel** Public Relations Officer: Ms Jilly Easterby. Gallery & Events Administrator: Mrs Carol Worth.
*Falmouth College of Arts is a specialist University Sector College with an international reputation for excellence. Recently, the College achieved maximum marks in the Quality Assurance Agency's subject review of its art and design programmes, which further enhances this reputation. The College offers an innovative range of programmes of study in the fields of art, design and media at undergraduate and postgraduate level. Its two campuses provide a rare chance to study in a serene and beautiful environment in West Cornwall.*
**Courses:**
**Art History. Ceramics. Contemporary Art. Design (3-D, Graphic, Interior, Photography, Textile, Theory). Fine Art. Illustration. Media. Multi-Media.**
**Qualifications:**
**Degree. Foundation. Postgraduate.**

## ▶ Glasgow University

History of Art Department, 7 University Gardens, Glasgow G12 8QQ.
**Tel** 0141 330 4097
**Fax** 0141 330 3513
**Email** J.Nicholson@arthist.arts.gla.ac.uk
**Ws** www.arts.gla.ac.uk/ArtHist/decarts.htm
**Nearest Station** Glasgow, Queen Street or Central.
**Personnel** Programme Director: Sally Rush.
*This is a one-year programme run in partnership with Phillips Auctioneers, combining practical, academic and curatorial approaches to the decorative arts. The programme, offering either Master of Philosophy or Diploma qualifications, covers decorative arts from the period 1550 to 1920, studied in national and international contexts. First-hand study of objects includes ceramics, glass, metalwork, textiles, Far Eastern decorative art and a sound academic background in the history of interiors. Visiting lecturers (designers, scholars, curators, dealers and collectors) keep the programme abreast of current developments in all aspects of the decorative arts. Vocational teaching is provided by the staff of Phillips Auctioneers, Glasgow Museums, Scottish heritage organisations and country houses. Lectures, seminars and study sessions are followed with regular visits to museums, country houses, auction rooms and private collections. Glasgow has the richest decorative art collections outside London.*
**Courses:**
**Art History.**
**Qualifications:**
**Postgraduate.**

## ▶ Goldsmiths College

Lewisham Way, New Cross, London SE14 6NW.
**Tel** 020 7919 7671 **Fax** 020 7919 7673
**Email** visualarts@gold.ac.uk
**Ws** www.gold.ac.uk/
**Nearest Underground** New Cross, New Cross Gate.
**Courses:**
**Fine Art. Textiles.**
**Qualifications:**
**Degree. Postgraduate.**

## ▶ Heatherley School of Fine Art

HEATHERLEY'S

80 Upcerne Road, Chelsea, London SW10 0SH.
**Tel** 020 7351 4190 **Fax** 020 7361 6945
**Email** info@heatherleys.org
**Ws** www.heatherleys.org
**Nearest Underground** Fulham Broadway or Sloane Square. Rail: Victoria
**Personnel** School Office: The Registrar. Marketing Assistant: Sarah Cloonan.
*Heatherley's is a small independent art school based in Chelsea. It offers a wide range of full-time and part-time Fine Art courses for both beginners and experienced artists. Professional artists specialised in their academic field tutor the courses. The classes are small and have a high tutor to student ratio. Other courses include Painting, Drawing, Life Drawing, Portraiture, Sculpture, Watercolour/Pastel, Printmaking, Art History, The Heatherleys Print Workshop, the Heatherley Diploma in Portraiture, the Heatherley Diploma in Figurative Sculpture, Continuing Studies and a structured one-year Foundation course. There is an open studio for life and portrait drawing and painting.*
**Courses:**
**Fine Art (Art History, Drawing, Painting, Printmaking, Sculpture). Painting.**
**Qualifications:**
**Adult Education. Foundation. Heatherley's Diploma in Portraiture. Heatherley's Diploma in Figurative Sculpture. Pre-foundation. Practical.**

## ▶ The Institute

Hampstead Garden Suburb, Central Square, London NW11 7BN.
**Tel** 020 8455 9951 **Fax** 020 8201 8063
**Email** office@hgsi.ac.uk
**Ws** www.hgsi.ac.uk
**Nearest Underground** Golders Green.
**Personnel** Head of Art & Creative Studies: Bob Rothero. Course Director: Barbara Jackson.
*Prefoundation and Portfolio – September to March. This course in the visual arts consists of two structured terms, 27 hours per week, designed to prepare students for an art foundation course or an art degree at university. The course is suitable either for school leavers or for those mature students who wish to experience the total commitment of a full-time course in art and creative studies. Regular tutorials will be given to students as well as practical guidance and career advice. Some basic materials will be made available by The Institute but students should provide a portfolio and basic drawing equipment. A list of materials and equipment needed will be sent to successful students on acceptance to the course. Access to Art – April to June. This one-term course is aimed at students interested in pursuing art to a higher level with the possibility of progressing onto the Pre-foundation Course.*
**Courses:**
**Art History. Ceramics. Contemporary Art. Decorative Art. Design (Craft, Furniture, Interior, Museums & Exhibitions, Photography, Theatre). Fine Art (Art History, Ceramics, Drawing, Painting, Photography, Sculpture). Furniture. Jewellery/Silversmithing. Multi-Media. Painting. Photography. Architectural Stained Glass.**
**Qualifications:**
**Adult Education. Pre-foundation. Practical.**

## ▶ Kingston University, Faculty of Design

Knights Park, Kingston upon Thames KT1 2QJ.
**Tel** 020 8547 2000, direct line: 020 8547 7127/8
**Fax** 020 8547 7330
**Email** P.Amendt@kingston.ac.uk
**Nearest Station** Kingston upon Thames.
**Personnel** Head of School: Prof. Bruce Russell.
*Four areas: painting, sculpture, intermedia and print. Emphasis on student self-management and professional practice. Photography and computer-assisted imaging inductions first year. First year structured, project-led, second and third years personal research. Second year transatlantic and European exchange programme. All students contribute to public art/town and gown programme, art loan scheme and faculty-wide interdisciplinary project. 'Aftercare' graduate students network. In-house gallery showing staff and student self-curated shows and Stanley Picker Gallery. All courses modular.*
**Courses:**
**Ceramics. Fine Art (Artists' Books, Art Theory, Art History, Drawing, Installation, Painting, Photography, Printmaking, Sculpture, Video). Furniture. Painting.**
**Qualifications:**
**Degree.**

## ▶ Lancaster University, School of Creative Arts, The Art Department

Lonsdale Hall, Bailrigg, Lancaster LA1 4YW.
**Tel** 01524 593 056 **Fax** 01524 592 259
**Email** artists@lancaster.ac.uk
**Ws** www.lancs.ac.uk/users/art/
**Nearest Station** Lancaster.
**Personnel** Head of Department: Professor Nigel Whiteley. Admissions Tutor: Tony Heward.
**Courses:**
**Art History. Fine Art. Painting.**
**Qualifications:**
**Degree. Postgraduate.**

## ▶ Leeds College of Art and Design

Jacob Kramer Building, Blenheim Walk, Leeds LS2 9AQ.
**Tel** 0113 202 8000 **Fax** 0113 202 8001
**Email** info@leeds-art.ac.uk
**Ws** www.leeds-art.ac.uk
**Nearest Station** Leeds.
**Personnel** Marketing Assistant: Helen Sanders.
*A small, friendly college, based in one of the most vibrant cities in the country, Leeds College of Art and Design has played a central role in providing specialist education and training in art, design and the crafts for more than 150 years. Our aim is to offer you a creative environment, supported by experienced, committed staff and dedicated learning resources, which will help you realise your personal ambitions.*
**Courses:**
**Art History. Design (Fashion, Furniture, Graphic, Interior, Photography, Surface Decoration, Textile). Fine Art (Art History, Ceramics, Drawing, Painting, Photography, Sculpture, Textiles, Time-based Media). Furniture. Jewellery/Silversmithing. Multi-Media. Photography. Architectural Stained Glass. Textiles.**
**Qualifications:**
**Adult Education. Degree. Foundation. Pre-foundation. HNC. HND.**

## ▶ Nottingham Trent University

Nottingham Trent School of Art and Design, Dryden Street, Nottingham NG1 4FZ.
**Tel** 0115 848 2485 **Fax** 0115 948 6403
**Email** lisa.howes@ntu.ac.uk
**Ws** www.ntu.ac.uk/vpa
**Nearest Station** Nottingham.
**Personnel** Dean: Prof. Simon Lewis.
**Courses:**
**Animation. Architecture. Ceramics. Contemporary Art. Decorative Art. Design (Craft, 3-D, Fashion, Furniture, Graphic, Interior, Photography, Product, Public Art, TV & Film, Textile, Theatre). Fine Art. Furniture. Illustration. Media. Multi-Media. Painting. Photography. Textiles.**
**Qualifications:**
**Degree. Foundation. Pre-foundation. HND. Postgraduate.**

## ▶ Plymouth College of Art and Design

Tavistock Place, Plymouth PL4 8AT.
**Tel** 01752 203 434 **Fax** 01752 203 444
**Email** enquiries@pcad.plym.ac.uk
**Ws** www.pcad.plym.ac.uk
**Nearest Station** Plymouth.
**Personnel** Principal: Ms Lynne Stanley-Brookes. Admissions Officer: Mrs Jean Edmonds.
*Plymouth College of Art and Design is a specialist provider of art and design education and training and offers a wide range of full- and part-time programmes at Further and Higher Education levels. The college is composed of five subject-focused Schools, which are: Graphic Communication; Media and Photography; Decorative and Fine Arts; and Industrial Arts and Applied Arts.*
*Links with the community and local industry are encouraged to ensure that students are kept up to date with the latest developments, and there is also a gallery at its main site where former and current students as well as local artists can exhibit their work.*
**Courses:**
**Ceramics. Design (3-D, Fashion, Graphic, Interior, Typographic). Fine Art. Jewellery/Silversmithing. Media. Multi-Media. Photography.**
**Qualifications:**
**Adult Education. Degree. Foundation. HND.**

### ▶ The Prince's Foundation
19–22 Charlotte Road, London EC2A 3SG.
**Tel** 020 7613 8500 **Fax** 020 7613 8599
**Email** rsuzuki@princes-foundation.org
**Ws** www.princes-foundation.org
**Nearest Underground** Old Street.
**Personnel** Director: Dr Khaled Azzam. Administrator: Ms R. Suzuki.
*The VITA courses offer a unique opportunity to study both the theory and practice of visual Islamic and traditional arts at higher educational level. As well as PhD and MPhil degress, the following two courses (each lasting two years) are validated by the University of Wales: (1) MA (Practical Course) (2) MA (Project Course – half practical, half theory).*
*The study of the theory and meaning of the traditional arts are a special feature of the VITA programme. The course work is suported by first-hand experience of the traditional arts through field trips and working sessions with traditional artists and craftsmen. Students are encouraged to pursue their own particular skills, whether it be painting, wood carving, jewellery, stained glass, or ceramics, at the same time as attending the classes in geometry, calligraphy, arabesque and others.*
**Courses:**
**Fine Art.**
**Qualifications:**
**Postgraduate.**

### ▶ Ravensbourne College of Design and Communication
Walden Road, Elmstead Woods, Chislehurst, Bromley BR7 5SN.
**Tel** 020 8289 4900 **Fax** 020 8325 8320
**Email** info@rave.ac.uk
**Ws** www.rave.ac.uk
**Nearest Station** Elmstead Woods.
**Personnel** Marketing and PR Officer: Ms Cath Baldwin.
**Courses:**
**Design (3-D, Fashion, Furniture, Graphic, Interactive, Interior, Product, TV & Film, Textile). Furniture. Media. Multi-Media.**
**Qualifications:**
**Degree. Foundation. HND. Postgraduate. Practical.**

### ▶ Reigate School of Art and Design
127 Blackborough Road, Reigate RH2 7DE.
**Tel** 01737 766 137 **Fax** 01737 768 643
**Ws** www.esc.org.uk
**Nearest Station** Redhill, Reigate.
**Personnel** Programme Area Manager: Mr Mike Williams. Faculty Assistant: Annette Scoble.
**Courses:**
**Design (Craft, 3-D, Fashion, Graphic, Interior, Photography, Product, Surface Decoration, Textile, Theory, Typographic). Fine Art. Illustration. Jewellery/ Silversmithing. Photography. Textiles.**
**Qualifications:**
**Adult Education. Foundation. HND.**

### ▶ Ruskin School of Drawing and Fine Art
74 High Street, Oxford OX1 4BG.
**Tel** 01865 276 940 **Fax** 01865 276 949
**Email** vanda.wilkinson@ruskin-school.ox.ac.uk
**Ws** www.ruskin-sch.ox.ac.uk/
**Nearest Station** Oxford.
*The Ruskin School is the Fine Art Department at Oxford University. It benefits from a strong academic foundation, with a particular emphasis on prominent visiting lecturers, and treats the boundaries between media as permeable. Of particular note is The Laboratory, the School's research wing, which supports the production of new work deriving from collaborations between artists and experts from the worlds of science, technology and the humanities. The Laboratory is administered by Paul Bonaventura and organises The Joseph Beuys Lectures and the Arts Council of England Helen Chadwick Fellowship on an annual basis.*
**Courses:**
**Fine Art (Art Theory, Art History, Drawing, Installation, Painting, Photography, Printmaking, Sculpture, Video).**
**Qualifications:**
**Degree. Postgraduate.**

### ▶ Rycotewood College
Priest End, Thame OX9 2AF.
**Tel** 01844 212 501
**Fax** 01844 218 809
**Email** jmcintyre@rycote.ac.uk
**Ws** www.rycote.ac.uk
**Nearest Station** Thame and Haddenham Parkway.
**Personnel** Principal: Mrs J. McIntyre.
**Courses:**
**Design (Furniture). Furniture.**
**Qualifications:**
**Adult Education. Foundation. HND.**

### ▶ Slade School of Fine Art
University College London, Gower Street, London WC1E 6BT.
**Tel** 020 7679 2313
**Fax** 020 7679 7801
**Email** slade.enquiries@ucl.ac.uk
**Ws** www.ucl.ac.uk/slade/
**Nearest Underground** Euston, Euston Square, Warren Street.
**Personnel** Co-ordinator of Academic Affairs: Ms Caroline Nicholas.
*Slade School of Fine Art, founded in 1871, is a department of University College London. Slade offers a BA in Fine Art (four years, full-time) and, at graduate level, an MA and MFA (two years, full-time), a Graduate Diploma (one year, full-time) and MPhil and PhD degrees. Students are taught by professional artists of distinction and distinguished staff teaching art history and theoretical studies. Students may specialise either in Painting, Sculpture or Fine Art Media (including film, video, printmaking, photography and electronic media).*
**Courses:**
**Art History. Fine Art (Media, Painting, Photography, Printmaking, Sculpture, Time-based Media, Video).**
**Qualifications:**
**Degree. Postgraduate.**

### ▶ Sotheby's Institute
30 Oxford Street, London W1D 1AU.
**Tel** 020 7462 3232 **Fax** 020 7580 8160
**Email** education@sothebys.com
**Ws** www.sothebys.com/education
**Opening times** Mon–Fri 9–5.
**Nearest Underground** Tottenham Court Road.
*Sotheby's Institute of Art in London offers a unique environment where the study of art begins by looking at the work itself, both in the galleries and museums of London and at Sotheby's auction house, where students are allowed special access to this ever-changing resource. Our internationally recognised degree courses include BA in Fine & Decorative Art and MAs in Art Business, Asian Art, Contemporary Art and Fine & Decorative Art, and are designed for those who aim to work in the art world as auctioneers, dealers, gallery owners, curators or critics. In addition to full-time courses, we offer a wide range of part-time, evening and summer courses.*
**Courses:**
**Art History. Ceramics. Contemporary Art. Decorative Art. Fine Art (Art Theory, Art History). Furniture. Jewellery/Silversmithing. Textiles.**
**Qualificatons:**
**Adult Education. Degree. Postgraduate.**

### ▶ SPACE Studios
8 Hoxton Street, London N1 6NG.
**Tel** 020 7613 1925
**Fax** 020 7613 1996
**Email** mail@spacestudios.org.uk
**Ws** www.spacestudios.org.uk
**Opening times** 10–6 Mon–Fri.
**Personnel** Director: Charlotte Robinson. Studios Manager: Fiona Furness.
*SPACE Studios, founded in 1968, is an arts and educational charity providing affordable studios and support for over 400 visual artists at 15 sites in East London. SPACE's Artists' Resource Centre, SPACE Place in Fish Island, E3, helps artists to bridge the gap between producing and making a living. SPACE Place provides IT training, exhibition space, commissions studio, seminars, careers advice (ViA), and community and education projects for artists and the local community. SPACE receives core funding from London Arts. SPACE Place was made possible by the European Regional Development Fund.*

### ▶ Swansea Institute of Higher Education
Faculty of Art and Design, Townhill Road, Swansea SA2 0UT.
**Tel** 01792 481 285 **Fax** 01792 205 305
**Email** du.lake@SIHE.ac.uk
**Ws** www.sihe.ac.uk
**Nearest Station** Swansea.
**Personnel** Head of School of Art & Design: Mrs Andrea Liggins.
*As a major centre of excellence for art and design higher education in Wales, the Faculty provides opportunities for students to study a wide variety of vocational and professional subjects or to undertake more academically oriented studies by choosing alternative theoretical and historical subjects. There is also an Art and Design Foundation programme for students preparing for higher education entry, as well as future possibilities to study for a taught postgraduate degree leading to an MA or the research degrees of MPhil and PhD. Undergraduate awards include the BA (Hons) and HND, and these are available on both a full-time and part-time basis.*
**Courses:**
**Animation. Archeological Illustration. Art History. Ceramics. Contemporary Art. Decorative Art. Design (Display, Graphic,**

**Interactive, Photography, Public Art, Surface Decoration, Textile, Theory, Typographic). Fine Art (Art Theory, Art History, Ceramics, Drawing, Installation, Media, Painting, Photography, Printmaking, Textiles, Time-based Media, Video). Illustration. Media. Multi-Media. Painting. Photography. Architectural Stained Glass. Textiles.**
**Qualifications:**
**Adult Education. Degree. Foundation. HND. Postgraduate.**

### ▶ University of Central England in Birmingham

Birmingham Institute of Art & Design, Corporation Street, Gosta Green, Birmingham B4 7DX.
**Tel** 0121 331 5878 **Fax** 0121 359 0423
**Email** Helen.Annetts@uce.ac.uk
**Ws** www.biad.uce.ac.uk
**Nearest Station** New Street.
**Personnel** Publicity Officer: Miss Helen Annetts.
*Birmingham Institute of Art & Design is one of the largest centres for art, design and media education in the UK. BIAD is rated within the top 10 UK institutions and has been rated 'Excellent' by the Government's Quality Assurance Agency. Nearly 4,000 full-time and part-time students presently study on five recently renovated and refurbished sites. BIAD offers a comprehensive choice of pregraduate, undergraduate and post-graduate courses and a well-established higher research degrees programme.*
**Courses:**
**Animation. Art History. Ceramics. Design (3-D, Fashion, Furniture, Graphic, Interior, Photography, Product, Surface Decoration, TV & Film, Textile, Theatre). Fine Art (Art Theory, Art History, Ceramics, Drawing, Installation, Media, Painting, Photography, Printmaking, Sculpture, Textiles, Time-based Media, Video). Furniture. Illustration. Jewellery/ Silversmithing. Media. Multi-Media. Painting. Photography. Textiles.**
**Qualifications:**
**Adult Education. Degree. Foundation. Pre-foundation. HND. Postgraduate. Teacher Training.**

### ▶ University of Plymouth

Faculty of Arts and Education, Earl Richards Road North, Exeter EX2 6AS.
**Tel** 01392 475 022 **Fax** 01392 475 012
**Email** fae-admissions@plymouth.ac.uk
**Ws** www.plymouth.ac.uk
**Nearest Station** Exeter St Davids, Exeter Central.
**Personnel** Publicity: Ms Sue Try.
*Based in Exeter and Exmouth, the University of Plymouth's Faculty of Arts and Education offers a wide range of courses in arts and design disciplines at undergraduate, postgraduate and research level. The Art and Design programme includes: Fine Art; Fine Art Contextual Practice; Design and Italian; Graphic Communication; Illustration; Photography; Typography; 3D Design; Designer Maker; Furniture and Interior Design; and Product Design. The Combined Arts programme includes: Art History and Visual Studies; Popular Culture; Media Arts; and Visual Studies, all of which can be studied as single or joint honours, majors, or options with another subject. Art and Design is also a subject specialism in the Teacher Education programmes at primary and secondary level.*
**Courses:**
**Art History. Design (3-D, Furniture, Graphic, Interior, Photography, Product, Typographic). Fine Art (Art History, Media, Painting, Photography, Printmaking, Sculpture, Textiles, Time-based Media, Video). Furniture. Illustration. Media. Multi-Media. Painting. Photography.**
**Qualifications:**
**Degree. Postgraduate. Teacher Training.**

### ▶ Westminster College

Battersea Park Road, London SW11 4JR.
**Tel** 020 7556 8000 **Fax** 020 7556 8082
**Email** admissions@westminster-cfe.ac.uk
**Ws** www.westminster-cfe.ac.uk
**Nearest Underground** Battersea Park.
**Personnel** Head of School: Ms Deborah See. Head of Art & Fashion: Linnia Khemdoudi.
**Courses:**
**Design (Fashion, Graphic, Interior, Photography, Textile). Fine Art. Illustration. Media. Multi-Media. Photography. Textiles.**
**Qualifications:**
**Adult Education. Foundation. HND.**

### ▶ York College

Tadcaster Road, Dringhouses, York YO24 1UA.
**Tel** 01904 770 200 **Fax** 01904 770 499
**Email** cbrace@yorkcollege.ac.uk
**Ws** www.yorkcollege.ac.uk
**Nearest Station** York.
**Personnel** Curriculum Manager Art, Design & Crafts: Mr Chris Brace. Curriculum Manager Graphics, Media & Performing Arts: Mrs Jenny Troyna.
*Full-time art and design courses available from York College include (All courses are EDEXCEL BTEC):*
*GNVQ Foundation in Art and Design*
*GNVQ Intermediate in Art and Design*
*GNVQ Advanced in Art and Design*
*Diploma in Foundation Studies*
*Higher National Diploma in Design Crafts*
*National Diploma in 3D Design: Furniture, Product, Interior, Ceramics, Jewellery and Fine Art*
*National Diploma in Graphic Design*
*Higher National Diploma in Graphic Design*
*National Diploma in Fashion Design*
*Higher National Diploma in Fashion Design*
*National Diploma in Media Studies*
*National Diploma in Performing Arts*
*National Certificate in Art and Design*
*AS/A level Art and Design*
*A level Textiles*
**Courses:**
**Animation. Art History. Ceramics. Design (3-D, Graphic, Interior, Photography, Typographic). Fine Art. Furniture. Illustration. Jewellery/Silversmithing. Media. Multi-Media. Painting. Photography. Architectural Stained Glass. Textiles.**
**Qualifications:**
**Adult Education. Foundation. Pre-foundation. HND.**

# Art Management and Promotion

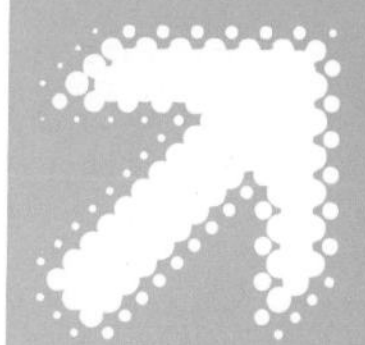

NOTES

# Tracking Stolen Art

Domestic burglaries in the UK have decreased recently by more than 25 per cent but the trend in Europe is the opposite, because insurers there have less influence on protection. In excess of 25 per cent of all the Art Loss Register's (ALR) recoveries are made in countries other than those where the theft occurred, hence the international nature of the problem.

Before there was a central database of stolen and looted art and antiques, the art trade (auctioneers and dealers) had to rely on questioning the vendor to try and ascertain an item's provenance, and purchased only from 'reputable sources'. This system was not effective, as stolen items moved up the chain of respectability and there was no real test of due diligence.

For the last 10 years, there has been a more systematic back-up in the form of the ALR's database, used rigorously by the major auction houses for whom over 300,000 lots per annum are checked out, or 'searched'. The existence of the ALR has resulted in a substantial reduction in the number of stolen items consigned by criminals or fences, as they have become aware of the search technique.

Searching is now being extended into the provincial UK and overseas auction houses, but the amount of searching by dealers of items purchased not at the major auction houses but from other members of the trade or private individuals remains disappointing. Pressure is being brought to bear by some of the major fairs in Maastricht, Basle, Zurich, Cologne and London, who encourage exhibitors to have items searched to prevent prejudicing the reputation of the fair.

Many major museums and private collectors are now insisting on an ALR search certificate, and the defective title insurance provided to the trade would usually require that the ALR be consulted.

To deter art theft, searching must become the usual custom and practice of the trade. Objections on grounds of practicality when buying at short notice, and a general resentment of the invasion of computers and self-regulation, are more than outweighed by the support which the ALR can give to dealers to prevent potential embarrassment.

Unfortunately, making the database open for the trade to search without any advice, audit trail or proof of access has not been successful, either for the the police, the original victims, or the trade itself. The details of some stolen items can be circulated to help increase awareness, but there is no effective alternative to a due diligent search of the database.

Julian Radcliffe
Chairman
Art Loss Register

## ART CONSULTANTS

### ▶ Alexandra Wettstein C
138 Ladywell Road, London SE13 7NS.
**Tel** 020 8690 9556, mobile 07711 400 021
**Fax** 020 8690 7959
**Email** alexandra.wettstein@virgin.net
**Ws** graffiti.virgin.net/alexandra.wettstein/
**Opening times** 9–6 and by appointment.
**Nearest Underground** Ladywell (Rail), Brockley.
**Personnel** Proprietor: Alexandra Wettstein.
**Services and Facilities** Art Consultancy. Art for Offices. Commissioning Service. Parking. Valuation.
**Work Stocked and Sold** Cer. Dr. Pa. Pr. Sc.
**Price range** £50–£150,000
For artists see Commercial Gallery Artists.

### ▶ Anne Berthoud
Flat 4, 1 Stanley Gardens, London W11 2ND.
**Tel** 020 7229 8400 **Fax** 020 7221 8185
**Opening times** By appointment.
**Nearest Underground** Notting Hill Gate.
**Personnel** Director: Anne Berthoud.
**Services and Facilities** Art Consultancy. Commissioning Service. Valuation.
**Work Stocked and Sold** Cer. Dr. Pa. Ph. Pr. Sc.
*Contemporary British and international paintings, drawings, prints, sculpture, ceramics and photographs. Agency and organisation of exhibitions. Anne Berthoud is also personally available for consultancy services.*

### ▶ Art Contact Ltd.
2 Rickett Street, London SW6 1RU.
**Tel** 020 7381 8655
**Fax** 020 7386 9015
**Email** jt@artcontact.co.uk
**Ws** www.artcontact.co.uk
**Opening times** Office hours, by appointment.
**Personnel** Director: Julian Thomas.
**Services and Facilities** Art Consultancy. Art for Offices. Commissioning Service. Framing. Restoration.
**Work Stocked and Sold** Dec. Dr. Pa. Ph. Pr. Sc. Tx.
**Price range** £10–£100,000
*Art Contact is one of the UK's most experienced and resourceful art consultancies. We work with corporate, design and private clients and are associated with over 1,000 highly talented up-and-coming artists.*
*We offer full project management, leaving our clients with a pleasant process of choice, including: original works; commissions; sculpture; wall hangings; glass art; limited editions; 19th-century oils; restrikes; and framing and installation. The rental option is available.*

### ▶ Art For Offices C
International Art Consultants,The Galleries, 15 Dock Street, London E1 8JL.
**Tel** 020 7481 1337 **Fax** 020 7481 3425
**Email** enquiries@afo.co.uk
**Ws** www.afo.co.uk
**Opening times** Mon–Fri 9.30–5.30.
**Nearest Underground** Tower Hill, Aldgate, Aldgate East.
**Personnel** Directors: Andrew Hutchinson, Peter Harris. Amanda Basker.
**Services and Facilities** Art Consultancy. Art for Offices. Commissioning Service. Framing. Parking.
**Work Stocked and Sold** Cer. Cra. Dr. Gla. Pa. Ph. Pr. Sc. Tx. Wd.
**Price range** £100–£50,000
For artists see Commercial Gallery Artists.
*We have 20 years experience advising architects, designers and corporate clients on the planning and implementation of art programmes. Our 10,000 sq ft galleries provide a central source of art, enabling clients and specifiers to view a comprehensive range of art on a single visit to one location. We deal directly with over 800 artists and have a large visual reference library covering art in all media which is cross-referenced by style and price. This makes it possible to research works of art, or artists for commission quickly and effectively. Art can be purchased, commissioned or acquired on a flexible rental basis.*

### ▶ Artists in Residence
The Jointure Studios, 11 South Street, Ditchling BN6 8UQ.
**Tel** 01273 841 244 **Fax** 01273 841 244
**Email** studios@artsistsinresidence.co.uk
**Ws** www.artistsinresidence.co.uk
**Opening times** Gallery open by appointment.
**Personnel** Co-ordinator: Shirley Crowther.
**Services and Facilities** Art Consultancy. Art for Offices. Commissioning Service. Gallery space for hire.
*An art service which specialises in commissioning portraits of architecture, gardens and landscape, working on private and corporate projects: homes, offices, shops, hotels, industrial sites, public buildings and illustrated plans. We have a wide range of artists and illustrators on our books from which we help clients find a style of work and approach that is right for them and their project, setting up and co-ordinating the commission. The Agency can also advise on presentation, promotional opportunities and reproduction, and works with other artists and galleries to offer a wider consultancy service.*

### ▶ Brandler Galleries C
1 Coptfold Road, Brentwood CM14 4BN.
**Tel** 01277 222 269 **Fax** 01277 222 786
**Email** John@Brandler-Galleries.com
**Ws** www.brandler-galleries.com and www.thesaurus.co.uk/brandler
**Opening times** Tue–Sat 10–5.30.
**Nearest Station** Brentwood 400 yds, Shenfield 1 mile.
**Personnel** Director: John Brandler. Linda Rodrigues.
**Services and Facilities** Art Consultancy. Art for Offices. Commissioning Service. Framing. Parking. Restoration. Valuation.
**Work Stocked and Sold** Cer. Dr. Pa. Pr. Sc.
**Price range** £50–£65,000

### ▶ Business Art Galleries C
New Academy Gallery, 34 Windmill Street, Fitzrovia, London W1T 2JR.
**Tel** 020 7323 4700 **Fax** 020 7436 3059
**Email** business@curwen.gallery.com
**Ws** www.curwengallery.com
**Opening times** Mon–Fri 10–6 (Thurs 10–8), Sat 11–5 (closed bank holiday weekends).
**Nearest Underground** Goodge Street, Tottenham Court Road.
**Personnel** Directors: John Hutchings, Jill Hutchings. Contact: Anna Cusden.
**Services and Facilities** Art Consultancy. Art for Offices. Commissioning Service. Framing.
**Work Stocked and Sold** Dr. Pa. Ph. Pr. Sc. Tx.
**Price range** £50–£20,000
For artists see Commercial Gallery Artists.

*James Gutch, Mobile for BP AMOCO European Headquarters.*

*Business Art Galleries was founded within the Royal Academy of Art in 1978 and is Britain's longest-established art consultant. Now an independent company, we offer a comprehensive corporate art service including free consultations and on-site presentation, a flexible hire scheme, and special commissions. Our two sister galleries, The New Academy Gallery and Curwen Gallery, provide us with an extensive permanent stock of work as well as a changing monthly programme of exhibitions (including our highly esteemed Northern Graduates show in August). This includes painting, limited edition prints and sculpture from both leading and up-and-coming contemporary British artists.*

### ▶ Christopher Wood C
20 Georgian House, 10 Bury Street, London SW1Y 6AA.
**Tel** 020 7839 3963 **Fax** 020 7839 3963
**Email** cwood@christopherwoodgallery.com
**Ws** www.christopherwoodgallery.com
**Opening times** 9.30–5.30 by appointment.
**Nearest Underground** Green Park.
**Personnel** Director: Christopher Wood.
**Services and Facilities** Art Consultancy. Bookshop. Lectures. Valuation.
**Work Stocked and Sold** Cer. Dr. Fur. Pa. Sc.
**Price range** £500–£250,000
For artists see Commercial Gallery Artists.
*Christopher Wood has over 30 years experience in the art world. He is a member of SLAD, the Society of London Art Dealers, and BADA, the British Antique Dealers Association. Former Director of Christie's and Mallett, Christopher Wood specialises in Victorian and Pre-Raphaelite paintings, watercolours and drawings; also arts and crafts movements, gothic revival furniture, sculpture and ceramics. The Christopher Wood Gallery was founded in Motcomb Street, Belgravia, in 1977; Christopher Wood now works privately from an address in Bury Street, St James's. He is the author of* The Dictionary of

Victorian Painters, Paradise Lost, The Pre-Raphaelites, Tissot, Painted Gardens, *and numerous other books. He also presented a TV series,* Painters to the People, *on Channel Four Television in 1990, and appears regularly on Antiques Roadshow.*

## ▶ Conservation Management Ltd

10 Wilton Street, London SW1X 7AF.
**Tel** 020 7823 2331
**Fax** 020 7823 2285
**Email** slescher@compuserve.com
**Opening times** By appointment.
**Nearest Underground** Victoria/ Hyde Park Corner.
**Personnel** Director: Sally Lescher, MA (Courtauld). Thalia Kennedy MA (Edinburgh).
**Services and Facilities** Art Consultancy. Art for Offices. Commissioning Service. Framing. Lectures. Restoration. Valuation.
*Sally Lescher and associates assist private and corporate clients in putting together interesting collections of works of art. Expertise ranges from Old Master Paintings to 20th-century British and contemporary art. They also provide specialist cataloguing, restoration and conservation services to museums and collectors.*

## ▶ Contemporary Art Holdings C

The Old Chapel, 14 London Road, Cirencester GL7 1AL.
**Tel** 01285 644 990
**Fax** 01285 644 992
**Email** CAH@contemporary-art-holdings.co.uk
**Ws** www.contemporary-art-holdings.co.uk
**Opening times** 9.30–5.30 Mon–Fri by appointment.
**Personnel** Celia Wickham. Janet Sheridan. Suzanne Hern.
**Services and Facilities** Art Consultancy. Art for Offices. Commissioning Service.
**Work Stocked and Sold** Cer. Gla. Pa. Pr. Sc. Tx.
**Price range** £200–£50,000

*Contemporary Art Holdings offers 10 years experience in corporate art consultancy. Working closely with artists, architects and designers, the consultancy offers a highy individual and personal service. The company specialises in identifying the effect of the image on corporate identity and can recommend interesting and innovative solutions within reasonable budgets. CAH is constantly attracting new artists and is able to source work from a wide range of disciplines including printmaking, painting, photography, contemporary glass, ceramics and site-specific installation. Fabric wall hangings, banners and tapestries are also available. Commissions are an integral part of the consultancy's practice.*

## ▶ de Putron Art Consultants Ltd.

27 Pattison Road, London NW2 2HL.
**Tel** 020 7431 1125 or 07050 611 025
**Fax** 020 7431 1125
**Email** art@dpac.demon.co.uk
**Ws** www.art@dpac.demon.co.uk
**Opening times** By appointment only.
**Nearest Underground** Hampstead/ Golders Green.
**Personnel** Director: Laura de Putron. Company Secretary: Tim de Putron.
**Services and Facilities** Art Consultancy. Art for Offices. Commissioning Service.
**Work Stocked and Sold** App. Cer. Dr. Gla. Pa. Pr. Sc. Tx. Wd.
**Price range** £100–£50,000
For artists see Commercial Gallery Artists.

## ▶ Dickson Russell Art Management

23 St Peter's Square, London W6 9NW.
**Tel** 020 8741 9577 **Fax** 020 8563 9249
**Email** dickson.russell@virgin.net
**Opening times** By appointment.
**Nearest Underground** Stamford Brook
**Personnel** Directors: Rachel Dickson, Emma Russell.
**Services and Facilities** Art Consultancy. Art for Offices. Commissioning Service. Framing. Restoration. Valuation.
*Dickson Russell provides a complete range of art management services for both corporate and private clients, to include art acquisition, exhibition curation, project management for commissioned works, and maintenance of existing collections. Art of all media and from across all periods can be sourced to suit the client's business, profile and location. Additional services can include professional packing, shipping, restoration, framing, installation and photographing of artwork; catalogue literature, insurance updates and valuations are also undertaken. A professional fee is charged; no commission is taken on purchased artworks.*

## ▶ Egee Art Consultancy C

9 Chelsea Manor Studios, Flood Street, London SW3 5SR.
**Tel** 020 7351 6818 **Fax** 020 7376 3510
**Email** egee.art@btinternet.com
**Ws** www.egeeart.com
**Opening times** Mon–Fri 8.30–5.30, Sat by arrangement. By appointment.
**Nearest Underground** Sloane Square or South Kensington.
**Personnel** Director: Dale Egee. Sales: Yvonne Eklund. Art Consultant: Kate Brown. Administrator: Barbara Allen.
**Services and Facilities** Art Consultancy. Art for Offices. Commissioning Service. Framing. Restoration. Valuation.
**Work Stocked and Sold** Cra. Dr. Pa. Ph. Pr. Sc. Tx.
**Price range** £50–£35,000
For artists see Commercial Gallery Artists.

## ▶ Federation of British Artists

Mall Galleries, 17 Carlton House Terrace, London SW1Y 5BD.
**Tel** 020 7930 6844 **Fax** 020 7839 7830
**Ws** www.mallgalleries.org.uk
**Personnel** Chairman: Tom Muir. Commission Consultant: Katy Letman.

## ▶ Howick Contemporary Art Ltd (Contemporary Art Consultants)

The Side House, 18 Parkhill Road, London NW3 2YN.
**Tel** 020 7284 2614 **Fax** 020 7267 7861
**Email** alistair@howickart.co.uk
**Opening times** By appointment only.
**Nearest Underground** Belsize Park.
**Personnel** Directors: Louisa Howick, Alistair Howick.
**Services and Facilities** Art Consultancy. Art for Offices. Commissioning Service. Framing. Parking.
**Work Stocked and Sold** Cer. Cra. Dec. Dr. Fur. Gla. Pa. Ph. Pr. Sc. Tx. Wd.

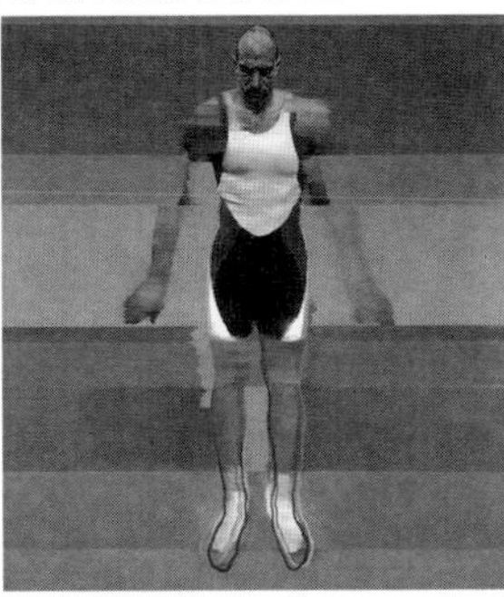

*Justin Mortimer,* Steve Redgrave, *oil on canvas, 183 x 152 cm, 1998.*

*A professional art consultancy providing a comprehensive and personal service to architects, interior designers and corporate clients on a wide range of art works. Imaginative well-researched solutions, including commissions, purchasing, and rentals within set budgets.*

## ▶ Kings Road Gallery

436 Kings Road, London SW10 0LJ.
**Tel** 020 7381 2983 **Fax** 020 7610 2255

## ▶ Lynne Stern Associates Art Consultancy and Management

46 Bedford Row, London WC1R 4LR.
**Tel** 020 7491 8905 **Fax** 020 7624 3749
**Email** art@lynnstern.com
**Services and Facilities** Art Consultancy. Art for Offices. Commissioning Service. Lectures.
*A professional, independent and comprehensive service; in-depth art expertise combined with long-term proven business experience (including managing the business art section at the Royal Academy of Arts). Specifically work with corporate clients, architects, designers and project managers. Art project management: includes art selection through on-site presentations from wide-ranging sources; managing site-specific commissions of art in all media to schedule and within art and construction budget. Maintaining new and existing art collections: includes developing client's art-allied corporate programme and handling related services: framing, installation, restoration, photography,*

*copyright and managing art inventories and insurance revaluations.*
*Awarded the Art and Work Award 1996 and Award Commendation 1998 for art projects achieved for clients.*
*Price range: comprehensive.*

### ▶ Moreton Contemporary Art C

40 Moreton Street, London SW1V 2PB.
**Tel** 020 7834 7773/7775 **Fax** 020 7834 7834
**Email** sales@frasco.co.uk
**Ws** www.moretonart.com
**Opening times** 9–6 Mon–Fri, 12–4 Sat.
**Services and Facilities** Art Consultancy. Art for Offices. Commissioning Service. Disabled Access. Framing. Gallery space for hire.
*Moreton Contemporary Art operates a comprehensive art consultancy service catering to private individuals, interior designers, hotel groups and the corporate sector. Clients are advised on the purchase of artwork to suit their needs and specifications. The service includes sourcing and commissioning artwork from our large portfolio of artists. This is not restricted to contemporary work but also includes work from any period or style.*
*Full framing and installation services are also provided. Work can be viewed at our Gallery space or appointments can be made to visit clients.*

### ▶ Sarah Myerscough Fine Art Gallery & Consultancy C

15–16 Brooks Mews, Mayfair, London W1Y 1LF.
**Tel** 020 7495 0069 **Fax** 020 7629 9613
**Email** sarah@smyerscough.freeserve.co.uk
**Opening times** 10–6 Mon–Fri, 11–2 Sat.
**Nearest Underground** Bond Street.
**Personnel** Director: Sarah Myerscough. Consultant: Dan Seymour-Davies.
**Services and Facilities** Art Consultancy. Art for Offices. Commissioning Service. Framing.
**Work Stocked and Sold** App. Cer. Cra. Dr. Gla. Pa. Ph. Pr. Sc. Tx. Wd.
**Price range** £300–£30,000

*The Gallery in Brooks Mews.*
*Sarah Myerscough Fine Art provides a comprehensive consultancy service. We show a mixture of established artists and affordable work by recent graduates from colleges all over the country. Every October we host the DLA Art Award, a show of the best graduates nationwide. Our consultancy side caters to both private and corporate clients, so whether you are looking for a couple of paintings for your house or enough to fill an office, we can source original and high quality work for you.*

### ▶ Sheeran Lock, Specialist Independent Art Consultants

The Mansion House, Church Lane, Market Hill, Framlin & Ham IP13 9BD.
**Tel** 01728 621 126 **Fax** 01728 724 942
**Email** imogenlock@sheeranlock.com
**Ws** www.sheeranlock.com
**Personnel** Curator: John Sheeran. Marketing & Communications Director: Imogen Lock. Projects & Collections Manager: Alison Newell. Business Development Manager: Kate Hunt.
*Sheeran Lock's services, described in detail on its website, comprise: corporate art collections management; art book, catalogue and visual database production; bespoke art exhibitions; corporate entertainment and sponsorship brokerage; art education outreach projects; and innovative corporate communications strategies using art. Its high-quality art projects and events provide businesses and other organisations with positive promotional and marketing opportunities, and enhanced social and cultural identity. Projects have included the Official 50th Birthday Exhibition of HRH The Prince of Wales at Hampton Court Palace, sponsored by Asprey & Garrard; and The United Nations Millennium Art Exhibition at the UN, New York, in aid of UNICEF.*

### ▶ Thomas Corman Arts

24 Daleham Gardens, London NW3 5DA.
**Tel** 020 7433 1339
**Fax** 020 7433 1339
**Email** tca@btinternet.com
**Ws** www.thomascormanarts.com
**Opening times** Any time by appointment.
**Nearest Underground** Swiss Cottage, Finchley Road, Belsize Park.
**Personnel** Partners: Ruth Corman, Christopher Thomas.
**Services and Facilities** Art Consultancy. Art for Offices. Commissioning Service. Framing.
**Work Stocked and Sold** Cer. Cra. Dec. Gla. Pa. Ph. Pr. Sc. Tx. Wd.
**Price range** £100–£50,000

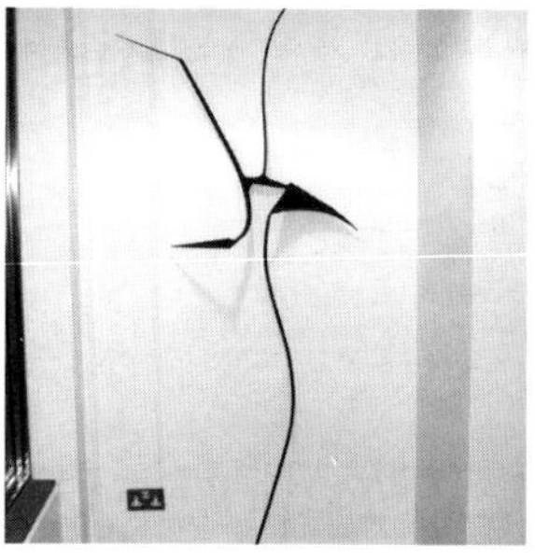

*Marko Kratohril, untitled, ground and brushed steel, 2 m 20 cm x 1 m 50 cm, 2000, £2400.*

*Thomas Corman Arts provides a professional service, working with corporate clients, architects, designers, and private collectors. Dealing directly with over 400 young and established artists and makers from the UK and overseas, TCA has gained a reputation for working effectively with clients from the initial free consultation to the installation of artworks. Our role is to make your acquisition of art easy. TCA will source art to suit your budget, your location and your image.*

### ▶ The Unicorn Gallery C

Unicorn Pictures Ltd, 8 Hollywood Road, London SW10 9HY.
**Tel** 020 7376 3195 **Fax** 020 7352 4120
**Email** unicornlondon@freeuk.com
**Opening times** Mon–Fri 11–7, Sat 1–7. Any other time by appointment.
**Nearest Underground** Fulham Broadway, South Kensington, Earls Court.
**Personnel** Founder: John Simmons FRSA. Director: P. J. Clarke.
**Services and Facilities** Art Consultancy. Art for Offices. Commissioning Service.
**Work Stocked and Sold** Cer. Dr. Gla. Pa. Pr. Sc. Tx.
**Price range** £100–£8,000

*Michael Forbes,* Rocket Dog, *oil on canvas, 20" x 30", 1999.*
*Unicorn Pictures (established 1961) provides new and adventurous paintings and sculpture by award-winning British artists with rising reputations to Parliamentary, corporate and private collections from their gallery in Chelsea, creates in-house exhibitions in corporate premises, organises promotional events, and provides a renowned artist-in-residence scheme.*

## ART MANAGEMENT

### ▶ Art For Offices C

International Art Consultants, The Galleries, 15 Dock Street, London E1 8JL.
**Tel** 020 7481 1337 **Fax** 020 7481 3425
**Email** enquiries@afo.co.uk
**Ws** www.afo.co.uk
**Opening times** Mon–Fri 9.30–5.30.
**Nearest Underground** Tower Hill, Aldgate, Aldgate East.
**Personnel** Director: Andrew Hutchinson. Director: Peter Harris. Amanda Basker.
**Services and Facilities** Art Consultancy. Art for Offices. Commissioning Service. Framing. Parking.
**Work Stocked and Sold** Cer. Cra. Dr. Gla. Pa. Ph. Pr. Sc. Tx. Wd.
**Price range** £100–£50,000

*We have 20 years experience advising architects, designers and corporate clients on the planning and implementation of art programmes. Our 10,000 sq ft galleries provide a central source of art, enabling clients and specifiers to view a comprehensive range of art on a single visit to one location. We deal directly with over 800 artists and have a large visual reference library covering art in all media which is cross-referenced by style and price. This makes it possible to research works of art or artists for commission quickly and effectively. Art can be purchased, commissioned or acquired on a flexible rental basis.*

## COMPUTER SOFTWARE SYSTEMS

### ▶ Hallett Independent
5 Solent Place, Bath Road,
Lymington SO41 3RU.
**Tel** 01590 672 888 **Fax** 01590 673 222
**Email** info@halettindependent.com
**Opening times** 9–6.
**Personnel** Director: Louise Hallett.
**Services and Facilities** Art Consultancy.
*Specialist services for the art world – insurance and computer software. Expert and unbiased insurance consultant for galleries, dealers, collectors, museums and exhibitions – from someone with a history of working in the art world. Make sure you have the best deal available. Also, advice on gallery/dealer and collection management computer software – know what the choice is and what's right for you. The best insurance and the best management software cut the costs of running your business.*

## INFORMATION SERVICES

### ▶ AOP (Association of Photographers)

81 Leonard Street, London EC2A 4QS.
**Tel** 020 7739 6669 **Fax** 020 7739 8707
**Email** general@aophoto.co.uk
**Ws** www.aophoto.co.uk
**Opening times** Mon–Fri 9.30–6.
**Personnel** Marketing: Sascha Howard.
CEO: Gwen Thomas.
*You've found it! Whether you're a professional photographer, an assistant, an agent or a graduate – the Association of Photographers is here to work for you. What is the Association of Photographers? It began in 1968, as the Association of Fashion, Advertising and Editorial Photographers. Then, it was a small group of photographers united by a common interest – to promote the highest standards of work and practice throughout the industry and to protect and improve the rights of all professional photographers based in the UK. Today, it's the Association of Photographers (AOP), with over 1,700 photographers and photographic assistants as members. It's supported by agents, printers, manufacturers and suppliers of photographic equipment, as well as affiliated colleges. Though our principal aim has not changed in over 30 years, our areas of influence have expanded dramatically!*

### ▶ The Art Loss Register
12 Grosvenor Place, London SW1X 7HH.
**Tel** 020 7235 3393 **Fax** 020 7235 1652
**Email** artloss@artloss.com
**Ws** www.artloss.com
**Opening times** 8.30–6.30 (NY 2–10).
**Nearest Underground** Hyde Park Corner, Victoria.
**Personnel** Managing Director: James Emson.
**Services and Facilities** Art Consultancy.

### ▶ Artists' General Benevolent Institution
Burlington House, Piccadilly, London W1V 0DJ.
**Tel** 020 7734 1193 **Fax** 020 7734 9926
**Personnel** Secretary: Miss April Connett-Dance.

### ▶ Axis
Leeds Metropolitan University, 8 Queen Square, Leeds LS2 8AJ.
**Tel** 0113 245 7946 **Fax** 0113 245 7950
**Email** axis@lmu.ac.uk
**Ws** www.axisartists.org.uk
**Opening times** Mon–Fri 9–5.
**Nearest Station** Leeds.
**Personnel** Principal Information Officer: Robin Bourne.

### ▶ International Arts Bureau
4 Baden Place, Crosby Row, London SE1 1YW.
**Tel** 020 7403 7001 **Fax** 020 7403 2009
**Email** enquiry@international-arts.org
**Ws** www.international-arts.org
**Opening times** 9.30–5.30.
**Nearest Underground** London Bridge.
**Personnel** Director: Rod Fisher.
Manager: Valerie Synmoie.
**Services and Facilities** Art Consultancy.

### ▶ National Irish Visual Arts Library
100 Thomas Street, Dublin 8.
**Tel** 00353 1 6364200 **Fax** 00353 1 6364207
**Email** annehodge@ncad.ie
**Ws** www.ncad.ie
**Opening times** Mon 10–1, Tue, Wed 10–1, 2–5, Thu 2–8, Fri 10–1, 2–8.
**Personnel** Administrator: Anne Hodge.
Librarian: Edward Murphy.
**Services and Facilities** Disabled Access.

## MARKETING SERVICES AND PR

### ▶ In West Ltd - Pro Art
218 New Kings Road, London SW6 4NZ.
**Tel** 020 7384 2461 **Fax** 020 7731 6562
**Email** proartconsultants@netscapeonline..co.uk
**Opening times** Mon–Fri 9–5.
**Nearest Underground** Putney Bridge.
**Personnel** Director: Vesna Petkovic.
**Services and Facilities** Art Consultancy. Bookshop. Commissioning Service. Lectures.

### ▶ Layzell Public Relations for the Arts
2A Tuam Road, London SE18 2QU.
**Tel** 020 8776 6650 **Fax** 020 8317 0905
**Email** layzellpr@compuserve.com
**Personnel** Director: Alistair Layzell.
*Layzell Public Relations for the Arts specialise in publicity for art exhibitions and events, artists and books on the arts. Marketing services.*

### ▶ Parker Harris Partnership
15 Church Street, Esher KT10 8QS.
**Tel** 01372 462 190 **Fax** 01372 460 032
**Email** info@parkerharris.co.uk
**Ws** www.parkerharris.co.uk
**Opening times** Daily 9–5.
**Nearest Station** Esher
**Personnel** Partners: Penny Harris, Emma Parker. Rachel Mapplebeck. Siobhan Kneale.
**Services and Facilities** Art Consultancy.
*Parker Harris and Company specialise in all aspects of arts administration, exhibition organising, press and public relations. As well as organising national touring events such as the Jerwood Painting Prize, The Hunting Art Prizes, the Singer Friedlander/Sunday Times Watercolour Competition, The Discerning Eye, The Garrick/Milne Prize, The Jerwood Sculpture Prize, and The Laing Art Competition, they also arrange, market, and publicise exhibitions throughout the UK and Europe.*

## PUBLIC ART AGENCIES

### ▶ Art For Offices C
International Art Consultants, The Galleries, 15 Dock Street, London E1 8JL.
**Tel** 020 7481 1337 **Fax** 020 7481 3425
**Email** enquiries@afo.co.uk
**Ws** www.afo.co.uk
**Opening times** Mon–Fri 9–5.
**Nearest Underground** Tower Hill, Aldgate, Aldgate East.
**Personnel** Directors: Andrew Hutchinson, Peter Harris. Amanda Basker.
**Services and Facilities** Art Consultancy. Art for Offices. Commissioning Service. Framing. Parking.
**Work Stocked and Sold** Cer. Cra. Dr. Gla. Pa. Ph. Pr. Sc. Tx. Wd.
**Price range** £100–£50,000
*We have 20 years experience advising architects, designers and corporate clients on the planning and implementation of art programmes. Our 10,000 sq ft galleries provide a central source of art, enabling clients and specifiers to view a comprehensive range of art on a single visit to one location. We deal directly with over 800 artists and have a large visual reference library covering art in all media which is cross-referenced by style and price. This makes it possible to research works of*

*art or artists for commission quickly and effectively. Art can be purchased, commissioned or acquired on a flexible rental basis.*

### ▶ Artangel
36 St John's Lane, London EC1M 4BJ.
**Tel** 020 7336 6801 **Fax** 020 7336 6802
**Email** info@artangel.co.uk
**Ws** www.innercity.demon.co.uk

### ▶ Cardiff Bay Arts Trust
123 Bute Street, Cardiff CF1 6AE.
**Tel** 029 2048 8772 **Fax** 029 2047 2439
**Email** Arts.Trust@ENABLIS.co.uk
**Opening times** Daily office hours.
**Personnel** Director: Carole-Anne Davies.
**Services and Facilities** Art Consultancy. Art for Offices. Commissioning Service. Gallery space for hire. Guided Tours. Lectures.

### ▶ Cywaith Cymru. Artworks Wales
Crichton House, 11–12 Mount Stuart Square, Cardiff CF10 5EE.
**Tel** 029 2048 9543 **Fax** 029 2046 5458
**Email** info@cywaithcymru.org
**Ws** www.cywaithcymru.org
**Personnel** Director: Tamara Krikorian.
**Services and Facilities** Art Consultancy. Commissioning Service.
*Cywaith Cymru. Artworks Wales was established in 1981 to encourage the placing of art in the environment through commissions, exhibitions and residencies. The wide range of work covered by the organisation is supported by a strong commitment to the cultural life of Wales, seeking to bring about new work which is particular to its environment and which reflects the culture from which it comes. Cywaith Cymru works closely with local authorities, industry, environmental groups and arts organisations. It encourages creative collaboration between artists, architects, landscape architects and developers. Registered charity No. 512006.*

### ▶ Free Form Arts Trust
38 Dalston Lane, London E8 3AZ.
**Tel** 020 7249 3394 **Fax** 020 7249 8499
**Email** freeform@ffat1.globalnet.co.uk
**Nearest Underground** Dalston Kingsland.
**Personnel** Associate Director: Barbara Wheeler-Early. Training Co-ordinator: Patrick Burton.
**Services and Facilities** Art Consultancy. Commissioning Service.

### ▶ Public Art Development Trust
3rd Floor, Kirkham House,
12–14 Whitfield Street, London W1P 5RD.
**Tel** 020 7580 9977 **Fax** 020 7580 8540
**Personnel** Director: Sandra Percival. Chairman: Gordon Edington.

# Art Services

# NOTES

# Art Insurance

For most people, insurance is all about financial compensation; but for the inheritor or the serious collector, risk prevention is of much greater significance.

Whereas the custodian of a historic collection of Old Masters may feel a certain responsibility in terms of the national heritage, the more modest collector aims to conserve the items for his or her own family. Both aims are equally valid.

Art insurance differs from mass-market insurance, where formulaic rates and cover apply. There is no retail price index for Iznik pottery, no match test for a Regency bergère. Art is an international business and, in common with the stock exchange, values can be subject to dramatic fluctuations influenced by confidence and fashion. Specialist brokers and underwriters who appreciate these complexities design their policies accordingly. But fine art insurance doesn't just mean a premium cheque at the end of each year. Specialist insurers, such as AXA Nordstern Art, are exposed daily to claims of all kinds and are in a unique position to offer advice on conservation and protection.

Sadly, art theft has increased and contrary to popular belief, this is not an elitist crime. Nor is there such a thing as a picture too obscure or too famous to steal. Even the best security will not keep the professional thief at bay. But it's not just burglary that the collector needs to protect against. Common reasons for claims are fire or even the damaging effects of a bath overflowing. This is when the service your insurance company offers will be put to the test. A non-specialist insurer will not understand either the true value of your collection or how its loss can best be indemnified. Art insurers have the breadth of knowledge to understand and compensate correctly for depreciation following damage.

'New for old' is a common basis for settlement in household insurance; however, it is totally inappropriate as compensation for the loss of antiques. All claims should be handled by cash settlement, the insurance company having agreed the value prior to the claim directly with the client and having monitored it throughout the life of the policy. With this high level of service, surely specialist insurance is expensive and will be well in excess of covering household contents? The reverse is in fact true. The price of insuring a private collection of paintings worth £1 million can be as little as £1,500.

Clare Pardy
Development Manager
AXA Nordstern Art Insurance Limited

## INSURANCE BROKERS

### ▶ Aon UK
Briar Cliff House, Kings Head,
Farnborough GU4 7TE.
**Tel** 01252 807 321
**Fax** 01252 807 330

### ▶AXA Art Insurance
**Tel** 020 7626 5001
**Fax** 020 7626 4606
**Email** helen.george@axa-art.co.uk
**Ws** www.axa-art.co.uk

### ▶ Blackwall Green (Jewellery and Fine Art)
Lambert Fenchurch House, Friary Court,
Crutched Friars, London EC3N 2NP.
**Tel** 020 7560 3381
**Fax** 020 7560 3649
**Email** cstephens@lfgroup.co.uk
**Personnel** Martin Owen. Camilla Stephens. Robert Graham. Robert Hepburne-Scott. Adam Prideaux.

### ▶ Byas Mosley & Co. Ltd.
International Fine Art Division, William
Byas House, 14–18 St Clare Street,
London WC3N 1JX.
**Tel** 020 7481 0101
**Fax** 020 7480 5303

### ▶ Crowley Colosso
Friary Court, Crutched Friars,
London EC3N 2NP.
**Tel** 020 7560 3000
**Fax** 020 7560 3655

### ▶ HSBC Insurance Brokers Ltd
Bishops Court, 27/33 Artillery Lane,
London E1 7LP.
**Tel** 020 7661 2360 **Fax** 020 7377 2175
**Email** bob.diggory@HSBC.com
**Opening times** 9.30–5.30 Mon–Fri.
**Nearest Underground** Liverpool Street.
**Personnel** Andrew Nunn. Tony Barratt.
*Specialist insurance brokers for Art Dealers; Antique Dealers; Auction Houses; Shippers and Packers; Art Galleries and Museums; Historic Houses; Private Collections; Corporate Collections; Exhibitions; Transits; Art Trade Fairs; and Jewellery. A member of the HSBC Group.*

### ▶ Jardine Insurance Brokers International Ltd
Jardine House, 6 Crutched Friars,
London EC3N 2HT.
**Tel** 020 7528 4100, 020 7528 4444
**Fax** 020 7528 4746

### ▶ Needham Jobson & Co.
Byron House, 102 Wimbledon Hill Road,
London SW19 7PB.
**Tel** 020 8944 8870 **Fax** 020 8944 8816

### ▶ SBJ Speciality Limited
100 Whitechapel, London E1 1JG.
**Tel** 020 7816 2000
**Fax** 020 7816 2121
**Personnel** Directors: Christopher Bailey-West, David Lock.

### ▶ Sedgwick Fine Art
Sedgwick House, The Sedgwick Centre,
London E1 8DX.
**Tel** 020 7377 3456
**Fax** 020 7377 3199

### ▶ Sneath, Kent & Stuart Ltd
Stuart House, 53/55 Scrutton Street,
London EC2A 4QQ.
**Tel** 020 7739 5646
**Fax** 020 7739 6467

### ▶ Willis Corroon Fine Art
10 Trinity Square, London EC3P 3AX.
**Tel** 020 7975 2173
**Fax** 020 7975 2447
**Email** hallettl@wcg.co.uk
**Opening times** Mon–Fri 9.30–5.30.
24-hour answering machine.
**Personnel** Account Executive: Louise Hallett.
**Services and Facilities** Valuation.

### ▶ Windsor Insurance Brokers Ltd, Fine Art and Antiques Division
Lyon House, 160–166 Borough High Street,
London SE1 1JR.
**Tel** 020 7407 7144
**Fax** 020 7378 6676
**Email** paul.tasker@windsor.co.uk
**Opening times** 8–6.
**Nearest Underground** London Bridge.
**Personnel** Account Executives: David Beck, Peter Clifford.

## INSURANCE COMPANIES

### ▶ Hiscox plc
1 Great St Helen's, London EC3A 6HX.
**Tel** 020 7448 6000
**Fax** 020 7448 6797
**Email** enquiry@hiscox.co.uk
**Ws** www.hiscox.co.uk
**Personnel** Annabel Fell-Clark. Elizabeth Seeger.
**Services and Facilities** Café.
*Hiscox plc is one of the leading specialist insurers in the UK, representing 30 years experience and knowledge of providing individually tailored insurance. By combining efficiency of service, speed and fairness of claims payment, Hiscox offers an unparalleled ranged of products to the discerning individual.*

### ▶ Nordstern Art Insurance Ltd.
78 Leadenhall Street, London EC3A 3DH.
**Tel** 020 7626 5001
**Fax** 020 7626 4606
**Personnel** Clare Pardy.

## INSURANCE CONSULTANCY

### ▶ Special Insurance Schemes Agency
PO Box 168, London SW20 8LE.

### ▶ Hallett Independent
5 Solent Place, Bath Road,
Lymington SO41 3RU.
**Tel** 01590 672 888 **Fax** 01590 673 222
**Email** info@hallettindependent.com
**Opening times** 9–6.
**Personnel** Director: Louise Hallett.
**Services and Facilities** Art Consultancy.
*Specialist services for the art world – insurance and computer software. Expert and unbiased insurance consultant for galleries, dealers, collectors, museums and exhibitions – from someone with a history of working in the art world. Make sure you have the best deal available. Also, advice on gallery/dealer and collection management computer software – know what the choice is and what's right for you. The best insurance and the best management software cut the costs of running your business.*

# Conservation

## CONSERVATORS AND RESTORERS

### ▶ Clare Finn & Co.
38 Cornwall Gardens, London SW7 4AA.
**Tel** 020 7937 1895 **Fax** 020 7937 4198

### ▶ Connaught Galleries
44 Connaught Street, London W2.
**Tel** 020 7723 1660 **Fax** 020 7723 1660
**Opening times** Mon–Fri 10–6.30, Sat 10–1.
**Nearest Underground** Paddington, Lancaster Gate, Marble Arch.
**Personnel** Partner: Michael Hollamby.
**Services and Facilities** Art for Offices. Framing. Gallery space for hire. Parking. Restoration. Shop. Workshop Facilities.

### ▶ Conservation Management Ltd
10 Wilton Street, London SW1X 7AF.
**Tel** 020 7823 2331 **Fax** 020 7823 2285
**Opening times** By appointment.
**Nearest Underground** Victoria/ Hyde Park Corner.
**Personnel** Director: Sally Lescher, MA (Courtauld).
**Services and Facilities** Art Consultancy. Art for Offices. Commissioning Service. Framing. Lectures. Restoration.

### ▶ The Conservation Studio
Sparsholt, Winchester, SO21 SQH.
**Tel** 01962 776 495 **Fax** 01962 776 495
**Email** WinStudio@aol.com
**Opening times** By appointment only.
**Personnel** Paul Congdon-Clelford.
**Services and Facilities** Art Consultancy. Parking. Restoration.

### ▶ De Beer Studios
9 Old Bond Street, London W1X.
**Tel** 020 7629 1470

### ▶ Deborah Bates Paper Conservation & Gallery
191 St John's Hill, Battersea, London SW11 1TH.
**Tel** 020 7223 1629 **Fax** 020 7207 1330
**Email** djbates42@hotmail.com
**Opening times** Studio: Mon–Fri 10–6. Gallery: Mon–Sat 10–4.
**Nearest Station** Clapham Junction.
**Personnel** Proprietor: Deborah Bates AIC MIPC.
**Services and Facilities** Restoration.
*Established in 1980, the conservation practice offers studio and on-site conservation and restoration of works of art on paper: watercolours, prints, drawings and pastels for private collectors, galleries and institutions. All staff fully qualified. Large, well-equipped studio. Insurance work undertaken (flood and fire damage). Appraisal and estimates are given free. Condition and treatment reports. Framing service and advice on storage and display for preventative conservation. Delivery and collection can be arranged. Member of the Institute of Paper Conservation and listed on the register maintained by the Museum & Galleries Commission. Gallery specialising in contemporary art.*

### ▶ G. Bignell Paper Conservation
45 Coronet Street, London N1.
**Tel** 020 7729 3161

### ▶ Graeme Storey
The Grange, Maesbrook, Oswestry SY10 8QP.
**Tel** 0169 185 260

### ▶ Hahn & Son
47 Albemarle Street, London W1X 8FE.
**Tel** 020 7493 1630/020 8429 7320

### ▶ James Wray Picture Conservation
Wood Farm, Ipswich Road, Otley, Ipswich.
**Tel** 01473 890 286

### ▶ John Jones Artsauce C
Stroud Green Road (corner of Morris Place), Finsbury Park, London N4 3JG.
**Tel** 020 7281 5439
**Fax** 020 7281 5956
**Email** info@johnjones.co.uk
**Ws** www.johnjones.co.uk
**Opening times** Mon–Fri 9.30–6, Sat 10–5.
**Nearest Underground** Finsbury park.
**Personnel** Jason Mackie.
**Services and Facilities** Framing. Parking. Restoration. Shop.
**Work Stocked and Sold** Pa.
*Specialist frame design and consultation. Conservation and restoration. Sculpture protection and display. Fine Art photographic serice. Two-level art materials store stocking premium brands. Ample parking. Efficient collection and delivery service. Art materials mail order department*

### ▶ Lees Fine Art Restorers
Unit 11, Wellington Close, Ledbury Road, London W11.
**Tel** 020 7229 3521

### ▶ Lowe & Butcher
Neckinger Mills, 162–164 Abbey Street, London SE1.
**Tel** 020 7237 1113

### ▶ Patricia Garner
Arragon Conservation Studio, 55 Arragon Road, Twickenham TW1 3NG.
**Tel** 020 8286 6153
**Fax** 020 8296 9377
**Opening times** Mon–Fri 9–5.30 or by appointment.
**Nearest Station** Twickenham.
**Personnel** Director: Patricia Garner.
**Services and Facilities** Art for Offices. Framing. Parking. Restoration.

### ▶ Paul Mitchell Ltd
99 New Bond Street, London W1Y 9LF.
**Tel** 020 7493 8732/0860
**Fax** 020 7409 7136

### ▶ Plowden and Smith
190 St Ann's Hill, Wandsworth, London SW18 2RT.
**Tel** 020 8874 4005 **Fax** 020 8874 7248

### ▶ Preservations Solutions
60 Queens Gardens, London W2.
**Tel** 020 7724 4744

### ▶ Rankins (Glass) Company Ltd
The London Glass Centre, 24–34 Pearson Street, London E2 8JD.
**Tel** 020 7729 4200
**Fax** 020 7729 7135/9197
**Email** info@rankinsglass.co.uk
**Ws** www.rankinsglass.co.uk
**Opening times** 9–5.
**Nearest Underground** Old Street/ Liverpool Sreet.
**Personnel** Marketing Manager: Stephanie Graham.
*Holders of the Royal Warrant for supplying low-reflective glass, Rankins are independent glass processors and glaziers situated in the east end of London. We specialise in fire-resistant, conservation and low-reflective glass and carry substantial stocks of these and all standard float glass products. With our vast range of equipment we can offer all the different forms of glass processing required by the end user as well as design advice when required.*
*For further information, please call the Rankins Sales Office.*

### ▶ S. Firnberg Paper Conservation
Home Farm, Salters Lane, Ludgershall, near Aylesbury, HP18 9NY.
**Personnel** Sarah Firnberg.

### ▶ Simon R. Gillespie
16 Albemarle Street, London W1X.
**Tel** 020 7493 0988 **Fax** 020 7493 0955
**Email** Simon.R.Gillespie@btinternet.com
**Ws** www.art-connection.com
**Opening times** Mon-Fri 9–6.
**Nearest Underground** Green Park.
**Personnel** Partner: Simon Gillespie.
**Services and Facilities** Art Consultancy. Art for Offices. Framing. Restoration. Valuation.

### ▶ Sophia Fairclough
Studio 5, Whitehouse Mews, 37–39 Westminster Bridge Road, London SE1 7QD.
**Tel** 020 7261 0735 **Fax** 020 7261 0735

# Fine Art Printers

## FINE ART PRINTERS

### ▶ Abacus (Colour Printers) Ltd
Lowick Green, Lowick, Ulverston, LA12 8DX.
**Tel** 01229 885 361 **Fax** 01229 885 348
**Opening times** Mon–Sat 9–5.
**Personnel** Directors: John Sutcliffe, Vicki Sutcliffe.
**Services and Facilities** Parking.
*Mail order postcards, greetings cards, posters, catalogues from your own art work. All work is in-house to ensure maximum print quality and accuracy of colour to the original art work. Print members of the Fine Art Trade Guild for 10 years.*

### ▶ Amica Fine Art Printing Ltd
F1 Park Hall, 40 Martell Road, London SE21 8EN.
**Tel** 020 8670 6060 **Fax** 020 8670 0060
**Nearest Underground** Tooting Broadway. Rail: Earlsfield.
**Personnel** Directors: Agnes Pindelski, Chris Silcock, Andrew Usill.

### ▶ BAS Printers Ltd
Over Wallop, Stockbridge SO20 8JD.
**Tel** 01264 781 711 **Fax** 01264 781 116
**Email** bas@basprint.sonnet.co.uk
**Nearest Station** Andover.
**Personnel** Managing Director: David Gumn. Sales Director: Paul Gumn.

### ▶ Broad Oak Colour
Units A & B, 254 Broad Oak Road, Canterbury CT2 7QH.
**Tel** 01227 767 856 **Fax** 01227 762 599
**Personnel** Directors: Terry Tilbury, Simon Young.

### ▶ Dayfold Fine Art Printers
Dayfold House, Black Moor Road, Verwood BH31 6BE.
**Tel** 01202 827 141 **Fax** 01202 825 841
**Email** dayfold@aol.com

### ▶ Fidelity Colour Fine Art Prints
8–10–12 Hornsby Square, Southfields, Lamdon SS15 6SD.
**Tel** 01268 544 066 **Fax** 01268 418 977
**Personnel** Sue Brown.

### ▶ J. Thomson Colour Printers
14 Carnoustie Place, Glasgow G5 8PB.
**Tel** 0141 429 1094 **Fax** 0141 429 5638
**Personnel** Nicholas Thomson.

### ▶ Loudmouth Postcards
The Workstation, 15 Paternoster Row, Sheffield S1 2BX.
**Tel** 0114 275 3175 **Fax** 0114 281 5464
**Email** info@loudworld.co.uk
**Ws** www.loudworld.co.uk
**Opening times** 9–5.30.
**Personnel** Chet Cunago.
*Postcard printers to the art world for 11 years. Prices start at £89 for 1,000 postcards. Huge discounts on group/multiple orders. Artwork can be taken from your disk/photo/transparency. Call 0114 275 3175 for a free sample pack or visit us at www.loudworld.co.uk and blow your own trumpet loud!*

### ▶ Napier Jones Ltd
187 Gordon Road, London SE15 3RT.
**Tel** 020 7277 8677
**Fax** 020 7639 3320
**Email** print@napierjones.ltd.uk
**Personnel** Managing Director: Jennifer Jones. Director: Peter Clements.

### ▶ Newcastle Fine Art Printers
9A Marquis Court, Low Prudhoe.
**Tel** 01661 831 086
**Personnel** Cherie Holpen.

### ▶ Northumberland Fine Art Printers
West Farm, Kenton Bar, Ponteland Road, Newcastle-upon-Tyne NE3 3EJ.
**Tel** 0191 286 2596
**Personnel** Colin Ashton.

### ▶ The Pale Green Press
Unit 30, Cranwell Close, Violet Road, London E3 3QY.
**Tel** 020 7538 0330
**Fax** 020 7538 3691
**Personnel** Ben Craze.

### ▶ Penshurst Press
Longfield Road, Tunbridge Wells.
**Tel** 01892 537 315
**Fax** 01892 511 424
**Personnel** Barry Wright.

### ▶ The Postcard Company Limited
51 Gortin Road, Omagh BT79 7HZ.
**Tel** 028 8224 9222
**Fax** 028 8224 9886
**Email** sales@thepostcardcompany.com
**Ws** www.thepostcardcompany.com
**Opening times** Mon–Thu 8.30–5.15, Fri 8.30–1.15.
*Manufacturers of high-quality full-colour and black and white postcards, product cards, greetings cards, business cards and promotional material to artists, craftspeople, photographers and graphic designers in the UK, Ireland and Europe. Offering an unrivalled service with a quick order turn-around of 10 working days and the lowest prices in UK and Ireland. For example, 500 postcards for £67+VAT. PHONE NOW FOR OUR FREE SAMPLE PACK!*

### ▶ Ranelagh Colour Printers
Park End, South Hill Park, London NW3 2SG.
**Tel** 020 7435 4400 **Fax** 020 7435 5635
**Personnel** Robert Zeffman.

### ▶ Severnside Printers Ltd
Upton-upon-Severn WR8 0HG.
**Tel** 01684 594 521 **Fax** 01684 594 344
**Personnel** Betty Williams.

### ▶ St Ives Printing & Publishing Company
High Street, St Ives, TR26 1RS.
**Tel** 01736 798 951 **Fax** 01736 793 536
**Opening times** Mon–Fri 9–5.
**Personnel** Director: Toni Carver. Contact: Andrew Richards.
*Situated as we are amongst the 'Art Colony' of St Ives, our printing craftsmen are fully aware of the needs of individual painters, photographers and galleries to have their work reproduced to the highest standard. It is through meeting these high expectations that St Ives Printing & Publishing Company has gained a national reputation for its quality of fine art reproduction, while at the same time keeping its prices competitive.*
*Phone now for our free sample pack and price list.*

### ▶ Walker Print Ltd
Dept. AR, Classic House, 4th Floor, 174 Old Street, London EC1V 9BP.
**Tel** 020 7253 1200 **Fax** 020 7253 0890
**Personnel** Sarah Harries.

## FINE ART PRINTERS – ART CARDS

### ▶ Petrol Cards
The Island, Moor Road, Chesham, HP5 1NZ
**Tel** 01494 775 849
**Fax** 01494 777 930
**Email** petrolcards@mediadial.co.uk
**Ws** www.petrolcards.com
**Nearest Station** Chesham. Metropolitan line.
**Personnel** Gordon Baird-Maclaren, Sue Neate.
*17 years of print and design for the arts and entertainment world, producing postcards, business cards, product cards, posters, private view cards, catalogues and related promotional material. 500 gloss laminated postcards for only £65 + VAT. Huge discounts for group orders. Design, artwork and print finishing services. 24 hour turnaround digital print service available. PHONE NOW FOR YOUR FREE SAMPLE PACK 08000 72 66 72.*

### ▶ Thought Factory
Group House, 40 Waterside Road, Hamilton Industrial Park, Leicester LE5 1TL.
**Tel** 0116 276 5302 **Fax** 0116 246 0506
**Email** kpegroup@aol.com
**Ws** www.kpegroup@aol.com
**Opening times** Mon–Thu 8.30–5.30, Fri 8–1.30.
**Nearest Station** Leicester London Road.
**Personnel** Director: Elaine King.

### ▶ Westside Creative Services
32 Great Pulteney Street, London W1R 3DE.
**Tel** 020 7437 1533/7437 1542
**Fax** 020 7437 1542
**Personnel** Ian Brewster.
*Private view and production postcards – from £125 for 1,000 full colour cards including black text on the reverse. We also supply presentation folders, envelopes, invoice pads, stationary, posters, and catalogues. Design, artwork and finishing services available.*

# Founders

## FINE ART FOUNDERS

### ▶ AB Fine Art Foundry
1 Fawe Street, London E14 6PD.
**Tel** 020 7515 8052
**Fax** 020 7987 7339
**Email** jerry@abfineart.demon.co.uk
**Personnel** Henry Abercrombie. Jerry Hughes.
*AB Fine Art Foundry Ltd employs only craftspeople with a fine art background, ensuring an empathy with individual sculptors and their work. The foundry offers a complete range of services: scaling up, armature building, mould making, lost wax and sand casting, patination, repair and restoration etc.*
*We have a record of reliability in meeting deadlines and maintaining high quality and good value for money. 1,700 sq ft. studio available for individual projects. If casting your work into bronze interests you and you would like to visit the workshops or discuss any projects, please phone and we will be happy to help and advise.*

### ▶ Alden Arts
8 Reynolds Place, Crawley.
**Tel** 01293 535 411

### ▶ AMTeC Co-Op Ltd
The Foundry The Historic Dockyard, Chatham ME4 4TZ.
**Tel** 01634 832 627 **Fax** 01634 832 627
**Email** danagh@msn.com
**Opening times** Various.
**Personnel** Director: Mrs Dana Goodburn-Brown. Director: Andrew Lacy. Artist/founder: ATTAS.
**Services and Facilities** Lectures. Restoration.
*Ancient Materials Technology and Conservation: an art and archaeometallurgical bronze foundry. We offer workshops in ancient and modern casting techniques, the production of replicas, didactic displays and fine art sculptures, mould making and bronze casting.*

### ▶ Art Bronze Foundry (London) Ltd
1 Michael Road, London SW6.
**Tel** 020 7736 7292

### ▶ Art Cast
36 Southwell Road, London SE5.
**Tel** 020 7733 8424

### ▶ Beltane Studios Ltd
2 Soonhope Farm Holdings, Peebles EH45 8BH.
**Tel** 01721 724 888
**Personnel** Paul Fraser.

### ▶ Bronze Age Sculpture Foundry
272 Island Row, Limehouse, Docklands, London E14 7HY.
**Tel** 020 7538 1388 **Fax** 020 7538 9723
**Email** duncanh@netcomuk.co.uk
**Ws** www.netcomuk.co.uk/-duncanh
**Opening times** 9–6.
**Nearest Underground** Limehouse (Docklands Light Rail).
**Personnel** Proprietor: Mark Kennedy.
**Services and Facilities** Parking.

### ▶ Black Isle Bronze
Newton of Belivat, Nairn IV12 5PT.
**Tel** 01309 651 260
**Fax** 01309 651 260
**Email** blackislebronze@totalise.co.uk
**Ws** www.blackislebronze.co.uk
*A busy scupture foundry, specialising in lost-wax and sand casting techniques, with an on-site moulding service. Black Isle Bronze is responsible for many large sculptures throughout Britain today. Please call, or check out our website for more information.*

### ▶ The Bronze Works
13 Derbyshire Lane, Sheffield S8 9EH.
**Tel** 0114 255 4376 **Fax** 0114 276 1769

### ▶ Burleighfield Arts Limited
Sculpture Casting Studio, Loudwater, High Wycombe HP10 9RF.
**Tel** 01494 521 341 **Fax** 01494 461 953
**Email** burleighfield@compuserve.com
**Ws** www.polestarltd/sculpture/
**Opening times** Weekdays 8–5.
**Personnel** Paul Dimishky.

### ▶ Casteck Ltd
61 Caroline Street, Birmingham B3 1UF.
**Tel** 0121 233 1334 **Fax** 0121 523 7469
**Personnel** Barry Leach.

### ▶ Castle Fine Arts Foundry
Tanat Foundry, Llanrhaeadr YM, Oswestry SY10 0AA.
**Tel** 01691 780 261 **Fax** 01691 780 563
**Personnel** Chris Bulter.

### ▶ Century Bronze
9 Camton Street, Birmingham BAT 6AR.
**Tel** 0121 212 0840

### ▶ Colin Reid Glass
New Mills, Stod Road, Stroud GL3 1RN.
**Tel** 01453 751 421

### ▶ Euro Cast
Michael House, 48 Carver Street, Birmingham B1 3AS.
**Tel** 0121 233 2266 **Fax** 0121 233 9731

### ▶ Firth Rixon
PO Box 6, Heath Road, Darleston, Wednesbury.
**Tel** 0121 568 6222

### ▶ Harrison Castings Ltd
Gough Road, Leicester.
**Tel** 01533 769 351

### ▶ John Longbottom (Ironfounders)
Broomhill Road, Bonnybridge FK4 2AN.
**Tel** 01324 812 860

### ▶ Leander Architectural
Fletcher Foundry, Hallsteads Close, Doves Holes, Buxton.
**Tel** 01298 814 941 **Fax** 01298 814 970
**Email** ted@leanderarch.demon.co.uk
**Ws** www.leanderarch.demon.co.uk
**Opening times** 8–5.30.
**Nearest Station** Dove Holes.
**Personnel** Partner: Ted McAvoy.
**Services and Facilities** Disabled Access. Parking. Workshop Facilities.
*Leander operate a sand cast bronze and aluminium foundry specialising in plaques and bas reliefs. The company has in-house pattern and modelling facilities and a wide range of graphic production techniques. Leander has acquired a deserved reputation for undertaking complex and graphically precise castings in any quantity and to tight schedules. Clients include sculptors, community arts groups, English Heritage, CADW and many local authorities. Many plaques and signs are cast for export because of the foundry's experience in working with different languages and script forms.*

### ▶ Livingstone Art Founders
Maidstone Road, Matfield, Tonbridge TN12 7LQ.
**Tel** 01892 722 474 **Fax** 01892 722 474
**Opening times** 7.30–5.
**Nearest Station** Paddock Wood.
**Personnel** Director: W. B. Livingstone.
**Services and Facilities** Commissioning Service. Restoration. Workshop Facilities.

### ▶ LS Sculpture Casting
Unit 367, Westcott Venture Park, Westcott HP18 0XB.
**Tel** 01296 658 884 **Fax** 01296 658 882
**Personnel** David Challis.
*Over the years we have built a good reputation in the field of bronze resin casting, giving a high-quality service to professional sculptors and crafts people alike. We are generally recommended to clients by sculptors who have used us and been particularly pleased with our work – particularly the patinations.*
*Although most of our work is moulding and casting in bronze resin, other finishes are available. We also offer sculpture-related services such as modelling and enlarging.*

### ▶ Lunts Castings Ltd
Middlemore Road, Birmingham B21 0BJ.
**Tel** 0121 551 4301 **Fax** 0121 523 7954
**Email** info@luntscastings.co.uk
**Ws** www.luntscastings.co.uk
**Opening times** 7.30–5.
**Nearest Station** Birmingham New Street.
**Personnel** Managing Director: A. J. Limb.
*Lunts Castings Ltd have built on an enviable reputation for quality and service at very competitive prices, enabling the sculptor to price to sell. We offer a collection/delivery service of both waxes and bronze. Casting is carried out for most non-ferrous and precious metals, ie bronze, brass, silver and gold. Many well-known*

*sculptors are moving to the Lunts complete casting service, so put us to the test.*

### ▶ Mike Davis Foundry

St James Street, New Bradwell,
Milton Keynes MK13 0BW.
**Tel** 01908 315 841 **Fax** 01908 511 363
**Personnel** Mike Davis.

### ▶ Morris Singer Ltd

Highfield Industrial Estate,
Church Lane, Lasham GU34 5SQ.
**Tel** 01256 381 033 **Fax** 01256 381 565
**Email** morrissinger@btclick.com
**Opening times** 7.30–4.30
**Nearest Station** Basingstoke.
**Personnel** Directors: David J. Vallance, Chris Boverhoff.
**Services and Facilities** Disabled Access. Workshop Facilities.
*Whenever you place a commission with Morris Singer Ltd, you have the confidence of knowing that it has the backing of almost 150 years of experience and many of the great artists within that time have commissioned the services of Morris Singer. Whether your work is large or small, anywhere in the world, we will be happy to enlarge, cast, erect on site and provide all the comprehensive services you would expect from the foremost company. We are very close to exit 6 on the M3.*

### ▶ Nautilus Fine Art Foundry Ltd

Head Office and Works, 11 Swinborne Drive,
Springwood Industrial Estate,
Braintree CM7 2YP.
**Tel** 01376 343 222 **Fax** 01376 348 480
**Email** enquiries@nautilus-foundry.co.uk
**Ws** www.nautilus-foundry.co.uk
**Opening times** 7.30–5.30.
**Nearest Station** Braintree.
**Personnel** Manager: Paul Joyce.
*Nautilus is now recognised as a leader in the art casting profession. By employing only those considered to be the best in their respective disciplines, we achieve a quality that is second to none. The facilities we can offer and the range of materials, processes and patinations available, together with our studio facilities in both Braintree and London, has resulted in us becoming one of the most comprehensive of any art foundry. To fully appreciate all that Nautilus can offer, with an opportunity to discuss your requirements with our production team, please contact Paul Joyce to arrange a visit.*

# Framing

Choosing the perfect frame for a piece of artwork can seem to be quite a daunting task when surrounded by hundreds of different corner samples, especially when the work to be framed could look great in most of them – or, on the other hand, totally out of place in any of them! Should you frame to suit the picture or frame to suit the decoration? Do you frame to suit the artist's wishes, or frame to suit what you've chosen before? These are just a few of the typical dilemmas facing the owner the day he or she takes a painting, drawing or photograph to the framer's.

It is likely to be the very same day the framer is consulting or tendering for a project to frame 200 individual pieces for a contemporary gallery show next month; the exhibition may include works by artists as diverse as Victor Pasmore and Chris Ofili. In both cases the framing styles would be based on existing specifications co-designed by the artist, the gallery and the framing consultant. Repeating recognised framing instructions such as these will always help towards keeping a consistent identity for each piece.

Does the piece require some breathing space around it? Does it require an elaborate antiqued white gold leafed finish? Would it look best sat behind an acid-free off-white mount contained in a thin hand-welded aluminium frame with a polished face and brushed sides? Clearly, the number of choices can be alarming.

One of the main points to bear in mind is that the artwork is the feature and the frame should support its every aspect. Achieving the balance between what the piece needs and what enhances its subject matter is the key to finding the perfect frame. This may be done by using a particular colour or highlight within the painting and bringing it out in the finish of the wood stain. Bear in mind too that to 'frame' can sometimes limit the expression within the artwork. The piece could look superb elevated within a very simple box.

In this sense, simplicity can be a prime ingredient towards enhancing the space that the work is to be housed in. Creating a frame that disguises its internal mechanics is another example of the intrigue of framing.

Tim Blake
Consultant
John Jones Art Centre

## DRY MOUNTERS

### ▶ A. Bliss
5 Bakers Yard, Bakers Row, London EC1R 3HF.
**Tel** 020 7837 4959 **Fax** 020 7837 8244
**Email** edward@abliss.co.uk
**Ws** www.abliss.co.uk
**Opening times** Mon–Fri 9–6.
**Nearest Underground** Farringdon.
**Personnel** Partner: Edward Mawby.
**Services and Facilities** Framing.
*A. Bliss are dry mounting specialists with over 40 years experience. Our workshops in Clerkenwell (with off-street parking) are equipped with the largest and most up-to-date machinery whilst retaining a traditional hot mounting facility, indispensable for many types of work. We are aware of conservation issues and can advise on the most appropriate methods of mounting most types of media onto a wide variety of materials, including aluminium, glass and cloth.*

## FRAMERS

### ▶ Academy Arts Centre C
Winton Road, Petersfield GU32 3HA.
**Tel** 01730 261 624 **Fax** 01730 231 499
**Email** nixy@compuserve.com
**Opening times** Mon–Sat 9–5.30.
**Nearest Station** Petersfield.
**Personnel** Gallery Director: Nick Yellop. Art Centre Manager: Geoff Harris.
**Services and Facilities** Art for Offices. Bookshop. Commissioning Service. Framing. Gallery space for hire. Parking. Shop. Workshop Facilities.

### ▶ Academy Framing Royal Academy of Arts
Burlington House, Piccadilly, London W1V 0DS.
**Tel** 020 7300 5646/5647
**Fax** 020 7300 8001
**Ws** www.royalacademy.org.uk
**Opening times** Mon–Fri 10–5.
**Nearest Underground** Green Park, Piccadilly Circus.
**Personnel** Manager: C. Sims. Assistant Manager: E. Hannagan. Framers: T. Breen, D. Hegarty. Mount Cutter: M. Taylor. Fitter: C. Medhurst.
**Services and Facilities** Framing. Restoration.

### ▶ Alec Drew Picture Frames Ltd
5/7 Cale Street, Chelsea Green, London SW3 3QT.
**Tel** 020 7352 8716 **Fax** 020 7352 8716
**Email** adrew@hugill.demon.co.uk
**Ws** www.hugill.demon.co.uk/adrew.htm
**Opening times** Mon–Fri 9–5, Wed 9–6, Sat 9.30–1.
**Nearest Underground** Sloane Square/ South Kensington.
**Personnel** Director: Mr David Hughes.
**Services and Facilities** Framing. Restoration.
*We are well situated bespoke framers, working to a conservation standard offering a wide range of traditional and modern factory mouldings and hand-made frames. We can also put you in touch with restorers, picture hangers, or other specialists.*

### ▶ Arnold Wiggins & Sons Ltd
4 Bury Street, London SW1.
**Tel** 020 7925 0195

### ▶ Art & Soul
G14 Belgravia Workshops, 157–163 Marlborough Road, London N19 4NF.
**Tel** 020 7263 0421 **Fax** 020 7263 0421
**Opening times** Tue–Fri 9–5, closed 1–2. Sat: am (phone to check time/holidays).
**Nearest Underground** Archway, Finsbury Park.
**Personnel** Owner: Rebecca Bramwell.
**Services and Facilities** Framing. Parking.

### ▶ Art & Wood Supplies
220 North End Road, London W14.
**Tel** 020 7385 4683

### ▶ Art Works
50 High Street, Walton-on-Thames KT12 1BY.
**Tel** 0800 834 409

### ▶ Artbeat
703 Fulham Road, London SW6.
**Tel** 020 7736 0337

### ▶ Artbook London
The Chambers, Chelsea Harbour, London SW10 0XF.
**Tel** 020 7349 0666 **Fax** 020 7349 0202
**Personnel** Dainae Leaman.
**Work Stocked and Sold** Pa. Pr. Sc.

### ▶ Artefact Picture Framers
36 Windmill Street, London W1P 1HF.
**Tel** 020 7580 4878, Freephone 0500 850 085

### ▶ Artistic Impressions
62a Queens Road, London SE15.
**Tel** 020 7580 4878

### ▶ Ashworth & Thompson
12 Baron Street, London N1.
**Tel** 020 7837 6836

### ▶ Belgravia Frameworks
9 Kinnerton Street, Belgravia, London SW1X 8EA.
**Tel** 020 7245 1112 **Fax** 020 7245 1156

### ▶ Bishopsgate Framing Gallery
228 Bishopsgate, London EC2M 4QD.
**Tel** 020 7247 2320 **Fax** 020 7247 2320

### ▶ Bloomsbury Framing Co.
42 Theobalds Road, London WC1.
**Tel** 020 7404 8140

### ▶ Blue Jay Frames
Possingworth Craft Workshops, Blackboys East, Heathfield TN22 5HE.
**Tel** 01435 866 258 **Fax** 01435 868 473
**Opening times** Mon–Fri 8.30–5.30.
**Nearest Station** Uckfield.
**Personnel** Managing Director: Simon Hayes Fisher.
**Services and Facilities** Framing. Restoration.

### ▶ C. C. Galleries
420 Roman Road, London E3.
**Tel** 020 7980 2888

### ▶ Chelsea Frame Works
106 Finborough Road, London SW10.
**Tel** 020 7373 0180

### ▶ Circa 48
17b Brecknock Road, London N7.
**Tel** 020 7485 9249

### ▶ Connaught Galleries
44 Connaught Street, London W2.
**Tel** 020 7723 1660 **Fax** 020 7723 1660
**Opening times** Mon–Fri 10–6.30, Sat 10–1.
**Nearest Underground** Paddington, Lancaster Gate, Marble Arch.
**Personnel** Partner: Michael Hollamby.
**Services and Facilities** Art for Offices. Framing. Gallery space for hire. Parking. Restoration. Shop. Workshop Facilities.

### ▶ Cork Street Framing
8 Bramber Street, London W14.
**Tel** 020 7381 9211

### ▶ The Cottage Gallery
11/12 High Street, Huntingdon PF18 6TE.
**Tel** 01480 411 521 **Fax** 01480 386 521
**Opening times** Mon–Sat 9–5.30, Sun 10–4.
**Nearest Station** Huntingdon.
**Personnel** Proprietor: John Nind. Manageress: Amanda Burrell.
**Services and Facilities** Commissioning Service. Framing. Restoration. Shop. Valuation. Workshop Facilities.

### ▶ Court Frames Mayfair
8 Bourdon Street or 5–7 Sedley Place (off Berkeley Square), London W1X 9HX.
**Tel** 020 7493 3265 **Fax** 020 7493 8369
**Personnel** Mark Fisher.

### ▶ Coutts Framing
75 Blythe Road, Hammersmith, London W14.
**Tel** 020 7603 7475

### ▶ Dixon Bate Framing
94–98 Fairfield Street, Manchester M1 2WR.
**Tel** 0161 273 6974 **Fax** 0161 274 4865
**Opening times** Mon–Fri 8.30–5.30, Sat 9–1.
**Personnel** Managing Director: Jon Davies.
**Services and Facilities** Framing. Parking.

*One of the finest contemporary framers in the country. Bespoke hand-finished frames for the fine art market. Specialists in natural hardwoods and softwoods, stained/coloured/gilded/finished to your requirements. The largest selection of frames available in the North West, all produced with individual attention. Full conservation framing service to the highest possible standards. Servicing artists, dealers, galleries, and private and public collections nationwide. Outstanding and beautiful framing at a sensible price.*

### ▶ Frame Designs
57 Ebury Street, London SW1.
**Tel** 020 7730 0533/7823 6521

### ▶ Frame Emporium
589–591 Holloway Road, London N19 4DJ.
**Tel** 020 7263 8973 **Fax** 020 7281 1766

### ▶ Frame Factory
1E Gleneagle Road, London SW16.
**Tel** 020 8677 1882

### ▶ Frameworks
9 Kinnerton Street, London SW1.
**Tel** 020 7245 1112

### ▶ Glaze & Frame
408 Harrow Road, London W9 2HU.
**Tel** 020 7266 5379

### ▶ Harvard Enterprises
36–40 York Way, London N1.
**Tel** 020 7278 7138

### ▶ Holborn Galleries
70 Chancery Lane, London WC2A.
**Tel** 020 7404 0678

### ▶ International Art Supplies
CP House, Otterspool Way, Watford WD2 8HG.
**Tel** 01923 210 042 **Fax** 01923 240 899

### ▶ Islington Frames
8 Essex Road, London N1.
**Tel** 020 7359 8031

### ▶ John Davies Framing Ltd
8 Bury Street, London SW1.
**Tel** 020 7930 7795

### ▶ John Gilbert
30–34 Woodfield Place, London W9.
**Tel** 020 7289 3198

### ▶ John Jones Artsauce P
Stroud Green Road (corner of Morris Place), Finsbury Park N4 3JG.
**Tel** 020 7281 5439 **Fax** 020 7281 5956
**Email** info@johnjones.co.uk
**Ws** www.johnjones.co.uk
**Opening times** Mon–Fri 9.30–6. Sat 10–5.
**Nearest Underground** Finsbury Park.
**Services and Facilities** Framing. Parking. Restoration. Shop.
*Specialist frame design and consultation. Conservation and restoration. Sculpture protection and display. Fine Art photographic service. Two-level art materials store stocking premium brands. Ample parking. Efficient collection and delivery service. Art materials mail order department.*

### ▶ Kevin D'arts
Unit 6, Southern Row, London W10.
**Tel** 020 8964 0238

### ▶ Kingsbridge Arts
141 Dawes Road, London SW6.
**Tel** 020 7381 1133

### ▶ Lenny Villa
386a York Way, London N7 9LW.
**Tel** 020 7700 5010

### ▶ Little Venice Frames
12 Clifton Road, London W9.
**Tel** 020 7286 6500

### ▶ Mainline Mouldings
Unit 3, Hollygate Lane Industrial Park, Cotgrave, Nottingham NG12 3JW.
**Tel** 0115 989 0076 **Fax** 0115 989 9488

### ▶ Mosta Posta
86 Southwark Street, London SE1.
**Tel** 020 7620 4070

### ▶ New Frames
37 Beak Street, London W1.
**Tel** 020 7437 8881

### ▶ Old Church Galleries
320 Kings Road, London SW3 5UH.
**Tel** 020 7351 4649 **Fax** 020 7351 4449
**Services and Facilities** Framing.

### ▶ Oxford Exhibition Services
Station Road, Uffington SN7 7QD.
**Tel** 01367 820 713 **Fax** 01367 820 504
**Services and Facilities** Framing.
*A comprehensive framing service for museums and galleries. Also at Unit G6, Tavern Quay, Rope Street, Rotherhithe, London SE16 1TD. Tel: 0171 237 5646, fax: 0171 232 2254.*

### ▶ Portobello Framers
316 Portobello Road, London W10 5RU.

### ▶ Simon Beaugié Picture Framers
Manor Farm Workshops, Hamstreet Road, Shadoxhurst, Ashford TN26 1NW.
**Tel** 01233 733 353 **Fax** 01233 732 354
**Email** framing@simonbeaugiepictureframes.com
**Ws** www.simonbeaugiepictureframes.com
**Opening times** Mon–Fri 9.30–6.
**Personnel** Framing Consultants: Simon Beaugie, Norman Wass.
**Services and Facilities** Framing.
*Picture framers specialising in conservation of art on paper, canvas or board. Guilding service, frame design, sculpture plinths. Free consultation/collection/delivery within central London.*

### ▶ Steve Maddox Specialist Picture Framers
Hardy House, 62 Trafalgar Road, Moseley, Birmingham B13 8BU.
**Tel** 0121 449 3868
**Personnel** Proprietor: Steve Maddox.

## GALLERY HANGING SUPPLIES

### ▶ Frank B. Scragg & Co.
68 Vittoria Street, Birmingham B1 3PB.
**Tel** 0121 236 7219 **Fax** 0121 236 3633
**Email** sales@frankscragg.co.uk
**Ws** www.frankscragg.co.uk
**Personnel** Mr John Lewis.
*Frank B. Scragg & Company are a long-established company dealing in a wide range of supplies for framing and hanging pictures. For galleries, there is brass rail with hooks and chain, together with a system of sliding rods and adjustable hooks, available in various finishes. Scragg's also supply all manner of framing accessories, including wire, cord, hooks and rings. A free illustrated catalogue and price list is available on request.*

# Materials and Equipment

## ARTISTS' MATERIALS

### ▶ Academy Arts Centre C
Winton Road, Petersfield GU32 3HA.
**Tel** 01730 261 624 **Fax** 01730 231 499
**Email** nixy@compuserve.com
**Opening times** Mon–Sat 9–5.30.
**Nearest Station** Petersfield.
**Personnel** Gallery Director: Nick Yellop. Art Centre Manager: Geoff Harris.
**Services and Facilities** Art for Offices. Bookshop. Commissioning Service. Framing. Gallery space for hire. Parking. Shop. Workshop Facilities.

### ▶ Alec Tiranti Ltd
27 Warren Street, London W1.
**Tel** 020 7636 8565
**Fax** 020 7636 8565
**Email** sales@tiranti.co.uk
**Ws** www.tiranti.co.uk
**Opening times** Mon–Fri 9–5.30, Sat 9.30–1.
**Personnel** Managing Director: Susan Tiranti Lyons, ACIS. Director: Jonathan Lyons.
**Services and Facilities** Shop.

### ▶ Connaught Galleries
44 Connaught Street, London W2.
**Tel** 020 7723 1660
**Fax** 020 7723 1660
**Opening times** Mon–Fri 10–6.30, Sat 10–1.
**Nearest Underground** Paddington, Lancaster Gate, Marble Arch.
**Personnel** Partner: Michael Hollamby.
**Services and Facilities** Art for Offices. Framing. Gallery space for hire. Parking. Restoration. Shop. Workshop Facilities.

### ▶ Cowling & Wilcox Ltd.
26–28 Broadwick Street, London W1V 1FG.
**Tel** 020 7734 9557
**Fax** 020 7434 4513
**Email** art@cowlingandwilcox.com
**Ws** www.cowlingandwilcox.com
**Opening times** Mon–Fri 9–6, Sat 10–5.
**Nearest Underground** Oxford Circus, Piccadilly Circus.
**Personnel** Sales: Jane Wallace.
**Services and Facilities** Shop.

### ▶ John Jones Artsauce C
Stroud Green Road (corner of Morris Place), Finsbury Park N4 3JG.
**Tel** 020 7281 5439 **Fax** 020 7281 5956
**Email** info@johnjones.co.uk
**Ws** www.johnjones.co.uk
**Opening times** Mon–Fri 9.30–6, Sat 10–5.
**Nearest Underground** Finsbury Park.
**Services and Facilities** Framing. Parking. Restoration. Shop.
*Specialist frame design and consultation. Conservation and restoration. Sculpture protection and display. Fine Art photographic service. Two-level art materials store stocking premium brands. Ample parking. Efficient collection and delivery service.Art materials mail order department.*

### ▶ Lamley Art Supplies
5 Exhibition Road, London SW7 2HE.
**Tel** 020 7589 1276

### ▶ Langford & Hill
4th Floor, Hardy House, 16–18 Beak Street, Regent Street, London W1R.
**Tel** 020 8439 0181

### ▶ Liquitex UK
Ampthill Road, Bedford MK42 9RS.

### ▶ London Graphic Centre
254 Upper Richmond Road, London SW15 6TQ.
**Tel** 020 7785 9797

### ▶ Product Caran D'ache/ Jakar International Ltd
Hillside House, 2–6 Friern Park, London N12 9BX.
**Tel** 020 8445 6376
**Fax** 020 8445 2714
**Personnel** General Manager: D. W. Finney.

### ▶ Russell & Chapple Ltd, 'The Artists Canvas Company'
68 Drury Lane, London WC2B 5SP.
**Tel** 020 7836 7521
**Fax** 020 7497 0554
**Opening times** Mon–Fri 8.30–5. Sat 10–5.
**Services and Facilities** Shop.

### ▶ Staedtler (UK) Ltd
Pontyclun CF72 8YJ.
**Tel** 01443 237 421
**Fax** 01443 237 440

## CONSERVATION MATERIALS

### ▶ Conservation By Design
Timecare Works, 5 Singer Way, Woburn Road Industrial Estate, Kempston, Bedford MK42 7AW.
**Tel** 01234 853 555
**Fax** 01234 852 334
**Email** info@conservation-by-design.co.uk
**Ws** www.conservation-by-design.co.uk
**Personnel** Managing Director: Stuart Welch. Special Projects Manager: Philip Charnock. Sales Co-ordinator: Rachel Bridger.
*Conservation By Design is a company dedicated to the design and supply of high-quality conservation, storage and display products including acid-free boxes, safe transparent polyester album pages, acid-free papers and mounting board, and a wide range of furniture including plan chests, picture racking, mobile shelving and museum-standard glass showcases.*

### ▶ Preservation Equipment Ltd.
Vinces Road., Diss, Norfolk, IP22 4HQ
**Tel** 01379 647 400 **Fax** 01379 650 582
**Ws** www.preservationequipment..com

## FRAMING SUPPLIES

### ▶ Arqadia Ltd
2 Wolseley Road, Kempston, Bedford MK42 7AD.
**Tel** 01234 857 488/+44 (0) 1234 852777
**Fax** 01234 840 190
**Email** sales@arqadia.co.uk
**Ws** www.arqadia.co.uk
**Personnel** Marketing: Pauline Hutchinson. National Sales Managers: John Thornton, Steve Burke.
*For over 25 years, Arqadia has provided unrivalled experience and expertise in the UK framing industry. We now offer more than 2000 different mouldings and a full range of frames and mountboards. We are very proud of our position within the market place, which has been achieved through our commitment to exceptional design, competitive pricing and professional friendly service. In 2000 we acquired the complete range of Larson-Juhl mouldings, which can be purchased directly from Arqadia. To view our product range visit our website at www.arqadia.co.uk. Our products database includes full text -search facilities and covers Mouldings, Mountboards, Ready-made Frames and Equipment.*

### ▶ Connaught Galleries
44 Connaught Street, London W2.
**Tel** 020 7723 1660 **Fax** 020 7723 1660
**Opening times** Mon-Fri 10-6.30, Sat 10–1.
**Nearest Underground** Paddington, Marble Arch.
**Personnel** Partner: Michael Hollamby.
**Services and Facilities** Art for Offices. Framing. Gallery space for hire. Parking. Restoration. Shop. Workshop Facilities.

### ▶ Frank B. Scragg & Co.
68 Vittoria Street, Birmingham B1 3PB.
**Tel** 0121 236 7219 **Fax** 0121 236 3633
**Personnel** Mr J. B. Lewis.

### ▶ Norfolk Mouldings Limited

Beeston Road, Mileham, King's Lynn PE32 2PZ.
**Tel** 01328 700 200 **Fax** 01328 700 777
**Opening times** 9–5.
**Personnel** Managing Director: Bevil Granville. Ian Skipp.
*Manufacturers of the highest quality plain wood mouldings for the bespoke framer. Free catalogue available. Comprehensive range of 300 plain wood profiles in obeche, pine, ramin, ash, oak, cherry, black walnut, maple and beech. We can quote on your custom profiles, made in the wood of your choice.*

# Packers and Shippers

At the last count there were over 60 companies in the UK offering a 'quality' service for the transport, handling and installation of fine art. Quality in this sense is totally subjective, which means that whatever a customer's requirements, there is a company which will offer exactly the level of service sought at an affordable price.

One of the most significant factors to affect the industry in the last couple of decades was initiated by our museums adopting preventative measures for the care of collections as a whole, rather than the costly restoration of individual works of art. The increasing demand from the new breed of conservators for the best services that money can buy has provided consistent quality work for those companies with an empathy for the policy – those with a willingness to invest in the latest technology and, of course, the know-how to do so. Thus, the specialist fine art handler was born.

Improved training for the fine art technicians, vastly superior equipment and a more structured approach to risk management have all resulted in a much safer journey for works of art. In turn, the demand for loans to increasingly ambitious exhibitions has been met. The Tate Modern is a clear example of this success story.

Traditionally, auction houses, art galleries, private collectors and dealers have been governed by more commercial considerations, although all were quick to take full advantage of improved service levels during a booming art market at the end of the 1980s and many continue to do so.

More recently, the international success of the YBAs has also made an impact on the art service industry in the UK. Meticulous research by the museum community into the effects of shock, vibration, changes in temperature and relative humidity on oil on canvas had not prepared us for a 14 ft tiger shark in a tank of formaldehyde weighing in at 20 tonnes, not to mention flies, cows, pigs, sheep, frozen human blood, elephant dung, kebabs and fresh fruit and vegetables. Charles Saatchi's Sensation! exhibition, which contained all the above, proved hugely successful in London, Berlin and New York, albeit with a certain amount of controversy. Contemporary artists continue to tax the expertise and problem-solving capability of the specialist art handler, and long may it continue – it is what makes the job interesting.

While fine art handling may be a science, managing risk against budget at the same time as concentrating on the fragility of an artwork, rather than its current value or perceived importance, is a juggling act and practically an art form in itself.

Scot Blyth
Managing Director
Momart

## PACKERS & SHIPPERS

### ▶ 01 Art Services
Unit 2, Towcester Road, Bow, London E3 3ND.
**Tel** 0700 401 ART/020 7515 7510
**Fax** 020 7538 2479
**Email** art01.services@virgin.net
**Opening times** Mon–Fri 9-6.
**Personnel** Elizabeth Cooper.
*01 Art Services Ltd is a reputable company specialising in fine art transportation and installation in London and the UK. Handling and installation of single works and exhibitions. Storage space available.*

### ▶ All Wheel Drive
4 Clevedale, Downend, Bristol B216 2SQ.
**Tel** 01836 627 520/01272 570 158
**Fax** 01272 820 505

### ▶ Anglo Pacific International Plc
Unit 1, Bush Industrial Estate, Standard Road, North Acton, London NW10 6DF.
**Tel** 020 8838 8008 **Fax** 020 8453 0225
**Email** gerryward@anglopacific.co.uk
**Opening times** 8–6.
**Nearest Underground** North Acton.
**Personnel** Gerry Ward.
*Specialist packers and shippers serving the whole world from a London head office. Offering a full range of services to meet the needs of artists, dealers, collectors, exhibitions organisers etc. Contact Gerry, Mary or Malcolm for a free estimate or just friendly advice.*

### ▶ Art Handle
9 Sophia's Walk, Cathedral Road, Cardiff CF1 9LL.
**Tel** 029 2023 3390, mobile 07850 681 004
**Fax** 029 2023 3390
**Services and Facilities** Restoration.

### ▶ Art Move Ltd
Unit 3, Grant Road, London SW11 2NU.
**Tel** 0700 278 6683/020 7585 1801
**Fax** 020 7223 0241
**Email** mail@artmove.co.uk
**Ws** www.artmove.co.uk
**Opening times** Mon–Fri 9–5.30 and by appointment.
**Nearest Station** Clapham Junction.
*Local, national and international transport. Climate-controlled secure storage approved by Museum and Galleries Commission. Worldwide shipping. Picture hanging and sculpture installation for trade, corporate and private clients. Packing and case making. Photography, gilding, conservation, framing and restoration.*

### ▶ Artlink Transport
102 Main Street, Milngavie, Glasgow.
**Tel** 0141 956 5320

### ▶ C'ART
Unit 7, Brunel Court, Enterprise Drive (off Station Road), Four Ashes, Wolverhampton WV10 7DF.
**Tel** 01902 791 797 **Fax** 01902 790 687
**Email** info@cart.uk.com
**Ws** www.cart.uk.com
**Personnel** Angus Macdonald.
*Ideally placed on the M6/M5 axis for competitive art and craft transport throughout Britain in custom built vehicles; onward transport to Europe. Shipping and airfreight arranged worldwide. Packing and casemaking available. Hanging of single works or exhibitions; public art installation.*

### ▶ Cadogan Tate Fine Art Services
Cadogan House, 2 Relay Road, London W12 7SJ.
**Tel** 020 8735 3700 **Fax** 020 8735 3701
**Email** fineart@cadogantate.com
**Ws** www.cadogantate.com
**Opening times** 9–5.
**Personnel** Director: Simon Sheffield. Associate Director: Bill Telfer-Smollett. Marketing: Shane Alabaster.
*Cadogan Tate Fine Art Services have over 25 years experience and expertise in the carriage, storage and shipping of fine art worldwide. Our clients include many of London's leading auction houses, dealers and private collectors, all of whom regularly use our services to manage their fine art collections. As market leaders, our professional and helpful staff will provide solutions for all aspects of fine art management. Our new central London office and warehouse complex offers secure individually alarmed private room storage and our on-site skilled packers provide a quality service to ensure that your possessions are shipped safely to any destination.*

### ▶ Constantine
134 Queens Road, London SE15 2HR.
**Tel** 020 7635 7555
**Fax** 020 7737 2631
**Email** ReesM@ArtServices.co.uk
**Ws** www.artservices@ukbusiness.com
**Opening times** 8.30–5.30.
**Personnel** Manager: Rees Martin. National Transport (0171 635 2130): Steve Glynn. International Transport (0171 635 2137): Jo Pearson. Storage and Installation: Patrick Onione.

### ▶ Davies Turner Worldwide Movers Ltd
49 Wates Way, Mitcham CR4 4HR.
**Tel** 020 7622 4393
**Fax** 020 7720 3897
**Email** N.Hickman@daviesturner.co.uk
**Personnel** Nigel Hickman.

### ▶ Hedley's Humpers Ltd
Units 2, 3 & 4, 97 Victoria Road, London NW10 6ND.
**Tel** 020 8965 8733
**Fax** 020 8965 0249
**Email** steve@hedleyshumpers.com
**Ws** www.hedleyshumpers.com
**Opening times** 8–6.
**Nearest Underground** North Acton.
**Personnel** Managing Director: Steve Hedley. Art Department: Peter Bessant.
*Fine art packers and shippers. Weekly part-load services to Europe. Weekly service by sea to New York. Twice weekly service to and from Paris. Offices in London, Paris, New York and Nice.*

### ▶ Momart Limited (A wholly owned subsidiary of Momart International Plc)
199–205 Richmond Road, London E8 3NJ.
**Tel** 020 8986 3624 **Fax** 020 8533 0122
**Email** enquiries@momart.co.uk
**Personnel** Managing Director: Scot Blyth. Director of Exhibitions: Anna Maris.
**Services and Facilities** Workshop Facilities.
*Specialists in all aspects of fine art handling; experts in packing, case making, import and export services, private and exhibition installation, national and international transport (using air ride, climate control, fine art vehicles), and high-security storage.*

### ▶ MTEC International Ltd
MTEC House, Oaklands Industrial Estate, Essex Road, Hoddesdon, EN11 0BX.
**Tel** 01992 463 580 **Fax** 01992 448 363
**Email** mtec2000@aol.com
**Ws** www.arttransport.com
**Opening times** Mon–Fri 8–7.
**Nearest Station** Hertford East.
**Personnel** Managing Director, Transport and Shipping: David Williams. Special Projects: Jack Turner. Packing: Tony Stone. Storage: Chris Williams.
**Services and Facilities** Parking.
*Specialising in all aspects of the transportation and installation of paintings and sculptures for private and public exhibitions. Case packing, shipping, storage, national and international transport using air-ride temperature control. Box vans and covered HIAB vehicles.*

### ▶ T. Rogers & Co. Ltd
PO Box 8, 1a Broughton Street, London SW8 3QL.
**Tel** 020 7622 9151 **Fax** 020 7627 3318
*Storage, packing, removal, shipping and forwarding of all works of art. Customs bonded warehousing.*

### ▶ Trans Euro Amertrans Fine Art Divsion

Transeuro Amertrams Fine Art Division, Drury Way, London NW10 0JN.
**Tel** 020 8784 0100 **Fax** 020 8459 3376
**Email** richard.edwards@transeuro.com
**Ws** www.transeuro.com
**Opening times** Mon–Fri 9–6.
**Nearest Underground** Wembly Park
**Personnel** Richard Edwards.
*Providing specialist packing and worldwide transportation services for the safe movement of works of art of all kinds. Secure environment-controlled storage available for short and long terms. 'Climate Controlled' UK and European transport on 'Air Ride' vehicles.*

# Photographers

## PHOTOGRAPHERS

### ▶ A. C. Cooper
10 Pollen Street, London W1R 9PH.
**Tel** 020 7629 7585

### ▶ Alan Crumlish
11 Kirklee Terrace Lane, Glasgow G12 0TL.
**Tel** 0141 339 5790

### ▶ Anthony Marshall
2 Riverside Cottages, New Lumford, Bakewell DE45 1GH.
**Tel** 01629 814 787
**Personnel** Anthony Marshall.

### ▶ Antonia Reeve
11 Grosvenor Crescent, Edinburgh EH12 5EL.
**Tel** 0131 337 4640
**Personnel** Antonia Reeve.

### ▶ ASP Photography
281 Sydenham Road, London SE26 5EN.
**Tel** 020 8676 0836;
Mobile 07956 897 302
**Personnel** Cliff Birtchnell.

### ▶ b2 Photographic
5 Peary Place (off Roman Road), Bethnal Green, London E2 0QW.
**Tel** 020 8983 1109

### ▶ Chris Boyle
272 Newchurch Road, Rawtenstall BB4 7SN.
**Tel** 01706 215 958/0161 832 2244 ext 245;
Mobile 0802 680 601
**Personnel** Chris Boyle.

### ▶ Coopers of Regent Street
207 Regent Street, London W1R 7DD.
**Tel** 020 7629 6745
**Fax** 020 7493 4488
**Personnel** Managing Director: Mr K. J. Romer.

### ▶ Davies Colour Ltd
168 Sloper Road, Cardiff CF1 8AA.
**Tel** 029 2023 0565

### ▶ Dawes & Billings Photographic
42 Goldstone Road, Hove BN3 3RH.
**Tel** 01273 722 971 **Fax** 01273 722 971

### ▶ Dennis Gilbert
11/15 Furmage Street, London SW18 4DF.
**Tel** 020 8870 9051

### ▶ Frank Thurston Photography
c/o Royal College of Art, Kensington Gore, London SW7.
**Tel** 020 7584 5020 ext 286/020 7584 7881

### ▶ Gabriel Weissman Applied & Fine Art
21 Cable Street Studios, 566 Cable Street, London E1 9HB.
**Tel** 020 7780 9096

### ▶ Graham P. Matthews
Delfyd Farm, Llangennith, SA3 1JL.
**Tel** 01792 386 217 **Fax** 01792 386 295

### ▶ Ian Jackson Photography
Oakgate, Southampton Road, Cadnam SO4 2NA.
**Tel** 023 8081 4010
**Fax** 023 8081 4002
**Personnel** Ian Jackson.

### ▶ Imagetrend
12 Chesterford Gardens, London NW3 7DE.
**Tel** 020 7435 7383

### ▶ Incorporated Photographer
14 East Rise, Llanisben, Cardiff CP4 5RJ.
**Tel** 029 2075 1368
**Personnel** Michael Pugh.

### ▶ J. R. Photography
15 Westward Close, Uttoxeter ST14 7BJ.
**Tel** 01889 565 061; Mobile 0836 717 783
**Fax** 01889 567 039
**Personnel** John Roberts.

### ▶ John Carmichael
2 Scotts Avenue, Bromley BR2 0LQ.
**Tel** 020 8464 5869
**Personnel** John Carmichael.

### ▶ John Hoodless
36 Seymour Avenue, Morden SM4 4RD.
**Tel** 020 8330 3234/01323 762 547;
Mobile 0378 385 732
**Personnel** John Hoodless.

### ▶ John Penna
2 Hylands Road, Epson KT18 7ED.
**Tel** 01372 721 678
**Personnel** John Penna.

### ▶ John R. Simmons
21 Park Mansions, Prince of Wales Drive, London SW11.
**Tel** 020 7622 0448

### ▶ Keith Meadley Photography
2 Sadberge Court, Osbaldswick, York YO1 3DR.
**Tel** 01904 611 109
**Personnel** Keith Meadley.

### ▶ Kenneth Smith
6 Lussielaw Road, Edinburgh EH9 3BX.
**Tel** 0131 667 6159
**Personnel** Kenneth Smith.

### ▶ Matthew Hollow Photography
10 Brackendale Court, Park Road, Beckenham BR3 1QX.
**Tel** 020 8658 6763 (mobile 07956 374 029)
**Fax** 01689 876 907

### ▶ Michael Hoppen Photography
Alexandra Studios, 3 Jubilee Place, London SW3 3TD.
**Tel** 020 7352 3649 **Fax** 020 7352 3669
**Personnel** Michael Hoppen.

### ▶ Mike Smith
Durham University Oriental Museum, Elvet Hill, Durham DH1 3TH.
**Tel** 0191 374 7911

### ▶ Norman R. Kent
Unit 5, 14 Castelnau, Barnes, London SW13 9RU.
**Tel** 020 8741 9133

### ▶ P. J. Gates Photography Ltd
Unit H, The London Stone Business Estate, Broughton Street, London SW8 3QR.
**Tel** 020 7498 8233 **Fax** 020 7498 8649
**Opening times** Mon–Fri 9.30–5.30.
**Nearest Underground** Battersea Park or Queenstown Road.
**Personnel** Peter J. Gates FBIPP. Phillip Paddock ABIPP.

### ▶ Peter Waltham
Lincolnshire Archives, St Rumbolds Street, Lincoln LN2 5AB.
**Tel** 01522 526 204
**Personnel** Peter Waltham.

### ▶ The Photography of Art
159 Kennington Lane, London SE11 4EZ.
**Tel** 020 7735 2432/0705/007 0216
**Fax** 020 7735 2627
**Email** gillian@mcmail.com
**Ws** www.books.mcmail.com/photo.htm
**Opening times** By appointment only.
**Nearest Underground** Kennington.
**Personnel** Director: Gillian Cargill. Co-ordinator: Jenny Camilleri.

### ▶ Prudence Cuming Associates
28–29 Dover Street, London W1X 3PA.
**Tel** 020 7629 6430

### ▶ Raymond Fifield
12 Lutton Bank, Lutton, Spalding PE12 9LJ.
**Tel** 01406 363 951

### ▶ Rodney Todd-White & Son
3 Clifford Street, London W1X 1RA.
**Tel** 020 7734 9070 **Fax** 020 7287 9727
**Opening times** 9–6.
**Personnel** Michael Todd-White.

# Space for Hire

## GALLERY SPACE FOR HIRE

### ▶ Abbott & Holder
30 Museum Street, London WC1A 1LH.
**Tel** 020 7637 3981 **Fax** 020 7631 0575
**Email** abbott.holder@virgin.net
**Ws** www.artefact.co.uk/AaH.html
**Opening times** Mon–Sat 9.30–6, Thu 9.30–7.
**Nearest Underground** Tottenham Court Road.
**Personnel** Partners: Phillip Athill, John Abbott.
**Services and Facilities** Art Consultancy. Framing. Gallery space for hire. Restoration. Valuation.
**Work Stocked and Sold** Pr.
**Price range** £50–£5,000

### ▶ The Air Gallery
32 Dover Street, London W1X 3RA.
**Tel** 020 7409 1255 **Fax** 020 7409 1856
**Email** admin@airgallery.co.uk
**Ws** www.airgallery.co.uk
**Opening times** 10–6.
**Nearest Underground** Green Park.
**Services and Facilities** Art Consultancy. Art for Offices. Commissioning Service. Gallery space for hire.

### ▶ Alchemy Gallery
157 Farringdon Road, London EC1R 3AD.
**Tel** 020 7278 5666 **Fax** 020 7278 9666
**Personnel** Daniela de Vendictis.

### ▶ AOP (Association of Photographers)
81 Leonard Street, London EC2A 4QS.
**Tel** 020 7739 6669 **Fax** 020 7739 8707
**Ws** www.aophoto.co.uk
**Opening times** Mon–Fri 9.30–6, Sat 12–4.
**Personnel** Gallery Manager: Susan Bright. Gallery Assistant: Nick Jones. Marketing: Sascha Howard.
**Work Stocked and Sold** Ph.
**Price range** From £100
*The AOP Gallery is an extremely attractive venue available for hire by the week for photographic exhibitions. All exhibition proposals must be submitted to the Gallery Committee. The space is also available for evening hire events and is ideal for such events as book launches, workshops, meetings and private parties. For information on prices and availability please contact 020 7739 3631.*

### ▶ Art Connoisseur Gallery
95–97 Crawford Street, London W1H 1AN.
**Tel** 020 7258 3835 **Fax** 020 7258 3532
**Nearest Underground** Baker Street.
**Personnel** Clare Grossman.

### ▶ Artbank Gallery C
114 Clerkenwell Road, London EC1M 5SA.
**Tel** 020 7608 3333 **Fax** 020 7608 3060
**Email** info@artbank.com
**Ws** www.artbank.com
**Opening times** Tue–Fri 11.30–6, Sat 12–4 or by appointment.
**Nearest Underground** Farringdon/Barbican.
**Personnel** Directors: Ann-Kathrin Durgé, Rick Goodale.
**Services and Facilities** Art Consultancy. Art for Offices. Gallery space for hire.
**Work Stocked and Sold** Pa. Pr. Sc.
**Price range** £300–£10,000

### ▶ Atrium Gallery, Whiteleys
Whiteleys, Queensway, London W2 4YN.
**Tel** 020 7229 8844 **Fax** 020 7792 8921

### ▶ Bird & Davis Ltd
45 Holmes Road, Kentish Town, London NW5 3AN.
**Tel** 020 7485 3797 **Fax** 020 7284 0509
**Opening times** Gallery 10–4. Workshop factory 8–5.30.
**Personnel** Directors: Roberto Orsi, Jayne Orsi.

### ▶ Charlotte Street Gallery C
28 Charlotte Street, Fitzrovia, London W1 2NA.
**Tel** 020 7255 2828 **Fax** 020 7580 2828
**Email** gallery@28charlottestreet.com
**Ws** www.28charlottestreet.com
**Opening times** 10–6 Mon–Sat.
**Personnel** Director: Rebecca Hossack.
**Services and Facilities** Art Consultancy. Bookshop. Commissioning Service. Framing. Gallery space for hire.
**Work Stocked and Sold** Ab. App. Cer. Cra. Jew. Pa. Ph. Pr. Sc.
**Price range** £200–£2,000
*The Charlotte Street Gallery is located in the heart of the West End in Fitzrovia, which has traditionally been London's artistic centre. It is now home to some of London's best-known galleries and most famous restaurants. The Charlotte Street Gallery features beautifully furnished large double frontage windows looking onto a bustling thoroughfare. The gallery has been refurbished to the highest standard, with state-of-the-art lighting and excellent presentation. A mailing list is available to hirers and in-house PR and exhibition services are available on request.*

### ▶ Collins & Hastie C
5 Park Walk, London SW10 0AJ.
**Tel** 020 7351 4292 **Fax** 020 7351 7929
**Email** caroline@chelseaart.co.uk
**Ws** www.chelseaart.co.uk
**Opening times** 10–6 Mon–Fri, 11–4 Sat.
**Nearest Underground** South Kensington.
**Personnel** Director: Caroline Hastie. Diana Collins.
**Services and Facilities** Art for Offices. Commissioning Service. Disabled Access. Gallery space for hire.
**Work Stocked and Sold** Dec. Pa.
**Price range** £300–£20,000
*Well located in the heart of Chelsea, off the strip of the Fulham Road known as 'The Beach', a lively and fashionable area attracting many young cosmopolitan professionals. There are other well-known art galleries in Park Walk, as well as Paper & Paints, one of London's leading suppliers to interior designers and decorators. The gallery is conveniently situated next to several top restaurants (including the celebrated Aubergine). It is an excellent exhibition space: large, light, and recently refurbished.*

### ▶ The Coningsby Gallery
30 Tottenham Street, London W1 9PN.
**Tel** 020 7636 7478 **Fax** 020 7580 7017
**Opening times** Mon–Fri 11–6.
**Nearest Underground** Goodge Street.
**Personnel** Andrew Coningsby.
**Services and Facilities** Art Consultancy. Art for Offices. Commissioning Service. Gallery space for hire.
**Work Stocked and Sold** App. Cra. Dr. Pa. Ph. Pr. Sc.
**Price range** £200–£8,000

### ▶ Connaught Galleries
44 Connaught Street, London W2.
**Tel** 020 7723 1660 **Fax** 020 7723 1660
**Opening times** Mon–Fri 10–6.30, Sat 10–1.
**Nearest Underground** Paddington, Lancaster Gate, Marble Arch.
**Personnel** Partner: Michael Hollamby.
**Services and Facilities** Art for Offices. Framing. Gallery space for hire. Parking. Restoration. Shop. Workshop Facilities.

### ▶ Ebury Galleries
200 Ebury Street, London SW1.
**Tel** 020 7730 8999
**Personnel** John Adams.

### ▶ Fine Art Commissions Ltd C
107 Walton Street, Knightsbridge, London SW3 2HT.
**Tel** 020 7589 4111 **Fax** 020 7589 3888
**Email** info@fineartcommissions.com
**Ws** www.fineartcommissions.com
**Opening times** By appointment 10–6.
**Nearest Underground** South Kensington or Knightsbridge.
**Personnel** Director: Sara Stewart. Assistant: Alice Palmer.
**Services and Facilities** Art Consultancy. Art for Offices. Commissioning Service. Framing. Gallery space for hire. Restoration.
**Work Stocked and Sold** Dec. Pa. Sc.
**Price range** £700–£20,000
For artists see Commercial Gallery Artists.
*Independent specialists in works of art by commission. Free advice starting with choice of artist to framing. Our subjects include Portraiture, Houses, Sporting art, Sculpture, Landscapes and Murals. With an office conveniently situated in Knightsbridge, we also advise on Restoration, Framing, Copies and Auction Consultancy. Our gallery for hire is at 23 Cork Street, London W1.*

### ▶ Gallery 47
47 Great Russell Street, Bloomsbury, London WC1B 3PA.
**Tel** 020 7637 4577/8663 6746
**Personnel** Mrs Fitzwilliam.

### ▶ The Gallery in Cork Street and Gallery 27 C
28 Cork Street, London W1S 3NG.
**Tel** 020 7287 8408 **Fax** 020 7287 2018
**Email** enquiries@galleryincorkst.com
**Ws** www.gallery27.com
**Opening times** Mon–Fri 10–6, Sat 11–4.

**Nearest Underground** Green Park/Piccadilly.
**Personnel** Manager: Caroline Edwards.
**Services and Facilities** Gallery space for hire.
*The Gallery in Cork Street and Gallery 27 are two stunning galleries of international reputation in 'Europe's Leading Art Street'. The Gallery in Cork Street Ltd offers our clients a unique opportunity to hold exhibitions entirely under their control in Cork Street. The Gallery in Cork Street: 125 sq m of versatile prime display area, 60 linear metres of wall space, full height double window frontage. Gallery 27: 100 sq m of versatile prime display area, 50 linear metres of wall space, large window frontage. Excellent presentation. Full management and facility support. Exclusive mailing list. Organisation services available by arrangement.*

## ▶ Hanover Galleries

11–13 Hanover Street, Liverpool L1 3DN.
**Tel** 0151 709 3073
**Opening times** Tue–Sat 10.30–5.
**Nearest Station** Lime Street.
**Personnel** Director: E. P. Austin.
**Services and Facilities** Gallery space for hire.
*Two spacious and prestigious galleries of exceptional standard, on ground and first floors, interconnected by a spiral staircase, wall run 85 ft and 81 ft respectively. Both have good natural light and 30 fully adjustable track spots per gallery.*
*Applications, enclosing slides or photographs, to Mrs. E. P. Austin, Director. Details of charges for the galleries available on 0151 709 3073*

## ▶ Highgate Gallery

11 South Grove, Highgate, London N6 6BS.
**Tel** 020 8340 3343
**Fax** 020 8340 5632
**Email** admin@hlsi.demon.co.uk
**Opening times** Wed–Fri 1–5, Sat 11–4, Sun 11–5.
**Nearest Underground** Archway and Highgate.
**Personnel** Gallery Administrator: Tasja Gardner. Gallery Chairman: Mary Shurman.
**Services and Facilities** Disabled Access. Gallery space for hire.
*This unique 19th-century vaulted gallery is housed in the Highgate Literary and Scientific Institution, a busy social and cultural centre in Highgate Village, London N6. There is a spacious 75 x 6 ft of clear hanging area. The gallery is top-lit from a large glass lantern and also has excellent purpose-built exhibition lighting.*
*Rates are reasonable. There are nine exhibitions a year, usually of two weeks each. Slides and/or photos plus a CV should be sent to the Art Gallery Committee. Ring the Administrator on 020 8340 3343 for further details.*

## ▶ Lauderdale House, Arts & Education Centre PS

Waterlow Park, Highgate Hill, London N6 5HG.
**Tel** 020 8348 8716/8341 2032
**Fax** 020 8442 9099
**Opening times** Tue–Fri 11–4, Sun 12–5 (check events). Saturdays dependent on private bookings.
**Nearest Underground** Archway.
**Personnel** Director: Carolyn Naish. General Manager: Katherine Ives. Arts Education Assistant: Lucy Ribeiro. Bookings Officer: Sarah Tresidder.
**Services and Facilities** Café. Friends Society. Gallery space for hire. Restaurant. Workshop Facilities.

## ▶ Limehouse Arts Foundation

Towcester Road, London E3 3ND.
**Tel** 020 7515 9998
**Fax** 020 7515 9998
**Email** david.laf@virgin.net
**Services and Facilities** Gallery space for hire. Workshop Facilities.
*Located in Bow, East London, 5 minutes from Underground, DLR and bus services. Limehouse Arts Foundation is an arts charity that rents out 35 reasonable-cost, heated studio spaces to visual artists of all media. It hires out its fully heated gallery space of circa 15 meters x 21 meters for exhibitions of contemporary art. With 3-phase supply, direct internal access for vehicles, a 5-meter-high ceiling and no supporting pillars – allowing a good aspect ratio – the space is ideal for video and film shoots as well as performance rehearsals and workshops.*

## ▶ Mall Galleries

17 Carlton House Terrace, London SW1Y 5BD.
**Tel** 020 7930 6844 **Fax** 020 7839 7830
**Email** jdestonmallgalleries@pipex.com.uk
**Ws** www.mallgalleries.org.uk
**Nearest Underground** Charing Cross, Piccadilly Circus
**Personnel** Gallery and Events Manager: John Deston.
**Services and Facilities** Art Consultancy. Commissioning Service. Friends Society. Gallery space for hire. Guided Tours. Lectures. Workshop Facilities.
*The Main, East and North Galleries, totalling over 500 sq m, are available for hire separately or in any combination. The Galleries meet British Library conditions with colour correct lighting, air conditioning and moveable screens. Please contact the above administrative address for details. See also entries under London Galleries, Art Consultants and Art Societies as 'Federation of British Artists'.*

## ▶ Merriscourt Gallery C

Merriscourt Farm, Sarsden, Chipping Norton OX7 6QX.
**Tel** 01608 658 989
**Fax** 01608 659 734
**Email** merriscourtpaintings@btinternet.com
**Ws** www.merriscourt.com
**Opening times** Tue–Sun 11–6. Closed Mon.
**Nearest Station** Kingham.
**Personnel** Partner: Nick Clements.
**Services and Facilities** Disabled Access. Parking.
**Work Stocked and Sold** Cer. Dr. Pa. Pr.
**Price range** £150–£4,000
For artists see Commercial Gallery Artists.

## ▶ Open Space Gallery

131 Lower Marsh, London SE1 7AE.
**Tel** 020 7261 1353

## ▶ Royal Hibernian Academy PS

Gallagher Gallery, 15 Ely Place, Dublin 2.
**Tel** 00353 1 661 2558
**Fax** 00353 1 661 0762
**Email** rhagallery@eircom.net
**Ws** www.royalhibernianacademy.com
**Opening times** 10–5 Tue–Sat. Sun 2–5. Thu late opening until 8.
**Services and Facilities** Disabled Access. Friends Society. Gallery space for hire. Guided Tours. Lectures.

## ▶ SPACE Studios

8 Hoxton Street, London N1 6NG.
**Tel** 020 7613 1925 **Fax** 020 7613 1996
**Email** mail@spacestudios.org.uk
**Ws** www.spacestudios.org.uk
**Opening times** 10–6 Mon–Fri.
**Personnel** Director: Charlotte Robinson. Studios Manager: Fiona Furness.
**Services and Facilities** Commissioning Service. Disabled Access. Gallery space for hire.
*SPACE Studios, founded in 1968, is an arts and educational charity providing affordable studios and support for over 400 visual artists at 15 sites in East London. SPACE's Artists' Resource Centre, SPACE Place in Fish Island, E3, helps artists to bridge the gap between producing and making a living. SPACE Place provides IT training, exhibition space, commissions studio, seminars, careers advice (ViA), and community and education projects for artists and the local community. SPACE receives core funding from London Arts. SPACE Place was made possible by the European Regional Development Fund.*

## ▶ Sackville Gallery

26 Sackville Street, London W1X 1DA.
**Tel** 020 7734 8104
**Fax** 020 7734 8104
**Personnel** Nathan Smith.

## ▶ South London Gallery

SLG

65 Peckham Road, London SE5 8UH.
**Tel** 020 7703 6120, recorded information line: 020 7703 9799
**Fax** 020 7252 4730
**Email** mail@southlondonart.com
**Ws** www.southlondonart.co.uk
**Opening times** Tue, Wed and Fri 11–6, Thu 11–7, Sat and Sun 2–6.
**Services and Facilities** Art for Offices. Friends Society. Gallery space for hire. Lectures.
*The South London Gallery is one of London's foremost contemporary art exhibition spaces, committed to a challenging curatorial programme showing the work of local, national and international living artists. It also holds in storage an extensive collection that extends from work by John Everett Millais and Frederic Leighton to*

*contemporary artists including Anish Kapoor, Tracey Emin and Tom Phillips.*
*In the past decade, exhibitions of work by artists including Gilbert and George, Gavin Turk and Julian Schnabel have established the South London Gallery as an important national and international forum for the extension of the debate around contemporary art. Forthcoming shows include solo exhibitions of work by Bill Woodrow and Ross Sinclair, live art performances, the annual Goldsmiths' exhibition, and several group exhibitions.*
*The gallery also provides a range of debates, seminars, talks and performances by artists and key figures in the fields of art journalism, broadcasting and curatorship. Recent speakers at the gallery have included Richard Cork, art critic for* The Times; *artist Julian Schnabel; Gill Hedley, Director of the Contemporary Arts Society; and Tim Marlow, Editor of* Tate *magazine and television arts presenter.*

### ▶ Westminster Gallery PS
Central Hall, Storey's Gate, London SW1 9NH.
**Tel** 020 7222 8010
**Fax** 020 7222 6883
**Email** events@wch.co.uk
**Ws** www.wch.co.uk
**Opening times** Various.
**Nearest Underground** Westminster, St James's Park. Within walking distance of Victoria, Charing Cross and Waterloo main line stations.
**Personnel** Senior Events Manager: Ms Cathy Williamson. General Manager: Michael Sharp.
**Services and Facilities** Café. Disabled Access. Gallery space for hire. Guided Tours.

*Central Hall, Westminster*
*The Westminster Gallery offers an elegant, spacious and versatile exhibition area. The three rooms the gallery occupies can be hired individually or as a whole and are available throughout the year. Lighting, hanging and display facilities are easily managed. The adjacent café is open daily and is very happy to assist with refreshments for your private viewings.*

### ▶ Yarrow Gallery
Art Department, Oundle School, Glapthorn Road, Oundle, Peterborough PE8 4EN.
**Tel** 01832 274 034 **Fax** 01832 274 034
**Ws**www.oundleschool.org.uk/school/arts/yarrow/yarrow htm.
**Opening times** Mon–Fri 10.30–1 and 2.30–5, Sun 2.30–5.
**Nearest Station** Peterborough.
**Personnel** Director: Roger Page.
**Services and Facilities** Gallery space for hire.

## STUDIO SPACE FOR HIRE

### ▶ ACME
44 Copperfield Road, London E3 4RR.
**Tel** 020 8981 6811 **Fax** 020 8983 0567

### ▶ The Cable Street Studios
Thames House, 566 Cable Street, Limehouse, London E1 9HB.
**Tel** 020 7790 1309 **Fax** 020 7790 1309
**Personnel** Michael Cubey.

### ▶ Florence Trust Studios
St Saviour's, Aberdeen Park, Highbury, London N5 2AR.
**Tel** 020 7354 4771
**Fax** 020 7354 4771
**Nearest Underground** Highbury & Islington.
**Personnel** Director: Rod McIntosh.

### ▶ Great Western Studios
Westbourne Park, London W2.
**Tel** 020 7221 0100

### ▶ Hertford Road Studios
12–14 Hertford Road, London N1.
**Tel** 020 7241 0651

### ▶ Roseangle Gallery
17 Roseangle, Dundee.
**Tel** 0138 322 429

### ▶ SPACE Studios
8 Hoxton Street, London N1 6NG.
**Tel** 020 7613 1925 **Fax** 020 7613 1996
**Email** mail@spacestudios.org.uk
**Ws** www.spacestudios.org.uk
**Opening times** 10–6 Mon–Fri.
**Personnel** Director: Charlotte Robinson. Studios Manager: Fiona Furness.
**Services and Facilities** Commissioning Service. Disabled Access. Gallery space for hire.
*SPACE Studios, founded in 1968, is an arts and educational charity providing affordable studios and support for over 400 visual artists at 15 sites in East London. SPACE's Artists' Resource Centre, SPACE Place in Fish Island, E3, helps artists to bridge the gap between producing and making a living. SPACE Place provides IT training, exhibition space, commissions studio, seminars, careers advice (ViA), and community and education projects for artists and the local community. SPACE receives core funding from London Arts. SPACE Place was made possible by the European Regional Development Fund.*

### ▶ Sculpture House
54–56 Mill Place,
Kingston upon Thames KT1 2LR.

### ▶ South and North Arts
133 Rye Lane, Peckham, London SE15 4ST.
**Tel** 020 7635 8742

### ▶ Studio Voltaire
1A Nelson's Row London SW4.
**Tel** 020 7622 1294

# Publishing

# Magazines

Information is everywhere in the 21st century. Although the Internet promised a garden of earthly delights, many in the sector now realise it to be far from a virtual paradise. Due to the enormity of the world wide web, plagued as it is by user-unfriendliness, the net delivers less clear, less concise information than was originally hoped. Traditional print publishers have not had to retreat into the production of esoteric pamphlets because of Internet publishing; rather, they continue to launch more magazines, books and catalogues every year.

*Art World Directory* aims to provide the sort of listings information that cannot be replicated on the web in such a clear, usable format. Its sister publication, *Art Review*, was conceived over 50 years ago as a newspaper, *Art News and Review*, with the same intent – to provide comprehensive information on the art world. Together, *Art World Directory* and *Art Review* magazine cover all the news, events, movements, services, personalities and opinions that matter to the contemporary art enthusiast. This publishing vision has changed little since Lawrence Alloway and Patrick Heron wrote on the hot topics of the day for *Art News and Review* all those years ago; but the amount of information presented and the ways to access it have attracted greater audiences.

For 2002, *Art Review* will consolidate its mission to report and inform on current trends, with more focus on the primary sources – the works of art themselves – and the next most important factor, the artist.

Ossian Ward
Deputy Editor
*Art Review*

## ART BOOK PUBLISHERS

### ▶ Academy Group Ltd
Academy Editions, 42 Leinster Gardens, London W2 3AN.
**Tel** 020 7402 2141

### ▶ AN Publications
1st Floor, Turner Building, 7–15 Pink Lane, Newcastle-upon-Tyne NE1 5DW.
**Tel** 0191 241 8000
**Fax** 0191 241 8001
**Email** an@anpubs.demon.co.uk

### ▶ Art Sales Index Ltd
16 Luddington Avenue, Virginia Water GU25 4DF.
**Tel** 01344 841 750
**Fax** 01344 841 760
**Email** info@art-sales-index.com
**Ws** www.art-sales-index.com

### ▶ Ashgate Publishing Group incorporating Lund Humphries
Gower House, Croft Road, Aldershot GU11 3HR.
**Tel** 01252 344 405
**Fax** 01252 368 595
**Email** info@ashgatepub.co.uk
**Ws** www.ashgate.com
**Personnel** Sarah Stilwell. Helen Kennedy.
*Editorial: Mecklenburgh House, 11 Mecklenburgh Square, London WC1N 2AE.*
*Tel: 020 7841 9800; Fax: 020 7837 6322.*
*Contact: Lucy Myers, Publishing Director.*

### ▶ British Museum Press
46 Bloomsbury Street, London WC1B 3QQ.
**Tel** 020 7323 1234

### ▶ BT Batsford
583 Fulham Road, London SW6 5BY.
**Tel** 020 7486 8484

### ▶ Cambridge University Press
The Edinburgh Building, Shaftesbury Road, Cambridge CB2 2RU.
**Tel** 01223 312 393

### ▶ Cassell Plc
Wellington House, 125 Strand, London WC2R 0BB.
**Tel** 020 7420 5582

### ▶ Collins & Brown Publishers
London House, Parkgate Road, London SW11 4NQ.
**Tel** 020 7924 2575
**Personnel** Charlotte Morgan. Sonia Pugh.

### ▶ Conran Octopus Ltd
2–4 Heron Quays, London E14 4JP.
**Tel** 020 7531 8400 **Fax** 020 7531 8627

### ▶ Constable and Company
3 The Lanchesters, 162 Fulham Palace Road, London W6 9ER.
**Tel** 020 8741 3663

### ▶ Craft Galleries Guide
Burton Cottage Farm, East Coker, Yeovil BA22 9LS.
**Tel** 01935 862 731
**Fax** 01935 862 731
**Email** caroline@craftgalleries.co.uk
**Ws** www.707.co.uk/craftgalleries
**Personnel** Editor/Publisher: Caroline Mornement.

*A lavishly illustrated guide to Craft galleries and their makers throughout the UK. Updated every other year.*
*Also publish* Second Steps, *a guide to careers in the craft world.*

### ▶ David & Charles
Brunel House, Forde Road, Newton Abbott TQ1Z 4PN.
**Tel** 01626 323 200

### ▶ Dorling Kindersley
9 Henrietta Street, London WC2E 8PS.
**Tel** 020 7836 5411

### ▶ Faber & Faber
3 Queen Square, London WC1N 3AU.
**Tel** 020 7465 0045

### ▶ Garnet Publishing
8 Southern Court, South Street, Reading RG1 4QF.
**Tel** 01189 597 847
**Fax** 0118 959 7356

### ▶ Gerald Duckworth Publishers
61 Frith Street, London W1D 3JL.
**Tel** 020 7434 4420

### ▶ Hamlyn Octopus
2–4 Heron Quays, London E14 4JP.
**Tel** 020 7531 8573
**Fax** 020 7531 0514

### ▶ Hodder & Stoughton
Hodder Headline Book Publishing Ltd, 338 Euston Road, London NW1.
**Tel** 020 7873 6000

### ▶ J. A. B. Publishing
Suite 2, Arran Place, Valnord Road, St Peter Port GU1 1TL.
**Tel** 01481 722 460

### ▶ Little, Brown & Company
Brettenham House, Lancaster Place, London WC2E 7EN.
**Tel** 020 7911 8000

### ▶ Macmillan Online Publishers Ltd. The Dictionary of Art
The Macmillan Building, Porters South, Crinan Street, London N1 9XW.
**Tel** 020 7881 8356 **Fax** 020 7881 8357
**Email** tda@macmillan.co.uk or eh@macmillan.co.uk
**Ws** www.macmillan.com

### ▶ Manchester University Press
Oxford Road, Manchester M13 9NR.
**Tel** 0161 273 5539 **Fax** 0161 274 3346

### ▶ Methuen London Ltd
Michelin House, 81 Fulham Road, London SW3 5DT.
**Tel** 020 7581 9393

### ▶ The MIT Press Ltd
Fitzroy House, 11 Chenies Street, London WC1E 7ET.
**Tel** 020 7306 0603

### ▶ Octopus Books Ltd
2–4 Heron Quays, London E14 4JP.
**Tel** 020 7531 8400

### ▶ Orion Publishing
Orion House, 5 Upper St Martins Lane, London WC2H 9EA.
**Tel** 020 7240 3444

### ▶ Oxford University Press
Great Clarendon Street, Oxford OX2 6DP.
**Tel** 01865 556 767 **Fax** 01865 556 646
**Ws** www.oup.co.uk

### ▶ Paragon Press
92 Horwood Road, London SW6 4QH.
**Tel** 020 7736 4024
**Personnel** Charles Booth-Aibborn.

### ▶ Pavilion
26 Upper Ground, London SE1 9DP.
**Tel** 020 7620 1666

### ▶ Phaidon Press
Regents Wharf, All Saints Street, London N1 9PA.
**Tel** 020 7843 1000

### ▶ Random House Publishing
20 Vauxhall Bridge Road, London SW1V 2SA.
**Tel** 020 7973 9670

### ▶ Reaktion Books
79 Farringdon Road, London EC1M 3JU.
**Tel** 020 7404 9930

### ▶ Routledge
11 New Fetter Lane, London EC4P 4EE.
**Tel** 020 7583 9855

### ▶ Sansom & Company/ Art Dictionaries Ltd
81g Pembroke Road, Clifton, Bristol BS8 3EA.
**Tel** 0117 973 7207 **Fax** 0117 973 8991
**Personnel** Publishing Director: John Sansom.

### ▶ Second Steps
Burton Cottage Farm, East Coker, Yeovil BA22 9LS.
**Tel** 01935 862 731 **Fax** 01935 862 731
**Email** caroline@craftgalleries.co.uk
**Ws** www.707.co.uk/craftgalleries
**Personnel** Editor/Publisher: Caroline Mornement.

*Revised and updated second edition of the guide to careers in the craft world: a one-stop resource book for recent graduates, covering everythong from CVs to business plans. Illustrated with case studies by gallery owners and makers. Includes a wide selection of addresses, telephone contacts and book titles for reference, plus new section on internet marketing and more pricing details.*

### ▶ Thames & Hudson
181A High Holborn, London WC1V 7QX.
**Tel** 020 7845 5000 **Fax** 020 7845 5050
**Email** sales@thameshudson.co.uk
**Ws** www.thameshudson.co.uk/ www.world-of-art.com

### ▶ V&A Publications
160 Brompton Road, London SW3 1HW.
**Tel** 020 7942 2966 **Fax** 020 7942 2977
**Email** vapubs.ifo@vam.ac.uk
**Ws** www.vandashop.co.uk/books
**Personnel** Head of Publications: Mary Butler. Marketing: Jane Smith.

### ▶ Yale University Press
23 Pond Street, London NW3 2PN.
**Tel** 020 7431 4422

## ART BOOKSHOPS

### ▶ Atrium Bookshop
5 Cork Street, London W1.
**Tel** 020 7495 0073

### ▶ Beyond Words
42–44 Cockburn Street, Edinburgh EH1 1PB.
**Tel** 0131 226 6636 **Fax** 0131 226 6676
**Opening times** Tue–Sat 10–8, Sun–Mon 12–5.
**Nearest Station** Edinburgh Waverley.
**Personnel** Proprietor: Neil McIlwraith.
**Services and Facilities** Bookshop. Friends Society. Gallery space for hire.

### ▶ Blackwell's Art & Poster Shop
27 Broad Street, Oxford OX1 2AS.
**Tel** 01865 792 792 **Fax** 01865 794 143
**Opening times** Mon–Sat 9–6, Tue 9.30–6, Sun 11–5.

### ▶ Book Club Associates (The Arts Guild)
Greater London House, Hampstead Road, London NW1 7TZ.
**Tel** 020 7760 6500 **Fax** 020 7760 6501

### ▶ Dillons Arts Bookshop
8 Long Acre, London WC2.
**Tel** 020 7836 1359
**Opening times** Mon–Sat 10–7.45.

### ▶ Foyles Bookshop
Charing Cross Road, London WC2H 0EB.
**Tel** 020 7437 5660

### ▶ Hayward Gallery Bookshop
Hayward Gallery, South Bank, London SE1.
**Tel** 020 7928 3144

### ▶ ICA Bookshop
Institute of Contemporary Arts, The Mall, London SW1.
**Tel** 020 7930 0493

### ▶ Paisley Fine Books
17 Corsebar Crescent, Paisley PA2 9QA.
**Tel** 0141 884 2661
**Personnel** Bernard Murrayfield.

### ▶ Waterstone's Bookshop
193 Kensington High Street, London W8.
**Tel** 020 7937 8432

### ▶ Zwemmers
24 Litchfield Street, London WC2M 9NJ.
**Tel** 020 7379 7886/7240 6995/7240 4158

## FINE ART MAGAZINES

### ▶ Art Monthly
4th Floor 28 Charing Cross Road, London WC2B 0DG.
**Tel** 020 7240 0389 **Fax** 020 7497 0726
**Email** artmonthly@compuserve.com
**Ws** www.artmonthly.co.uk
**Personnel** Editor: Patricia Bickers.

### ▶ The Art Newspaper
70 South Lambeth Road, London SW8 1RL.
**Tel** 020 7735 3331 **Fax** 020 7735 3332
**Personnel** Editor: Anna Summers - Potts.

### ▶ Art Review
Hereford House, 23–24 Smithfield Street, London EC1A 9LF.
**Tel** 020 7236 4880
**Fax** 020 7236 3370/3371
**Email** info@art-review.co.uk
**Ws** www.art-review.co.uk
**Personnel** Editor: Meredith Etherington-Smith.
*[Britain's leading monthly art magazine. Annual UK subscription £38; two years £66.50; three years £89.50. Students one year £25; two years £45; three years £57. Overseas one year £48; two years £86; three years £122. Also publishers of the* Art Review Art World Directory.

### ▶ Artists & Illustrators (A&I)
The Fitzpatrick Building, 188–194 York Way, London N7 9QR.
**Tel** 020 7700 8500
**Fax** 020 7700 4985
**Email** aim@quarto.com
**Personnel** Publisher: Ben Lane. Editor: James Hobbs. Sales Manager: Paul Harris. Events Manager: Alison Hamlett.
*The UK's best-selling magazine for practising artists, A&I provides amateur and professional artists and illustrators with inspiration and information on a wide range of fine art materials and techniques. Demonstrations and interviews provide insight into working methods and the Business File covers aspects of a career in art. Plus, keep up to date with exhibitions, competitions, book reviews and courses. Cover price: £2.60. One year's subscription: £25 (saving £6.20) – call 01858 435 307 for details. Also organisers of the annual A&I Exhibition held annually at Olympia, this year from 26–29 July; call 020 7700 8548 for details.*

### ▶ AN
1st Floor, Turner Building, 7–15 Pink Lane, Newcastle-upon-Tyne NE1 5DW.
**Tel** 0191 241 8000
**Fax** 0191 241 8001.
**Personnel** Publisher: Susan Jones.

### ▶ The Artists' Publishing Company
Caxton House, 63–65 High Street, Tenterden, TN30 6BD.
**Tel** 01580 763 315/3673
**Fax** 01580 765 411
**Personnel** Managing Director: Dr Sally Bulgin.

## ▶ Circa Art Magazine

Unit 102, MacAvoy House,
17 Ormeau Ave, Belfast.
**Tel** 028 9023 0375
**Fax** 028 9043 4135
**Email** editor@recirca.com
**Ws** www.recirca.com
**Personnel** Editor: Peter Fitzgerald.
Administrator: Daan Brujiel.
Circa *is Ireland's leading magazine for contemporary visual culture, with news, reviews, features and comment on all aspects of art from Ireland and abroad. Circa is full colour, appears quarterly and is sold by subsciption and in bookshops and galleries.*

## ▶ Circa Art Magazine

Arthouse, Curved Street, Temple Bar, Dublin 2.
**Tel** 00353 1 679 7388
**Fax** 00353 1 679 7388
**Email** editor@recirca.com
**Ws** www.recirca.com
**Personnel** Editor: Peter Fitzgerald.
Administrator: Daan Brujiel.

## ▶ Crafts Magazine

Crafts Council, 44a Pentonville Road, Islington, London N1 9BY.
**Tel** 020 7278 7700
**Fax** 020 7837 0858
**Email** crafts@craftscouncil.org.uk
**Ws** www.craftscouncil.org.uk
**Nearest Underground** Angel.
**Personnel** Editor: Geraldine Rudge.
Sales & Marketing Manager: Chantal Serhan.
**Services and Facilities** Commissioning Service.
*From the avant-garde to classic collector's pieces, from domestic pottery to public art commissions on the grand scale,* Crafts *is the only British magazine to highlight and explore the very best of the decorative and applied arts. Disciplines covered include textiles, jewellery, wood, ceramics, metalwork, furniture, fashion accessories, calligraphy, glass, and automata. Published bi-monthly by the Crafts Council,* Crafts *is the essential reference for both specialists and those with a general interest in visual culture.*

## ▶ Frieze

21 Denmark Street, London WC2H 8NE.
**Tel** 020 7379 1533 **Fax** 020 7379 1521
**Personnel** Editor: Matthew Slotover.

## ▶ Image Magazine

Association of Photographers,
81 Leonard Street, London EC2A 4QS.
**Tel** 020 7739 6669 **Fax** 020 7739 8707
**Email** gavinb@aophoto.co.uk
**Ws** www.aophoto.co.uk
**Opening times** Mon–Fri 9.30–6.
**Personnel** Editor: Gavin Blyth.
Marketing: Sascha Howard.
Image *is the only industry magazine written by photographers for photographers. Each month includes interviews with leading photographers, the latest industry news, technical reviews and advice, and exhibition and book reviews.*

## ▶ Modern Painters

Universal House, 251 Tottenham Court Road, London W1P 9AD.
**Tel** 020 7636 6058 **Fax** 020 7580 5615
**Personnel** Editor: Karen Wright.

## ▶ Print Quarterly Publications

80 Carlton Hill, London NW8 0ER.
**Tel** 020 7625 6332 **Fax** 020 7624 0960
**Opening times** Daily 9–1.
**Nearest Underground** Maida Vale.
**Personnel** Editor: David Landau. Carolyn Gill.

## ▶ RA Magazine

Royal Academy of Arts, Piccadilly, London W1.
**Tel** 020 7439 7438 **Fax** 020 7287 9023
**Personnel** Editor: Nick Tite.

## ▶ Tate Magazine

Avon House, Kensington Village,
Avonmore Road, London W14 8TS.
**Tel** 020 7906 2002
**Personnel** Editor: Tim Marlow.

# Commercial Gallery Artists

*This section lists, by gallery, a sample of the artists the gallery represents, stocks or sells.*

198 GALLERY
(Page 82 and 57)
**Aliyu,** Hassan
**Asante,** Barby
**Avni,** Sigal
**Essel,** Papa
**Ettienne,** Glen
**Hilton,** Joshua
**Keegan,** Rita
**Kelly,** George
**Kojima,** Miwa
**Lewisohn,** Cedar
**Mandiz,** Carlos
**Manning,** Jenni
**Mikame,** Takuro
**Oyetunde,** Dokun
**Padilha**
, Eduardo
**Palma Rodriguez,** Fernando
**Russell,** Salome

ABBOTSBURY STUDIOS
(Page 115)
**Skinner,** John

ABBOTT & HOLDER
(Page 57 and 266)
**Absolon,** John
**Adam,** Robert
**Ardizzone,** Edward
**Austin,** Samuel
**Barrett,** George
**Becker,** Harry
**Bourne,** James
**Brangwyn,** Frank
**Callow,** William
**Carmichael,** John W.
**Clausen,** George
**Collins,** Cecil
**Cox,** David
**De Wint,** Peter
**Devis,** Anthony
**Dibdin,** Thomas
**du Maurier,** George
**Emett,** Rowland
**Farington,** Joseph
**Faulkner,** John
**Fielding,** A.V. Copley
**Fraser,** (Family)
**Fripp,** George
**Frost,** George
**Glover,** John
**Goodall,** Edward A.
**Hills,** Robert
**Holland,** James
**John,** Augustus
**La Cave,** Peter
**Lear,** Edward
**Lessore,** Thérèse
**Minton,** John
**Monro,** Dr. Thomas
**Morley,** Harry
**Pitchforth,** Vivian
**Pont,** Graham Laidlaw
**Reynolds,** Alan
**Rowbotham,** Thomas L.
**Rowlandson,** Thomas
**Sandby,** Paul
**Searle,** Ronald
**Sickert,** Walter
**Strang,** William
**Sunderland,** Thomas
**Topolski,** Feliks
**Varley,** John
**Vaughan,** Keith
**Welch,** Denton
**Wood,** Christopher

ACKERMANN & JOHNSON
(Page 57)
**Alken,** Henry
**Anderson,** Douglas
**Boultbee,** John
**Bright,** Henry
**Bush,** Harry
**Chambers,** George
**Constable,** John
**Cooke,** Arthur Claude
**Cooke,** Edward William
**Cotman,** John Sell
**Crome,** John
**Ferneley,** John F.
**Gainsborough,** Thomas
**Gilpin,** Sawrey
**Glover,** John
**Goodwin,** Albert
**Hayman,** Francis
**Herring,** J.F.
**Howard,** Ken
**Huggins,** William
**Ladbrooke,** John Berney
**Leader,** Benjamin Williams
**Luny,** Thomas
**Marshall,** Ben
**McBey,** James
**Morland,** George
**Munnings,** Sir Alfred
**Nasmyth,** Alexander
**Nasmyth,** Patrick
**Prinsep,** Edward
**Pritchett,** Edward
**Sartorius,** Francis
**Sartorius,** John Nost
**Schetky,** John Christian
**Smythe,** Edward Robert
**Smythe,** Thomas
**Stannard,** Joseph
**Stark,** James
**Turner,** J.M.W.
**Walton,** Henry
**Ward,** James
**Watts,** George Frederick
**Webb,** James
**Wolstenholme,** Dean

ADAM GALLERY BATH
(Page 111)
**Andre,** Carl
**Ayres,** Gillian
**Beuys,** Joseph
**Bond,** Marj
**Cartwright,** Richard
**Cockrill,** Maurice
**Davie,** Alan
**Delaunay,** Sonia
**Denaro,** Melita
**Foord,** Susan
**Francis,** Sam
**Frost,** Sir Terry
**Graham,** Brian
**Harvey,** Gail
**Heron,** Patrick
**Hilton,** Roger
**Hitchens,** Ivon
**Hockney,** David
**Hoyland,** John
**Kent,** Colin
**Lanyon,** Peter
**Macmiadhachain,** Padraig
**Marini,** Marino
**McDowell,** Leo
**Mei Lin,** Hsiao
**Moore,** Henry
**Newton,** Algernon
**Nicholson,** Ben
**Philipson,** Sir Robin
**Picasso,** Pablo
**Piper,** John
**Piper,** John
**Roberts,** William
**Robertson,** James
**Scott,** William
**Selby,** William
**Suddaby,** Rowland
**Sutherland,** Graham
**Witt,** Sol Le
**Wood,** Christopher

ADVANCED GRAPHICS LONDON
(Page 57, 172,180)
**Aitchison,** Craigie
**Beattie,** Basil
**Bellany,** John
**Benjamins,** Paul
**Bennett,** Mick
**Canning,** Neil
**Caulfield,** Patrick
**Fraser,** Donald Hamilton
**Frost,** Anthony
**Frost ,** Terry
**Hammick,** Tom
**Hopkins,** Clyde
**Hoyland,** John
**Hugonin,** James
**Irvin,** Bert
**Jones,** Trevor
**Keane,** John
**Klein,** Anita
**McLean,** John
**Moon,** Mick
**Radford,** Matthew
**Richardson,** Ray
**Setch,** Terry
**Walker,** John
**Whiteford,** Kate
**Wragg,** Gary

AGNEW'S
(Page 57)
**Dunstan,** Bernard
**Finer,** Stephen
**Gadd,** Andrew
**Gall,** Neil
**Le Brocquy,** Louis
**McFadyen ,** Jock
**Wonnacott,** John

ALAN CRISTEA GALLERY
(Page 57)
**Albers,** A
**Albers,** J
**Ayres,** Gillian
**Baselitz,** Georg
**Blake,** Peter
**Braque,** Georges
**Caulfield,** Patrick
**Chillida,** Eduardo
**Craig-Martin,** Michael

**Dibbets,** Jan
**Dine,** Jim
**Dubuffet,** Jean
**Flanagan,** Barry
Francis
**Fulton,** Hamish
**Gabo,** Naum
**Hamilton,** Richard
**Hockney,** David
**Hodgkin,** Howard
House
**Hoyland,** John
**Inshaw,** David
**Johns,** Jasper
**Jones,** Allen
**Koons,** Jeff
Langlands and Bell
**Lichtenstein,** Roy
**Matisse,** Henri
**McKeever,** Ian
**Milroy,** Lisa
**Miró,** Joan
**Moon,** Mick
**Motherwell,** Robert
**Nauman,** Bruce
**Nicholson,** Ben
**Opie,** Julian
**Paladino,** Mimmo
**Phillips,** T
**Picasso,** Pablo
**Rauschenberg,** Robert
**Scully,** Sean
**Self,** Colin
**Stella,** Frank
**Tapiès,** Antoni
**Tilson,** Joe
Turnbull
**Walker,** John
**Warhol,** Andy
Yass

ALBANY GALLERY
(Page 144)
**Ganz,** Valerie
**Howard,** Ken
**Josef,** Herman
**Piercy,** Rob
**Roberts,** Will
**Selwyn,** William
**Thomas,** Gareth
**Tress,** David
**Williams,** Kyffin

ALBEMARLE GALLERY
(Page 58)
**Alarcon,** Aracely
**Alderliesten,** Kees
**Barlow,** Jeremy
**Berber,** Mersad
**Dominguez,** Goyo
**Escofet,** Miriam
**Faulkner,** Iain
**Gallarda,** Michael
**Gatherer,** Stuart Luke
**Gosling,** Annabel
**Gran,** Elena & Michel
**Hurtado,** Fabio
**King,** Alan
**Landa,** Julien
**Liepke,** Malcolm
**Liu,** Jincheng
**Markus,** Csaba
**McDowell,** Leo
**McKean,** Graham
**Narkevich,** Elena
**Roldan,** Alfredo
**Saunders,** Robert
**Smuling,** Ingrid
**Van Hoylandt,** Werner
**Williams,** Antony

ALEXANDRA GALLERY
(Page 58)
**Amor,** Steven
**Ashley,** Stuart
**Atkins,** John
**Black,** Simon
**Carter,** Sue
**Clinton,** Joanna
**Cockayne,** Anthony
**Cullen,** Patrick
**Daniel,** Jane
**Earle,** Nigel
**Garland,** Peter
**Grant,** Cliff
**Haggard,** Henry
**Hunt,** Peggy
**Loader,** Sue
**May,** Jane
**Mei-Yim,** Chris
**Palao,** Edmond
**Pollak,** Norma
**Richardson,** Ilana
**Tchenega,** Mikhail
**Wildman,** P.

ALEXANDRA WETTSTEIN
(Page 234)
**Bailey,** Belinda
**Barker,** Dale Devereux
**Caulfield,** Patrick
**Chadwick,** Lynn
**Cooper,** Eileen
**Frost,** Sir Terry
**Garfield,** Rachel
**Jones,** Allen
**Keiller,** Anna
**Kitaj,** R.B.
**Kowalsky,** Elaine
**Matisse,** Henri
**McKellar,** Robert
**Miró,** Joan
**Moore,** Henry
**Newington,** Charles
**Paolozzi,** Eduardo
**Pasmore,** Victor
**Picasso,** Pablo
**Piper,** Edward
**Piper,** John
**Redfern,** June
**Sutherland,** Graham
**Sykes,** Sandy
**Tilson,** Joe
**Wakita,** Aijiro

ALPHA GALLERY
(Page 115)
**Brown,** Bonnie
**Harris,** Nick
**Hunter,** Jim
**Joyce,** Peter
**Mirza,** Jill
**Potter,** David
**Tuszynska,** Virginia

ALRESFORD GALLERY
(Page 118)
**Ashley,** Raymond
**Atkins,** David
**Bates,** Joan
**Berry,** June
**Boden,** Richard
**Brown,** Bob
**Coates,** Tom
**Cuming,** Fred
**Dicker,** Molly
**Eurich,** Richard
**Evans,** Ray
**Fazakerley,** Pauline
**Glanville,** Christopher
**Goodman,** Sheila
**Handley,** Paul
**Holt,** Rod
**Hughes,** Kevin
**Huntly,** Moira
**Jackson,** Mary
**Johnsen,** Arabella
**Kay,** Pamela
**Knowler,** Brian
**Lindley,** Brian
**McKiveragan,** Terry
**Millar,** Jack
**Pikesley,** Richard
**Tilmouth,** Sheila
**Walker,** Sandra
**Whittlesea,** Michael

ANDERSON GALLERY
(Page 122)
**Bowen,** Clive
**Bowman,** Sarah
**Campbell,** James
**Cardew,** Ara
**Cardew,** Seth
**Cookson,** Delan
**Doherty,** Jack
**Dunbar,** Emma
**Fieler,** Helen
**Goldsmith,** Robert
**Hilton,** Roger
**Hitchens,** Ivon
**Hodge,** Anthony
**Holland,** Michael
**Howard,** Ashley
**Jeffrey,** Jill
**Lambert,** Nigel
**Millais,** Fiona
**Morrell Barnett,** Christine
**Moy,** Judith
**Nicholson,** Ben
**Nicholson,** Winifred
**Piper,** John
**Prosser,** Debbie
**Purser,** Keith
**Rowe,** Judith
**Sickert,** Walter
**Stephens,** Jenny
**Stevenson,** Paul
**Vaughan,** Keith
**Wells,** John

ANDERSON O'DAY GRAPHICS
(Page 172)
**Ackroyd,** Norman
**Bishop,** Brian
**Crossley,** Anthony
**Daniels,** Harvey
**Davey Winter,** Jean
**Delderfield,** Delia

**Farrow,** Carol
**Frost,** Sir Terry
**Irvin,** Bert
**Jones,** Ian
**McLean,** Bruce
**Neiland,** Brendan
**Neville,** Alison
**O'Neill,** Mary Rose
**Piper,** John
**Rowe,** Carl
**Shave,** Terry
**Virgils,** Katherine
**Wilkinson,** Donald

ANDREW MUMMERY GALLERY
(Page 58)
**Akkerman,** Philip
**Bach,** Michael
**Blane,** Frances
**Butler,** Jeremy
**Chevska,** Maria
**Edlund,** Krista
**Goto,** John
**Harding,** Alexis
**Hemington,** Tim
**Holubitschka,** Hans-Jorg
**Hopkins,** Louise
**Hughes,** Ian
**Kane,** Paula
**Kennedy,** Mark
**Marchan,** Javier
**Morton,** Victoria
**Rhodes,** Carol
**Staff,** Craig
**Todd,** Graeme

ANNE FAGGIONATO
(Page 58)
**A Bamgboye ,** Oladele
**Bacon,** Francis
Balthus
**Cattrell,** Annie
**Giacometti,** Alberto
**Hepworth,** Barbara
**Hirst,** Damien
**Howard,** Rachel
**Jebb,** Katerina
**Lichtenstein,** Roy
**Matisse,** Henri
**Miró,** Joan
**Monet,** Claude
**Moore,** Henry
**Moynihan,** Danny
**Picasso,** Pablo
**Warhol,** Andy
**Whiteread,** Rachel

ANNELY JUDA FINE ART
(Page 58)
**Ackling,** Roger
**Caro,** Anthony
**Charlton ,** Alan
**Chillida,** Eduardo
Christo
**Clough,** Prunella
**Cohen,** Nathan
**Friedmann,** Gloria
**Fulton,** Hamish
**Funakoshi,** Katsura
**Gabo,** Naum
**Green,** Alan
**Hall,** Nigel
**Hockney,** David
**Iida,** Yoshikuni
**Kadishman,** Menashe
**Kalkhof,** Peter
**Kawamata,** Tadashi
**Kossoff,** Leon
**Lago,** Darren
**Leapman,** Edwina
**Malevich,** Kasimir
**Michaeledes,** Michael
**Moholy-Nagy,** Laszlo
**Nash,** David
**Popova,** Liubov
**Reynolds,** Alan
**Rodchenko,** Alexander
**Saito,** Yoshishige
**Shinoda,** Toko
**Shiraga ,** Kazuo
**Shiraishi,** Yuko
**Vordemberge-Gildewart,** Friedrich
**Williams,** Graham

ANTHONY D'OFFAY GALLERY
(Page 58)
**André,** Carl
**Baselitz,** Georg
**Beuys,** Joseph
**Boltanski,** Christian
**Clemente,** Francesco
**De Kooning,** Willem
**Gallagher,** Ellen
Gilbert & George
**Hamilton,** Richard
**Hodgkin,** Howard
**Johns,** Jasper
**Kelly,** Ellsworth
**Kiefer,** Anselm
**Klein,** Yves
**Koons,** Jeff
**Kounellis,** Jannis
**Lichtenstein,** Roy
**Long,** Richard
**McLean,** Bruce
**Merz,** Mario
**Miyajima,** Tatsuo
**Mucha,** Reinhard
**Nauman,** Bruce
**Orozco,** Gabriel
**Patterson,** Richard
**Polke,** Sigmar
**Post,** Lisa May
**Richter,** Gerhard
**Smith,** Kiki
**Turrell,** James
**Twombly,** Cy
**Viola,** Bill
**Warhol,** Andy
**Webb,** Boyd
**Weiner,** Lawrence

ART ARENA GALLERY
(Page 180)
**Kianush,** Katy

ART EXPOSURE GALLERY
(Page 136)
**Burns,** Gerard
**Cockburn,** Tim
**Edgar,** Annette
**Evans,** Bryan
**King,** Alan
**Macaulay,** James
**Monaghan,** John
**Nardini,** Peter
**Pattullo,** Lin

ART FIRST
(Page 58)
**Barns-Graham,** Wilhelmina
**Cooper,** Eileen
**Elwes,** Luke
**Gardiner,** Anna
**Grant,** Alistair
**Gundle,** Kimberley
**Harvey,** Jake
**Hunter,** Margaret
**Lawrence,** Eileen
**Lever,** Gillian
**Lewty,** Simon
**Macalister,** Helen
**Macdonald,** Bridget
**Maclean,** Will
**Maqhubela,** Louis
**McAleer,** Clement
**Milroy,** Jack
**Nel,** Karel
**Pierce,** Janet
**Prentice,** David
**Rae,** Barbara
**Robertson,** Iain
**Tomkins,** Ridvan
**Trembath,** Su
**Welsh,** Ian
**Whishaw,** Anthony

ART FOR OFFICES
(Page 234)
**Benbow,** Zoe
**Blik,** Maurice
**Booth,** Martin
**Brown,** John
**Canning,** Neil
**Carter,** Lara
**Cinalli,** Ricardo
**Duffy,** Terry
**Ford,** Anita
**Freshwater,** Sally
**Godwin,** Mark
**Hayes,** Peter
**Hewitson,** Eric
**Hewitt,** Annabel
**Homma,** Kaori
**Humphreys,** Ian
**Jacobson,** David
**Jennings,** Helyne
**Jones,** Graham
**Krikhaar,** Anthony
**Lichterman,** Heidi
**Lucien,** Simon
**Marriot,** Neale
**Olins,** Rob
**Palin,** Les
**Plummer,** Brian
**Ribbons,** Ian
**Seligman,** Lincoln
**Simpson,** Chris
**Stok,** William
**Virgils,** Katherine
**Whadcock,** Richard

KINGS ROAD GALLERY
(Page 59)
**Allen,** Richard
**Aung,** Min Wae
**Bligh,** Olivia Clifton
**Dung,** Hong Viet
**Eyton,** Anthony

**Hocking,** Susan-Jayne
**Hung,** Bui Huu
**Kuhnlein,** Andreas
**Monnier,** Katarina
**Tsai,** Chiu Ya
**Warmoth,** Pip Todd
**Xin,** Yin

ART ON THE LINKS GALLERY
(Page 138)
**Aun-Teh,** Hock
**Batchelor,** Mary
**Birrell,** George
**Boag,** Francis
**Bryning,** Hugh
**Cook ,** David
**Edgar,** Annette
**Fiddes Watt,** Alastair
**Gallagher,** Mary
**Hanna,** Naol
**Jones,** Andrea
**MacDonald,** Hamish
**McIntyre,** Joe
**Morrison,** John Lowrie
**Morrocco,** Jack
**Phillips,** Deborah
**Walker,** Monteith
**Young,** Georgie

THE ART SUPERMARKET
(Page 59)
**Avsec,** Naomi
**Braga,** Celio
**Chapman,** Kevin
**Codina,** Joseph
**Colombo,** Cecile
**Cooper,** Lucien
**Duffin,** John
**Ellis,** Carl
**Eustace,** David
**Halsey,** Mark
**Hargrave,** Jane
**Knubley,** Alex
**Kuehne,** Judith
**Lazzerini,** Giuliana
**Lei-Lei,** Qu
**Leone,** Liviana
**Mayes,** Emerson
**Milne,** Christine
**Notman,** Marion
**Panays,** Angela
**Prat,** Jordi
**Read,** James
Sabala
**Thompson,** Ian
**Tschallener,** Yara
**West,** Sarah
**Wieland,** Christine

THE ARTISTS STUDIO
(Page 148)
**Parsons,** Keith Malcolm

ARTIZANA
(Page 99)
**Baier,** Fred
**Bray,** Charles
**Broadbent,** Stephen
**Holmes,** Andrew
**Hough,** Catherine
**Layton,** Peter
**Mach,** David
**Makepeace,** John

**Middlemiss,** Jon
**Moustafa,** Ahmed
**Nigoumi,** Siddig
**O'Dwyer,** Kevin
**Odundo,** Magdalene
**Peters,** Alan
**Reid,** Colin
**Stead,** Tim
**Thor,** Gun
**Warren,** Verina
**Winteringham,** Toby
**Woodman,** Rachel

ARTS CENTRE
(Page 107)
**Ansell,** Jane
**Aynsley,** Susannah
**Burnup,** Eve
**Dixon,** Jon
**Ferguson,** Izzy
**Fownes,** Sue
**Gater,** Claire
**Lambert,** Liz
**Moncrieff,** Alan
**Richardson,** Joanne
**Ritchey,** Jean
**Rowden,** Ken

ARTWORKS GALLERY
(Page 115)
**Bates,** Merete
**Frost,** Kevin
**Greenup,** John
**Guildford,** Richard
**Hughes,** Susan
**Launder,** June
**McKee,** Samantha
**Sealy,** Gina
**Yates,** Suzanne

ATHOLL GALLERY
(Page 138)
**Anderson,** Anne
**Armstrong,** Anthony
**Awlson,** Walter
**Barr,** Shona S.M.
**Birnie,** William
**Bourne,** Peter
**Cheape,** Malcolm
**Clark,** Donald
**Gillespie,** Joan
**Gordon,** Anne
**Harrigan,** James
**Harvey,** Gail
**Innes,** Robert
**Kirkwood,** Terry
**Law,** Frances
**Macfarlane,** Alice
**Macmillan,** Sheila
**Mitchell,** Gordon K.
**Morrice,** Ilona
**Paterson,** Anda
**Ross,** Iain
**Spence,** James
**Thomson,** Alastair W.
**Turner,** Helen
**Webster,** Beth
**Wiatrer,** Richard

ATLANTIC GALLERY
(Page 114)
**Armstrong,** Robin
**Buckett,** Mathew

**Coughman,** Jill
**Crossley,** Bob
**Dalton,** Mary
**Davis,** Mike
**Deakin,** Chris
**Dubrey,** Henrietta
Eustace
**Hughes,** Fiona
**Ivory,** Evan
**Lenkiewicz,** Robert
**McBride,** Wendy
**Moss,** Michael
**Nevitt,** Diane
**Preston,** Norman
**Skinner,** John
**Spence,** Les
**Sproule,** Lyn
**Symons,** Judy

AVALON ART
(Page 113)
**Beer,** David
**Bray,** Barrie
**Bray,** Heather
**Dalgarno,** Barbara
**Dayton,** John
**Dunstan,** Sarah
**Evans,** Bernard
**Fisher,** Tom
**Frost,** Luke
Gore & Flumeri
**Hawkes,** Gabrielle
**Hiddleston,** Stephen
**Hoskin,** Amanda
**Hoskin,** Catherine
**Laurie,** Ian
**Lodey,** Richard
**McClary,** Louise
**Pilcher,** Esther
**Scott,** Carol
**Sherlock,** Darrel
**Smith,** Jason
**Smith,** Nicole
**Styles,** Linda
Styles & Ward
**Talbot,** Sarah
**West,** Oliver
**Wilson,** Ges
**Winterton,** Claire

AVENUES-OF-SIGHT.COM
(Page 180)
**Armitstead,** Karen
**Longlands,** Sarah
**Singleton,** Alan

BARN GALLERIES
(Page 120)
**Cook,** Rosemary
**Goode,** David
**Grevatte,** Michael
**Gunn,** Fion
**January,** Libby
**Jevons,** Sheilagh
**Jonathan,** Antony
**Lossock,** Neil
**Macrae,** Stephen
**Morgan,** David
**Nicholson,** Sarah
**Roscoe-Hudson,** Susan
**Ryan,** Lucy
**Sinclair,** Helen
**Stobart,** Louise

**Sweeney,** Jan
**Taylor,** Frank
**Watson,** Simon

BCA - BOUKAMEL CONTEMPORARY ART
(Page 59)
**Braham,** Philip
**Castelli,** Luciano
**Chia,** Sandro
**Currie,** Ken
**Daniels ,** Beverley
**Delebecque,** François
**Delprat,** Hélène
**Fetting,** Rainer
**Lüpertz,** Markus
**Mourad,** Joumana
**Nele,** E.R.
**Olanier,** Cyril
**Sicilia,** Jose Maria
**Tatafiore,** Ernesto
**Traquandi,** Gérard

BEATRICE ROYAL CONTEMPORARY ART AND CRAFT
(Page 120)
**Aburrow,** Michele
**Akroyd,** Stuart
**Allen,** Ingrid
**Andrew,** Nick
**Baptist,** Gerry
**Brewster,** Martyn
**Cutts,** Susan
**Griffiths,** Michael
**Harrington,** Heidi
**Hayzer,** Geoffrey
**Hearn,** Stewart
**Heath,** Andrew
**Heber,** Jeremy
**Hewitson,** Eric
**Hole,** Marcus
**Hope,** Zoe
**Huit,** Mark
**Kay,** Sarah
**Miller,** Linda
**Morgan,** David
**Morris,** Elizabeth
**Peace,** Carol
**Plowman,** Chris
**Prindl,** Chris
**Rankle,** Alan
**Roles,** Diana
**Sainty,** Peter
**Smith,** Andrew
**Spare,** Richard
**Theobald,** Helen
**Waller,** Carole
**Watson,** Lucy
**Wynne-Jones,** Jenny

BEAUX ARTS BATH
(Page 111)
**Adams,** Norman
**Ayrton,** Michael
**Barker,** Patrick
**Bealing,** Nicola
**Bellany,** John
**Blackadder,** Elizabeth
**Boydell,** Lucy
**Buxton,** Judy
**Chadwick,** Lynn
**Crocker,** Andrew
**Entwistle,** Mark
**Evans,** Susan
**Fedden,** Mary
**Frink,** Elisabeth Dame
**Frost,** Sir Terry
**Garden,** Simon
**Gilbert,** Mark
**Halls,** Roxana
**Hanscomb,** Brian
**Hartley,** Ben
**Haste,** Kendra
**Herman,** Josef
**Jammet,** Lin
**MacPherson,** Neil
**Mazzotta ,** Anna
**McDonald,** James
**McLean,** Donna
**McRae,** Jennifer
**Mount,** Paul
**Musgrave,** Olivia
**Nisser,** Daniel
**Pearce,** Bryan
**Piper,** John
**Richardson,** Ray
**Simmons,** Anna
**Volk,** Patricia
**Von Stumm,** Johannes
**Williams,** Charles

BEAUX ARTS LONDON
(Page 59)
**Adams,** Norman
**Ayrton,** Michael
**Bellany,** John
**Chadwick,** Lynn
**Cinalli,** Ricardo
**Crowley,** Graham
**Dillon,** Angela
**Frink,** Elisabeth
**Frost,** Sir Terry
**Gifford,** Jane
**Hardie,** Gwen
**Harper,** Andy
**Harris,** Philip
**Hepworth,** Barbara
**Heron,** Patrick
**Hilton,** Roger
**Hitchens,** Ivon
**Jolly,** Nicholas
**Leaman,** Jonathon
**Leapman,** David
**Piper,** John
**Richards,** Ceri
**Scott,** William
**Spiller,** David
**Sutherland,** Graham
**Vaughan,** Keith

BERNARD JACOBSON GALLERY
(Page 60)
**Abrahams,** Ivor
**Bomberg,** David
**Cockrill,** Maurice
**Cummins,** Gus
**Finer,** Stephen
**Hitchens,** Ivon
**Lanton,** Peter
**McKeever,** Ian
**Scott,** William
**Smith,** Richard
**Spencer,** Stanley
**Sutherland,** Graham
**Tillyer,** William
**Williams,** Glynn

BETTLES GALLERY
(Page 119)
**Andrews,** Tim
**Ashby,** David
**Batterham,** Richard
**Bayer,** Svend
**Bowen,** Clive
**Burgess,** Do
**Carter,** Chris
**Davidson,** Andrew
**Dodd,** Mike
**Doherty,** Jack
**Frith,** David
**Gardiner,** Karen
**Graham,** Brian
**Hall,** Sam
**Hill,** Andrew
**Howard,** Ashley
**Jolly,** Linda
**Joyce,** Peter
**Keeler,** Walter
**Keeley,** Laurel
**Kellam,** Colin
**Leach,** David
**Leach,** John
**Maltby,** John
**Marshall,** Anne Marie
**Marshall,** William
**Mason,** Andrew
**Mommens,** Ursula
**Mundy,** Sue
**Myers,** Emily
**Noël,** Anna
**Noël,** Sarah
**Philps,** Emmie
**Pollex,** John
**Ray,** Amanda
**Rees,** Nick
**Rich,** Mary
**Rogers,** Phil
**Trey,** Marianne de
**Waal,** Edmund de
**Wallwork,** Alan
**Wardell,** Sasha
**White,** David
**Woolner,** Robert

BILSTON CRAFT GALLERY AND MUSEUM
(Page 124)
**Colquitt,** Jenny
**Graveson,** Sarah
**McKay,** Iain
**Peevor,** Carol
**Westwood,** Karen

THE BLACK SHEEP GALLERY
(Page 146)
**Anderson,** Ian
**Bailey,** Sylvia
**Boyce,** Kay
**Casey,** Sandra
**Chaloner,** Clinton
**Collins Shone,** Keith
**Cook,** David
**Davies,** Gareth
**Earnshaw,** Wilfred
**Fox,** Judith
**Gadd,** Gerald V.
**Gardner,** Linda
**Gee,** Arthur
**Goodwin,** Christopher
**Green,** Andrew
**Hale,** Vernon
**Haynes,** David

Heath, Jim
Henderson, Bob
Hughes, Phil
Hughes, Richard
Kitchin, Mervyn
Ladell, George
Leyens, Petra
MacMillan, Gregory
McCarthy, Linda
McKinnon Day, Tricia
Miller, Michael
Mosley, Tony
Munslow, Angela
Paskin, John
Peake, Eric
Perkins, David
Pickering, Polly Anna
Pitt, Alison
Pugh, Leuan
Rudd, Brian
Shaugnessy, Clare
Snow, Philip
Symington, Rob
Taylor, Brian
Tuffrey, Marion
Walker Barker, David
Walton, Ian
Watkins, Meurig
White, Harry
Wilson, Eric
Wooding, Tony
Woolf, Colin

BLACKTHORN GALLERIES
(Page 103)
Abbot & Ellwood, Mike & Kim
Ashton, Lee
Bearman, Paul
Beavan, Jenny
Becci, Nicola
Birchwood, Tracy
Briscoe, Mike
Cookson, Delan
Darach, Peter
Davies, Peter
Duffy, Terry
Fleming, Jim
Goldsborough, Bob
Grant, Ken
Hillhouse, David
Hodder, Grant
Jennings, Helyne
Jones, Stephen
Kuwano, Naho
Langan, Jane
Liddell, Stuart
McGillivray, Joe
McKellar, John
Meikle, Annabel
Mitchelhill, Noon
Moore, Jane
Morris, Nigel
Nash, Mandy
Newton, Simon
O'Dare, Emma
Oakley, Peter
Quigley, Lawrence
Rana, Mah
Ratcliffe, Sally
Reeves, Stephen
Rennie, Edward
Robinson, Kay
Rowe, Dot
Rowe, Les
Rushworth, Helen
Shillito, Anne Marie
Sirvio, Joonas
Stanley, David
Van Heel, Elizabeth
Warren, Penny
Warshaw, Josie
Wheeldon, John
Williams, Wendy

BOHUN GALLERY
(Page 120)
Bartlett , Charles
Bond, Marj
Fedden, Mary
Fraser, Donald Hamilton
Frink, Elisabeth
Hambling, Maggi
Houston, John
Littlejohn, William
Piper, Edward
Piper, John
Ramshaw, Wendy
Redfern, June
Remfry, David
Trevelyan, Julian
Turpin, Louis
Volk, Patricia

BOUNDARY GALLERY, AGI KATZ FINE ART
(Page 60)
Bomberg, David
Bornfriend, Jacob
Breuer-Weil, David
Brodzky, Horace
Cozens-Walker, Mary
Dubsky, Mario
Epstein, Jacob
Gotlib, Henryk
Hayden, Henri
Herman, Josef
Jackson, Davina
Kestelman, Morris
Klein, Anita
Koenig, Ghisha
Kramer, Jacob
Lawson, Sonia
Louden, Albert
MacPherson, Neil
Meninsky, Bernard
Pacheco, Ana Maria
Prendergast, Peter
Redfern, June
Tress, David
Wolmark, Alfred

BOURNE GALLERY
(Page 110)
Ball, Gerry
Barlow, Jeremy
Borkowski, Lissa
Brummell Smith, Tony
Campbell, Raymond
Easton, Arthur
Easton, Timothy
Fazakerley, Pauline
Fitzgerald, Sue
Flynn, Dianne
Fountain, Cheryl
Goode, Mervyn
Graham, Peter
Jose, Mary
Lane-Davies, Hugh
Moroney, Ken
Napp, David
Pieroni, Bella
Putman, Salliann
Russell, Christine
Sapp, Prue
Skea, Janet
Smith, Richard
Sykes, Lois
Symonds, Peter
Thompson, Liam
Thorn, Richard
Valentine-Daines, Sherree
Walker, Sandra
Wheatley, Jenny
Yardley, Bruce
Yardley, John

THE BOW HOUSE GALLERY
(Page 60)
Allbrook, Colin
Andrew, Nick
Baker, Richard
Brown, John
Carsberg, Natasha
Clarke, Jonathan
Clarke, Peter
Davey, Caroline
Davies, Phyllis
Ellis, Kate
Felts, Shirley
Foxhall, Peter
Gallwey, Kate
Goldbacher, Fiona
Gould, Cheryl
Griffiths, Mary
Hawken, Anthony
Hoare, Wendy
Holt, John
Horsfall, Andrew
Hubbard, Deirdre
Huggins, John
Lidzey, John
Loxton, Polly
Marsters, Geoff
Mayer, Charlotte
Milborrow, Jim
Moon, Liz
Newman, Ros
Nicoll, Judith
Onians, Dick
Peasnall, Claire
Richards, Christine-Ann
Shutter, Timothy
Sinclair, Helen
Sweeney, Jan
Sykes, David
Symmonds, Susan
Wesselman, Frans
Weston, David
Westwood, Dennis
Wynne, Althea
Yedigaroff, Marina

BRANDLER GALLERIES
(Page 95)
Abrahams, Ivor
Bowyer, William
Bratby, John
Brown, Ralph
Camp, Jeffrey
Casson, Sir Hugh

Cockrill, Maurice
Constable, John
Cox, Paul
Cuming, Fred
Dring, William
Dunlop, Ronald O.
Dunstan, Bernard
Eurich, Richard
Fedden, Mary
Frink, Elisabeth
Gainsborough, Thomas
Gore, Frederick
Gosse, Sylvia
Green, Anthony
Hartill, Brenda
Hayes, Colin
Hepple, Norman
Hitchens, Ivon
Hockney, David
Howard, Ken
Jacklin, Bill
John, Augustus
Kenny, Michael
Larusdottir, Karolina
Lawrence, John Frederick
Lowry, L.S.
Millar, John
Moore, Henry
Phillips, Tom
Piper, John
Potter, Beatrix
Rooney, Mick
Russell, Calvin
Shepard, E. H.
Shepherd, David
Smith, Stan
Stage, Ruth
Sutherland, Emma
Sutton, Linda
Sutton, Philip
Tindle, David
Turner, J.M.W.
Weight, Carel

BREWHOUSE THEATRE & ARTS CENTRE
(Page 117)
Benson, Rosemary
Hind
Jones, David
Kollwitz, Käthe
Mowat, Jane
Nilsson, Jonas
Ollsson, Eva
Shape
Steinberg, Barbera
Woolner, John

BRIAN SINFIELD GALLERY
(Page 119)
Armfield, Diana
Arnup, Sally
Cordery, Don
Crook, P.J.
Cuming, Fred
Hemingway, Andrew
Herman, Josef
Ryder, Sue
Smith, Richard
Tabner, Len
Ward, John
Williams, Jacqueline
Wootton, Olive

BROUGHTON HOUSE GALLERY
(Page 94)
Aked, G. D.
Balzola, Asun
Bennett, Michael
Benveniste, Pip
Blumenfield, Helaine
Borlase, Deirdre
Caine, Alan
Campbell, Gordon
Cornford, Christopher
Cunliffe, Christopher
English, Andy
Griffin , Jackie
Hanley, Liam
Hartley, Marie
Hazelwood, David
Hellewell, Jack
Hemming, Caroline
Jesson, Robin
Kennedy, Richard
Kraczyna, Swietlan
Lawrence, John
Lewis, Ffiona
Lickfold, Gail
Lodge, Jean
Mattioli, Carlo
McGuinness, Tom
Mommens, Norman
Morsman, Phil
Muñoz, Rie
Newbolt, Thomas
Nicholson, Anthony
Piper, John
Raverat, Gwen
Richards, Ceri
Rothestein , Michael
Sansoni, Barbara
Schloss, Edith
Shreve, Peter
Vannithone, Soun
Watson, Jacqueline

BURFORD WOODCRAFT
(Page 165)
Atkinson, Tim
Batty, Stuart
Booker, David
Brown , Jim
Bryan, James
Dawson, Brian
Dumolo, Andrew
Dunworth, Rod
Furlong, Robin
Gosden, Colin
Green , Andrew
Howard, Mary
Irons, Phil
Johnson, Helen
Key, Ray
Lane, Graham
Langworth, Stewart
Lewin , Robert
Lister, Peter
Lythgoe, Michael
Mainwaring, John
Marsh, Bert
Neal, Laurence
Neill, Bob
Pidgen, Martyn
Sheppard, Glynn
Shorrock, John
Suffield, Max
Tattersall, Jules
Way, Colwin
White, Don
Williams, Ralph
Winteringham , Toby
Wroot , Peter
Young Jones

BUSINESS ART GALLERIES
(Page 234)
Atherton, Barry
Barry, Jo
Bawden, Edward
Bigger, Clare
Blackburn, Kenneth
Blackmore, Clive
Blake, Naomi
Boyd Harte, Glynn
Brokenshire, John
Corsellis, Jane
Creswell, Alexander
Dingwall, Phoebe
Dover, Peter
Dunstan, Bernard
Fraser, Donald Hamilton
Frink, Elisabeth
Gibbs, Jonathan
Gore, Frederick
Hansbro, Brendan
Hartill, Brenda
Hepworth, Barbara
Herman, Josef
Hocking, Susan-Jayne
Holliday, Sarah
Holmes, Katherine
Hoyland, John
Jawahirilal, Lallitha
Jones, Stanley
Kotzen, Thirza
Macara, Andrew
Macmiadhachain, Padraig
Mandl, Anita
Martin, Ruth
Martina, Toni
Moore, Henry
Neville, Alison
Noach, Michèle
Norris, Linda
Oki, Yuji
Piper, John
Richards, Ceri
Richmond, Robin
Roberts, Keith
Ryan, Paul
Schwarz, Hans
von Stumm, Johannes
Walker, Richard
Willis, Lucy
Wouda, Marjan
Wray, Peter

CADOGAN CONTEMPORARY ART
(Page 60)
Alcock, Emma
Baird, Charlie
Ballard, Brian
Bealing, Nicola
D'vatz, Timur
Grant, Keith
Johnstone, Andrew
Le Grice, Jeremy
Leaman, Bridget
Mann, Sargy

**McClure,** Daphne
**McClure,** Emma
**Montgomery,** Kate
**Neal,** Arthur
**Webb,** R.A.
**Yavorsky,** Sveta

CARNINGLI CENTRE
(Page 148)
**Batt,** Richard
**Coles,** Bill
**Farrell,** Alan
**Flack,** James
**Greenhalgh,** Annabel
**Horton,** Sheila
**Hughes,** Robert
**King,** Michael
**Leeke,** Desmond
**Mason,** Ann
**Orton,** Joe
**Swinfield,** Simon
**Whitaker,** Rita

CCA GALLERIES
(Page 109)
**Bartlett,** Stephen
**Blow RA,** Sandra
**Caddick,** Kathleen
**Cook,** Beryl
**Cornish,** Charlotte
**Crew,** Lee
**Davis,** Emma
**Dunbar,** Emma
**Frost RA,** Sir Terry
**Furneaux,** Alan
**Goodwin,** Alison
**Görg,** Jürgen
**Hamilton Fraser,** Donald
**Howard RA,** Ken
**König,** Heidi
**Kotsireas,** Stavros
**Mark,** Johnston
**McMurray,** Katty
**Millington,** Terence
**Piper,** John
**Richardson,** Ilana
**Sheppard,** Estienne
**Spare,** Richard
**Spence,** Annora
**Swain,** Hannah
**Taylor,** Frank
**Tribe,** Maria
**Tuff,** Richard

CCA GALLERIES LTD
(Page 60)
**Blow,** Sandra
**Cook,** Beryl
**Cook,** Beryl
**Cornish,** Charlotte
**Crew,** Lee
**Davis,** Emma
**Frost,** Sir Terry
**Goodwin,** Alison
**Görg,** Jürgen
**Hamilton Fraser,** Donald
**Howard RA,** Ken
**Howard RA,** Ken
**König,** Heidi
**Kotsireas,** Stavros
**Mc Murray ,** Katty
**McMurray,** Katty
**Millington,** Terence
**Piper,** John
**Piper,** Luke
**Poulton,** Jane
**Richardson,** Ilana
**Sheppard,** Estienne
**Spare,** Richard
**Spence,** Annora
**Swain,** Hannah
**Taylor,** Frank
**Tuff,** Richard
**Vettriano,** Jack

CHANTRY HOUSE GALLERY
(Page 127)
**Allen,** David
**Anderson,** Athena
**Barker,** Neville
**Berzins,** Valteris
**Braithwaite,** Kevin
**Crossley,** Donald
**Cudworth,** Jack
**Curgenven,** Michael
**Durkin,** Tom
**Gray,** Len
**Halsey,** Mark
**Haste,** J. Barrie
**Howell,** David
**Jones,** Mike
**Keeton,** Richard
**Lazzerini,** Giuliana
**Logan,** Georgina
**Logan,** Lynda
**Logan,** Terry
**Mayes,** Emerson
**Nettleship,** Patrick
**Parkin,** John
**Roxby,** Brian
**Rush,** Maureen
**Saville,** Michael
**Schofield,** Helen
**Sibson,** John
**Simone,** Neil
**Velard,** Paula
**Whatmore,** Nel

THE CHAPEL GALLERY, THE NATIONAL TRUST
(Page 165)
Abbott & Ellwood
**Anderson ,** Blandine
**Arnold,** Brdget
**Bayer,** Svend
**Bedding,** John
**Benatt,** Fran & Frank
**Besher,** Holly
**Betowski,** Noel
**Bowen,** Clive
**Chapple,** Dan
**Chivers,** Bruce
**Chris,** Prindl
**Cockram,** Roger
**Collins,** Nic
**Cooper,** Prue
**Copeland ,** Alex
**De Burlet,** Philippa
**de Choisy,** Kevin
**Deakin,** Chris
**Delan,** Cookson
**Fletcher ,** Sian
**George,** Mary
**Glover,** Carole
**Godfrey,** Richard
**Gordon,** Jo
**Hale,** Jennie
**Hammond,** Lisa
**Hawkins,** Chris
**Hesketh,** Fiona
**Huggett,** Barry
**Hyde,** Marylin
**Jackson,** Paul
**Johnson,** Vanessa
**Jones,** Robert
**Keeley,** Laurel
**Kendall,** Jessamine
**Lilley,** Rachel
**Martin,** Jane
**Moss,** Michael
**Napiorkowska,** Danka
**Noguchi,** Hikaru
**Polybank,** Rebecca
**Polyblank,** Veronica
**Price,** Trevor
**Reeves,** Peter
**Schwartz,** Chuck
**Smith,** Rita
**Stein,** Gillian
**Sumner ,** Mary & Rachel
TAJA
The Rudge Family

THE CHAPEL OF ART / CAPEL CELFYDDYD
(Page 147)
**Aplin,** Kay
**Boenigk,** Dagmar
**Brown,** Celia
**Cheshire,** Richard
**Clay,** Andie
**Coles,** Howard
**Elsworth,** Carole
**Evans,** Polly Marix
**Frith,** David
**Gardner,** Jan
**Gould,** Teena
**Grosvenor,** David
**Hamer,** Frank
**Hamer,** Janet
**Ingham,** Eta
**John,** Linda
**Kay,** Jay F.
**King,** Sue
**Kojelyté,** Diava
**Morgan,** Ann
**Morris,** Nancy
**Napier,** Jean
**Piatigorsky,** Max
**Pritchard,** David
**Reading,** John
**Rice,** Bill
**Snape,** Alan
**Spashett,** Anne
**Swann,** Bill
**Templeman,** Angharad
**Templeman,** Rhian
**Watkins,** Jim
**Wilkinson,** Fiona Brown
**Wilkinson,** Ray
**Williams,** Karen
**Williams-Ellis,** Bronwyn

THE CHILFORD HALL SCULPTURE CENTRE
(Page 202)
**Auvinen,** Matti Kalevi
**Benedetto,** Michele
**Blumenfeld,** Helaine
**Cpajak,** Goran
**Cpakak,** Giorgie
**Cun-Sun,** Park

**Grassi,** Andrea
**Neidermann,** Zoya
**Otero,** Camilo
**Penalba,** Alicia
**Sato,** Akiko
**Schonk,** Aart
**Tarabella,** Viliano

CHRIS BEETLES
(Page 61)
**Archer,** Val
**Badmin,** Stanley
**Barton,** Rose
**Bateman,** H.M.
**Beerbohm,** Max
**Blake,** Quentin
**Brabazon,** Hercules Brabazon
**Brookes,** Peter
**Drew,** Simon
**Dulac,** Edmund
**Elgood,** G.S.
**Foreman,** Michael
**Foster,** Birket
**Fotherby,** Lesley
**Giles,** Carl
**Girvan,** Geraldine
**Goodwin,** Albert
**Greenaway,** Kate
**Hammond,** Roy
**Hilder,** Roland
**Hunt,** Cecil Arthur
**Ivory,** Lesley Anne
**Knight,** Charles
Larry
**Pemberton,** Muriel
**Piper,** John
**Rackham,** Arthur
**Robinson,** William Heath
**Rowlandson,** Thomas
**Scarfe,** Gerald
**Shepard,** E. H.
**Soper,** Eileen
**Soper,** George
**Steadman,** Ralph
**Studdy,** George "Bonzo"
**Tarrant,** Margaret
**Tyndale,** Walter
**Wain,** Louis
**Wyllie,** William L.

CHRISTOPHER WOOD
(Page 234)
**Allingham,** Helen
**Anderson,** Sophie
**Bligh,** Jabez
**Bond,** William Joseph
**Boodle,** Walter
**Breakspeare,** William A
**Burne-Jones,** Sir Edward Coley
**Calthorp,** Dion Clayton
**Carse,** Ducan
**Cayley,** Neville
**Chase,** Marian
**Ciardi,** Emma
**Clarke ,** Maud U.
**Corbould ,** Alfred
**Cruikshank,** William
**Dicksee,** Sir Frank
**Frampton,** Edward Reginald
**Frith ,** William Powell
**Gale,** William
**Grimshaw,** John Atkinson
**Hammond,** Gertrude D
**Haughton ,** Benjamin
**Henderson,** Thomas
**Hicks,** George Elgar
**Hillingford,** Robert Alexander
**Hughes ,** A Foord
**Jobling,** Robert
**Kilburne,** George Goodwin
**Laurens ,** Joseph Augustin
**Leader ,** Benjamin Williams
**Loder of Bath,** James
**Lott,** Frederick Tully
**Lucas,** John Templeton
**Ludovici,** Albert
**Moore,** Henry
**Oliver,** William
**Parsons ,** Alfred
**Parsons,** Beatrice
**Pratt ,** Jonathan
**Roberts,** David
**Rosetti,** Dante Gabriel
**Shayer ,** William
**Sowerby ,** John
**Stanier,** Henry
**Stannard,** Henry John Sylvester
**Thornycroft,** Helen
**Topham,** Frank William Warwick
**Tovey,** Samuel Griffiths
**Underwood ,** Thomas Richard

THE CITY GALLERY
(Page 92)
**Abbot & Ellwood,** Mike & Kim
**Bell,** Cressida
**Betts,** Malcolm
**Bottle,** Neil
**Carnac,** Helen
**Complin,** Jo
**Corbett,** Henrietta
**Currell,** Anthony
**Downes,** Charlie
**Griffin,** James
**Grigor,** Rachel
**Hammond,** Lisa
**Harding,** Angela
**Harrison,** Steve
**Hauksdottir,** Valgerdur
**Hawkins,** Amanda
**Hodgkinson,** Trevor
**Holmes,** Michelle
**Impey,** Jill
**Jennings,** Helyne
**Keeler,** Walter
**Kirby,** Sarah
**Levi Marshall,** Will
**McKibbin,** Marlene
**McSwiney,** Sharon
**Miller,** Linda
**Murphy,** Kathie
**Packington,** Sarah
**Park,** Rowena
**Rana,** Mah
**Rice,** Liz
**Rivans,** Maria
**Roberts,** Hilary
**Ross,** Vivienne
**Sellars,** Julie
**Smith,** Mark
**Stephens,** Ian
**Stoddart,** Rosalind
**Walter,** Josie
**Williams,** Penny
**Williams,** Sophie
**Wood,** Paul
**Wood,** Philip
**Young,** A & J

CLARGES GALLERY
(Page 61)
**Armfield,** Diana
**Bevan,** Robert
**Cooper,** Egerton
**Cox,** David
**Denholm Armour,** G.
**Dunstan,** Bernard
**Hunt,** Cecil Arthur
**Kemp-Welch,** Lucy
**Marshall,** Menzies
**Owen,** Samuel
**Piper,** John
**Prout,** Samuel
**Watson,** Harry
**Williams,** Terrick

COLIN JELLICOE GALLERY
(Page 101)
**Abbott,** Nolan
**Baumforth,** David
**Bell,** John
**Blenkinsopp,** John
**Bocai,** Maria Daniela
**Brady,** Flo
**Brown,** Sally
**Cousset,** Jean-Marie
**Cownie,** Allan
**Davey,** Peter Granville
**Dobson,** Martin
**Gardner,** Reg
**Gilbert,** Colin
Granville
**Granville,** Nicholas
**Harrison,** Michael
**Hesketh,** Michael
**Higginson,** Cliff
**Hill,** Debbie
**Jellicoe,** Colin
**Jones,** Alwyn Dempster
**Kelly,** Francis
**Lawley,** Christine
**Leigh,** Teresa
**Martin,** Christina
**Mayer,** William
**McPake,** John
**Mitchell,** Sue
**Na'el,** Shahrokll
**Naughton,** James
**Noble,** Chris
**Persson,** Katriona
**Picking,** John
**Porter,** Robert
**Ritchie,** Paul
**Rothmer,** Dorothy
**Sharf,** Fua
**Simione,** Giovanni
**Skovgaard,** Kim
**Stanley,** Dave
**Thornton,** Barry
**Tonge,** Emma
**Whittall,** Sylvia
**Williams,** Enid
**Williams,** Jackie
**Williams,** Peter

COLLECTIONS OF HARPENDEN
(Page 165)
**Aldridge ,** Lara
**Aston,** Dan

**Attridge,** Claire
**Beadsmoore,** May Ling
**Beer,** Yolande
**Bramble,** Chris
**Burn,** Bryony
**Buus,** Marianne
**Carnegy,** Daphne
**Charles,** Jane
**Cummings,** Christine
**Darby ,** Louise
**Dupuy,** Phyllis
**Dyer ,** Sue
**Farquharson,** Angela
**Foard,** Tony
**Gale,** Liz
**Galloway Whitehead,** Stephen
**Gilbert ,** Jennie
**Glanville,** Don
**Goodwin Jones,** Richard
**Hollidge,** Jane
**Howells ,** Joanna
**Ingley,** Martin
**Jones,** David
**Knowles,** Jayne
**Langley,** Siddy
**Layton,** Peter
**Lloyd ,** William
**Mannings Cox,** Gillian
**Mason,** Andrew
**Miller,** Sean
**Munro,** Keith
Orchard Pottery
**Patel ,** Kirti
Penkridge Fruits
**Rana,** Mah
**Rudge ,** Lawson
**Saba,** Suleyman
**Salmon,** Antonia
**Sibun,** Caroline
**Smith,** Daniel
**Sollis,** Rob
**Spearman,** John
**Storey,** Michael
**Sutcliffe ,** Malcolm
**Tattersall,** Jules
**Whittington,** Gilly
**Wild,** Michelle
**Withers,** Sara
**Wolfe Murray,** Tessa

THE CONINGSBY GALLERY
(Page 61)
**Bellingham,** Barbara
**Burston,** Oliver
**Crowther,** Peter
**Fraser,** Ewan
**Friedman,** Jim
**Gissing,** Nicky
**Haygarth,** Stuart
**Hoogslag,** Nanette
Huntley/Muir
**Jarzbowska,** Tamsin
**Kitching,** Alan
**Loco,** Gone
**Marsham,** Sophie
**Maynard,** Peter
**Quinnell,** Peter

CONNAUGHT BROWN
(Page 61)
**Bonnard,** Pierre
**Chadwick,** Lynn
**Chagall,** Marc
**Degas,** Edgar
**Dubuffet,** Jean
**Dufy,** Raoul
**Hitchens,** Ivon

**Hockney,** David
**Holsoe,** Carl
**Matisse,** Henri
**Miró,** Joan
**Moore,** Henry
**Picasso,** Pablo
**Pissarro,** Lucien
**Renoir,** Pierre-Auguste
**Richards,** Paul
**Van Dongen,** Kees
**Vuillard,** Edouard
**Warhol,** Andy

CONTEMPORARY APPLIED ARTS
(Page 82)
**Adam,** Jane
**Amsell,** Galia
**Aust,** Rushton
**Aylieff,** Felicity
**Behennah,** Dail
**Betts,** Malcolm
**Blee,** Kate
**Brennand-Wood,** Michael
**Brown,** Christie
**Brown,** Lucy
**Bryant,** Anthony
**Buus,** Marianne
**Carnac,** Helen
**Clarke,** David
**Crooks,** Bob
**Curneen,** Claire
**de Quin,** Rebecca
**de Waal,** Edmund
**Dixon,** Stephen
**Dowling,** Gaynor
**Dupree,** Dawn
**Gordon,** Anna
**Greaves-Lord,** Sally
**Hackney,** Katy
**Hearn ,** Stewart
**Hope,** Zoe
**Illsley,** Bryan
**Jamison,** Nuala
**Keeler,** Walter
**Koch,** Gabriele
**La Trobe- Bateman,** Richard
**Mann,** Ptolemy
**Martin,** Malcolm
**McCallum,** Alistair
**McKibbin,** Marlene
**McNichol,** Carol
**O Kelly,** Angela
**Partridge,** Jim
**Pennell,** Ronald
**Ramshaw,** Wendy
**Rana,** Mah
**Reid,** Colin
**Restieaux,** Mary
**Sara ,** McDonald
**Solven ,** Pauline
**Spira,** Rupert
**Stair,** Julian
**ten Hompel,** Simone
**Waller,** Carole
**Woodman,** Rachel
**Yamamoto,** Koichiro

CONTEMPORARY ART HOLDINGS
(Page 172)
**Barber,** Karen
**Baxter,** Joan
**Carpenter ,** Pip
**Cornish ,** Charlotte
**Crew ,** Lee
**Donlin,** Martin
**Edwards ,** John D
**Farrow,** Kieron
**Ford,** Anita
**Gibb,** Kate
**Godwin,** Mark
**Harvey,** Vanda
**Hedger,** Ray
**Hogarth OBE RA ,** Paul
**Hurst ,** Mary
**Kennewell ,** Sue
**Lee,** Jessie
**Lichterman ,** Heidi
**Lynton,** Katy
**Mason,** Barry
**Philips ,** Annie
**Price,** Trevor
**Rennie,** Edward
**Ridge,** Sue
**Short ,** Tanya
**Van Open ,** Gisela
**Watson,** Howard

CONTEMPORARY PRINT GALLERY
(Page 173)
**Ayres,** Gillian
**Bassett,** Clare
**Baxter,** Sandra
**Blackadder,** Elizabeth
**Blake,** Peter
**Braunton,** Nicki
**Brett,** Simon
**Byrne,** John
**Carpenter,** Pip
**Clark,** Leigh
**Cox,** Alan
**Day,** Gill
**De Bulat,** Fiona
**Ferguson-Lees,** Dominic
**Fielding,** Jim
**Ford,** Peter
**Fraser,** Donald Hamilton
**Frost,** Sir Terry
**Hammick,** Tom
**Houston,** John
**Hoyland,** John
**Huxley,** Jonathan
**Ingamells,** Andrew
**Irvin,** Bert
**Jones,** Trevor
**Kalinovich,** Konstantin
**Kantaris,** Rachael
**Klein,** Anita
**Koenig,** Heidi
**Kosowicz,** Peter
**Kudryashov,** Oleg
**Le Brun,** Christopher
**Lee,** Jessie
**Lewandowski,** Simon
**McLean,** Bruce
**Meyer,** Klaus
**Moxley,** Susan
**Mumberson,** Stephen
**O'Brien,** Patricia
**Paolozzi,** Eduardo
**Perring,** Susie
**Petterson,** Melvyn

**Rae,** Barbara
**Rego,** Paula
**Richardson,** Ray
**Rollo,** Sonia
**Rowley,** Kevin
**Russell,** Victoria
**Sykes,** Sandy
**Thompson,** Emma

CORRYMELLA SCOTT GALLERY
(Page 105)
**Douthwaite,** Peter
Jolomo
**Oram,** Ann

COSKUN & CO. LTD.
(Page 61)
**Braque,** Georges
**Chagall,** Marc
**Dali,** Salvador
**Dine,** Jim
**Giacometti,** Alberto
**Léger,** Fernand
**Matisse,** Henri
**Miró,** Joan
**Picasso,** Pablo
**Warhol,** Andy

THE COTTAGE GALLERY
(Page 95)
**Bartlett,** Mikaela
**Beaver,** David
**Berry Patterson,** Penny
**Cameron,** Barbara
**Carsberg,** Natasha
**Castellano-Haycock,** Cinzia
**Coles,** Fiona
**Garner,** Olivia
**Gosling,** Oliver
**Hawdon,** Paul
**Maberley,** James
**Marsters,** Geoff
**Morse,** Colin
**Murfin,** Michael
**Osborne,** Tricia
**Richardson,** Phillip
**Ronaldson,** Bruce
**Ross,** Nigel
**Sewell,** Marc
**Smith,** Jane
**Street,** Cynthia
**Tracey,** Sue
**Waters,** Alan
**White,** Peter
**Winbolt,** Pam

CRANE KALMAN GALLERY
(Page 61)
**Bomberg,** David
**Dubuffet,** Calder
**Franklin,** Jenny
**Hayter,** S.W.
**Hofmann,** Hans
**Lowndes,** Alan
**Lowry,** L.S.
**Moore,** Henry
**Newcomb,** Mary
**Nicholson,** Ben
**Nicholson,** Winifred
**Picasso,** Pablo
**Ra'anan,** Levy
**Rouault,** Georges
**Smith,** Sir Mathew
**Spear,** Ruskin
**Stamos,** Theodoros
**Sutherland,** Graham
**Wallis,** Alfred
**Wood,** Christopher

CREFTOW GALLERY
(Page 112)
**Beecroft,** Jane
**Dunstan,** Sarah
**Fisher,** Tom
**Gingell,** Lynne
**Makinen,** Seija
**Mullaly,** Ann
**Owers,** Dione
**Pilcher,** Esther
**Scott,** Carol
**Searle,** Dorothy
**Sheldon-Fenten,** Angela
**Sherlock,** Darrel
**Taylor,** Theo
**Wadsworth,** Paul
**Wicks,** Jenny

CROSS KEYS ART GALLERY & COFFEE HOUSE
(Page 139)
**Baxter,** Brian
**Biazotti,** Sue
**Borland,** Joyce
**Bryning,** Hugh
**Clark,** Linda
**Davies,** Tim
**Duff,** Margaret
**Duncan,** Liz
**Duncan,** Perri
**Edgar,** Annette
**Farey,** Lizzie
**Foote Watts,** Enid
**Forrester,** Laurie
**Frewin,** Ken
**Goodall,** Oscar
**Harkess,** Claire
**Houston,** Falconer
**Johnston,** Amaryllis
**Johnston,** Janet
**Johnstone,** John
**Kinnear,** Ian
**Kinnear,** Maggie
**Lightwood,** Anne
**MacDonald,** Angus
**McCarthy,** Liz
**McDougall,** Yvonne
**McStay,** Adrienne
**Morrocco,** Elizabeth
**Persson,** Katriona
**Phillips,** Deborah
**Phillips,** Douglas
**Reid,** Honor
**Rennie,** Gordon
**Roberts,** Diane
**Robertson,** Barbara
**Scott,** Ian M.
**Scott Martin,** David
**Sharp,** Elizabeth
**Silver,** Chris
**Soutar,** Derek
**Stepinska,** Barbara
**Stoa,** John
**Thomson,** Jean
**West,** Katy
**Williams,** Doreen
**Wilson,** Gillian
**Wolfson,** Alma
**Younger,** Elspeth

CUPOLA GALLERY
(Page 127)
**Aylward,** Jo
**Bassett,** Clare
**Baxter,** Sandra
**Briggs,** Jessica
**Brokenshire,** John
**Brown,** Jo
**Brown,** Olivia
**Bryan,** Victoria
**Button,** Corinna
**Carson-Shaw,** David
**Casey,** Jo
**Darling,** Michael
**Daval,** Valerie
**Dowe,** Virginia
**Fay,** Helen
**Gladden,** Peter
**Grover,** Emma
**Hardwick,** Bruce
**Haxworth,** Hetty
**Hodnett,** Lyn
**Howells,** Joanna
**Hudson,** Caroline
**Jackson,** Brian
**Klein,** Anita
**Langford,** Martin
**Lee,** Jacky
**Lee,** Jessie
**Martin,** Victoria
**McAlpine,** Heather
**McCarthy ,** Simon
**McDade,** Sarah
**McQueen,** Derek
**Morgan,** Kate
**Oda,** Mari Ruth
**Palliser,** Neil
**Parrott,** Helen
**Riorden,** Daniel O.
**Roberts,** Hilary
**Ross,** Vivienne
**Salmon,** Chris
**Westergaard,** Hanne
**Wood,** Paul

THE CURWEN STUDIO
(Page 175)
**Beattie,** Basil
**Cheese,** Chloe
**Clough,** Prunella
**Cohen,** Alfred
**Corsellis,** Jane
**Dunstan,** Bernard
**Frink,** Elisabeth
**Frost,** Anthony
**Hawkes,** Justin
**Herman,** Josef
**Hilton,** Matthew
**Hogarth,** Paul
**Irvin,** Albert
**Kindersley,** David
**Lim,** Kim
**Lysycia,** Tony
**Paolozzi,** Eduardo
**Procktor,** Patrick
**Sutton,** Philip
**Williams,** Nicholas

CURWEN GALLERY
(Page 61)
**Bawden,** Edward

**Beattie,** Basil
**Blackburn,** Kenneth
**Boyd Harte,** Glynn
**Cheese,** Chloe
**Clough,** Prunella
**Dingwall,** Phoebe
**Farrow,** Kieron
**Frink,** Elisabeth
**Gibbs,** Jonathan
**Hansbro,** Brendan
**Hepworth,** Barbara
**Herman,** Josef
**Hoyland,** John
**Irvin,** Albert
**Jawahirilal,** Lallitha
**Jones,** Stanley
**Kotzen,** Thirza
**Martin,** Ruth
**Martina,** Toni
**McRae,** Jennifer
**Moore,** Henry
**Neville,** Alison
**Oki,** Yuji
**Piper,** John
**Richards,** Ceri
**Richmond,** Robin
**Rizvi,** Sophia
**Ryan,** Paul
**von Stumm,** Johannes
**Willis,** Lucy
**Wouda,** Marjan

THE CYNTHIA CORBETT GALLERY
(Page 62)
**Blackwood,** Simon
**Bowman,** Day
**Burgess,** Andrew
**Hourwich,** Sasha
**Howard,** Ghislaine
**Knoll,** Geoffrey
**Kupferman,** David
**Lanyon,** Deborah
**Monks,** John
**Moore,** Nicholas
**Pattie,** Tuëma
**Shaft,** Robert
**Wiggins,** Colin

CYRIL GERBER FINE ART
(Page 136)
**Banks,** Lesley
**Bellany,** John
**Cadell,** F.C.B
**Cameron,** D.Y.
**Cowie,** James
**Eardley,** Joan
**Fergusson,** J.D.
**Gaudier-Brzeska,** Henri
**Gill,** Eric
**Gillies,** William G.
**Herman,** Josef
**Hilton,** Roger
**Howson,** Peter
**Hunter,** Leslie
**Kay,** James
**Knox,** Jack
**Lanyon,** Peter
**Lavery,** John
**McCance,** William
**Melville,** Arthur
**Morrocco,** Alberto
**Paterson,** James
**Peploe,** S.J.
**Redpath,** Anne
**Schilsky,** Eric
**Shanks,** Tom
**Vaughan,** Keith

DANIEL KATZ LTD
(Page 62)
**Canova,** Antonio
Clodion
**Da Fiesole,** Mino
**Da Ravenna,** Severo
**Fanelli,** Francesco
**Foggini,** G-B
Giambologna
**Gibson,** John
**Lombardo,** Tullio
**Susini,** Antonio
**Tacca,** Ferdinand
**Tacca,** Pietro
**Thorwaldsen,** Bertel
**Wilton,** Joseph

DANSEL GALLERY
(Page 166)
**Berry,** Chris
**Brewer,** Jane
**Bromilon,** Caroline
**Butler,** Nicholas
**Chapman,** Robert
**Curtis,** Hannah
**Dalby,** Peter
**Darby,** William
**Dawson,** Brian
**Dugdale,** Peter
**Dumolo,** Andy
**Dunworth,** Robert
**Gallimore,** Adam
**Gosden,** Colin
**Hales,** Dennis
**Hancock,** Brian
**Henderson,** Stephen
**Henshaw,** Nicola
**Hibbert,** Louise
**Hunnex,** John
**Jackson,** Ted
**Johnson,** Helen
**Jolliffe,** Lionel
**Kilvington,** Robert
**King,** Ian
**Lancaster,** Perry
**Langworth,** Stewart
**Lucraft,** Nigel
**Markley,** Alan
**Marsh,** Bert
**Marston,** James
**Martyn,** Ralph
**McEwan,** Robin
**Moore,** Andrew
**Moth,** David
**Nicoll,** Judith
**Oxley,** Ted
**Pickard,** Simon
**Pidgen,** Martin
**Roy,** Peter
**Sanders,** Jan
**Scott,** Mike
**Smith,** Robert
**Soan,** Jeff
**Stanley,** David
**Tattersall,** Jules
**Teed,** Simon
**Try,** Kevin
**Vickers,** Christopher
**White,** Don

DAVIS GALLERY
(Page 157)
**Cahill,** Patrick
**Clear,** Ciaran
**Crowe,** Dee
**Davis,** Gerald
**Hayes,** Olivia
**Kelly,** Joe
**Klitz,** Tony
**Oakley,** George
**Pearson,** Peter
**Treacy,** Liam
**Viale,** Patrick

DE PUTRON ART CONSULTANTS LTD.
(Page 235)
**Adams,** Alastair
**Amin,** Sherif
**Aplin,** Kay
**Aust,** Rushton
**Becker,** Bernard
**Bennett,** Austin
**Bisset,** Anna
**Black,** Simon
**Brason,** Paul
**Bryon,** Beverly
**Carpanini,** David
**Churchill,** Martin
**Clay,** Andie
**David,** Michele
**Davies,** Ivor
**Davis,** Paul Marc
**Dwyer,** Judy
**Farquharson,** Mo
**Ferrey,** Petrina
**Fiennes,** Susannah
**Godlieb,** Jennifer
**Hamilton,** Susie
**Harrington,** Heidi
**Hawken,** Anthony
**Jarvis,** Martin
**Jones,** Catrin
**Killin,** Mhairi
**Kinley,** Susan
**Kirby,** Rick
**Klapez,** Ivan
**Larsen,** Patricia
**Lord,** Bernard
**Maclean,** Diane
**Masoero,** Jeanne
**Maxwell,** Mark
**McNiven,** Peter
**Medway,** Sarah
**Morgan,** Howard
**Morland,** Louise
**Morris,** Stuart
**Nicholas,** Peter
**O'Leary,** Clare
**Patsalides,** John
**Pavlenko,** Sergei
**Pearse,** Deborah
**Phillips,** Annie
**Piatigorsky,** Max
**Radford,** Diane
**White,** Laura
**Willson,** Graeme

THE DEAN CLOUGH GALLERIES
(Page 128)
**Attree,** Jake
**Babayan,** Karen

**Binder,** Doug
**Brown,** Jo
**Brown,** Olivia
**Cronshaw,** Edward
**Darnley,** Frank
**Dawson,** Stuart
**Gaffney,** Sheila
**Gorner,** Jo
**Gratton,** Ralph
**Jameson,** Katherine
**Judd,** Ian
**Lockey,** Jayne
**North,** Suzanne
**O'Boyle,** Sarah
**Rados,** Ivan
**Roberts,** Sarah
**Sacker,** Chris
Sahaja
**Schwab,** Linda
**Seaman,** Julie
**Sykes,** Barbara
**Taylor,** Chris
**Vine,** Ghris
**Weigert,** Gaby
**Wincer,** Richard
**Wood,** Tom

DEVON GUILD OF CRAFTSMEN
(Page 166)
**Anderson,** Blandine
**Andrews,** Tim
**Bowen,** Clive
**Bowen,** Clive
**Cockram,** Roger
**De Trey,** Marianne
**Edmunds,** Rebecca
**Highet,** Hilary
**Hone,** Juliet
**Honnor,** Michael
**Keeley,** Laurel
**Kellam,** Colin
**Kendall,** Jessamine
**Langley,** Siddy
**Leach,** David
**Leach,** John
**Lloyd,** Andrew
**Maltby,** John
**Mann,** Tony
**Martin,** Malcolm
**McKay,** Ian
**Peters,** Alan
**Regester,** Dave
**Searle,** Teresa
**Stoyel,** Janet
Taja
**Vincent,** Carole

DEXTERITY
(Page 103)
**Adam,** Jane
**Aldridge,** Lara
**Berkowitz,** Maggie
**Brett,** Kate
**Brock,** Hilary
**Browne,** Piers
**Bruce,** Susan
**Brunsdon,** John
**Calver,** John
**Curtis,** Eddie
**Dunbar,** Emma
**Dunn,** John
**Eden,** Mike & Vicky
**Forrester,** Trevor
**Giarrusso,** Veronique
**Gibson,** Lynne
**Goldsmith,** Robert
**Hamlyn,** Jane
**Hanson,** Helen
**Hartill,** Brenda
**Holder,** Guy
**Jolly,** Linda
**Kellam,** Colin
**Kershaw,** John
**King,** Mary
**Lane,** Peter
**Langley,** Siddy
**Layton,** Peter
**Lear,** Susie
**Leech,** Kenneth
**Lennox,** Grainne
**MacDonell,** Alasdair Neil
**MacDonell,** Sally
**Maltby,** John
**Moxon,** Debbie
**Rogers,** Paul
**Rudge,** Dillon
**Rudge,** Keza
**Rudge,** Lawson C.
**Rudge,** Lawson E.
**Rushbrooke,** Karlin
**Smith,** Jane
**Stones,** Alan
**Van Reigersberg-Versluys,** Carlos
**Walton,** Jackie
**West,** Linda
**Westgate,** Jo
**White,** David
**Whiterod,** Karen
**Williams,** Julian

DUKES OAK CONTEMPORARY ART GALLERY
(Page 99)
**Bailey,** Caroline
**Cooper,** Lucien
**Davis,** Paul
**Fleming,** Jim
**Heath,** Donna
**Leese,** Charlotte
**Midgley,** Julia
**Moate,** Fiona
**Mowat,** Lyn
**Newhouse,** Jan
**Noble,** Lewis
**Nowakowski,** Ondre
**Pearson,** Janette
**Pickering,** Dorothy
**Seba Smith,** Frances
**Spencer,** Liam
**Stuart Smith,** Elizabeth
**Turner,** Bridget

EGEE ART CONSULTANCY
(Page 235)
**Al Fakhri,** Patricia
**Azzawi,** Dia
**Berchere,** N.
**Carter,** Owen
**Contreras,** Don Rafael
**Cooke,** Jonathan
**Corrodi,** Hermann
**Deutsch,** Lugwig
**Diab,** Rachid
**Eastham,** Peter
**Ermes,** Ali Omar
**Forray,** Count Ivan
**Fromentin,** Eugéne
**Géricault,** Théodore
**Harrison,** Christopher
**Hartman,** Lesley Ann
**Hugronje,** Snouck
**Iacovleff,** Alexandre
**Kebir,** Abdeldrim
**Koreichi,** Rachid
**Lamplough,** A.O.
**Lewis,** Jane
**Lubroth,** Mil
**Marrash,** Hania
**Massoudy,** Hassan
**McNab,** Tiffany
**Miller,** Francis St. Clair
**Murphy,** James
**Nasiri,** Rafa
**Neville,** Alison
**Newington,** Charles
**Niati,** Houria
**Noire,** Maxim
**Pascale,** P.
**Philippoteau,** Felix
**Preziosi,** Amedeo
**Prisse D'Avennes,** A.C.T.
**Racim,** Mohammed
**Raymonde,** A.M.
**Richmond,** Ernest
**Roberts,** David
**Rousseau,** Henri
**Shimy,** Awad El
**Siti,** Walid Mustafa
**Van Loo,** Carle
**Vernet,** Horace
**Von Mayr,** Heinrich
**Warren,** Sarah
**Wyld,** William
**Zenderoudi,** Hussein

ELIZABETH HARVEY-LEE - ORIGINAL PRINTS c.1490 - c.1940.
(Page 173)
**Anderson,** Stanley
**Beckman,** Max
**Bella,** Stefano della
**Blampied,** Edmund
**Bone,** Muirhead
**Bonnard,** Pierre
**Brangwyn,** Frank
**Brockhurst,** Gerald Leslie
**Buhot,** Felix
**Callot,** Jacques
**Cameron,** David Young
**Carracci ,** Agostino
**Carracci,** Annibale
**Colqhoun,** Robert
**Copley,** John
**Corinth,** Lovis
**Corot,** J.B.C.
**Cowern,** R. T.
**Dix,** Otto
**Dodd,** Francis
**Dürer,** Albrecht
**Fry,** Roger
**Gabain,** Ethel
**Goeneutte,** Norbert
**Goltzius,** Hendrik
**Goya,** Francisco
**Grosz,** George
**Hayter,** Stanley William
**Hollar,** Wenceslaus
**Kandinsky,** Wassily
**Lalanne,** Maxime
**Legrand,** Louis

**Liebermann,** Max
**Manet,** Edouard
**Menpes,** Mortimer
**Meryon,** Charles
**Munch,** Edvard
**Nevinson,** C.R.W.
**Pechstein,** Max
**Piranesi,** Giovanni Battista
Rembrandt
**Reni,** Guido
**Roualt,** Georges.
**Short,** Sir Frank
**Sutherland,** Graham
**Tiepolo,** Giovanni Battista
**Tissot,** Jacques Joseph
**Toulouse-Lautrec ,** Henri
**Tschudi,** Lill
**Tunnicliffe,** Charles Frederick
**Valadon,** Suzanne
**Whistler,** J. McNeill

ENID LAWSON GALLERY
(Page 63)
**Abbey,** David
**Abbot,** Cathy
**Calver,** John
**Chan,** Philip
**Clayton,** Inge
**Coates,** Russell
**Cooke,** Jonathan
**Cross,** Diane
**Drakeford,** Bridget
**Dupuy,** Phyllis
**Grant,** Mary
**Harvey,** Rebecca
**Irving,** Alvin
**Johnstone,** Hazel
**König,** Heidi
**Lambirth,** Alan
**Laverick,** Tony
**Lee,** James
**Moore,** Bridget
**Musso,** Anne
**Myers,** Emily
**Nash,** Gareth
**Richardson,** Philip
**Rushall,** Harvey
**Salmon,** Antonia
**Smith,** Christine
**Wheeldon,** John
**Wilson,** George
**Wolfe Murray,** Tessa

FAIRFAX GALLERY
(Page 109)
**Armitage,** David
**Atkins,** David
**Matoff,** Theo
**Newington,** Charles
**Rankle,** Alan
**Scrutton,** Alice
**Sinclair,** Helen
**Wicks,** Sara

FALMOUTH ART GALLERY
(Page 112)
**Atkins,** Geraldine
**Barnes,** Howard
**Beecroft,** Jane
**Glover,** William
**Hawkes,** Gabrielle
**Hendra,** Hilary
**Hicks,** June
**Jones,** Robert
**Lyle,** Janet
**Newstead,** Keith
**Oaten,** Kate
**Prosser,** Deborah
**Schofield,** Julia
**Scott-Dickens,** Janine
**Spooner,** Paul
**Steiner,** Minou
**Stevenson,** Richard Lee
**Styles,** Sally
**West,** Oliver

FINE ART COMMISSIONS LTD.
(Page 266)
**Adams,** Alastair
**Alsop,** Roger
**Barrow,** Julian
**Bashall,** Nick
**Benney,** Paul
**Boggis Rolfe,** Camilla
**Browning,** Mary
**Churchill,** Robert
**Curry,** Anne
**Dufort,** Antony
**Dyer,** Simon
**Farquharson,** Mo
**Foster,** Richard
**Gilbert,** Terence
**Grenville,** Hugo
**Heseltine,** Michael
**Hilleary,** Alasdair
**Hodge,** Marcus
**James,** Andrew
**Laubin,** Carl
**Lester,** Guy
**Leveritt,** Tom
**Mackie,** Hamish
**Maley,** Tom
**McCall,** Sheena
**Millner,** Etienne
**Morgan,** Hazel
**Morgan,** Howard
**Munslow,** Angela
**Noakes,** Michael
**Oakshett,** Anthony
**Odescalchi,** Tin
**Paik,** Anna
**Pavlenko,** Sergei
**Pearson Cooper,** Michelle
**Pearson,** Jemma
**Philipps,** Clare
**Philipps,** Nicky
**Philipps,** Susie
**Platt,** Theo
**Rampling,** Madeleine
**Rukavina,** Tim
**Scott Bolton,** Tim
**Sergeant,** Emma
**Terry,** Francis
**Tkachuk,** Alla
**Turville,** Owen
**Williams-Ellis,** David
**Wise,** Tom
**Yeo,** Jonathan

FLOWERS EAST
(Page 63)
**Barton,** Glenys
**Bellany,** John
Boyd & Evans
**Chambers,** Stephen
**Clough,** Prunella
**Cohen,** Bernard
**Cuddihy,** Mikey
**Daley,** Anthony
**Dutkiewicz,** Edward
**Faulkner,** Amanda
**Forster,** Noel
**Frost,** Sir Terry
**Gibbons,** John
**Gouk,** Alan
**Hahn,** Friedemann
**Hepher,** David
**Herman,** Josef
**Hicks,** Nicola
**Hirst,** Derek
**Hodgson,** Carole
**Howson,** Peter
**Hughes,** Patrick
**Jeffries,** Neil
**Jones,** Lucy
**Jones,** Trevor
**Keane,** John
**Kirby,** John
**Kondracki,** Henry
**Lewis,** Tim
**Loker,** John
**Mara,** Tim
**McLean,** John
**Neagu,** Paul
**Osuga,** Jiro
**Paolozzi,** Eduardo
**Payne,** Freya
**Phillips,** Tom
**Robertson,** Carol
**Rothenstein,** Michael
**Schierenberg,** Tai-Shan
**Sinnott,** Kevin
**Smith,** Jack
**Smith,** Richard
**Stahl,** Andrew
**Sutton,** Trevor
**Tait,** Renny
**Wall,** Brian
**Watt,** Alison
**Wragg,** Gary

FRAMES CONTEMPORARY GALLERY
(Page 139)
**Bourne,** Peter
**Gray,** Janice
**Littlejohn,** William
**Mackintosh,** Archie Dunbar
**MacQueen,** Charles
**Woodside,** Christine

FRANCIS GRAHAM-DIXON
(Page 63)
**Andersen,** Emily
**Berger,** Sybille
**Carter,** John
**Dring,** Rowena
**Francoise,** LaCampagne
**Girling,** Sheila
**Hopkins,** Clyde
**Ingham,** Bryan
**Kudryashov,** Oleg
**Langley,** Jane
**Morris,** Mali
**Roberts,** Derek
**Smallhorn,** Sophie
**Thesiger,** Amanda
**Verran,** Virginia
**Zechner,** Johanes

Frederick Gallery
(Page 97)
**Burman,** John
**Campbell,** Andrew
**Chatten,** Geoffrey
**Cherry,** Maureen
**Darley,** Paul
**Durban,** Ronald
**Glass,** Margaret
**Green,** Jasmine
**Hann,** Hannah
**Hazelwood,** David
**Jarret,** Andy
**Jarret,** Sarah
**King,** Andrew
**Lomax,** Patricia
**Midson,** Dorothy
**Patchett,** John
**Quantrill,** David
**Richardson,** Ann
**Richardson,** Louise
**Riley,** Sue
**Russell,** Tassie
**Smith,** Madeline
**Stocker,** Tony
**Woodard,** Adrian

Galerie Moderne / le Style Lalique
(Page 64)
**Lalique,** René

Gallery Different
(Page 64)
**Begbie,** David
**Chamoreau,** Claire
**Cooper,** Carlotta
**Everitt,** Adrian
**McClaren,** Joan
**Pearse,** Deborah
**Scannell,** Aine

The Gallery Dorchester
(Page 115)
**Barry,** Jo
**Brown,** Stephen
**Cadman,** Michael
**Clemson,** Katie
**Cuthbert,** Ros
**Desmet,** Anne
**Ellis,** Edwina
**Emerson,** Keyna
**Fulleylove,** Rein
**Gradidge,** Daphne
**Hicklin,** Jason
**Hill,** Dennis
**Hogan,** Eileen
**Jesty,** Ron
**Lunn,** Jean
**Newberry,** John
**Pikesley,** Richard
**Simpson,** Alan
**Toms,** Peter
**Uht,** John
**Webster,** John
**Willey,** Colin
**Worth,** Leslie
**Yardley,** Bruce
**Yardley,** John

Gallery Duncan Terrace
(Page 64)
**Carnegie,** Andrew
**Clossick,** Peter
**Crosby,** Dido
**Espley,** Tom
**Evans,** Geth
**Holden,** John
**Jack,** Jim
**Nicol,** Brian
**O'Donnell,** John
**Olsen,** Geoffrey
**Olverson,** Vicki
**Rendle-Short,** Hephzibah
**Spayol,** Lucy
**Theobald,** Dom
**Volley,** Jo

Gallery Gilbert
(Page 115)
**Ball,** Peter Eugene
**Constantinides,** Joanna
**Henderson,** Ewen
**Howard,** Ian
**Lovell,** Margaret
**Maclean,** Will
**Nicholson,** Ben
**Portway,** Douglas
**Ribas,** Antonio
**Rie,** Lucie
**Ward,** John

Gallery K
(Page 64)
**Alexandrakis,** Alexandros, the Estate of
**Apergis,** Antonis
**Bell,** Edward
**Brice,** Ian
**Cambanis,** Marcos
**Caras,** Christos
**Charalambides,** Andreas
**Dennison,** Lynn
**Dichefalos,** Costos
**Foster,** Barbara
**Georgiou,** Costis
**Ghisi,** Maria
**Hodson,** Millicent
**Hurm,** Carl
**Kalorkotis,** Panayiotis
**Kanakaki,** Hero, the Estate of
**Kiki,** John
**Koch,** Gabriele
**Kyriacou,** George
**Loizou,** Renos
**Moore,** Nicholas
**Moraki,** Ifigenie
**Nicolaou,** Andreas
**Pantaleon,** Theodoros,
**Papayiannis,** Theodoros
**Pennisi,** Paul
**Samios,** Pavlos
**Vlassopoulou,** Tina
**Watson,** Christine
**Yayannos,** Abostolos
**Zengellis,** Zoe

The Gallery Manchester's Art House
(Page 101)
**Aubrey,** Kirsteen
**Baggaley,** Kristan
**Bailey,** Caroline
**Brown,** Peter
**Davies,** Miles
**Decent,** Martin
**Dingle,** Stephanie
**Fuster ,** Jose
**Goode,** Liv
**Halsey,** Mark
**Hampson,** Roger
**Henley,** David
**Higginbotham,** Pat
**Hipkins,** Michael
**Hodgkinson,** Trevor
**Huit,** Mark
**Isherwood,** Lawrence
**Lennon,** John
**Lowndes,** Alan
**Lowry,** L.S.
**MacDonald,** Hamish
**Major,** Theodore
**McGuigan,** Bernard
**Portelli,** Guy
**Rosenblatt,** Rosalind
**Sollis,** Rob
**Spofforth,** Colin
**Turner,** Sheila
**Vallette,** Adolphe
**Verlarde,** Paula
**Was,** Tadeusz
**Watts,** E.B.
**Wilde,** Tony
**Williams,** Kyffin
**Woodford,** David

Gallery of Modern Art
(Page 64)
**Allen,** St. Claire
**Bauman,** Lydia
**Boulting,** Bridget
**Brogan,** Honor
**Bruguera,** Lluis
**Burke,** Peter
**Carswell,** Robbie
**Clarke,** Pat
**Davis,** Derek
**Davis,** Ruth
**Freeman,** Barbara
**Freudenthal,** Peter
**Gill,** Bobby
**Gratz,** Thomas
**Hamilton-Finlay,** Ian
**Harley Peters,** Jonet
**Harvey,** Jake
**Hirvimaki,** Veiko
**Hodgson,** Carole
**Holmsen,** Brit
**Holtom,** Robin
**Hulland,** Ann
**Hunt,** Helen
**Hunt,** Kate
**Jaquet,** Francoise
**Jones,** Mary Lloyd
**Katz,** Tamara
**McGowan,** Richard
**Mellon,** Erik
**Mulholland,** Susan
**O'Brien,** Donagh
**Parhizgar,** Monir
**Rogers,** John Boydell
**Royston,** Gwen Joy
**Shakspeare,** William
**Sivertsen,** Jan
**Williams,** Lois
**Willis,** Simon
**Wilson,** Julia

Gallery Pangolin
(Page 115)
**Abrahams,** Anthony
**Backhouse,** David

**Bibby**, Nick
**Brown**, Ralph
**Buck**, Jon
**Chadwick**, Lynn
**Coventry**, Terence
**Dashwood**, Geoffrey
**Kingdon**, Jonathan
**Mandl**, Anita
**Mayer**, Charlotte
**Ryder**, Sophie

THE GALLERY
(Page 110)
**Ambrose**, John
**Barker**, Jon
**Beecroft**, Yvonne
**Haas**, Pamela
**Hudson**, Sheila
**Markovich**, Violeta
**O'Keeffe**, Rory
**Organ**, Bryan
**Osborne**, James
**Relph**, Sue
**Strang**, Michael
**Walton**, Janice

THE GARDEN GALLERY
(Page 202)
**Ackroyd**, Jane
**Bawden**, Richard
**Bent**, Richard
**Berlin**, Greta
**Brown**, John
**Clahane**, Daniel
**Clarke**, Peter
**Constable**, Sasha
**Erland**, Sukey
**Falcke**, Emma
**Ford**, Susan
**French**, Neal
**Genders**, Carolyn
**Goodman**, Amy
**Hawken**, Anthony
**Hessenberg**, Karin
**Hodgson**, Carole
**Holmes**, Hannah
**Hubbard**, Deirdre
**James**, Harriet
**Jones**, Jenifer
**Konu**, Michael
**Leach**, Ben
**Lush**, Emma
**Maxwell**, Lyn Constable
**Mayer**, Charlotte
**McGuigan**, Bernard
**Milborrow**, Jim
**Moss**, Anne-Marie
**Mussi**, Cleo
**Peever**, Alec
**Penny**, Giles
**Plowman**, Chris
**Pryce**, Vivien ap Rhys
**Ralph**, Alex
**Richards**, Christine-Ann
**Sinclair**, Helen
**Skelton**, Helen Mary
**Vou Marx**, Maggie
**Woodford**, Johnny
**Wynne**, Althea

GLASGOW PRINT STUDIO GALLERY
(Page 136)
**Blackadder**, Elizabeth
**Byrne**, John
**Cook**, Ashley
**Currie**, Ken
**Duffin**, Stuart
**Gonzalez**, Roberto
**Houston**, John
**Howson**, Peter
**Lamb**, Elspeth
**Mach**, David
**Mackenzie**, Tom
**MacPherson**, Neil
**McDonald**, James
**McLean**, Bruce
**McLellan**, Abigail
**Rae**, Barbara
**Richardson**, Ray
**Taylor**, John
**Teh**, Hock-Avn
**Wiszniewski**, Adrian

GLASGOW PRINT STUDIO WORKSHOP
(Page 175)
**Blackadder**, Elizabeth
**Byrne**, John
**Campbell**, Stephen
**Carey**, June
**Cook**, Ashley
**Currie**, Ken
**Davie**, Joseph
**Duffin**, Stuart
**Gonzalez**, Roberto
**Houston**, John
**Howson**, Peter
**Lamb**, Elspeth
**Mathieson**, Norman
**McCulloch**, Ian
**McLean**, Bruce
**McPherson**, Neil
**Mistry**, Dhruva
**Mock**, Richard
**Rae**, Barbara
**Richardson**, Ray
**Robertson**, Murray
**Wiszniewski**, Adrian

THE GOLDEN PLOVER STUDIO GALLERY
(Page 148)
**Giardelli**, Arthur
**Giardelli**, Bim

THE GOLDMARK GALLERY
(Page 173)
**Ayrton**, Michael
**Bartolozzi**, Francesco
**Bawden**, Edward
**Brangwyn**, Frank
**Brannan**, Peter
**Burman**, Barry
**Chagall**, Marc
**Chapman**, George
**Cox**, Morris
**Farrington**, John
**Gibbings**, Robert
**Gill**, Eric
**Gillray**, James
**Graham**, Rigby
**Gross**, Anthony
**Grosz** , George
**Jones**, David
**Kokoschka**, Oskar
**Kossoff**, Leon
**Large**, George
**Matisse**, Henri
**Menary**, Derek
**Miró**, Joan
**Moore**, Henry
**Moreton**, Nicolas
**Picasso**, Pablo
**Piper**, John
**Piranesi**, Giovanni Battista
**Richards**, Ceri
**Rouault**, Georges
**Stringer**, Simon
**Sutherland**, Graham
**Trevelyan**, Julian
**Wootton**, Olive

GOMSHALL GALLERY
(Page 110)
**Bannina**, Paul
**Cole**, Jane
**Langley**, Siddy
**McGowan**, Lawrence
**Midgley**, Colin
**Millard**, Helen
**Moorcroft**, Lise
**Nicoll**, Judith
**Pannett**, Denis
**Peto**, Elaine
**Rudge**, Lawson
**Von Bertele**, Ulrich
**Wood**, Michael

GORING MILL GALLERY
(Page 119)
**Brazier**, Connie
**Cash**, Angela
**Chiles**, Trish
**Chilton**, Linda
**Clandon**, Penny
**Clements**, Caroline
**Coombs**, Trevor
**Couling**, Paula
**Dudding**, Valerie
**Emmerich**, Anita
**Farrell**, David
**Findlay**, Kate
**Firth**, Jo
**Foster**, Stephen
**Gillmore**, Olwen
**Hall**, Mary
**Hallett**, Ted
**Halliday**, Mary
**Handley**, Betty
**Hanson**, Helen
**Hulse**, Caroline
**Joslyn**, Bob
**Macaulay**, Kerry
**Marek**, Stanley
**Markin**, Mavis
**Millis**, Susan
**Monostori**, Helen
**Morgan**, David
**O'Neill**, Sarah
**Parkin**, Jane
**Pidoux**, Janet
**Piper**, Brenda
**Pitt**, Gale
**Rawlings**, Ray
**Rogerson**, Joyce
**Saward**, Ann
**Seddon**, Joyce
**Sim**, David
**Symes**, Marion
**Target**, Connie
**Ward**, Derek

**Welch,** Rosemary
**Whittle,** Janet
**Wyatt,** Joyce
**Zelin,** Linda

GOSSIPGATE GALLERY
(Page 103)
**Ablewhite,** Ron
**Armstrong,** Bob
**Ayre,** Ken
**Browne,** Piers
**Bull,** Simon
**Calver,** John
**Campbell,** John
**Campbell,** Robert
**Cawthorne,** Gillie
**Cresswell,** Janet
**Cross,** Shirley
**Crossley,** John Cartmell
**Curtis,** Eddie & Margaret
**Evans,** Judy
**Fry,** David
**Gundrey,** Walter
**Hughes,** Angela
**Jolly,** Tony
**King,** Michael
**Massie,** Ian Scott
**McDermot,** Andy
**Morgan-Clarke,** Paul
**Mountain,** Paul
**Podmore,** Peter
**Rhodes,** Kate
**Ridout,** Jim
**Rogers,** Mary Ann
**Rogers,** Paul
**Russell,** Andrew
**Stones,** Alan
**Tye,** Roger
**Walker,** Angela
**White,** David

GRAHAM CLARKE
(Page 108)
**Clarke,** Graham

GRANT FINE ART
(Page 156)
**Behan,** John
**Delaney,** Eddie
**Dillon,** Gerard
**Le Brocquy,** Louis
**McDonnell,** Hector
**O'Malley,** Tony
**O'Neill,** Dan
**Rowlett,** George
**Yeats,** Jack B.

GRAPHIC STUDIO DUBLIN GALLERY
(Page 157)
**Aghajanian,** Sophie
**Bardon,** Jean
**Benson,** Carmel
**Bewick,** Pauline
**Bourke,** Brian
**Breakey,** John
**Cooney,** Jackie
**Cronin,** John
**Crozier,** William
**Cuffe,** Grainne
**Cuffe,** Siobhan
**Cullen,** Charles
**Cullen,** Michael
**Delargy,** Diamuid
**Doyle,** Cliona
**Duncan,** Jead
**Egan,** Felim
**Farrell,** Michael
**Flood,** Taffina
**Frew,** Ivan
**Gorman,** Richard
**Grahame,** John
**Hannan,** Valerie
**Hanratty,** Alice
**Hickey,** Patrick
**Jones,** Peter
**Kane,** Michael
**Keating,** John
**Lane,** Jennifer
**Lawlor,** Stephen
**Le Brocquy,** Louis
**Lennon,** Ciaran
**Madden,** Anne
**Maguire,** Brian
**Maher,** Alice
**McCreary,** James
**Monreal,** Alfonso
**Nolan,** James O.
**O'Donnell,** Ruth
**O'Donoghue,** Tighe
**O'Malley,** Jane
**O'Malley,** Tony
**O'Neill,** Mary Rose
**Pye,** Patrick
**Reilly,** Marc
**Sheridan,** Vincent
**Simonds Gooding,** Maria
**Staunton,** Tracy
**Tyrrell,** Charles

GREENWICH PRINTMAKERS ASSOCIATION
(Page 173)
**Aida,** Emiko
**Alves,** Timothy
**Atkinson,** Jane
**Barham,** Jean
**Barratt,** Mychael
**Black,** Maureen
**Bowyer,** David
**Carpenter,** Pip
**Carreck,** Libby
**Coleborn,** Deanne
**Cossey,** Mary
**Croft,** Diana
**Crozier,** Kathleen
**Davies,** Louise
**De Monchaux,** Ruth
**Dell,** Mickey
**Gracia,** Carmen
**Graubart,** Ellen
**Hammond,** Audrey
**Hanson,** Helen
**Harris,** Donald
**Hawkes,** Soren
**Irvin,** Joanna
**Johnson,** Annette
**Klein,** Anita
**Lydbury,** Jane
**Marshall,** Elaine
**Morris,** Elizabeth
**Pateman,** Theresa
**Perring,** Susie
**Price,** Trevor
**Robson,** Sally
**Rollo,** Sonia
**Ronay,** Jenny
**Salmon,** Christopher
**Salter,** Anthony
**Sands,** Susan
**Scovell,** Audrey
**Shiomi,** Nana
**Solly,** Phillip
**Stone,** Kirsten
**Sullock,** Julie
**Weaver,** Felicity
**Wright,** Kevin
**Zaleki,** Barbara

GRESHAM STUDIO
(Page 173)
**Barns-Graham,** Wilhelmina
**Bellany,** John
**Blackadder,** Elizabeth
**Blake,** Peter
**Caulfield,** Patrick
**Clough,** Prunella
**Coe,** Sue
**Cohen,** Alfred
**Flanagan,** Barry
**Frost,** Anthony
**Gormley,** Antony
**Griffin,** Peter
**Hiller,** Susan
**Hilton,** Matthew
**Hoyland,** John
**Jammet,** Lin
**Jaquette,** Yvonne
**Kosuth,** Joseph
**Lanyon,** Ellen
**Lim,** Kim
**Long,** Richard
**Mach,** David
**Mclean,** John
**Miller,** Mellissa
**Nathan,** Janet
**Oldenburg,** Claes
**Paolozzi,** Eduardo
**Parker,** Cornelia
**Pearce,** Bryan
**Penney,** Bill
**Procktor,** Patrick
**Rego,** Paula
**Smith,** Kiki
**Taylor,** Jo
**Turnbull,** William
**Watt,** Alison
**Wunderlich,** Paul

HALES GALLERY
(Page 65)
**Beddington,** Sarah
**Bick,** Andrew
**Callan,** Jonathan
**Carter,** Claire
**Cooper,** Diana
**Dean,** Judith
**Dean,** Stephen
**Gabie,** Neville
**Hyde,** James
**Op de Beeck,** Hans
**Ravenscroft,** Ben
**Rolph,** Danny
**Stimson,** Myra
**Takahashi,** Tomoko
**Tunick,** Spencer
**Wilbraham,** Jane

HALLWARD GALLERY
(Page 157)
**Armstrong,** Robert

**Banahan,** Christopher
**Behan,** John
**Bell,** Sandra
**Benson,** Carmel
**bogan,** Vivienne
**Butler,** Joe
**Carr,** Eithene
**Clarke,** Robert
**Comerford,** Oliver
**Cooney,** Jackie
**Cullen,** Stephen
**Desmond,** Maurice
**Donnelly,** Mary
**Doran,** Paul
**Hanley,** James
**Harper,** Charles
**Kelly,** John
**Madden,** Bernadette
**Masterson,** Bernie
**Mooney,** Carmel
**Murray,** Coilin
**O'Kane,** Eamon
**Reihill,** Zita
**Richmond,** Helen
**Souter,** Michele
**Stanley,** Jacqueline
**Tobin,** Maghread
**Walker,** Sarah
**Wright,** Niall

HAMILTON'S GALLERY
(Page 65)
**Avedon,** Richard
**Bailey,** David
**Bassman,** Lillian
**Brandt,** Bill
**Erwitt,** Elliot
**Fuss,** Adam
**Groover,** Jan
**Horst,** Horst P.
**Horvat,** Frank
**Kertesz,** André
**Klein,** William
**Mapplethorpe,** Robert
**McCullin,** Don
**Newton,** Helmut
**Parkinson,** Norman
**Penn,** Irving
**Rheims,** Bettina
**Von Unwerth,** Ellen
**Wegman,** William
**Witkin,** Joel-Peter

HANGA TEN
(Page 65)
**Akiyama,** Iwao
**Brayer,** Sarah
**Colyer,** Ted
**Endo,** Susumu
**Hagiwara,** Hideo
**Hamanishi,** Katsunori
**Ihara,** Kaori
**Imamura,** Yoshio
**Iwami,** Reika
**Kaneko,** Kunio
**Kasai,** Masahiro
**Kelly,** Daniel
**Kinoshita,** Keisuke
**Kinoshita,** Taika
**Maki,** Haku
**Minami,** Masao
**Miyamoto,** Shufu
**Mori,** Yoshitoshi
**Nakayama,** Masako
**Nakazawa,** Shin'ichi
**Okamoto,** Shogo
**Ouchi,** Makoto
**Sawada,** Tetsuro
**Shimura,** Hiroshi
**Shinoda,** Toko
**Stewart,** Joel
**Sugiura,** Kazutoshi
**Tachibana,** Seiko
**Takahashi,** Rikio
**Tanaka,** Ryohei
**Wako,** Shuji
**Williams,** Brian
**Yamada,** Juliane
**Young,** Karyn

HANOVER FINE ARTS
(Page 133)
**Alred,** Richard
**Anderson,** Libby
**Arnstein,** Sylvia
**Banks,** Roger
**Bochkov,** Valery
**Bonn,** Gary
**Boyle,** Lorna
**Briggs,** Maureen
**Brydon,** Lindsay
**Cairncross,** Mike
**Clark,** Fay
**Conboy,** Kathleen
**Couper,** Carolyn
**Craig,** Ronald A.H.
**Crawford,** Anne
**Erlich,** Vladimir
**Fernandes,** Regina
**Fish,** Margo E.
**Hanley,** Lynn
**Hepworth,** Susan
**Jaques,** Avril
**Jaques,** Richard
**Johnstone,** Ian S.
**Kudriavtseva,** Natasha
**MacDonald,** Allan
**Magro,** Petro
**Mastin,** Ian
**McMillan,** Margaret
**Merrilees,** Roberta
**Neustein,** Ella
**O'Donnell,** Bernie
**Philip,** Jackie
**Philip,** Kate
**Phillips,** Sheena
**Sharp,** Elizabeth
**Shyshko,** Grygoriy
**Standen,** Peter
**Stevenson,** Wendy
**Strachan,** Una
**Sutherland,** Alan
**Tchubiy,** Nikolai
**Theys,** Freddy
**Tytenko,** Panas
**Watling,** John
**Watts,** Enid Foote
**Xia,** Yangjin
**Yalanskyi,** Andriy
**Znoba,** Valentin

HARDWARE GALLERY
(Page 65)
**Bullen,** Duncan
**Coleman,** Les
**King,** Rowland
**Klein,** Randy
**Lewandowski,** Simon
**Sykes,** Sandy
**Thomson,** Sarah
**Tyson,** Ian

HART GALLERY
(Page 65)
**Baldwin,** Gordon
**Bevan,** Jenny
**Blackburn,** David
**Bot,** G.W.
**Bowen,** Sian
**Buthod-Garcon,** Giséle
**Carter,** Chris
**Champy,** Claude
**De Waal,** Edmund
**Devereux,** Richard
**Dilworth,** Steve
**Doig,** Maxwell
**Draper,** Kenneth
**Freeman,** Barbara
**Graham,** Brian
**Greaves,** Derrick
**Hartman,** John
**Henderson,** Ewen
**Koch,** Gabrielle
**MacAlpine,** Jean
**Maltby,** John
**Middlemiss,** Jon
**Owen,** Elspeth
**Perry,** Richard
**Roberts,** David
**Rogers,** Phil
**Ross,** Duncan
**Sheppard,** Michael
**Stringer,** Simon
**Taylor,** Sutton
**Virot,** Camille
**Walker-Barker,** David
**West,** Jenny
**West,** Steve
**Whittaker,** Malcolm
**Wood,** Tom
**Wright,** Austin

HAYLOFT GALLERY
(Page 154)
**Allen,** Barbara
**Vallely,** J.B.

THE HENRY MOORE FOUNDATION
(Page 202)
**Moore,** Henry

HIGHGATE FINE ART
(Page 66)
**Adams,** Norman
**Andrewes,** Eliza
**Atkinson,** Anthony
**Bawden,** Richard
**Betowski,** Noel
**Blow,** Sandra
**Boyd,** Jamie
**Bratby,** John
**Brill,** Reginald
**Browne,** Piers
**Casson,** Hugh
**Cronyn,** Hugh
**Cuming,** Fred
**Cundall,** Charles
**Dinner,** Tony
**Donovan,** James

**Easton,** Arthur
**Feilden,** Lucy
**Flint-Shipman,** Andrew
**Géas,** Luce
**Gore,** Frederick
**Gowing,** Lawrence
**Green,** Anthony
**Guaitamacchi,** Bruno
**Harrison,** Claude
**Hay,** Ian
**Hepburn,** Alan
**Hobhouse,** Robert
**Howard,** Ken
**Ingamells,** Andrew
**Irwin,** Flavia
**Kenning,** David
**Lawton,** Teresa
**lowndes,** Rosemary
**McWhirter,** Ishbel
**Patterson,** Doug
**Pedraza,** Jorge
**Pettit,** Roy
**Pugno-Vandni,** Francesca
**Quirke,** Michael
**Richardson,** Philip
**Rizvi,** Jacqueline
**Robbins,** Richard
**Robinson,** Paul
**Roca,** Francesc
**Scherbakova,** Tanya
**Soan,** Hazel
**Sorel,** Agathe
**Whitehead,** Rhonda
**Wilson,** Stuart
**Wolfe,** Edward
**Wolff,** Phyllis
**Zeh,** Ulrich

HILARY CHAPMAN, 20TH CENTURY GALLERY
(Page 66)
**Andrews,** Sybil
**Austen,** Winifred
**Austin,** Frederick
**Austin,** Robert
**Ayrton,** Michael
**Badmin,** Stanley
**Blampied,** Edmund
**Brangwyn,** Frank
**Bresslern-Roth,** Norbertine
**Brockhurst,** Gerald
**Buckland-Wright,** John
**Cameron ,** David Young
**Craig,** Gordon E.
**Dodd,** Francis
**Farleigh,** John
**Fookes,** Ursula
**Gabain,** Ethel
**Gill,** Eric
**Griggs,** F.L.
**Hassall,** Joan
**Janes,** Norman
**John,** Augustus
**Leighton,** Clare
**Lumsden,** Ernest
**Malet,** Guy
**Nash,** John
**Nevinson,** C.R.W.
**O'Connor,** John
**Platt,** John Edgar
**Raverat,** Gwen
**Royds,** Mabel
**Seaby,** Allen
**Slater,** Eric
**Thorpe,** John Hall
**Tunnicliffe,** Charles Frederick
**Underwood,** Leon
**Urushibara,** Yoshijuro
**Walcot,** William
**Wales,** Geoffrey
**White,** Ethelbert
**Wyllie,** William L.

HILDEGARD FRITZ-DENNEVILLE FINE ARTS
(Page 66)
**Beckmann,** Max
**Constable,** John
**Corinth,** Louis
**Epstein,** Elizabeth I.
**Gaertner,** Eduard
**Kirchner,** Ernst Ludwig
**Klose,** Friedrich Wilhelm
**Liebermann,** Max
**Macke,** Auguste
**Meidner,** Ludwig
**Modersohn-Becker,** Paula
**Monet,** Claude
**Nolde,** Emil
**Olivier,** Ferdinand
**Pechstein,** Max
**Pissarro,** Camille
**Runge,** Philipp Otto
**Schad,** Christian
**Topffer,** Wolfgang-Adam
**Turner,** J.M.W.
**Von Dillis,** Johann Georg
**Von Hofmann,** Ludwig
**Von Kobell,** Wilhelm
**Von Menzel,** Adolf

HONOR OAK GALLERY
(Page 66)
**Ackroyd,** Norman
**Aida ,** Emiko
**Benson,** Rosemary
**Berry,** June
**Bisson,** Paul
**Blackadder,** Elizabeth
**Brockway,** Harry
**Cook,** Ashley
**Day,** Gill
**Devereux,** Jenny
**Drury,** Paul
**Evans,** David
**Glück,** David
**Graubert,** Ellen
**Hamerschlag,** Margareta Berger-
**Hartrick,** A. S.
**Hennell,** Thomas
**Houston,** John
**Jameson,** Sue
**Kortokraks,** Rudolph
**Larusdottir,** Karolina
**Leighton,** Clare
**Lewis,** Sanchia
**Lines,** Vincent
**Marton,** George Mayer-
**McNab,** Tiffany
**O'Connor,** John
**Price,** Trevor
**Richardson,** Linda
**Stamp,** Edward
**Tanner,** Robin
**Tout ,** Ann
**Wagner,** Erich
**Wardle,** Richard
**Winner,** Gerd
**Wiszniewski,** Adrian

HOULDSWORTH
(Page 66)
**Craik,** Michael
**Delafield Cook,** Jonathan
**Ford,** Laura
**Haughton,** Derrick
**Hodgson,** Paul
**Kidd,** Natasha
**McGinn,** Martin
**O'Riley,** Tim
**Pratt,** Katie
**Radford,** Matthew
**Steele,** Leon
**Wilson,** Robert

IAP FINE ART
(Page 66)
**Crayk,** Fred
**Gollon,** Chris
**Hambling,** Maggi
**Howson,** Peter

INGLEBY GALLERY
(Page 133)
**Aitchison,** Craigie
**Austen,** David
**Blondes,** Jeffrey
**de Waal,** Edmund
**Derges,** Susan
**Egan,** Felim
**Fabian Miller,** Garry
**Goldsworthy,** Andy
**Hamilton-Finlay,** Ian
**Heron,** Patrick
**Hill,** Harriet Mena
**Hodgkin,** Howard
**Hylton,** Nel
**Innes,** Callum
**Macdonald,** Patricia
**McLean,** John
**Mellis,** Margaret
**Murray-Orr,** Craig
**Schueler,** Jon
**Scully,** Sean
**Smith,** Ian McKenzie
**Spirn,** Rupert
**Stair,** Julian
**Watt,** Alison
**Young,** Emily

JILL GEORGE GALLERY
(Page 67)
**Benjamins,** Paul
**Brewster,** Martyn
**Bullen,** Duncan
**Butler Adams,** Louise
**Devereux Barker,** Dale
**Ensall,** Kathryn
**Fawcett,** Robert
**Firth,** Mark
**Frost,** Jill
**Gallie,** Sara
**Gillman,** Tricia
**Hodgson,** Paul
**Hosie,** David
**Jones,** Tony
**Judkins,** Rod
**Lambert,** Alison
**Leverett,** David
**Mach,** David
**Mihaylouich,** Alexander

**Orr,** Chris
**Ota,** Tsugumi
**Parsey,** Martha
**Ripley,** Simon
**Salter,** Rebecca
**Stibbon,** Emma
**Taylor,** Fraser
**Virgils,** Katherine
**Watson,** Tomas

THE JINNEY RING CRAFT CENTRE
(Page 122)
**Foard,** Tony
**Jandrell,** Ralph
**Lord,** Kirsten
**Margetts,** Paul
**Merchor,** Oswaldo
**Powers,** Mike
**Rudge,** Dillon
**Rudge,** Keza
**Rudge,** Lawson
**Scaldwell,** Debbie
**Sutcliffe,** Malcolm
**Wolsey,** Lindsay
**Yeomans,** Chris

THE JOHN DAVIES GALLERY
(Page 116)
**Aggett,** Lionel
**Bowman,** Michael
**Brown,** John
**Denton,** Kate
**Dudgeon,** Gerry
**Evans,** Peter
**Gordon,** Anne
**Grevatte,** Jenny
**Jackson,** Kurt
**Jones,** Robert
**Knight,** Geraldine
**Lloyd Griffith,** David
**Murphy,** Sandy
**Prentice,** David
**Scaldwell,** Deborah
**Selwyn,** William
**Shanks,** Duncan
**Taylor,** Frank
**West,** John

JOHN DENHAM GALLERY
(Page 67)
**Dachinger,** Hugo
**Kalm,** Erich
**Nessler,** Walter
**Wilezyska,** Katerina

JOHN MARTIN OF LONDON
(Page 67)
**Adlington,** Mark
**Collis,** Peter
**Duhan,** Mike
**Duncan,** Ana
**Gifford,** Andrew
**Gorman,** Des
**Griffiths,** Mary
**Hamel,** Francis
**Kelsey,** Robert
**Martin,** David
**Morrocco,** Leon
**Wraith,** Robert
**Yates,** Fred

JONATHAN COOPER
(Page 67)
**Abbott,** Paul
**Austin,** Michael
**Brasington,** Alan
**Bream,** Antony
**Kirkman,** Jay
**Mathews,** Binny
**Nessier,** Kate
**Newton,** William
**Ogilvy,** Susan
**Stinton,** Gary
**Tolley,** Nicholas
**Wraith,** Robert

JONATHAN POOLE
(Page 116)
**Ayrton,** Michael
**Cowie Sanders,** Jill
**Cowie-Sanders,** Jill
**Dalrymple,** Neil
**Davies,** Miles
**Davis,** Miles
**Fay,** Helen
**Illsley,** John
**Lennon,** John
**Lennon,** John
**Mackie,** Hamish
**Mills,** John
**Newman,** Ros
**Nicholas,** Peter
**Plazzotta,** Enzo
**Plisnier,** Bobby
**Plisnier,** Bobby
**Poole,** Jonathan
**Poole,** Jonathan
**Shepheard,** Jean
**Sweeney,** Jan
**Torres,** Tico
**Torres,** Tico
**Tweed,** Jill
**Voorman,** Klaus
**Wallis,** Vicky
**Wallis,** Vicky
**Westwood,** Dennis
**Westwood,** Dennis
**Wood,** Ronnie
**Wood,** Ronnie

JULIAN HARTNOLL
(Page 67)
**Blow,** Sandra
**Bratby,** John
**Burne-Jones,** Sir Edward
**Channing,** Stefan
**Coker,** Peter
**Crane,** Walter
**Glavurtic,** Kristina
**Greaves,** Derrick
**Leighton,** Frederick Lord
**Middleditch,** Edward
**Poynter,** Sir E. J.
**Setton,** Laurence
**Shaw,** John Byam
**Smith,** Jack
**Souza,** Francis N.
**Sturgess-Lieff,** Christopher
**Tilson,** Joe
**Waterhouse,** John William
**Watts,** George Frederick

JULIAN LAX
(Page 67)
**Auerbach,** Frank
**Blake,** Peter
**Buffet,** Bernard
**Chagall,** Marc
**Colquhoun,** Robert
**Fedden,** Mary
**Frink,** Elisabeth
**Frost,** Sir Terry
**Gear,** William
**Heron,** Patrick
**Hockney,** David
**Hodgkin,** Howard
**Kossoff,** Leon
**Léger,** Fernand
**Matisse,** Henri
**Miró,** Joan
**Moore,** Henry
**Nevinson,** C.R.W.
**Nicholson,** Ben
**Pasmore,** Victor
**Picasso,** Pablo
**Piper,** John
**Redpath,** Anne
**Roberts,** William
**Rouault,** Georges
**Scott,** William
**Sutherland,** Graham
**Vaughan,** Keith

KALEIDOSCOPE
(Page 67)
**Altsculer,** Gail
**Ankomah,** Eugene
**Baker,** Ian
**Barrie,** Karl
**Bartlett,** June
**Brand,** Maurice
**Burch,** Guy
**Creaye,** Janine
**Dali,** Salvador
**Duffin,** John
**Gorman,** James
**Harris,** Roger
**Hill,** Frank
**Icart,** Louis
**Lamb,** Judi
**Lebor,** Brenda
**Mann,** Maurice
**Moroney,** Ken
**Murray,** John
**Newman,** Susan
Scheherazade
**Selby,** Mark
**Stewart,** Alex
**Taggart,** Elizabeth
**Thomason,** Colin G.
**Weisbort,** George
**Wright,** Dominic

KATHARINE HOUSE GALLERY
(Page 121)
**Belleroche,** Albert
**Copley,** John
**Drury,** Paul
**Fishwick,** Clifford
**Fraser,** Eric
**Gill,** Eric
**Grant,** Duncan
**Hermes,** Gertrude
**Jones,** Barbara
**Jones,** David
**Knight,** Laura
**Nash,** John
**Paolozzi,** Eduardo
**Pissarro,** Orovida

**Spencer,** Stanley
**Tanner,** Robin
**Vaughan,** Keith

KENTMERE HOUSE GALLERY
(Page 128)
**Bawden,** Richard
**Brunsden,** John
**Evans,** Brenda
**Freer,** Roy
**Greenwood,** David
**Hellewell,** Jack
**Huckett,** Alfred
**Newcomb,** Tessa
**Palmer,** Robert
**Spencer,** Liam

KERLIN GALLERY
(Page 157)
**Appel,** Karel
**Boberg,** Oliver
**Clemente,** Francesco
**Cooke,** Barrie
**Cross,** Dorothy
**Doherty,** Willie
**Egan,** Felim
**Eun-Mo,** Chung
**Francis,** Mark
**Godbold,** David
**Gorman,** Richard
**Hapaska,** Siobhán
**Magill,** Elizabeth
**Maguire,** Brian
**McKenna,** Stephen
**McKeown,** William
**Ní Chiosáin,** Fionnuala
**Potter,** Carter
**Prendergast,** Kathy
**Scott,** William
**Scully,** Sean
**Seawright,** Paul
**Shanahan,** Séan
**Sugimoto,** Hiroshi

KILVERT GALLERY
(Page 149)
**Arscott,** Peter
**Bishop,** Peter
**Blake,** Carolyn
**Bolton,** Helen
**Bradford,** Geoffrey
**Bradford,** Sarah
**Burgoyne,** Claire
**Campbell,** Ann
**Campbell,** James
**Carter,** Howard
**Cecil,** Roger
**Christie,** Jonathan
**Cunning,** Robert
**Curneen,** Claire
**Fisk,** Eugene
**Foa,** Maryclare
**Folkard,** Edward
**Gosling,** Veronica
**Hawkins,** Richard
**Hicks-Jenkins,** Clive
**Howard,** Mark
**Lovegrove,** Elizabeth
**Lowery,** Dominic
**MacDonald,** Robert
**Marsh,** Roger
**Marsland,** Kim
**Matthews,** Sally
**Nice,** Derek
**Partridge,** Serena
**Payne,** Michael
**Pennell,** Betty
**Pennell,** Ronald
**Peppé,** Jonathan
**Phillipson,** Michael
**Popham,** Sheila
**Reid,** Dan
**Ridgway,** Elizabeth
**Robinson,** Paddy
**Rogers,** John Boydell
**Rowe,** Jean
**Shearer,** Charles
**Smith,** Thomasin
**Spowers,** Antonia
**Thwaites,** Sarah
**Troup,** Cally
**Wainwright,** Elsa
**Waite,** Caroline
**Windham,** Rachel
**Windley,** Richard
**Wright,** Joanna

KINGFISHER GALLERY
(Page 134)
**Anderson,** Anne
**Bailey,** Christopher
**Baillie,** William
**Ballantyne,** Margaret
**Balmer,** Barbara
**Barrie,** Mardi
**Birrell,** George
**Black,** Dorothy
**Boag,** Francis
**Bourne,** Peter
**Bridge,** Eoghan
**Conboy,** Kathleen
**Downham,** Sara
**Flynn,** Theresa
**Fraser,** Donald Hamilton
**Grossart,** Gay
**Harrigan,** James
**Jaques,** Avril
**Kelsey,** Robert
**Knox,** Liz
**Lassen,** Jeanette
**Lenaghan,** Brenda
**Littlejohn,** William
**Manby,** Simon
**Melrose,** Janet
**Miller,** Moray
**Paterson,** Anda
**Paterson,** Susie
**Pickard,** Baajie
**Pyrie,** Jenny A.
**Robertson,** Iain
**Simmers,** Connie
**Smith,** Andrew
**Spence,** James
**Stubbs,** Rosemary
**Thomson,** Alastair W.
**Wardman,** Clare
**Watt,** Tom
**Wegmuller,** Ann

LABURNUM CERAMICS
(Page 104)
**Akroyd ,** Stuart
**Armstrong,** Pat
**Astoul,** Eric
**Beadsmoore,** May Ling
**Bray ,** Charles
**Burgess,** Jan
**Calver,** John
**Charles,** Jane
**Cockram,** Roger
**Constantin White,** David
**Curtis,** Eddie & Margaret
**Dewar ,** Richard
**Dodd,** Mike
**Drewery,** David
**Dunne,** John
**Garet ,** Dominique
**Gibson,** John
**Glanville ,** Don
**Guillaume,** Claude & J
**Hardwick ,** Bruce
**Harrison,** Tobias
**Hill,** Andrew
**Hoogland,** Niek
**Illes,** Lazlo
**Inglehart,** Ed & Bob
**Irvine,** Alvin F
**Irvine,** Scott
**Janssens,** Netty
**Jensen,** Svein Hjorth
**Kemp ,** Paul
**Kinsman ,** Rowena
**Lyon,** Ron & Joyce
**Lyon,** Simone
**Malone ,** Jim
**Meanley ,** Peter
**Pearson,** Elli
**Pedley ,** Christine
**Potelune,** Didier
**Ramsay ,** Ian
**Reynolds,** Peter
**Scott,** Paul
**Selleslagh,** Mieke
**Smith ,** Mark
**Spitters,** Ardine
**Tudball ,** Ruthanne
**Ullrich,** Hans
**van Bussel,** Willy
**vanReigersberg,** Carlos
**Watson ,** Rob
**Woof ,** Karen

LAMONT GALLERY
(Page 68)
**Boydell,** Lucy
**Cooper,** Eileen
**Crayk,** Fred
**Crocker,** Andrew
**Crowley,** Graham
**Duffin,** John
**Gollon,** Chris
**Kavanagh,** Jim
**Kenny,** Michael
**Lawson,** Sonia
**Mannocci,** Lino
**Mason,** Robin
**McLean,** Bruce
**Medway,** Sarah
**Mistry,** Dhruva
**Moreton,** Nicholas
**Mullins,** Nigel
**Musgrave,** Oivia
**Noble,** Guy
**O'Keeffe,** Anthony
**Orr,** Chris
**Rooney,** Mick
**Simpson,** Abigail
**Speiser,** Kira

LENA BOYLE FINE ART
(Page 68)
**Brown,** Bonnie
**Byars,** Hugh
**Cary,** Caroline
**Clarke,** Jonathan
**Coghill,** Sarah
**Cohen,** Alfred
**Edwards,** Lawrence
**Fedden,** Mary
**Frink,** Elisabeth
**Gilbert,** Dennis
**Hall,** Clifford
**Hart,** Simon
**Herman,** Josef
**Howson,** Peter
**Hutton,** Sarah
**Inwood,** Derek
**John,** Augustus
**Johnstone,** Gwyneth
**Macmiadhachain,** Padraig
**McAdam Clark,** Caroline
**Moore,** Henry
**Muir,** Jane
**Newcomb,** Mary
**Newcomb,** Tessa
**Nice,** Derek
**Pasmore,** Mary
**Sell,** Charlotte
**Sutton,** Philip
**Trevelyan,** Julian
**Ward,** Henry
**Weight,** Carel

LINDA BLACKSTONE GALLERY
(Page 68)
**Allain,** Tony
**Bastin,** John
**Bernard,** Mike
**Blockley,** G. John
**Bloom,** Enid
**Bolton,** Richard
**Brennand,** Catherine
**Bridge,** Eoghan
**Brown,** John
**Butlin,** Anne-Marie
**Davis,** Pamela
**Dawson,** Peter
**Easton,** David
**Fazakerley,** Pauline
**Gyles,** Pauline
**Harrison,** Stephanie
**Huntly,** Moira
**Kavanagh,** Paul
**Kennedy,** Matt Barber
**Kent,** Colin
**King,** Robert
**Ledger,** Janet
**Lidzey,** John
**Manifold,** Debra
**McDowell,** Leo
**Milton,** Malcolm

**Neumann,** Dori
**Paine,** Ken
**Plincke,** J. Richard
**Price,** Harry
**Read,** Sue
**Roper,** Keith
**Simmonds,** Jackie
**Simpson,** Alan
**Sykes,** David
**Taylor,** Martin
**Thompson,** Andrew
**Tookey,** John
**Turner,** Jacquie
**Uht,** John

LINTON COURT GALLERY
(Page 127)
**Adams,** Norman
**Borlase,** Deirdre
**Butt,** Anna
**Cook,** David
**Holmes,** Katharine
**North,** Kitty
**Roberts,** Tony

LION GALLERY
(Page 123)
**Bamford,** Sara
**Blake,** Peter
**Casson,** Ben
**Chiswell,** Shelley
**Craddock,** Martin
**Crouch,** Andrew
**Drakeford,** Bridget
**Dupernex,** Alison
**Eastaugh,** Katie
**Ede,** Caroline
**Elliot,** George
**Fisher,** Sue
**Furminger,** Julie
**Gall,** Fiona
**Gilbert,** Wally
**Griffin,** Ardyn
**Hickman,** Ken
**Hodgson,** Lynn
**Hunt,** Anita
**Jagger,** Janette
**Jones,** David
**Jones,** Siobhan
**Keeble,** Victoria
**Kenny,** Mary
**Keogh,** Rozie
**King,** Deborah
**King,** Marie-Therese
**Kirkby,** Ruth
**Le Bailly,** Virginia
**Lynch,** Helen
**Mackinnon,** Blake
**McEvoy,** Brian
**Mee,** Hilary
**Mosse,** Michael
**Noble,** Chris
**Ohlsun,** Michelle
**Plumridge,** Caroline
**Price,** Judith
**Roberts,** Sue
**Robinson,** Yen
**Rosher,** Diane
**Rowlatt,** Christopher
**Spriggs,** Paul
**Sutcliffe,** Malcolm
**Vine,** Helen
**Wade,** Richard
**Wardle,** Richard
**Windley,** Richard
**Wrightson,** Ann

LISSON GALLERY
(Page 68)
**Allington,** Edward
Art & Language
**Baldessari,** John
**Bismuth,** Pierre
**Borland,** Christine
**Burgin,** Victor
**Burton,** Scott
**Casebere,** James
**Coleman,** James
**Collishaw,** Mat
**Cragg,** Tony
**Deacon,** Richard
**Dujourie,** Lili
**Floyer,** Ceal
**Francis,** Alÿs
**Gerber,** Gaylen
**Gordon,** Douglas
**Graham,** Dan
**Graham,** Rodney
**Grenville,** Davey
**Hilliard,** John
**Hosking,** Mark
**Houshiary,** Shirazeh
**Joseph,** Peter
**Judd,** Donald
**Kapoor,** Anish
**Kawara,** On
**Latham,** John
**Lewitt,** Sol
**Linke,** Simon
**Mangold,** Robert
**Martin,** Jason
**McCollum,** Allan
**McCracken,** John
**Monk,** Jonathan
**Mossman,** Anna
**Muñoz,** Juan
**Murphy,** John
**Newman,** Avis
**Opie,** Julian
**Oursler,** Tony
**Paolini,** Giulio
**Patterson,** Simon
**Schütte,** Thomas
**Ufan,** Lee
**Vercruysse,** Jan
**Wentworth,** Richard
**West,** Franz
**Wilson,** Jane & Louise

LLEWELLYN ALEXANDER (FINE PAINTINGS) LTD
(Page 68)
**Aggett,** Lionel
**Barlow,** Jeremy
**Bizon,** Edna
**Bone,** Ron
**Canti,** Oliver
**Fellows,** Elaine
**Ireland,** William
**Jardel,** Kristina
**Jeffrey,** Gary
**Johnson,** Rosalie
**Jordan,** Maureen
**King,** Fraser
**Large,** George
**Mcardle,** Peter
**Moseley,** Austin
**New,** Keith
**Spencer Pryse,** Tess
**Taylor,** Michael
**Tonks,** Godfrey
**Yardley,** John

LONG & RYLE ART INTERNATIONAL
(Page 68)
**Archer,** Nicholas
**Casson,** Simon

**Fernandez Saus,** Ramiro
**Fyodorou,** Sergei
**Gorky,** Maro
**Hoyer Millar,** Henrietta
**Humphries,** Ian
**Light,** Susan
**Patel,** Sunil
**Prouan,** Donald
**Rose,** Matthew
**Sayers,** Brian
**Stitt,** Sarah
**Thomas,** Dominic
**Zervudachi,** Manuela

LOOK GALLERY
(Page 127)
**Baglee,** Arthur
**Bailey,** Caroline
**Barker,** Neville
**Baumforth,** David
**Bell,** Catherine
**Bizon,** Edna
**Browne,** Piers
**Carruthers,** Rosemary
**Cheall,** John
**Egerton,** John
**Fearn,** Raymond
**Fowkes,** David
**Gillespie,** Bridget
**Gordon,** Frank
**Greenwood,** David
**Halsey,** Mark
**Heath,** Andrew
**Henley,** David
**Janin,** Philippe
**Jones,** Derek
**Jones,** Mike
**Lazzerini,** Giuliana
**Luckham,** Alan
**Mansion,** Dominique
**Massie,** Ian Scott
**McCarthy,** Peter
**Naylor,** John
**Oliver,** Raymond
**Parker,** Ian
**Pierson,** Rosalind
**Platts,** David
**Ruggeri,** Anne-Marie
**Skea,** Janet
**Taunton,** Adrian
**Tilling,** Robert
**Trowell,** Jonathan
**Tulloh,** Phoebe
**Turvey,** Simon
**Walton,** Jackie
**Westergaard,** Hanne

THE LOOK
(Page 114)
**Castle,** Josephine
**Cox,** Alison
**Henshall,** Jonty
**Penny,** Lisa
**Poucher,** Karen
**Sims,** Gentian
**Smith,** Dryden
**Sykes,** Bill

LUMLEY CAZALET
(Page 68)
**Belleroche,** Albert
**Braque,** Georges
**Chagall,** Marc
**Frink,** Elisabeth
**Helleu,** Paul
**Hockney,** David
**Matisse,** Henri
**Miró,** Joan
**Picasso,** Pablo
**Tissot,** J.J.

LUPTON SQUARE GALLERY
(Page 128)
**Abrahams,** Rosemary
**Bowman,** Malcolm
**Boyson,** Alan
**Brown,** Susan
**Burgess,** Jane
**Collier,** Maureen
**Court,** Stephen
**Cross,** Diane
**Fairchild-Woodard,** Roy
**Greenwood,** David
**Hutton,** Sarah
**Kirkby-Geddes,** Mick
**Mead,** Pauline
**Mountain,** Keith
**Muchan,** Paul
**North,** Suzanne
**Palliser,** Neil
**Pasmore,** Victor
**Rados,** Ivan
**Spence,** Annora
**Thornton,** Barry
**Walton,** Jackie

THE MAAS GALLERY
(Page 69)
**Alma-Tadema,** Sir Lawrence
**Anderson,** Sophie
**Brett,** John
**Burne-Jones,** Sir Edward
**Calderon,** Philip Hermogenes
**Crane,** Walter
**Dadd,** Richard
**De Morgan,** Evelyn
**Dicksee,** Sir Frank
**Doyle,** Charles Altamont
**Doyle,** Richard
**Draper,** Herbert James
**Etty,** William
**Fitzgerald,** John Anster
**Frith,** William Powell
**Frost,** William Edward
**Goodwin,** Albert
**Gotch,** Thomas Cooper
**Grimshaw,** Atkinson
**Hughes,** Arthur
**Hughes,** E.R.
**Hunt,** William Holman
**Landseer,** Sir Edwin
**Leighton,** Frederic Lord
**Maclise,** Daniel
**Millais,** Sir John
**Moore,** Albert Joseph
**Mulready,** William
**Murray,** Charles Fairfax
**Orchardson,** Sir William Quiller
**Osborn,** Emily Mary
**Paton,** Sir Joseph Noel
**Poynter,** Sir E. J.
**Richmond,** George
**Richmond,** Sir William Blake
**Rooke,** T.M.
**Rossetti,** Dante Gabriel
**Ruskin,** John
**Sandys,** Anthony Frederick Augustus
**Severn,** Arthur
**Smetham,** James
**Solomon,** Simeon
**Stillman,** Maria Spartali
**Strudwick,** John Melhuish
**von Herkomer,** Hubert
**Waterhouse,** John William
**Watts,** George Frederick
**Woolmer,** Alfred Joseph

MAINHILL GALLERY
(Page 139)
**Alexander,** Alan
**Alexander,** J.S.C.
**Ayrton,** Michael
**Carr,** Tom
**Coen,** John
**Fergusson,** J.D.
**Frink,** Elisabeth
**Gibbison,** Michael
**Gillies,** William
**Haig,** The Earl
**Johnstone,** William
**Kerr,** Henry Wright
**Lawrie,** Hamish
**Philipson,** Sir Robin
**Scott,** Tom
**Sinclair,** David
**Thomson,** Adam Bruce
**Walker,** Andrew
**Wood,** Frank
**Wood,** Watson and David

MARLBOROUGH GRAPHICS
(Page 69)
**Arikha,** Avigdor
**Auerbach,** Frank
**Bacon,** Francis
**Brandt,** Bill
Brassai
**Conroy,** Stephen
**Davies,** John
**Freud,** Lucian
**Hambling,** Maggi
**Hepworth,** Barbara
**Hockney,** David
**Jacklin,** Bill
**Kiff,** Ken
**Kitaj,** R.B.
**Kokoschka,** Oskar
**Le Brun,** Christopher
**Matisse,** Henri
**Miró,** Joan
**Moore,** Henry
**Nicholson,** Ben
**Oulton,** Thérèse
**Pasmore,** Victor
**Paul,** Celia
**Picasso,** Pablo
**Piper,** John
**Raphael,** Sarah
**Rego,** Paula
**Riley,** Bridget
**Sutherland,** Graham

MARTIN TINNEY GALLERY
(Page 144)
**Canning,** Neil
**Cecil,** Roger
**Chappell,** Dick
**Crowther,** Michael
**Davies,** Ivor

**Elwyn,** John
**Griffiths,** Mary
**Herman,** Josef
**Holland,** Harry
**James,** Shani Rhys
**John,** Augustus
**John,** Gwen
**Jones,** David
**Lloyd-Jones,** Mary
**Mabbutt,** Mary
**Macfarlane,** John
**Moore,** Sally
**Müller,** Sigrid
**Piper,** John
**Povey,** Edward
**Prendergast,** Peter
**Prichard,** Gwilym
**Richards,** Ceri
**Samuel,** Mark
**Sinnott,** Kevin
**Tudur,** Dewi
**Volk,** Patricia
**Williams,** Claudia
**Williams,** Emrys
**Williams,** Kyffin
**Williams,** Vivienne
**Zobole,** Ernest

MATTHIESEN FINE ART LIMITED
(Page 69)
**Artemesia,** Gentileschi
**Bassano,** Jacopo
**Batoni,** Pompeo
**Bellotto,** Bernardo
**Botticelli,** Sandro
**Boucher,** Francois
**Canaletto,** Antonio
**Carracciolo,** Giovanni Battista
**Chardin,** Jean-Baptiste-Siméon
**Corot,** Camille
**Courbet,** Gustave
**Daubigny,** Charles Francois
**De Chavannes,** Puvis
**Delacroix,** Eugène
**Di Paolo ,** Giovanni
**Dossi,** Dosso
**Farfin Lafour ,** Henri
**Fragonard,** Jean-Honoré
**Gaddi,** Agnolo
**Gentileschi,** Orazio
**Giaquinto,** Corrada
**Giordano,** Luca
**Ingres,** Jean-Auguste-Dominique
**Lanfranco,** Giovanni
**Longhi,** Pietro
**Manfredi,** Bartlolomeo
**Millet,** J.F.
**Nattier,** Jean-Marc
**Pater,** Jean Baptiste
**Romanino,** Girolamo
**Rosa,** Salvator
**Rousseau,** Theodore
**Sarto,** Andrea del
**Severini,** Gino
**Sisley,** Alfred
**Solimena,** Francesco
**Tiepolo,** Giambattista
**Vernet,** Horace
**Vouet,** Simon
**Wtewael,** Joachin

THE MCHARDY SCULPTURE COMPANY
(Page 69)
**Bell,** Sandra
**Bennett,** Holly
**Berelowitz,** Jill
**Bermejo,** Vega
**Blik,** Maurice
**Bodie,** Marc
**Brook,** Dorothy
**Buck,** Chris
**Cameron,** Ronald
**Chapman,** Richard
**Cohen,** Agi
**Cohen,** John
**Cregeen,** David
**Daniels,** Stephen
**Davies,** Alex
**Dickens,** Sophie
**Freeman,** Richard
**Frohlich-Wiener,** Irene
**Gioia,** Angelo
**Glendinning,** Lucy
**Godden,** Nicola
**Hooke,** Robert
**Hubbard,** Deirdre
**Huggins,** John
**Konu,** Michael
**Kreuder,** Loni
**Lecerf,** Odette
**Lovell,** Margaret
**MacDonell,** Alasdair Neil
**MacDonell,** Sally
**Newstead,** Keith
**Owen,** Glynis
**Penny,** Giles
**Pomeroy,** Tim
**Rae,** Ronald
**Rattenbury,** Jim
**Robinson,** Peter Lyell
**Roud,** Adam
**Samson,** Hana
**Sandys,** Edwina
**Spielman,** John
**Stern,** Deborah
**Sweeny,** Jan
**Thursby,** Peter
**Volk,** Patricia
**Wall,** Terence
**Wheeler,** Alexandra
**Willis,** Neil
**Wozniak,** Florian

THE MEDICI GALLERIES
(Page 69)
**Campion,** Sue
**Casseldine,** Nigel
**Casson,** Lucy
**Chandler,** Colin
**Crittenden,** James
**Deymonaz,** Andre
**Jameson,** Kerry
**Magill,** Anne
**Mann,** Tony
**Penny,** Charles
**Raybould,** Howard
**Raynes,** Polly
**Sanders,** Jeremy
**Soan,** Jeff
**Tonks,** Godfrey
**Whiteside,** Zöe
**Wilcox ,** Graeme

THE MEDICI SOCIETY LTD
(Page 174)
**Brett,** Molly
**Brueghel,** Pieter
**Constable,** John
**Edwards,** Carlotta
**Elsley,** Arthur
**Holbein,** Hans the Younger
**Lowry,** L.S.
**Millais,** Sir John
Raphael
**Renoir,** Pierre
**Scott,** Sir Peter
**Sherwin,** Frank
**Strevens,** John
**Tarrant,** Margaret
**Turner,** J.M.W.
**Ward,** Vernon

MERCURY GALLERY
(Page 70)
**Abbassy,** Samira
**Blackadder,** Elizabeth
**Boulton,** Janet
**Callender,** Robert
**Gentleman,** David
**Hirst,** Barry
**Houston,** John
**Laurie,** Simon
**Remfry,** David
**Rimmington,** Eric
**Sutherland,** Carol Ann

MERRISCOURT GALLERY
(Page 119)
**Bailey,** Julian
**Bicat,** André
**Fleming,** Lainy
**Foord,** Susan
**Gardiner,** Vanessa
**Goodwin,** Leslie
**Harrison,** Tim
**Hellewell,** Jack
**Heseltine,** Julia
**Hocking,** Susan-Jayne
**Johnstone,** Andrew
**McClean,** Fiona
**Neal,** Arthur
**Noble,** Lewis
**Owen,** Hermione
**Scott,** Manja
**Tutton,** Vince

MICHAEL HUE-WILLIAMS FINE ART
(Page 70)
**Bevan,** Tony
**Cooper,** Thomas Joshua
**Cox,** Stephen
**de Waal,** Edmund
**Derges,** Susan
**Eggleston,** William
**Esser,** Elger
**Estate of the Edwardian photographer ,** Charles Jones
**Goldsworthy,** Andy
**Light,** Michael
**Misrach,** Richard
**Muniz,** Vik
**Sicilia,** Jose Maria
**Sugimoto,** Hiroshi
**Turrell,** James
**Virtue,** John

MICHAEL WEBB FINE ART
(Page 144)
**Armfield,** Edward

**Armfield,** George
**Bond,** W.J.J.C.
**Breakspear,** John
**Browne,** E. of Coventry
**Calvert,** Henry
**Cleminson,** Robert
**Cockram,** George
**Cox,** David
**Duncan,** Edward
**Fielding,** A.V. Copley
**Fontville de**
**Breanski,** Alfred
**Foster,** Birket
**Fox,** Henry Charles
**Gregory,** George
**Hagarty,** Mary S.
**Hardy,** Thomas Bush
**Hart,** Thomas
**Holland,** James
**Holland,** John
**Howard,** Squire
**Ireland,** Thomas
**Jamieson,** Alex
**Kelly,** Talbot
**King,** H.J. Yeend
**Knell,** William Callcott
**Knowles,** Fred J.
**Lines,** Henry H.
**Maiden,** Joseph
**Martin,** E.H.
**Mason,** Frank H.
**Nightingale,** Basil
**Passey,** Charles
**Powell,** Alfred
**Richardson,** Charles
**Rickman,** Philip C.
**Roe,** Clarence
**Roe,** Colin Graeme
**Rope,** George Thomas
**Shalders,** George
**Sherrin,** Daniel
Simone
**Spencelash,** Charles
**Tunnicliffe,** Charles Frederick
**Valter,** Florence
**Wainwright,** T.F.
**Walker,** Eaton
**Wane,** Richard
**Watson,** Robert
**Watson,** William R.C. Jnr
**Williams,** Owen

Milmo-Penny Fine Art Ltd
(Page 157)
**Burke,** Augustus N.
**Forbes,** Stanhope
**Garstin,** Norman
**Guinness,** May
**Hamilton,** Eva
**Hamilton,** Letitia
**Henry,** Grace
**Henry,** Paul
**Hill,** Nathaniel
**Hone,** Evie
**Hone,** Nathaniel
**Jellett,** Mainie
**Kavanagh,** Joseph M.
**Lavery,** John
**Leech,** William J.
**Moynan,** Thomas
**O Brien,** Dermod
**O'Conor,** Roderic
**O'Kelly,** Aloysius
**O'Meara,** Frank
**O'Reilly,** Joseph
**Orpen,** William
**Osborne,** Walter
**Purser,** Sarah
**Russell,** George
**Somerville,** Edith
**Swanzy,** Mary
**Thaddeus,** Henry J.
**Yeats,** Jack B.
**Young,** Mabel

Modern Artists Gallery
(Page 117)
**Armitage,** David
**Bryson,** Katriona
**Daw,** Carol
**Griffiths,** Edla
**Kessling ,** Paul
**Schlee,** Nick
**Thomas,** Kathryn
**Williams ,** Helen

Montage Studio Gallery
(Page 126)
**Atkinson,** Sue
**Booker,** David
**Bryan,** Maureen
**Burden,** Alan
**Carter,** Barry
**Carter,** John
**Clark,** John Jake
**Clements,** Mark
**Cozens,** Ken
**Crawford,** Phillipa
**Cumming,** Anna
**Davies,** Roger
**Davis,** Alan
**Dickinson,** Kaff
**Draft,** Ernst
**Foard,** Tony
**Halsey,** Mark
**Herbert,** Stephen
**Hicks,** Peter
**Hidden,** Stella
**Howarth,** Anne
**Hurst,** Dagmar
**Iredale,** Steve
**Isaak,** Eryka
**Kershaw,** John
**Lindars,** Stephen
**Lowe,** Graham
**Mayes,** Emerson
**McCulley,** Ian
**Moss,** David
**Naughton,** James
**Palma,** Antonio
**Poskitt,** Pam
**Prosser,** Deborah
**Rookledge,** Gavin
**Routledge,** Guy
**Shaw,** Robert
**Shaw,** Sue
**Spencer,** Sheila
**Stevenson,** Matt
**Wilde,** Sue
**Zytka,** Gosia

The Museum Of Modern Art, Wales
(Page 149)
**Arnold,** Ann
**Arnold,** Graham
**Baines,** Glyn
**Bala,** Iwan
**Boydell Rogers,** John
**Briscoe,** Mike
**Burgess,** Cefyn
**Cecil,** Roger
**Davies,** Ogwyn
**Heeks,** Diana
**Holmes,** Clyde
**Isaac,** Bert
**Lloyd-Jones,** Mary
**Parry,** Iwan Gwyn
**Plant,** Laurie
**Prichard,** Gwilym
**Webster,** Catrin
**Williams,** Catrin
**Williams,** Claudia
**Yeomans,** Geoff

Mutch Art
(Page 180)
**Darke,** Sally
**Francis,** Lucy
**Mutch,** Gil
**Richards,** Sally
**Sloss,** Sheila

Nairi Sahakian Contemporary Art
(Page 70)
**Abovian,** Ruben
**Bagdassarian,** Samvel
**Barber,** Claire
**Cattle,** Rachel
**Curneen,** Claire
**Douglas Camp,** Sokari
**Gevorkian,** Armen
**Hamalbashian,** Sarkis
**Lewis,** Peter
**Niederberger,** Christina
**Sakuma,** Hana
**Sansom,** Peter

Neffe-Degandt
(Page 70)
**Bonnard,** Pierre
**Corot,** J.B.C.
**Degas,** Edgar
**Denis,** Maurice
**Dufy,** Raoul
**Guillaumin,** J.B.A.
**Luce,** Maximilien
**Marquet,** Albert
**Morisot,** Berthe
**Pissarro,** Camille
**Roussel,** Ker Xavier
**Signac,** Paul
**Vuillard,** Edouard

Nevill Gallery
(Page 108)
**Agoust,** Loes
**Alexander,** Gregory
**Alexander,** Matthew
**Arbus,** David
**Armour-Chelu,** Ian
**Bailey,** Clifford
**Bailey,** Dennis Rothwell
**Bellany,** John
**Bliss,** Ian
**Carey,** Shaun
**Chaplin,** Michael
**Clarke,** Graham
**Cuming,** Fred
**Fitzgerald,** Sue

**Flyn,** Diana
**Flyn,** Dianne
**Ginger,** Phillis
**Goodall,** John Strickland
**Goode,** Mervyn
**Greenwood,** Ernest
**Haskins,** John
**Hedley,** Paul
**Howat,** Andrew
**Jay,** Peter
**Johns,** Phil
**Junes,** Godfrey
**Kay,** Pamela
**Madgwick,** Clive
**Myers,** Bernard
**Napp,** David
**Raud,** Terrace
**Tyson,** Roul
**Wheeler,** Julie
**Yardley,** Bruce

NEW ACADEMY GALLERY AND BUSINESS ART GALLERIES
(Page 70)
**Atherton,** Barry
**Barry,** Jo
**Bigger,** Clare
**Blackmore,** Clive
**Blake,** Naomi
**Brokenshire,** John
**Chinnery,** Clare
**Corsellis,** Jane
**Creswell,** Alexander
**Dover,** Peter
**Dunstan,** Bernard
**Fraser,** Donald Hamilton
**Gore,** Frederick
**Grant,** Alistair
**Hartill,** Brenda
**Hocking,** Susan-Jayne
**Holliday,** Sarah
**Holmes,** Katherine
**Macara,** Andrew
**Macmiadhachain,** Padraig
**Mandl,** Anita
**Noach,** Michèle
**Norris,** Linda
**Piper,** John
**Rizvi,** Jacqueline
**Roberts,** Keith
**Rubens,** Zoe
**Schwarz,** Hans
**Vyner,** Tim
**Walker,** Richard
**Wray,** Peter

NEW ART CENTRE SCULPTURE PARK AND GALLERY
(Page 202)
**Adams,** Robert
**Armitage,** Kenneth
**Ayrton,** Michael
**Barratt,** Oliver
**Berman,** Brenda
**Breeze,** Gary
**Burke,** Peter
**Butler,** Reg
**Chadwick,** Lynn
**Colonna,** Marzia
**Cox,** Stephen
**Crowther,** Alison
**Dalwood,** Hubert
**Das Gupta,** John
**Davie,** Alan
**Deacon,** Richard
**Derges,** Susan
**Devereux,** Richard
**Frink,** Elisabeth
**Furuta,** Hideo
**Gormley,** Antony
**Hall,** Nigel
**Harrisson,** Tim
**Hepworth,** Barbara
**Jennings,** Martin
**Johns,** Greg
**Jones,** Allen
**Jones,** Jenifer
**Kennethson,** George
**King,** Phillip
**Kneale,** Bryan
**Kovats,** Tania
**Lasdun,** William
**Le Brun,** Christopher
**Long,** Richard
**Lowe,** Jean
**McCrum,** Bridget
**McWilliam,** F.E.
**Meadows,** Bernard
**Morris,** Derek
**Mount,** Paul
**Mowbray,** Joanna
**Nagare,** Masayuki
**Nash,** David
**Neilson,** John
**Nevelson,** Louise
**O'Connell,** Eilis
**Paladino,** Mimmo
**Paolozzi,** Eduardo
**Peever,** Alec
**Peever,** Fiona
**Perry,** Richard
**Rance,** Victoria
**Randall-Page,** Peter
**Rennertz,** Karl Manfred
**Renshaw,** Richard
**Roberts Holmes,** Paul
**Rosa,** Alvaro de la
Sadiq
**Salisbury,** James
**Shapiro,** Joel
**Spencer Watson,** Mary
**Stahler,** Franz
**Stirling,** Annet
**Thewlis,** Alan
**Thomas,** Simon
**Twyford,** Kit
**Viney,** Tony
**Watts,** Meical
**Wentworth,** Richard
**Whiteread,** Rachel
**Wilding,** Alison
**Wilding,** Alison
**Wilks,** Claire
**Woodrow,** Bill
**Woodrow,** Bill
**Wright,** Austin

NEW ASHGATE GALLERY
(Page 109)
**Angus,** Nancy
**Barlow ,** Phyllida
**Belmonte,** Julian
**Belsher,** Holly
**Blow,** Sandra
**Bond,** Marj
**Brown,** Ruta
**Bunzl,** Biddy
**Caines,** Susan
**Carpanini,** David
**Clapcott,** Helen
**Dean,** Graham
**Draper,** Kenneth
**Dunbar,** Emma
**Eastop,** Geoffrey
**Fairclough,** Michael
**Foord,** Susan
**Grevatte,** Jenny
**Hayes,** Peter
**Kiely,** David
**Klein,** Anita
**Lawson,** Sonia
**Lieberman,** Sybil
**Malenoir,** Mary
**Malenoir,** Mary
**Maltby,** John
**Martini,** Babette
**Millais,** Fiona
**Muszynski,** Leszek
**New,** Keith
**Newcomb ,** Tessa
**O' Casey,** Breon
**Parkinson,** Peter
**Phipps,** Howard
**Pye,** William
**Robertson,** Carol
**Ross,** Duncan
**Ross,** Vivienne
**Royle,** Guy
**Salmon,** Chris
**See-Paynton,** Colin
**Smith,** Pippa
**Spackman,** Sarah
**Theakston,** Anthony
**Tillotsen,** Edmund
**Vlassopoulis,** Tina
**Wawrzniak,** Ewa
**Whishaw,** Anthony
**Zelinski,** Pauline

NEW GRAFTON GALLERY
(Page 71)
**Adlington,** Mark
**Bailey,** Julian
**Bowey,** Olwyn
**Bowyer,** Jason
**Brooke,** Peter
**Campion,** Oliver
**Campion,** Sue
**Chalmers,** Sarah
**Coates,** Tom
**Craigmyl,** Anthea
**Cuming,** Fred
**Dowling,** Jane
**Dubery,** Fred
**Fedden,** Mary
**Gaa,** Christa
**Gammon,** Reg
**Greenham,** Peter
**Hall,** Christopher
**Hayes,** Colin
**Herman,** Josef
**Hocking,** Susan-Jayne
**Matthews,** Laura
**Nash,** John
**Newland,** Paul
**Pikesley,** Richard
**Rooney,** Mick
**Sloga,** Alison
**Spencer,** Liam

**Spencer,** Sarah
**Todd Warmouth,** Pip
**Trotter,** Josephine
**Weight,** Carel
**Williams,** Jacqueline
**Yeoman,** Martin

NEWLYN ART GALLERY
(Page 113)
**Annear,** Jeremy
**Armitage,** Catherine
**Atkins,** Ray
**Barns-Graham,** Wilhelmina
**Bealing,** Nicola
**Blackmore,** Clive
**Blow,** Sandra
**Bourne,** Bob
**Buxton,** Judy
**Calonder,** Rudolf
**Cook,** Barrie
**Cook,** Richard
**Dove,** Steve
**Dyson,** Julian
**Emanuel,** John
**Evans,** Audrey
**Evans,** Bernard
**Finn,** Michael
**Freeman,** Ralph
**Frost,** Anthony
**Frost,** Sir Terry
**Gilcrest,** Joan
**Hilton,** Rose
**Hogben,** Phil
**Jackson,** Kurt
**Joan,** Gilcrest
**Jones,** Robert
**Lanyon,** Andrew
**Mackenzie,** Alexander
**Maeckelberghe,** Margo
**McClary,** Louise
**McClure,** Daphne
**McDowall,** Carole
**Miles,** June
**Miller,** John
**O'Casey,** Breon
**Pearce,** Bryan
**Picard,** Biddy
**Piper,** John
**Praed,** Michael
**Ray,** Roy
**Stork,** Mary
**Symonds,** Ken
**Upton,** Michael
**Walker,** Roy
**Watkiss,** Gill
**Weyersberg,** Angela
**Yates,** Fred
**Zia,** Partou

NORSELANDS GALLERY
(Page 106)
**Browne-Wilkinson,** Fiona
**Cartmel-Crossley,** John
**Dobson,** Bruce
**Doherty,** Joan
**Evans,** Judy
**Gomar-Stone,** Barbara
**Gooderham,** Paul
**Kellam,** Colin
**Mallinson,** Pat
**Miles,** Gordon
**Rawlinson,** Veronica
**Sanders,** Andrew
**Trevena,** Shirley
**Wallace,** David
**Williams,** Julian
**Worthy,** Diana

NORTH DOWN VISITORS AND HERITAGE CENTRE
(Page 156)
**Devon,** Gary
**Priers,** Julian

NUMBER NINE THE GALLERY
(Page 122)
**Autiginof,** Vadimir
**Badham,** Glenn
**Begbie,** David
**Benjamins,** Arthur
**Black,** Antonia
**Blowzone,** Glass
**Brough,** Helen
**Chambers,** Mic
**Clarke,** Don
**Cockeyne,** Ruth
**Fountain,** Sarah
**Garrard,** Rose
**Gittens,** Paul
**Goodwin-Jones,** Richard
**Grant,** Keith
**Hoskins,** Knighton
**Keen,** Alice
**Keevil,** Melanie
**Lamba,** Juginder
**Linzel Smith,** Jules
**MacPherson,** Dolly
**Pearsh,** Kevin
**Phillips,** Tony
**Prentice,** David
**Prentice,** Dinah
**Roberts,** Brian
**Schrecher,** Jeremy
**Scott-Wilkie,** Pam
**Sutton,** Jake
**Sutton,** Philip
**Underhill,** Craig
**Walker,** Belle
**Willmott,** Charles

OBJECT 57
(Page 101)
**Constantine,** Elaine
**Cook,** Ben
**Dant,** Adam
**Diggle,** Philip
**Fry,** Nick
**Huws,** Elin
**Johnson,** Trevor
Lansley & Bendon
**O' Shaughnessy,** Michael
**Saville,** Peter
**Shard,** Jon
**Walsh,** Jon

THE OCTOBER GALLERY
(Page 71)
**Amaringo,** Pablo
**Anatsui,** El
**Aukomah,** Owusu
**Beckwith,** Carol
**Burroughs,** William S.
**Clarke,** LeRoy
**Cohen,** Ira
**Fame,** Ruki
**Glover,** Ablade
**Harding,** Marie
**Jegede,** Emmanuel Taiwo
**Kanage,** Mathias
**Kundun,** Gickmai
**Lalouschek,** Elisabeth
**Mendive,** Manuel
**Napangardi,** Eunice
**Odunlade,** Tunde
**Oloruntoba,** Z.O.
**Ouobrakpeya,** Bruce
**Quenum,** Gerard
**Rios,** Yando
**Rubio,** Julieta
**Seven Seven,** Twins
**Shawa,** Laila
**SINZOGAN,** Julieu
Wijdan
**Wilde,** Gerald
**Williams,** Aubrey
**Yoshida,** Kenji
**Zhong Min,** Xu

OGILVY & ESTILL
(Page 146)
**Chapman,** David
**Clarke,** Pat
**Clay,** Andie
**Cook,** Nalini Shanthi
**Cottrel,** David
**Duffy,** Terry
**Forbes,** Andrew
**Hocknell,** Shelley
**Jacobs,** Phillipa
**Jones,** Tom
**Lek,** Karel
**Lewis,** Ann
**Lloyd Griffith,** David
**Lloyd-Jones,** Mary
**Norris,** Linda
**Roberts,** Wilf
**Selwyn,** William
**Smith,** Alan Albert
**Wood,** Ray
**Wouda,** Marjan
**Wynne,** Bill

OLD TOWN HALL
(Page 96)
**Boon,** Anneli
**Clemmons,** Angela
**Cuthbert,** Julie
**Dobson,** Sue
**Geraghty,** Frances
**Hadland,** Michelle
**Hillier,** Christine
**Holloway,** Ley
**Human,** Paul
**Jones,** Sally-Ann
**Lord,** Daphne
**Marianne,** Nash
**Pheby,** Andrew
**Pragnall,** Kim
**Riley,** Fran
**Rolfe,** Peter
**Stern,** Jill
**Tipping,** Simon
**Wenman-Jones,** Joy
**Wright,** Charlotte

OPEN EYE GALLERY
(Page 134)
**Barnes,** Paul
**Bellany,** John
**Birnie,** William

**Black**, Colin
**Blackadder**, Elizabeth
**Bond**, Marj
**Bourne**, Peter
**Bowen**, Keith
**Bridge**, Eoghan
**Brown**, John
**Bushe**, Chris
**Carrington**, Sarah
**Christiansen**, Mary
**Donald**, George
**Fairley**, Rob
**Gibbs**, Jonathan
**Harrigan**, Claire
**Howson**, Peter
**Knox**, Jack
**Kondracki**, Henry
**Laurie**, Simon
**Lewis**, Whyn
**MacDonald**, Frances
**MacQueen**, Charles
**Mangan**, Stephen
**McInnes**, Jock
**McIntosh**, Archibald Dunbar
**McLellan**, Abigail
**Mitchell**, Gordon K.
**Morrocco**, Alberto
**Morrocco**, Leon
**Murphy**, Sandy
**Nagl**, Hazel
**Patrick**, Ann
**Philipson**, Sir Robin
**Rae**, Barbara
**Rodger**, Willie
**Roper**, Geoffrey
**Ross**, Ann
**Rossi**, Carlo
**Scofield**, David
**Scouller**, Glen
**Stirling**, Dorothy
**Stiven**, Charles
**Thompson**, Bonnie
**Withers**, Kirsty
**Woodside**, Christine
**Wyllie**, George

ORBOST GALLERY
**(Page 138)**
**Aldersley**, Jill
**Archbold**, John
**Kershaw**, Paul L.
**McMorrine**, Andrew
**Prosser**, David
**Roberts**, David
**Roberts**, Marion
**Stewart**, Angus
**Theys**, Freddy

ORIEL PLAS GLYN-Y-WEDDW
**(Page 147)**
**Ainsworth**, George
**Ap Tomos**, Gwynneth
**Baines**, Glyn
**Baines**, Glyn
**Ball**, Gerry
**Belshaw**, Beverley
**Bensken Mesher**, Sonia
**Bevan**, Vaughan
**Buff**, John
**Campbell**, Alex
**Clark**, Francis
**Clay**, Andie
**Coles**, Howard
**Davies**, Ivor
**Gadd**, Gerald
**Ganz**, Valerie
**Goble**, Tony
**Hedley**, John
**Herman**, Josef
**Hocknell**, Shelley
**Hunt** , Sue
**Huws**, Elin
**Iffla**, Kathy
**Jeffreys**, Elain
**Jones**, Aneurin
**Jones**, Cyril
**Jones**, Elfyn
**Jordan**, Valerie
**Kaldowski**, Mariusz
**Kelsey**, Gillian
**Kent**, Colin
**Lek**, Karel
**MacIntyre**, Donald
**McGutcheon**, Andrew
**Mroczkowska**, Alina
**Nechamkin**, Sarah
**Pell**, John
**Piercy**, Rob
**Pritchard**, Gwylim
**Roberts**, Will
**Sax-Ledger**, Maria
**Selwyn**, William
**Spafford**, George
**Spafford**, Iola
**Stevens**, Margaret
**Sutton**, Philip
**Ten Bosch**, Christina
**Thomas**, Gareth
**Thomas Williams**, David
**Tress**, David
**Williams**, Catrin
**Williams**, Claudia
**Williams Ellis**, Bronwen
**Williams**, James A
**Williams**, Kyffin
**Yates**, Jeremy

THE OSBORNE STUDIO GALLERY
**(Page 71)**
**Blackwell**, Tony
**Church**, Charles
**Cloherty**, Cloe
**Cursham**, Juliet
**De Watrigant**, Hubert
**Doyle**, John
**Evans**, Susan
**Gilbert**, Terence
**Golden**, Lynn
**Grieg**, Donald
**Halford-Thompson**, Constance
**Hemmings**, David
**Hurlbert**, Patricia
**Insoll**, Chris
**Jonas**, Johnny
**King**, John
**Koehler**, Henry
**Luff**, Ashley
**Maclean**, Sarah
**Matthews**, Harry
**Moore**, Margaret
**Newton**, Tom
**O'Sullivan**, Katie
**Parsons**, Elizabeth
**Penny**, Caroline
**Richards**, Colin
**Starey**, Penelope
**Taylor**, Jo
**Trowell**, Jonathon
**Upton**, Mark
**Whitcomb**, Susie
**Williams**, Martin

OTTERTON MILL GALLERY
**(Page 114)**
**Acworth**, Carol
**Carter**, Kenneth
**Cook**, Beryl
**Erland**, Sukey
**Golesworthy**, Joana
**Hartley**, Ben
**Lane**, Martin
**Lloyd**, Liz
**Silverthorne**, Penny
**Smith**, Keith
**Stafford**, John
**Stafford**, Sheila
**Watson**, Andrew

OXO TOWER WHARF
**(Page 167)**
**Burrows**, Pauline
**Fadda**, Caterina
**Selim**, Anne
**Watkins**, Miranda

PATON GALLERY
**(Page 71)**
**Clark**, Jake
**Guild**, Derrick
**Guy**, Alexander
**Hatton**, Nicholas
**Inglis**, Judy
**James**, Shani Rhys
**Langley**, Jane
**Mabbutt**, Mary
**Major**, Julie
**Ollivier**, Tim
**Palmer**, Kate
**Snell**, Rosie
**Vargas**, Cecilia
**Veness**, Alex

PENWITH GALLERIES
**(Page 113)**
**Barns-Graham**, Wilhelmina
**Bedding**, John
**Cardew**, Ara
**Cardew**, Seth
**Chandler**, Jill
**Clutterbuck**, Stephen
**Conn**, Roy
**Cooper**, Waistel
**Corser**, Trevor
**Cross**, Tom
**Crossley**, Bob
**Culwick**, Robert
**Dove**, Stephen
**Emanuel**, John
**Feiler**, Paul
**Freeman**, Ralph
**Frost**, Sir Terry
**John**, Alan
**Jones**, Robert
**Leach**, Janet
**Legrice**, Jeremy
**Maeckelberghe**, Margo
**Marshall**, William
**McClure**, Daphne
**McNally**, Kathy

**Miles,** June
**Mitchell,** Denis
**Mount,** Paul
**Nicholson,** Kate
**O'Casey,** Breon
**O'Malley,** Tony
**Oliner,** Sheila
**Pearce,** Bryan
**Piper,** John
**Praed,** Michael
**Ritman,** Lieke
**Semmens,** Jennifer
**Stork,** Mary
**Sumray,** Maurice
**Symonds,** Ken
**Walker,** Roy
**Ward,** Peter
**Wells,** John
**Wilson,** Vincent

PETER POTTER GALLERY
(Page 133)
**Ambrozevich,** Carmen
**Cohen,** Kirstie
**Demancyck,** Irma
**Frame,** Ian
**Gold,** Andrew
**Hall,** Marg
**Harrison,** Tobias
**Hemingsley,** David
**Henderson,** Ro
**Hunwick,** David
**Inglis,** Jamie
**Kinngar,** Maggie and Ian
**Laing,** Rowena
**Law,** Frances
**Lee,** Mandy
**Lenaghan,** Brenda
**Linstead,** Julia
**Lyon,** Simone
**Maguire,** John
**McLean,** Silvana
**Meikle,** Annabel
**Montgomery,** Pauline
**Muir,** Graham
**Outram,** Cat
**Phillips,** Sheena
**Ritchie,** Paul
**Robinson,** David
**Russell,** Neil
**Senior,** Susan
**Simmill,** Caroline
**Sinclair,** Carol
**Southall,** Ken
**Stephen,** Sheana
**Turquand,** Patti
**Watt,** Lorna
**Weightman,** Alison
**Westwick,** Pamela
**Whiteoaks,** Sue
**Whiteoaks,** Sue

PETERS BARN GALLERY
(Page 110)
**Bailey,** Walter
**Bailey ,** Walter
**Bryars,** Jill
**Chaikin,** Michael
**De Choisy,** Kevin
**Dupré,** Marie-Frédérique
**Farrar,** Simeon
**French,** Neal
**Gregory,** Ian
**Gregory,** Ian
**Hancox,** Jennie
**Homoky,** Nicholas
**Hoskins,** Stephen
**Hoskins,** Steven
**Jupp,** Mo
**Jupp,** Mo
**Keeler,** Walter
**Keeler,** Walter
**Keeney ,** Christie
**Knott,** Margaret
**Knott,** Margaret
**Lee-Turrell,** Elizabeth
**Lees,** Nicholas
**Mara,** Alice
**Munn,** Annabel
**Munn,** Annabel
**Murphy,** Kathie
**Ottey,** Piers
**Pearson,** Colin
**Pearson,** Colin
**Ramrayka,** Jacqui
**Schroeder,** Kjersti
**Scott,** Sally
**Sharpe,** Miranda
**Sula,** Artur
**Sutton,** Ann
**Turrell,** Elizabeth
**Wyndham,** Annabet
**Yufanli,** Jacqueline

PICCADILLY GALLERY LTD.
(Page 72)
**Berg,** Adrian
**Green,** Anthony
**Greenland,** Martin
**Held,** Julie
**Kelly,** John
**Morley,** John
**Murfin,** Michael
**Ovenden,** Graham
**Parker,** Alan
**Tumim,** Matilda
**Turnbull,** Peter
**Wilkins,** William

PICTURE HOUSE GALLERIES
(Page 113)
**Aspden,** Gail
**Bascombe,** Linda
**Christophers,** Julian
**Cockerall,** Rachel
**Cooper,** William
**Davies,** Emma
**Duplock,** Albert
**Garritt,** Daphne
**Glaister,** Fiona
**Hardings,** Sasha
**Hart,** Simon
**Holland,** Emma
**Hoskings,** David
**Kendrick,** Jane
**Micklethwaite,** Chrissie
**Richards,** Mark
**Ross,** Vivienne
**Saville,** Michael
**Shakspeare,** William
**Smith,** Nicole
**Wardell,** Sasha
**Windridge,** Eliza

PLAZZOTTA LTD
(Page 72)
**Plazzotta,** Enzo

PORTAL GALLERY
(Page 72)
**Allin,** John
**Aris,** Fred
**Broomfield,** Frances
**Byrne,** John
**Carter,** Bernard
**Castle,** Barry
**Castle,** Philip
**Cheepen,** David
**Clark,** Terry
**Cook,** Beryl
**Copas,** Ronnie
**Copeland,** Mark
**Cornner,** Haydn
**Cudworth,** Nick
**Easby,** Steve
**Grainger,** James
**Lawman,** Peter
**Layzell,** Peter
**Le Bas,** Philip
**Lewis,** Jane
**Lloyd,** James
**Lyon,** Charlotte
**McNaught,** James
**Neville,** Pat
**Pepper,** Reg
**Riches,** Lizzie
**Rozot,** Isabelle
**Taplin,** Guy
**Turpin,** Emma
**Ward,** Graham
**Williams,** Kit

POSK GALLERY
(Page 72)
**Baranowska,** Janina
**Borkowski,** Andrzej
**Dankiewicz,** Krystyna
**Dawidowski,** Andrzej
**Elaszkiewicz,** Andrzej
**Falkowski,** Wojciech
**Gierc,** Danuta
**Hojak-Mysko,** Elzbieta
**Jaczynska,** Maria
**Jaffe,** Ilona
**Lotringer,** Ludwig
**Lubomirski de Voux,** Stefan
**Lurczynski,** Mieczyslaw
**Nekanda-Trepko,** Halina
**Piesakowska,** Danuta
**Pytel,** Zygmunt
**Skolimowski,** Staszka
**Slaski,** Peter
**Smart,** Alan
**Werner,** Aleksander
**Zoltowski,** Adam
**Zwolinska-Brzeski,** Teresa

PRATT CONTEMPORARY ART/PRATT EDITIONS
(Page 174)
**Edalatpour,** Seyed M.S.
**Goncalves,** Pitagoras Lopes
**Kenny RA,** Michael
**Krokfors,** Kristian
**Nogueira Fleury,** Leonam
**Pacheco,** Ana Maria
**Rahmanzadeh,** Akram
**Rees Roberts,** Marcus

PRIMAVERA

(Page 167)
**Barker,** Patrick
**Batterham,** Richard
**Bauman,** Lydia
**Beard,** Peter
**Betts,** Malcolm
**Blanthorn,** Brian
**Bowen,** Clive
**Brennand Wood,** Michael
**Caines,** Susan
**Cartwright,** Ashley
**Constantinides,** Joanna
**Cornwell,** Jeremy
**Cowen,** Gina
**Creese,** Susannah
**Crouch,** Andrew
**De Waal,** Edmund
**Fanshawe Kato,** Jill
**Forrest,** Marianne
**Gilmour,** Judith
**Harris,** Charmain
**Henley,** Nicola
**Hough,** Catherine
**Hussey,** Dan
**Krinos,** Daphne
**Lambert,** Anna
**Layton,** Peter
**Leach,** David
**Long,** Maurice
**Mackmaidhachain,** Padraig
**Maltby,** John
**Mannheim,** Catherine
**Martin,** Guy
**McDowell,** Leo
**Meddings,** Camilla
**Newcomb,** Tessa
**Newell,** Stephen
**Owen,** Elspeth
**Pearson,** Colin
**Race,** Robert
**Ramshaw,** Wendy
**Ray,** Jane
**Scott,** Mike
**Spira,** Rupert
**Taplin,** Guy
**Tookey,** Fleur
**Watson,** Janet

PRYORY ART
(Page 72)
**Bennett,** Hafdis
**Berry,** Renu
**Burgess,** Andres
**Cardash,** Alan
**De Beaumorel,** G.
**Espeth,** Katrine
**Gerrard,** Charlotte
**Goldschuidt,** Eileen
**Goode,** Natalie
**Gori,** Emanuele
**Keulshiemer,** Pam
**Konyn,** Gillian
**Lass,** Cindy
**Lewers,** Jessica
**Lowe,** Roz
**Nastasic,** Drasan
**Oberheumer,** Christopher
**Parsons,** Stella
**Rockberger,** Polly
**Simler,** Marilyn
**Todd,** Janet

PURDY HICKS GALLERY
(Page 73)
**Budd,** Rachel
**Cockrill,** Maurice
**Di Stefano,** Arturo
**Egan,** Felim
**Fleck,** Ralph
**Hiscock,** David
**Jackowski,** Andrzej
**Johnson,** Glenys
**Kenny,** Paul
**Luzzati,** Mariannita
**Montag,** Daro
**O'Donoghue,** Hughie
**Porter,** Michael
**Smith,** Dillwyn
**Thompson,** Estelle
**Zimmer,** Bernd

PYMS GALLERY
(Page 73)
**Clausen,** George
**Forbes,** Stanhope
**Harpignies,** H.J.
**Henry,** Paul
**Hone,** Nathaniel
**Jellett,** Mainie
**John,** Augustus
**Keating,** Sean
**La Thangue,** H.H.
**Lavery,** John
**Leech,** William
**McDonnell,** Hector
**Millet,** Jean-Francois
**O'Conor,** Roderic
**Orpen,** William
**Osborne,** Walter
**Pryde,** James
**Sickert,** Walter
**Swanzy,** Mary
**Yeats,** Jack B.

REBECCA HOSSACK GALLERY
(Page 73)
**Audu,** Osi
**Bannantyne,** Aileen
**Benjamin,** Jason
**Bhatt,** Akash
**Boyd,** Arthur
**Bromley ,** David
**Brosnan,** Shaun
**Brownhall,** Robert
**Bullock,** Caroline
**Bushman,** African
**Casson,** Lucy
**Clark,** Peter
**Cronshaw,** Edward
**Davie,** Joseph
**Done,** Ken
**Farrar,** David
**Farrelly,** Jimmy
**Faucon,** Bernard
**Flockhart,** Helen
**Fransella,** Graham
**Hobden,** Catherine
**Kauage,** Mathias
**Landels,** Willie
**Law ,** Rodger
**Lewis,** Tracy
**MacFarlane,** Barbara
**Mackenzie,** Alexander
**McLellan,** Abigail
**Meddings,** Camilla
**Moore,** David
**Moriarty,** Paul
**Moss,** Nicola
**Nolan,** Sidney
**Pike,** Jinmy
**Pollock,** Fred
**Possum,** Clifford
**Small,** Pippa
**Smith,** Justine
**Stokes,** Ann
**Sutton,** Jilly
**Thompson,** Peter
**Trebinski,** Gabriella
**Udin,** Shaffique
**Wallace,** Alasdair
**Whittaker,** David
**Wood,** Christopher
**Wyllie,** George

REYNOLDS FINE ART
(Page 95)
**Bachmann,** David
**Bassingthwaighte,** Paul
**Durban,** Ronald
**Hare,** Derek
**Kennaway,** Emma
**Mantle,** Maureen
**Newton,** William
**Outram,** Steven
**Pinkster,** Anna
**Scott,** Henry
**Tong,** Belinda
**Yates,** John

ROGER BILLCLIFFE FINE ART
(Page 137)
**Ambery-Smith,** Vicki
**Behrens,** Reinhard
**Boyd,** John
**Bukvic,** Nina
**Bushe,** Chris
**Craxford,** Alan
**Durning,** Michael
**Edgar,** Norman
**Fullarton,** James
**Goudie,** Alexander
**Hicks,** Jeremy
**Howson,** Peter
**Laurie,** Simon
**Martin,** David
**McArthur,** Christine
**McInnes,** Sheila
**McIntosh,** Archibald Dunbar
**McIntosh,** Jane
**McQueen,** Charles
**Mitchell,** Gordon
**O'Dwyer,** Kevin
**Payne,** Brett
**Shanks,** Duncan
**Spira,** Rupert
**Squire,** Andrew
**Stewart,** Alison
**Whiteside,** Zoe
**Woodside,** Christine

ROYAL INTERNATIONAL PAVILION
(Page 146)
**Davies,** Maggie
**Dutton,** Tracey
**Griffith,** David
**Palmer,** Jane
**Price-Jones,** David

RUBICON GALLERY

(Page 158)
**Bolay,** Veronica
**Clear,** Felicity
**Collie,** Clifford
**Colman,** Eamon
**Copperwhite,** Diana
**Cotter,** Maud
**Drummond,** Blaise
**Du Pasquier,** Nathalie
**Gillian,** Mary Avril
**Groener,** Anita
**Hanlon,** Marie
**Harding,** Alexis
**Harrington,** Aoife
**Hughes,** Ronnie
**Jordan,** Eithne
**Kane,** Michael
**Miller,** Nick
**Molloy,** Tom
**Morrisson,** Margaret
**O'Donoghue,** Hughie
**Roche,** Vivienne
**Teskey,** Donald
**Walsh,** Samuel

RUSSIAN ARTS GALLERY - GZHEL (UK)
(Page 73)
**Bessonov,** B.
**Boyadzhan,** Alexander
**Cholaria,** Igor
**Galumov,** Edward
**Grasimov,** Alexander
**Ivanov,** Alexander
**Kakhiani,** Nugzar
**Kirilov,** A.
**Kiryanov,** Alexei
**Kiseleva,** Alla
**Konstantinov,** Fyodor
**Shapaev,** Feodor
**Sokolov,** H.
**Tutunov,** A.
**Tyagunov,** V.

RYE ART GALLERY
(Page 108)
**Adams,** Richard
**Bolton,** Michael
**Clarke,** Graham
**Cole,** Wally
**Cummins,** Gus
**Fanarof,** Sam
**Greenhalf,** Robert
**Hunnex,** John
**Newington,** Charles
**Nigoumi,** Vicki
**Pilcher,** Terry
**Purser,** Keith
**Smith,** Davida
**Soudain,** Annie
**Staermose,** Robert
**Tipple,** Barbara
**Townsend,** Keith
**Turpin,** Beryl
**Turpin,** Emma
**Turpin,** Louis

SABLE AND HOGG GALLERIES
(Page 149)
**Bennett,** Jane
**Conway,** Jennifer
**Egbers,** Michael
**Hodges,** Gary
**Joinson,** Gerald
**Keal,** Jenny
**King,** Michael
**Kinnersley,** Jim
**Preston,** James
**Stevens,** Meg
**Thomas,** Jonathan
**Wetherilt,** Terry
**Williams,** Alex

SALFORD MUSEUM & ART GALLERY
(Page 102)
**Lowry,** L.S.

SCHOOL HOUSE GALLERY
(Page 98)
**Abrahams,** Ruth
**Ackroyd,** Norman
**Benjamin,** Anthony
**Blanche,** Jean-Pierre
**Bolton,** Janet
**Boycott-Brown,** Michael
**Cohen,** Alfred
**Evans,** David
**Frink,** Elisabeth
**Fuller,** Moss
**Gill,** Eric
**Greaves,** Derrick
**Hill,** Andrew
**Hockney,** David
**Lee,** Dick
**Morris,** Derek
**Mutch,** Gil
**Neville,** Alison
**Newcomb,** Tessa
**Rubens,** Sula
**Smith,** Ivy
**Taylor,** Jo
**Theobald,** Dominic
**Tidman,** Bruer
**Weir,** Malcolm

SCOLAR FINE ART/GORDON SAMUEL
(Page 74)
**Aitchison,** Craigie
**Alechinsky,** Pierre
**Andrews,** Sybil
**Bacon,** Francis
**Bissiere,** Roger
**Bomberg,** David
**Buckland-Wright,** John
**Burton,** Richmond
**Chagall,** Marc
**Dickson,** Jane
**Flight,** Claude
**Frost,** Sir Terry
**Greengrass,** William
**Gross,** Anthony
**Hayter,** S.W.
**Hepworth,** Barbara
**Hermes,** Gertrude
**Hockney,** David
**Hughes-Stanton,** Blair
**Ingham,** Bryan
**Jones,** David
**kenny,** Michael
**Krut,** Ansel
**Lanyon,** Peter
**Matisse,** Henri
**Miró,** Joan
**Moore,** Henry
**Nash,** Paul
**Nevinson,** C.R.W.
**Nicholson,** Ben
**Nicholson,** Winifred
**O'Casey,** Breon
**Pacheco,** Ana Maria
**Picasso,** Pablo
**Piper,** John
**Powell,** Felicity
**Power,** Cyril
**Roberts,** William
**Rothenstein,** Michael
**Rouault,** Georges
**Sacco,** Graciela
**Storey,** Paul
**Sutherland,** Graham
**Tapies,** Antoni
**Trevelyan,** Julian
**Tschudi,** Lill
**Tunnard,** John
**Wadsworth,** Edward
**Wood,** Christopher

SCOTTISH GALLERY (AITKEN DOTT LTD.)
(Page 135)
**Barns-Graham,** Wilhelmina
**Bellany,** John
**Blackadder,** Elizabeth
**Blyth,** Robert Henderson
**Bryce,** Gordon
**Byrne,** John
**Cadell,** F.C.B.
**Carlisle,** Fionna
**Cowie,** James
**Crawford,** John Gardiner
**Crowe,** Victoria
**Cumming,** James
**Dees,** Stephanie
**Dees,** Stephanie
**Devlin,** George
**Douthwaite,** Pat
**Eardley,** Joan
**Edwards,** Dierdre
**Fergusson,** J.D.
**Findlay,** Denise
**Fojcik,** Brian
**Forrest,** Archie
**Fraser,** Alexander
**Gardner,** Alexandra
**Gillies,** William
**Gray,** Janice
**Haig,** The Earl
**Houston,** John
**Hunter,** Leslie
**Knox,** Jack
**Littlejohn,** William
**MacTaggart,** William
**McClure,** David
**McGill,** Alison
**Mclaren,** Peter
**McRae,** Jennifer
**Michie,** David
**Morrison,** James
**Morrocco,** Alberto
**Oram,** Ann
**Peploe,** Denis
**Peploe,** S.J.
**Philipson,** Sir Robin
**Rae,** Barbara
**Redfern,** June
**Redpath,** Anne
**Reid,** Paul
**Shanks,** Duncan
**Thomson,** Adam Bruce
**Wood,** Christopher

SCULPTURE AT GOODWOOD
(Page 202)
**Abrahams,** Ivor
**Allington,** Edward
**Ben-David,** Zadok
**Black,** Hamish
**Burke,** Peter
**Burton,** Andrew
**Caro,** Anthony
**Chadwick,** Lynn
**Cox,** Stephen
**Cragg,** Tony
**Culbert,** Bill
**Cutts,** George
**Davies,** John
**De Monchaux,** Cathy
**Dilworth,** Steve
**Finn-Kelcey,** Rose
**Firth,** Mark
**Furlong,** William
**Gernand,** Bruce
**Gibbons,** John
**Goldsworthy,** Andy
**Gregory,** Steven
**Hadcock,** Charles
**Hall,** Nigel
**Hartley,** Alex
**Hendy,** Sean
**Isherwood,** Jon
**Jones,** Allen
**King,** Phillip
**Kneale,** Bryan
**Logan,** Peter
**Mach,** David
**Maclean,** Diane
**Mayer,** Charlotte
**Nash,** David
**Neagu,** Paul
**O'Connell,** Eilis
**Palova,** Zora
**Pye,** William
**Ramshaw,** Wendy
**Rance,** Victoria
**Randall-Page,** Peter
**Sandle,** Michael
**Slee,** Richard
**Smallhorn,** Sophie
**Smith,** Keir
**Taylor,** Wendy
**Tebbenhoff,** Almuth
**Tucker,** William
**Whiteread,** Rachel
**Woodrow,** Bill

SIMMONS GALLERY
(Page 74)
**Cook,** Robert
**Dutton,** Ron
**Finke,** Leonda
**Fountain,** Marian
**Gunston,** Irene
**Hellegers,** Gustaaf
**Leski,** Pavel
**Lugossy,** Maria
**Moss,** Nicola
**Rank-Broadley,** Ian
**Solowiej,** Danuta
**Vaughan,** Avril

SIMON CAPSTICK-DALE FINE ART
(Page 74)
**Avery,** Milton
**Basquiat,** Jean-Michel
**Bomberg,** David
**Burra,** Edward
**Calder,** Alexander
**Caro,** Anthony
**Cocteau,** Jean
**De Kooning,** Willem
**De La Fresnaye,** Roger
**Derain,** André
**Dine,** Jim
**Dubuffet,** Jean
**Dyson,** Deirdre
**Flavin,** Dan
**Francis,** Sam
**Freud,** Lucian
**Gill,** Madge
**Grosz,** George
**Hepworth,** Barbara
**Hitchens,** Ivon
**Hoyland,** John
**Hume,** Gary
**Judd,** Donald
**Kitaj,** R.B.
**Kolar,** Jiri
**Lebasque,** Henri
**Leger,** Fernand
**Lichtenstein,** Roy
**Lurcat,** Jean
**Magritte,** René
**Matisse,** Henri
**Miró,** Joan
**Mitchel,** Joan
**Monet,** Claude
**Moore,** Henry
**Morley,** Malcolm
**Motherwell,** Robert
**Nevelson,** Louise
**Nevinson,** C.R.W.
**Nicholson,** Ben
**Olitski,** Jules
**Pearlstein,** Philip
**Picasso,** Pablo
**Piper,** John
**Roberts,** William
**Rothro,** Mark
**Ruscha,** Ed
**Steinberg,** Saul
**Warhol,** Andy
**Whiteread,** Rachel

SIR ALFRED MUNNINGS ART MUSEUM
(Page 95)
**Munnings,** Sir Alfred

SNAPE MALTINGS GALLERY
(Page 99)
**Allen,** James
**Bates,** Joan
**Bawden,** Richard
**Binks,** Stephen
**Brunsdon,** John
**Burman,** John
**Carlo,** Michael
**Coppillie,** Robert
**Dingle,** Jan
**Donaldson,** Ros
**Draper,** Jill
**Fuchs,** Tessa
**Gill,** George W
**Green** , David
**Hastings,** Eveline
**Henderson,** Sue
**Hodgkiss,** Joan
**Houghton,** Barrie
**Judge,** Janet
**Kempley,** Ken
**Laurance,** Martin
**Leech,** Kenneth
**McCarthy,** Peter
**Meade,** Clare
**Morgan,** Jane
**Neusten,** Barrie
**Palmer,** Alan W
**Paton,** Ann
**Paul,** Sylvia
**Reay,** John
**Richardson,** Linda
**Sayers,** Brian
**Spafford,** Iola
**Thomas,** Glynn
**Tookey,** John
**Wade,** Richard
**Westwood,** Neil
**Wincup,** Donald

THE SOLOMON GALLERY
(Page 158)
**Ballard,** Brian
**Bellany,** John
**Blackadder,** Elizabeth
**Blackshaw,** Basil
**Bond,** Marj
**Chihuly,** Dale
**Collis,** Peter
**Cope,** Elizabeth
**Duncan,** Ana
**Geoghegan,** Trevor
**Gillespie,** Rowan
Guggi
**Houston,** John
**Keown,** Mary Theresa
**Kingston,** Richard
**Kinney,** Desmond
**Longueville,** James
**Lynn,** Bob
**McAllister,** Therese
**McDonnell,** Hector
**McEntagart,** Brett
**McWilliam,** F.E.
**Mooney,** Martin
**Richardson,** Victor
**Spackman,** Sarah
**Stuart,** Imogen
**Warren,** Michael
**Wejchert,** Alexandra
**Yeats,** Jack B.

THE SPECIAL PHOTOGRAPHER'S COMPANY
(Page 74)
**Bingham,** Howard
**Boot,** Adrian
**Catany,** Toni
**Claxton,** William
**Clement,** Etienne
**Cryer,** Terry
**Cunnick,** Geraint
**Curtis,** Edward Sheriff
**Dayan,** Eddie
**Dow,** Beth
**Fonteyne,** Karel
**Fraser,** Ewan
**Gibson,** David H.
**Gilden,** Bruce
**Gorman,** Greg
**Greenfield,** Lois
**Gruen,** Bob
**Harris,** Graeme

**Hirschberg,** Tania
**Holland,** Tracey
**Jaques,** Ronny
**Lele,** Ouka
**Leonard,** Herman
**Lucas,** Cornel
**Mankowitz,** Gered
**Marsden,** Simon
**Mayne-Smith,** Sean
**McCabe,** Eamonn
**McCartney,** Mike
**Mcgee,** Tony
**Molins,** Sophie
**O'Neill,** Terry
**Paleologou,** Ettie
**Park,** Clare
**Parker,** Emma
**Reuter,** John
**Rivas,** Humberto
**Ryan,** Barry
**Samuel,** Deborah
**Suschitzky,** Wolfgang
**Tenneson,** Joyce
**Thorne-Thomsen,** Ruth
**Tunick,** Spencer
**Vargas,** Rafael
**Waite,** Charlie
**Waite,** Richard
**Warburton,** Holly
**Wesson,** Diane
**Wilmer,** Val
**Wilson,** Laura

### Square Gallery
(Page 115)
**Barnes,** Catherine
**Biggs,** Alan
**Frampton,** Russell
**Harley-Peters,** Jonet
**Hildren,** Ken
**Howell,** David
**Morgan,** Michael
**Rudge,** Dillon
**Rudge,** Lawson E.
**Wilson,** Mike

### St. Barnabas Press
(Page 176)
**Aarons,** Andrew
**Anderson,** Tom
**Cornish,** Charlotte
**De bay,** Galietta
**Durneen,** Ian
**Farooqui,** Yasmeen
**Grabham,** Alan
**Hill,** James
**Larkham,** Dorothy
**Martin,** Siobhan
**McKenzie,** Andy
**Moore,** Gabriella
**Preston,** John
**Rubans,** Sula
**Rubans,** Ursula
**Saunders,** Jenny
**Seymore,** Mary
**Shaw,** Gordon
**Smith,** Amanda
**Tait,** Jim
**Tedder,** Mike
**Thomas,** Fiona
**Warmsley,** Niel
**Westwood,** Lucy

### St. Brannock's Gallery
(Page 97)
**Baron,** Leofric
**Colinson,** Roy
**Gladwell,** James
**Godwin,** Sheila
**Partridge,** Ian
**Poole,** Doreen
**Salmons,** John
**Smith,** Michael
**Sparham,** Marie
**Symmons,** Barbara
**Townsend,** Christine

### St. David's Hall
(Page 144)
**Beard,** Leonard
**Chapman,** June
**Darlison,** John
**Dewsbury,** Gerald
**Evans,** David
**Giles Hobbs,** Annie
**Hawkins,** Des
**Howell,** Joyce
**Howells,** Pat
**Hughes-Williams,** Sylvia
**Hurn,** Daphne
**Hurst,** Dora
**Lowry,** Arnold
**Lush,** Helen
**McDonagh,** Sue
**Owen,** Cyril
**Owen,** Shirley Anne
**Traynor,** Mary
**Waugh,** Trevor
**Whalley,** Ann
**Williams,** David
**Woods,** Anne

### St. James's Gallery,
(Page 112)
**Baldwin,** Gordon
**Barry,** Jo
**Batterham,** Richard
**Bayer,** Svend
**Brown,** Bob
**Brown,** Stephen
**De Waal,** Edmund
**Dunn,** John
**Harris,** Charmian
**Hughes,** Kevin
**Kirk,** David
**Leach,** John
**Mcgreavy,** Mike
**McKibbin,** Marlene
**Morgan,** Ron
**Pollex,** John
**Royle,** Guy
**White,** David

### Star Gallery
(Page 107)
**Armitage,** David
**Blight,** John
**Cooper,** Michael
**Dubrey,** Henrietta
**Fedden,** Mary
**Hammick,** Tom
**Lloyd-Jones,** Mary
**Messer,** Peter
**Mockford,** Harold
**Rix,** Ruth
**Rooney,** Mick
**Traherne,** Margaret
**Williams,** Charles

### Stern Art Dealers
(Page 75)
**Armfield,** Edward
**Bale,** Thomas Charles
**Bates,** David
**Clark,** James
**Clemenson,** Robert
**Cousin,** Charles
**de Breanski,** Alfred
**de Breanski,** Gustave
**Ellis,** Edwin
**Epstein,** Jacob
**Goodall,** Frederick
**Haldon,** Trevor
**Hines,** Theodor
**Hollums,** Frances Mabel
**Horlor,** Joseph
**Hulk,** Abraham Jnr.
**Kadar,** Bela
**King,** H.J. Yeend
**Kramer,** Jacob
**Maze,** Paul
**Meadows,** William
**Morris,** Alfred
**Niemun,** Edward J.
**Paice,** George
**Parker,** Henry H.
**Passey,** Charles
**Perez,** Alonzo
**Pike,** Sidney
**Pissarro,** Camille
**Pissarro,** Georges Manzana
**Pissarro,** H. Claude
**Pissarro,** Lelia
**Pissarro,** Lucien
**Pissarro,** Ludovic-Rodo
**Pissarro,** Orovida
**Pissarro,** Paulemile
**Pollentine,** Alfred
**Schafer,** Henri
**Sherrin,** Daniel
**Spinks,** Thomas
**Steele,** Edwin
**Thornley,** William
**Vickers,** A.H.
**Walbourn,** Ernest

### Strathearn Gallery and Pottery
(Page 138)
**Awlson,** Walter
**Bell,** John
**Bourne,** Peter
**Bushe,** Chris
**Campbell,** Catriona
**Gray,** Janice
**Halstead,** Rebecca
**Harkess,** Claire
**Hollands,** Emma
**Maclean,** Sonas
**Maguire,** Fiona
**Maguire,** John
**McCarthy,** Liz
**McStay,** Adrienne
**Meikle,** Annabel
**Morrison,** John Lowrie
**Muir,** Graham
**Pretsell,** Philomena
**Robinson,** Neil
**Scobie,** Lara

STUDIO NINE
(Page 75)
**Hanley,** Cliff

THE STUDIO
(Page 145)
**Wilson,** David
**Wilson,** Guy

SUI GENERIS
(Page 116)
**Adams-Groom,** Paul
**Barnard,** Victoria
**Bellshaw-Langé,** Angela
**Brain,** Rick
**Breeze,** Linda
**Brown,** Sue
**Calvert,** John
**Carone,** Antonella
**Carpenter,** David
**Courtney,** Leanne
**Eagles,** Chris
**Fawlk,** Marion
**Feiler,** Christine
**Freeman,** Bob
**Granville-Edmunds,** Peter
**Hardy,** Charlotte
**Hirsh,** Cherry
**Honour,** Samantha
**Hoskins,** Sarah
**Houseago,** Natasha
**Loder,** Claire
**Love,** Adele
**Murphy,** Jaqueline
**O'Brien,** Martin
**Oakes,** Jonathan
**Osman,** Tony
**Palmer,** Jitka
**Parker,** Michelle
**Ratcliffe,** Valerie Ann
**Roberts,** Gill
**Robertson,** Nicholas
**Scarpa-Isles,** Antonella
**Shortland,** Kathleen
**Smith,** Traci
**Spencer,** Fran
**Stevens,** Michael
**Strachan,** David
**Taylor,** Alison
**Toogood,** Raymond
**Trevena-Jackson,** Emelie
**Whitaker,** Gillean
**Ziesler,** Sally

THE HAY MAKERS
(Page 166)
**Armstrong,** Chris
**Birks,** Pat
**Cartwright,** Catriona
**Griffin,** Pat
**Hiley Harris,** Sue
**Keeble,** Victoria
**Suffield,** Max
**Sutcliffe,** Nancy

THE RED GALLERY
(Page 167)
**Appleyard,** Annie
**Aylward,** Jo
**Bharrucha,** Julie
**Borsky,** Jiri
**Brown,** Sue
**Corbani,** Gabby
**Cork,** Angela
**Crew ,** Lee
**Deacon,** Rachel
**Dove,** Stanley
**Frew ,** Ivan
**Geoage,** Debbie
**Grover,** Emma
**Hardy,** Charlotte
**Jackson,** Paul
**Kantaris,** Rachel
**Klein,** Anita
**Konig,** Heidi
Lathem & Neve
**MacDonald,** Linda
**Matthew,** Katherine
**Mee,** Hillary
**Musson,** Peter
**Newell,** Elenor
**Potter,** Andrew
**Price,** Trevor
**Richardson,** Ray
**Ricketts,** Rachel
**Rollo,** Sonia
**Rudge,** Kesa
**Rudge,** Lawson
**Shaw ,** Simon
**Spence,** Annora
**Stuart Carke,** Norman
**Tayor,** Frank
**Trenwith,** Tobias
**Tye,** Roger
**Williams ,** Catherine

THE WYKEHAM GALLERY
(Page 121)
**Birch,** Lamorna
**Goode,** Mervyn
**Kennard,** David
**Knighton-Hammond,** Arthur
**Linfield,** John
**Maddison,** John
**McCrossan,** Mary
**Norrington,** Claire
**Palmer,** Robert
**Phipps,** Howard
**Rowe,** Ernest
**Wheatley,** Jenny
**White,** Ethelbert

THROSSELLS
(Page 75)
**Bulbis,** Ann
**Dennis,** Ann
**Harris,** Jane
**Kader,** Osman

TIB LANE GALLERY
(Page 102)
**Billsborough,** Jim
**Cebertowicz,** Janina
**Clayton,** Peter
**Ehrlich,** Georg
**Foerster,** Florian
**Freer,** Allen
**Frink,** Elisabeth
**Halliday,** Irene
**Henderson,** Sue
**Herman,** Josef
**Howard,** Ghislaine
**King,** Margaret
**Kramer,** Jacob
**Lloyd,** James
**Massey,** Ian
**McIntyre,** Donald
**McKinlay,** Don
**Nash,** John
**Ousey,** Harry
**Poulton,** Jane
**Radford,** Gordon
**Richardson,** Bob
**Rutherford,** Harry
**Sarkis,** Vera
**Selwyn,** William
**Shaw,** David Carson
**Sorrell,** Adrian
**Spafford,** George
**Spafford,** Iola
**Stubbs,** Rosemary
**Taylor,** Jo
**Thompson,** Alan
**Vallette,** Adolphe
**Vaughan,** Keith
**Wood,** Michael
**Woods,** Brian

TIDAL WAVE GALLERY
(Page 123)
**Barnett,** Christine
**Barry,** Jo
**Bellamy,** David
**Birtwhistle,** David
**Brown,** Bob
**Caddick,** Kathleen
**Clarke,** Graham
**Coates,** Tom
**Crawshaw,** Daniel
**Duprez,** Annie
**Fairchild,** Roy
**Farrell,** Jan
**Fedden,** Mary
**Gork,** Jurgen
**Ionescu,** Anca
**Jackson,** Mary
**Knapp-Fisher,** John
**Leverett,** David
**May,** Marianne
**McCarthy,** Charles
**Morris,** Anthony
**Perceval,** Alice
**Perceval,** Tessa
**Phillips,** Aubrey
**Pikesley,** Richard
**Putman,** Salliann
**Richardson,** Ilana
**Spain,** Mark
**Spare,** Richard
**Thornton-Jones,** Crispin
**Ward,** John
**Wardle,** Richard
**Williams,** Annie
**Wills,** Richard
**Woodthorpe,** Mariella
**Yardley,** Bruce
**Yardley,** John

TRINITY GALLERY
(Page 109)
**Bellchambers,** Lesley
**Black ,** Simon
**Brown,** Lucy
**Cairns,** Mary
**Clements,** Victor
**Cunligge,** Tom
**Gelidt,** Steve
**Grant,** Matthew
**Hambyln,** Amanda

**Hesmondhalgh,** Brendan
**Johnston,** Rachel
**Jury,** Sam
**Kettle,** Christopher
**Lloyd Jones,** Mary
**Matthews,** Rex
**May,** Elsie
**Mills,** Jon
**Nias,** Clare
**Rowe,** Julian
**Turner,** Stephen
**Underhill,** Emma
**Varvaro,** Anna
**Veillard,** Dominic
**Verdi,** Raj
**Wilcox ,** Carol
**Williams,** Jago Max
**Winbolt,** Pam
**Wright ,** Chris

TZB SOUTHBOURNE GALLERY
(Page 118)
**Dixon,** Morag
**Green,** Brian H.
**Hurley,** Rex
**Lough,** Daphne
**Macdonald,** Eleine
**Maguire,** W.E.
**Roberts,** Peter
**Sims,** Ronald H.
**Zwolinska-Brzeski,** Teresa

UNICORN PICTURES LTD.
(Page 76)
**Ashman,** Malcolm
**Black,** Simon
**Cameron,** Peter
**Carr,** Francis
**Cordero,** Philip
**Creswell,** Alexander
**Crocker,** Andrew
**Day,** Paul
**Elliott,** Richard
**Gallwey,** Kay
**Handon,** Paul
**Johnson,** Frank
**List,** Caroline
**Maconochie,** James
**Marshall,** Steven
**Roberts,** Trevor
**Rubinstein,** Gerda
**Rudd,** Bob
**Shanahan,** David
**Shiels,** Charlie
**Stevens,** Christopher
**Wiskey,** Joshua

UNIT 2 GALLERY
(Page 97)
**Allen,** Sarah
**Armstrong,** Pat
**Bailey,** Sylvia
**Barker,** Jane
**Barrow,** Martoz
**Bates,** Amanda
**Bourne,** Mary
**Bridge,** Ron
**Brown,** Chris
**Brown,** Sarah
**Clarke,** Shaun
**Cooke,** Arnold
**Cooke,** David
**Cooke,** Rosemarie
**Cox,** Hilary
**Crouchman,** Clare
**Eeles,** Tony
**Galanides,** Therasa
**Gandy,** Paul
**Heale,** Meg
**Hicks,** Peter
**Hilton,** Maggie
**Hurst,** Dagmar
**Illsley,** Will
**Knibs,** Vic
**Logan,** Frank
**Marix-Evans,** Polly
**McFarlane,** Kathleen
**Morgan,** Annette
**Peddie,** Crofton
**Plunkett,** Tim
**Skeels,** Rebecca
**Skinner,** Graham
**Spencer,** Lucy
**Spriet,** Cristal
**Thompson,** Fiona
**Warner,** Carmen
**Wassell,** Tony
**Waters,** Alan
**Wilson,** Andrew

THE UNIVERSITY GALLERY
(Page 105)
**Cornish,** Norman
**McGuinness,** Tom

UNIVERSITY OF LIMERICK - AV GALLERY
(Page 159)
**Baker,** Robert
**Blodau,** Dierer
**Blodau,** Peter
**Byrne,** Michael
**Donovan,** Jack
**Harper,** Charles
**Lilburn,** David
**MacMahon,** Des
**Murray,** Cóilin
**Sheemy,** Jim
**Shinnors,** John

VINCENT KOSMAN FINE ART
(Page 135)
**Armstrong,** John
**Bell,** Vanessa
**Bomberg,** David
**Brown,** Hugh Boycott
**Connard,** Philip
**Crosbie,** William
**Duncan,** John
**Dunlop,** Ronald O.
**Fedden,** Mary
**Fergusson,** J.D.
**Gertler,** Mark
**Gill,** Eric
**Gillies,** William
**Gore,** Frederick
**Gosse,** Sylvia
**Grant,** Duncan
**Hall,** Clifford
**Hamilton,** Maggie
**Harvey,** Harold
**Hayward,** Arthur
**Hilton,** Roger
**Houston,** George
**Kennedy,** Cecil
**Lee Hankey,** William
**Maitland,** Paul
**Manson,** James B.
**Maze,** Paul
**McClure,** David
**McIntyre,** Donald
**Meninsky,** Bernard
**Methuen,** Lord
**Morrocco,** Alberto
**Mostyn,** Tom
**Nicholson,** William
**Park,** James Stuart
**Park,** John A.
**Paterson,** James
**Paterson,** Viola
**Phillipson,** Robin
**Redpath,** Anne
**Robertson,** Eric
**Roussel,** Theodore
**Russell,** Gyrth
**Smith,** Matthew
**Trevelyan,** Julian
**Vaughan,** Keith
**Williams,** Terrick
**Wolfe,** Edward
**Wolmark,** Alfred
**Zinkeisen,** Doris

WADDINGTON GALLERIES
(Page 76)
**Albers,** Josef
**Albers,** Josef (The Estate of)
**Arp,** Jean
**Avery,** Milton
**Blake,** Peter
**Calder,** Alexander
**Caulfield,** Patrick
**Chamberlain,** John
**Chia,** Sandro
**Craig-Martin,** Michael
**Davenport,** Ian
**De Kooning,** Willem
**Degas,** Edgar
**Dubuffet,** Jean
**Ernst,** Max
**Flanagan,** Barry
**Flavin,** Dan
**Francis,** Sam
**Halley,** Peter
**Hepworth,** Barbara
**Heron,** Patrick
**Hockney,** David
**Hodgkin,** Howard
**Jones,** Zebedee
**Judd,** Donald
**Klee,** Paul
**Léger,** Fernand
**Lichtenstein,** Roy
**Lim,** Kim
**Lipchitz,** Jacques
**Magritte,** René
**Matisse,** Henri
**Milroy,** Lisa
**Miró,** Joan
**Moore,** Henry
**Nicholson,** Ben
**Paladino,** Mimmo
**Picabia,** Francis
**Picasso,** Pablo
**Rauschenberg,** Robert
**Samaras,** Lucas
**Schnabel,** Julian
**Spencer,** Stanley
**Tapiès,** Antoni
**Turnbull,** William

**Warhol,** Andy
**Wesselmann,** Tom
**Westermann,** H.C.
**Yeats,** Jack B.

THE WALK
(Page 76)
**Banks,** Nick
**Bartlett,** Adrian
**Carr,** David
**Clarke,** Denis
**Feilden,** Lucy
**Martin,** Sonia
**Milne,** Vincent
**Morris,** Sue
**Mortimer,** Sophie
**Sen,** Neera
**Snow,** Peter
**Wylan,** Marie

WARWICK GALLERY
(Page 168)
**Brunsdon,** John
**Burrows,** Hazel
**Cummings,** Christine
**Dingle,** Jan
**Dunn,** John
**Fairchild,** Michael
**Furminger,** Julie
**Hughes,** Alan
**Hughes,** John
**Kennedy,** Michael
**Mainwaring,** John
**Millington,** Terence
**Noble,** Chris
**Richecoeur,** Michael
**Roberts,** Ian
**Scaldwell,** Deborah
**Spain,** Mark
**Wilson,** Richard
**Wood,** Michael

THE WASHINGTON GALLERY
(Page 150)
**Bala,** Iwan
**Beard,** Leonard
**Davies,** Ivor
**Griffin,** Chris
**Howells,** Neale
**Husted,** Mary
**Muirden,** Phil
**Osmond,** Ozirhys
**Payne,** Michael Gustavius
**Phillips,** W.
**Selway,** John
**Sirota,** Monte
**Stuart Burns,** Brendan
**Traynor,** Mary
**Williams,** Sue

THE WEST END GALLERY
(Page 93)
**Hacker,** Sophie
**Hobbs,** Paul
**Lamb,** Jean

WEST WALES ARTS CENTRE,
(Page 147)
**Beard,** Leonard
**Campbell,** James
**Canning,** Neil
**Coker,** Peter
**Cramp,** Elizabeth
**Cramp,** Jonathan
**Cullen,** Stephen
**Curry,** Denis
**Henderson,** Ewen
**Jackson,** Dilys
**Loveday,** Ross
**MacKeown,** James
**Marsh,** Simon
**Partridge,** Josh
**Payne,** Michael
**Rich,** Simon
**Roberts,** Chris
**Robertson,** Ian
**Thurnham,** Chris
**Tress,** David
**Tudball,** Ruthanne
**Vaughan Jones,** Martyn
**Viale,** Patrick
**Ward,** John

WHITFORD FINE ART
(Page 76)
**Bendall,** Mildred
**Bissiere,** Roger
**Bogart,** Bram
**Boty,** Pauline
**Bradley,** Martin
**Bratby,** John
**Bunny,** Rupert
**Caulfield,** Patrick
Caziel
**Clarke,** Geoffrey
**Cockrill,** Maurice
**Davie,** Alan
**Dufresne,** Charles
**Francis,** Mike
**Frost,** Sir Terry
**Gear,** William
**Gilbert,** Stephan
**Heath,** Adrian
**Henri,** Adrian
**Herman,** Josef
**Heron,** Patrick
**Hilton,** Roger
**Hull,** John
**Jones,** Allen
**Kidner,** Michael
**Kisling,** Moise
**Lacasse,** Joseph
**Laing,** Gerald
**Lhote ,** Andre
**Lurcat,** Jean
**Mack,** Heinz
**Mara,** Pol
**Martin,** Henri
**Melville,** John
**Nolan,** Sir Sydney
**Paolozzi,** Eduardo
**Penrose,** Roland
**Phillips,** Peter
**Riley,** Bridget
**Russell,** John Peter
**Sedgley,** Peter
**Smith,** Matthew
**Souverbie,** Jean
**Survage,** Leopold
**Tilson,** Joe
**Tucker,** William
**Van Hoeydonck,** Paul
**Wall,** Brian
**Wilson,** Frank Awray

THE WILD HAWTHORN PRESS
(Page 174)
**Hamilton-Finlay,** Ian

WILL'S ART WAREHOUSE
(Page 76)
**Adams,** Lee
**Aiers,** Pauleen
**Bassett,** Clare
**Baxter,** Sandra
**Bevan,** Oliver
**Boyd,** Ron
**Cooke,** Jonathon
**Crook,** Craig
**Davy,** Lesley
**De Koniqswarter,** Steven
**Dickens,** Sophie
**Duffin,** John
**Dufton,** John
**Dumas,** Felise
**Edwards,** Nicola
**Elfick,** Pennie
**Fay,** Helen
**Gilvan,** Cartwright Christopher
**Grundy,** Bronwen
**Haring,** Ute
**Harris,** Ian
**Haxworth,** Hetty
**Jaffe,** Leanne
**James,** Simon
**Kennington,** Sue
**Langford,** Martin
**Leasor,** Joan
**Lee,** Jessie
**Liddell,** Caro
**Little,** Pauline
**Lodge,** Grace
**Mason,** Piers
**Midgley,** Julia
**Moxley,** Susan
**Nott,** Margaret
**Owen,** Rachel
**Pinkster,** Anna
**Piper,** Ruth
**Pullen,** Alison
**Robinson,** Julian
**Robinson,** Kate
**Rodriguez,** Cristina
**Smith,** Pippa
**Stalker,** Geoff
**Thomas,** Kate
**Timms,** Melissa
**Turnball,** Chris
**Urquhart,** Anne
**Wilson,** Robert
**Winter,** Tom

WINDOW GALLERY, FINE ART AND FRAMING
(Page 107)
**Atkin,** Michael
**Beattie,** David
**Bird,** Bebe
**Bowyer,** David
**Carreck,** Libby
**Child,** St. John
**Clatworthy,** Len
**Dunn,** John
**Dunn,** Philip
**Embden,** Michael
**Fenoughty,** Mary
**Green,** Kevin
**Hanson,** Helen
**Hartill,** Brenda
**Hill,** Linda

**Jameson,** Susan
**Myers,** Rick
**Price,** Trevor
**Richardson,** Ilana
**Ruffell,** Colin
**Snape,** Alan
**Spain,** Mark
**Thomas,** Glynn
**Tompkins,** Errol
**Trevena,** Shirley
**Tuff,** Richard
**Westcott,** Peter
**Whiting,** Cathi
**Wood,** Michael
**Woodhouse,** Ben

WISEMAN GALLERY
(Page 120)
**Allen,** Chrys
**Austin,** Allyson
**Butterwick,** Lucy
**Carpenter,** Pip
**Colbeck,** Joye
**Duffelen,** Fiona
**Dunbar,** Emma
**Fay,** Helen
**Guise,** Kirsty
**Gunning,** Annie
**Haxworth,** Hetty
**Henrys,** Sarah
**Jun-Im McLaughlin,** Kitty
**Knight,** David
**MacQueen,** Charles
**McAlpine,** Heather
**Millais,** Fiona
**Payne,** Martin
**Pearce,** David
**Perring,** Susie
**Price,** Trevor
**Rich,** Simon
**Rollo,** Andrew D.
**Rollo,** Sonia
**Stone,** Adam
**Tribe,** Marla
**Wallman,** Tessa

WISEMAN ORIGINALS
(Page 77)
**Aitchison,** Craigie
**Braque,** Georges
**Chagall,** Marc
**Freud,** Lucian
**Frink,** Elisabeth
**Frost,** Sir Terry
**Giacometti,** Alberto
**Heron,** Patrick
**Hockney,** David
**Hodgkin,** Howard
**Hoyland,** John
**Matisse,** Henri
**Miró,** Joan
**Moore,** Henry
**Picasso,** Pablo
**Scott,** William
**Scully,** Sean

WOODBINE COTTAGE GALLERY
(Page 97)
**Bailey,** Katy
**Bibby,** Rob
**Bramble,** Steven
**Colquitt,** Peter
**Curgenven,** Michael
**English,** Andy
**Foster,** Patience
**Goodwin,** Carolyn
**Gregory,** Mac
**Hatfield,** Richard
**Hicks,** Peter
**Hollinshead,** David
**James,** Glynne
**Johnston,** Steven
**Lale,** Hazel
**Lincoln,** John
**Micallef,** Antony
**Milliken,** Rob
**Moon,** Liz
**Moore,** Sarah
**Neal,** Richard
**Shields,** Sue
**Stump,** Mick
**Yorath,** Liz
**Yorath,** Rowan

WWW.AARTI.CO.UK
(Page 181)
**Addinall,** Ruth
**Baazham,** Robert
**Bailey,** Peter James
**Forbes-Cole,** Joy
**Handler,** Murry
**Husband,** Scott
**Johnson,** Don
**Jones,** Barrie
**Karta,** Nyoman
**Lana,** Imade
Lanus
**McCafferty,** Liz
**McLoughlin,** Amanda
**Middleton,** Susan
**Mikaiel,** Jay
**Mulberry,** John
**Noonan,** Michael
**Oxborrow,** Edmond
**Potts,** Suzi
**Putra,** R.
**Roundine,** Daniel
**Sherwood,** Sylvia
Su Drtawan
**Suadi,** Wyan
**Suja,** D. Made
**Sumbada,** Ketut
**Surata,** Pandle Alit
**Walsh,** Delores
**Wijaya,** Balik
**Yasa,** Maddika

ZINK EDITIONS
(Page 176)
**Abrahams,** Ivor
**Battye,** Chris
**Beattie,** Basil
**Cooper,** Eileen
**Cox,** Alan
**De Bulat,** Fiona
**Frost,** Sir Terry
**Paolozzi,** Eduardo
**Sinnott,** Kevin
**Smith,** Richard

# Commercial Galleries By Media

*This section lists, establishments by media speciality.*

*Use this section to find the gallery stocking the media you require.*

# COMMERCIAL GALLERIES BY MEDIA

## APPLIED ART



## ARTISTS BOOKS



## CERAMICS

## CRAFTS

## DECORATIVE ART



## DRAWING

## FURNITURE



## GLASS

## JEWELLERY



## PAINTING

## PHOTOGRAPHY

## PRINTS

## SCULPTURE

## TEXTILES



## WOOD

# Artists' Index

*This section lists by artist, the establishments where the artists' work may be bought*

# ARTISTS' INDEX

# NOTES

# General Index

*Alphabetical index to all entries*

## A



## B

## C

## D

## E



## F



## G

## T